Sliding Mask

Exam Tips:

1. Read each question carefully before looking at the possible answers.

2. After formulating an answer, determine which of the choices most nearly corresponds with that answer. It should completely answer the question.

3. Answer each question according to the latest regulations and procedures. You will receive credit if the regulations or procedures have changed. Computerized exams may be updated as regulations and procedures change.

4. There is only one answer that is correct and complete. The other answers are either incomplete or are derived from popular misconceptions.

5. If you do not know the answer to a question, try not to spend too much time on it. Continue with those you can answer. Then, return to the unanswered or difficult questions.

6. Unanswered questions will be counted as incorrect.

7. On calculator problems, select the answer nearest your solution. If you have solved it correctly, your answer will be closer to the correct answer than the other choices.

FAA AIRMAN KNOWLEDGE
INSTRUMENT RATING
TEST GUIDE

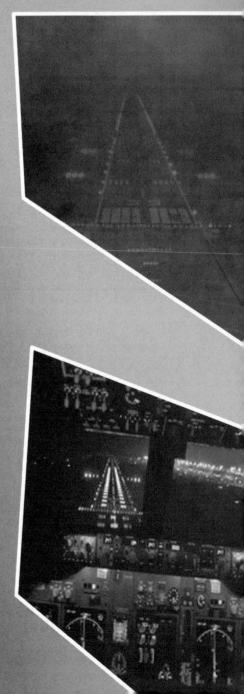

Jeppesen

Published in the United States of America
Jeppesen
55 Inverness Drive East, Englewood, CO 80112-5498
www.jeppesen.com

ISBN 978-0-88487-060-9

Jeppesen
55 Inverness Dr. East
Englewood, CO 80112-5498
Web Site: www.jeppesen.com
Email: Captain@jeppesen.com
Copyright © Jeppesen
All Rights Reserved. Published 1995-2009, 2011, 2015
Printed in the United States of America

TABLE OF CONTENTS

PREFACE

Thank you for purchasing the *Instrument Rating FAA Airman Knowledge Test Guide*. This test guide will help you understand the answers to the test questions so you can take the FAA knowledge test with confidence. The test guide contains the FAA instrument rating airplane test questions. Included are the correct answers and explanations, along with study references. Explanations of why the other choices are wrong are included where appropriate. Questions are organized by topic, with explanations conveniently located to the right side of each question. You can use the unique sliding mask to cover up the answers and test yourself. Full-color figures identical to those you will see on the FAA test are included together in Appendix 1 and 2 in the back of the book. Please note that this test guide is intended to supplement your instructor-led flight and ground training—it is not a stand-alone learning tool.

THE JEPPESEN TRAINING PHILOSOPHY

Flight training in the developing years of aviation was characterized by the separation of academics from flight training in the aircraft. For years, ground and flight training were not integrated. Students would consult a large number of books on different subjects, written by different authors, which resulted in a general lack of continuity in training material. The availability of **Jeppesen training products** changes this situation with professionally-integrated training materials that incorporate extensive research on teaching theory and on how adults learn most effectively. Some of the Jeppesen design features are:

- Objectives and completion standards included in every lesson.
- Teaching of complex skills using the **building block principle**.
- Incorporation of **meaningful repetition.** Each necessary concept or skill is presented several times throughout the instructional program.

You will find these features in Jeppesen syllabi, textbooks, videos, computer-assisted training (CAT), exercises, exams, and in this test guide. When these elements are combined with an instructor's class discussion and the skills learned in the simulator and airplane, you have an ideal integrated training system, with all materials coordinated.

People tend to retain about 10% of what they read, 20% of what they hear, 30% of what they see, and 50% of what they hear and see together. These retention figures can be increased to as high as 90% by including active learning methods. Active learning includes exercises, stage exams, student/instructor discussions, CAT, and practice in a simulator or airplane.

Levels of learning include rote, understanding, application, and correlation. One of the major drawbacks with test preparation courses that concentrate only on passing the test is that they focus on rote learning, the lowest level of learning. Jeppesen's approach raises the standard by challenging students to learn at the application and correlation levels. Our materials are challenging and motivating, maximizing knowledge and skill retention. More than 3 million pilots have learned to fly using our materials, which include:

TEXTBOOKS — Jeppesen pilot and maintenance training textbooks and e-books contain the answers to many of the questions you may have as you begin your training program. They are based on the **study/review** concept of learning. This means detailed material is presented in an uncomplicated way, then important points are summarized through the use of bold type and color. For best results, study the textbook as an integral part a coordinated package of materials. The textbook is the central component for academic study and is cross-referenced to video and CAT presentations.

ONLINE COURSES — Available for private, instrument, and commercial students, these engaging training courses teach you the academic knowledge needed for your pilot certificate or rating in straightforward, no-nonsense presentations. Strategic use of animation helps you understand concepts beyond what you can learn by just reading about them. Built-in maneuvers lessons show an animated overview of each maneuver, plus pilot's-eye videos that put you in the cockpit with an instructor. It is your best possible preparation prior to actual flight lessons.

VIDEOS — You can also purchase ground school DVDs that contain generous amounts of in-flight video and animated graphics. The DVDs complement the content in the textbook and online course, enabling you to review and reinforce essential concepts presented in the textbook.

SUPPORT COMPONENTS — Supplementary items include training syllabi, stage and end-of-course exams, CDs, FAR/AIM manuals or e-books, the *FARs Explained* book, these airman knowledge test guides, practical test study guides, question banks and airman knowledge testing supplements, the *Aviation Weather* textbook, the student record folder, computer, plotter, and logbook. Jeppesen Sanderson's training products are the most comprehensive pilot training materials available. In conjunction with your instructor, they help you prepare for the FAA exam and practical test; and, more importantly, they help you become a more proficient and safe pilot.

You can purchase our products and services through your Jeppesen dealer. For product, service, or sales information go to **www.jeppdirect.com.** If you have comments, questions, or need explanations about any component of our GFD Training System, we are prepared to offer assistance at any time. Contact us directly at: **TrainingServices@ Jeppesen.com**. You can also contact Jeppesen at the following addresses.

Jeppesen
55 Inverness Drive East
Englewood, CO 80112-5498
1-800-621-JEPP
303-799-9090

If you are in Europe, Africa, or the Middle East, contact us at:

Jeppesen & Co., GmbH
Frankfurter Strasse 233
63263 Neu-Isenburg, Germany
Tel: 011-49-6102-5070
Fax: 011-49-6102-507-999

UPDATES OF FAA QUESTIONS — You can obtain free updates for the FAA questions in this test guide by visiting Jeppesen's web site. These updates are generally valid within one year of book publication; if you are using an older test guide, the web site may not update all questions that have changed since the book was printed.

To find Test Prep Updates, go to **www.jeppesen.com/testprep.**

LATEST INFORMATION REGARDING AIRMAN KNOWLEDGE TESTS

In order to prevent students from memorizing the answers to the tests, the FAA randomizes the order of the answer choices to most questions in their knowledge tests. In addition, the FAA publishes only selected questions from their database, limiting the number of questions available to the public. Therefore, you might see questions on your knowledge test that are worded differently than those in this guide. This Jeppesen question bank contains the questions published on the FAA web site plus additional questions that should help you pass your airman knowledge test. If you are able to answer the questions in this guide, then you can reasonably expect to have the required knowledge to pass the FAA airman knowledge test.

Jeppesen has never encouraged its students to memorize answers to FAA questions. We provide comprehensive, nononsense study material that teaches you what you need to know to answer the test questions correctly. Our test prep materials always tell you why the correct answer is correct and, if it is not obvious, why the other answers are incorrect. When answering each FAA question, carefully read and evaluate each answer choice and choose the correct answer based on what you know from your study, not from that answer's position or wording.

INTRODUCTION

The Instrument Rating FAA Airman Knowledge Test Guide is designed to help you prepare for the Instrument Rating Knowledge Test. It covers FAA exam material that applies to airplanes, including pertinent Federal Aviation Regulations (FARs). Questions pertaining to helicopter, powered-lift, and airships are not included.

We recommend that you use this test guide in conjunction with the Guided Flight Discovery (GFD) Pilot Training System. The test guide is organized like the *GFD Instrument/Commercial* textbook, with eleven chapters and distinctive sections within each chapter. Questions are covered in the test guide generally in the same sequence as the material in the textbook. References to applicable page numbers in the textbook are included along with the answers. A separate chapter (Chapter 11) in the test guide is devoted to FAR questions and answers.

Within the chapters, each section contains a brief introduction. FAA test questions appear in the left column and answers and explanations are in the right column. Below is an example of a typical reference for a question.

[1]	[2]	[3]	[4]	[5]	[6]
4-59	**PLT016**	**4-59.**	**Answer C.**	**GFDIC 4B**	**AIM**
(FAA Question)		*(Explanation of FAA Question)*			

[1] Jeppesen designated test guide question number. The first number is the chapter where the question is located in the test guide. In most cases, this corresponds to the chapter in the GFD textbook. The second number is the question number within the chapter. In this example, the question is in Chapter 4 of the test guide and it is the 59th question.

[2] The FAA learning statement code. You can find a complete list of learning statements with learning statement codes in Appendix 3.

[3] The Jeppesen test guide number is repeated in the right hand column above the explanation.

[4] Correct answer to the question, in this case answer C is correct.

[5] The location where the question is covered in the GFD textbook. In this case, the question is covered in Chapter 4, Section B in the *GFD Instrument/Commercial* textbook.

[6] Abbreviation for the FAA or other authoritative source document. In this case, the reference is the Aeronautical Information Manual (AIM). Abbreviations used in the test guide are as follows:

AC	—	Advisory Circulars
A/FD	—	Airport/Facility Directory
AFH	—	Airplane Flying Handbook, FAA-H-8083-3A
AIM	—	Aeronautical Information Manual
ASI-SA##	—	Air Safety Institute (AOPA) Safety Advisor (By Number)
AW	—	Aviation Weather, AC 00-6A
AWS	—	Aviation Weather Services, AC 00-45
FAR	—	Federal Aviation Regulations
GFDIC	—	Guided Flight Discovery Instrument/Commercial Textbook
GFDPP	—	Guided Flight Discovery Private Pilot Textbook
IAP	—	Instrument Approach Procedure
IFH	—	Instrument Flying Handbook, FAA-H-8083-15
IPG	—	Instrument Procedures Guide (Jeppesen)
IPH	—	Instrument Procedures Handbook, FAA-H-8083-16
NAVWEPS	—	Aerodynamics for Naval Aviators
PHB	—	Pilot's Handbook of Aeronautical Knowledge, FAA-H-8083-25
RMH	—	Risk Management Handbook, FAA-H-8083-2
WBH	—	Aircraft Weight and Balance Handbook, FAA-H-8083-1
TERPS	—	U.S. Standard for Terminal Instrument Procedures

Below the reference line is the FAA question in the left column and the explanation in the right column. The explanation includes the correct answer followed by an explanation of why the answer is correct and if needed, why the other answers are wrong. In some cases, the incorrect answers are not explained. Examples include instances where the answers are calculated, or when the explanation of the correct answer obviously eliminates the wrong answers.

The answers in this test guide are based on official reference documents and, in our judgment, are the best choices of the available answers. Some questions that were valid when the FAA test was developed might no longer be appropriate due to ongoing changes in regulations or official operating procedures. The computer test that you take can be updated at any time. Therefore, when taking the FAA test, it is important to answer the questions according to the latest regulations or official operating procedures.

Three appendices from the FAA test materials are included in the back of the test guide. Appendix 1 provides legends from the appropriate airman knowledge testing supplement. These are an important resource for answering questions about charts and the *Airport/Facility Directory*; remember to look in the legends if you don't know the answer and remember that these legends will be available during your actual test. Appendix 2 contains the figures from the appropriate airman knowledge testing supplement that are needed to answer questions that refer to figures. Appendix 3 contains the FAA Learning Statement Codes and Learning Statements.

HOW TO PREPARE FOR THE FAA TEST
It is important to realize that to become a safe, competent pilot, you need more than just the academic knowledge required to pass a test. For a comprehensive ground training program, we recommend a structured ground school with a qualified flight or ground instructor. An organized course of instruction will help you complete the course in a timely manner, and you will be able to have your questions answered. The additional instruction will be beneficial in your flight training.

Regardless of whether you are in a structured ground training program, you will find this test guide is an excellent training aid to help you prepare for the FAA airman knowledge test. The test guide contains all of the airplane questions as they are presented in the FAA computerized test format. By reviewing the questions and studying the GFD Pilot Training materials, you should be well equipped to take the test.

You will also benefit more from your study if you test yourself as you proceed through the test guide. Cover the answers in the right-hand column, read each question, and choose what you consider the best answer. A sliding mask is provided for this purpose. Move the sliding mask down and read the answer and explanation for that question. You might want to mark the questions you miss for further study and review prior to taking the exam.

The sooner you take the exam after you complete your study, the better. This way, the information will be fresh in your mind, and you will be more confident when you actually take the FAA test.

WHO CAN TAKE THE TEST
When you are ready to take the FAA airman knowledge test, you must present evidence that you have completed the appropriate ground instruction or a home study course. This proof may be in the form of a graduation certificate from a pilot training course, a written statement, or a logbook entry by a certified ground or flight instructor. Although you are encouraged to obtain ground instruction, a home study course may be used. If you cannot provide one of the above documents, you may present evidence of a completed home study course to an FAA aviation safety inspector for approval.

You also must provide evidence of a permanent mailing address, appropriate identification, and proof of your age. The identification must include a current photograph, your signature, and your residential address, if different from your mailing address. You may present this information in more than one form of identification, such as a driver's license, government identification card, passport, alien residency (green) card, or a military identification card.

GENERAL INFORMATION — FAA COMPUTER TESTS
Detailed information on FAA computer testing is contained in FAA Order 8080.6, Conduct of Airman Knowledge Tests. This FAA order provides guidance for Flight Standards District Offices (FSDOs) and personnel associated with organizations that are participating in, or are seeking to participate in, the FAA Computer-Assisted Airman Knowledge Testing Program. You also may refer to FAA Order 8700.1, General Aviation Operations Inspector's Handbook, for guidance on computer testing by 14 CFR Parts 141 and 142 pilot schools that hold examining authority.

As an applicant, you don't need all of the details contained in FAA Orders, but you will be interested in some of the general information about computer testing facilities. A **Computer Testing Designee (CTD)** is an organization authorized by the FAA to administer FAA airman knowledge tests via the computer medium. A **Computer Testing Manager (CTM)** is a person selected by the CTD to serve as manager of its national computer testing program. A **Testing Center Supervisor (TCS)** is a person selected by the CTM, with FAA approval, to administer FAA airman knowledge tests at approved testing centers. The TCS is responsible for the operation of the testing center. A **Special Test Administrator (STA)** is a person selected by a CTD to administer FAA airman knowledge tests in unique situations and remote or isolated areas. A test proctor is a properly trained and qualified person, appointed by a TCS, authorized to administer FAA airman knowledge tests.

CTDs are selected by the FAA's Airman Testing Standards Branch. Those selected may include companies, schools, universities, or other organizations that meet specific requirements. For example, they must clearly demonstrate competence in computer technology, centralized database management, national communications network operation and maintenance, national facilities management, software maintenance and support, and technical training and customer support. They must provide computer-assisted testing, test administration, and data transfer service on a national scale. This means they must maintain a minimum of 20 operational testing centers geographically dispersed throughout the United States. In addition, CTDs must offer operational hours that are convenient to the public. An acceptable plan for test security is also required.

TEST MATERIALS, REFERENCE MATERIALS, AND AIDS
You are allowed to use aids, reference materials, and test materials within specified guidelines, provided the actual test questions or answers are not revealed. All models of aviation-oriented computers, regardless of manufacturer, may be used, including hand-held computers designed expressly for aviation use, and also small electronic calculators that perform arithmetic functions. Simple programmable memories, which allow addition to, subtraction from, or retrieval of one number from the memory, are acceptable. Simple functions such as square root or percent keys are also acceptable.

In addition, you may use any reference materials provided with the test. You will find that these reference materials are the same as those in your test guide. They include a printed airman knowledge testing supplement with the legend data and the applicable figures. You also may use scales, straight-edges, protractors, plotters, navigation computers, log sheets, and, as already mentioned, electronic or mechanical calculators that are directly related to the test. Permanently inscribed manufacturer's instructions on the front and back of these aids, such as, formulas, conversions, regulations, signals, weather data, holding pattern diagrams, frequencies, weight and balance formulas, and ATC procedures, are permissible.

WHAT TO EXPECT ON A COMPUTER TEST
Computer testing centers are required to have an acceptable method for the online registration of test applicants during normal business hours. They must provide a dual method, for example, keyboard, touch screen, or mouse, for answering questions. Features that must be provided also include an introductory lesson to familiarize you with computer testing procedures, the ability to return to a test question previously answered (for the purpose of review or answer changes), and a suitable display of multiple-choice and other question types on the computer screen in one frame. Other required features include a display of the time remaining for the completion of the test, a "HELP" function which permits you to review test questions and optional responses, and provisions for your test score on an Airman Knowledge Test Report.

On computer tests, the selection of questions is done for you, and you will answer the questions that appear on the screen. You will be given a specific amount of time to complete the test, which is based on past experience with others who have taken the exam. If you are prepared, you should have plenty of time to complete the test. After you begin the test, the screen will show you the time remaining for completion. When taking the test, keep the following points in mind:
1. Answer each question in accordance with the latest regulations and procedures. If the regulation or procedure has recently changed, you will receive credit for the affected question. However, these questions will normally be deleted or updated on the FAA computerized exams.

2. Read each question carefully before looking at the possible answers. You should clearly understand the problem before attempting to solve it.

3. After formulating an answer, determine which of the alternatives most nearly corresponds with that answer. The answer chosen should completely resolve the problem.

4. From the answers given, it may appear that there is more than one possible answer; however, there is only one answer that is correct and complete. The other answers are either incomplete or are derived from popular misconceptions.

5. Make sure you select an answer for each question. Questions left unanswered will be counted as incorrect.

6. If a certain question is difficult for you, it is best to proceed to other questions. After you answer the less difficult questions, return to those which were unanswered. The FAA computerized test format helps you identify unanswered questions, as well as those questions you wish to review.

7. When solving a calculator problem, select the answer nearest your solution. The problem has been checked with various types of calculators; therefore, if you have solved it correctly, your answer will be closer to the correct answer than the other choices.

8. Generally, the test results will be available almost immediately. Your score will be recorded on an Airman Knowledge Test Report form. [Figure A]

U.S. DEPARTMENT OF TRANSPORTATION
Federal Aviation Administration
Airman Knowledge Test Report

NAME: Jeffrey Scott   APPLICANT ID: 123456789

EXAM: Private Pilot-Airplane   EXAM ID: 90121120070468013

EXAM DATE: 12/11/2007   EXAM SITE: ABS80102

SCORE: 75%   GRADE: PASS   TAKE: 1

Below are learning statement codes which represent learning statements for incorrectly answered questions. For code descriptions, refer to the Learning Statement Reference Guide for Airman Knowledge Testing on the Internet: **www.faa.gov/education_research/testing/airmen/media/LearningStatementReferenceGuide.pdf** .

A single code may represent more than one incorrect response.

PLT012 PLT023 PLT090 PLT091 PLT141 PLT161 PLT173 PLT263 PLT366 PLT369 PLT420 PLT446

PLT447 PLT514

DO NOT LOSE THIS REPORT
(emboss here)

(Place red stamp above here)

EXPIRATION DATE: 12/31/2009

- -

Authorized instructor's statement. (If applicable)

On_____(date) I gave the above named applicant _____ hours of additional instruction in each subject area shown to be deficient and consider the applicant competent to pass the test.

Last_____ Initial _____ Cert. No. _____ Type _____
(Print clearly)

Signature _____

FRAUDULENT ALTERATION OF THIS FORM BY ANY PERSON IS A BASIS FOR SUSPENSION OR REVOCATION OF ANY CERTIFICATES OR RATINGS HELD BY THAT PERSON.

ISSUED BY: Computer Assisted Testing Service, CATS (01/06)

FEDERAL AVIATION ADMINISTRATION

Figure A. This sample Airman Knowledge Test Report shows the applicant's test results. Take 1 indicates this is the first time the applicant has taken this test. Learning statement codes for incorrect answers are included in the report, and an additional instruction section is included in the last part.

The Airman Knowledge Test Report includes learning statement codes for incorrect answers. To determine the knowledge area in which a particular question was incorrectly answered, compare the learning statement codes on this report to those in Appendix 1.

Computer testing designees must provide a way for applicants, who challenge the validity of test questions, to enter comments into the computer. The test proctor should advise you, if you have complaints about test scores, or specific test questions, to write directly to the appropriate FAA office. In addition to comments, you will be asked to respond to a critique form which may vary at different computer testing centers. The TCS must provide a method for you to respond to critique questions projected on the computer screen. [Figure B]

---

1. Did the test administration personnel give you an adequate briefing on testing procedures?

2. Was the "sign-on" accomplished efficiently?

3. Did you have any difficulty reading the computer presentation of test questions?

4. Was the test supplementary material (charts, graphs, tables, etc.) presented in a usable manner?

5. Did you have any difficulty using the "return to previous question for review" procedure?

6. Was the testing room noise level distracting?

7. Did you have adequate work space?

8. Did you have adequate lighting?

9. What is your overall evaluation of the computer testing experience?
   a. Unsatisfactory.
   b. Poor.
   c. Satisfactory.
   d. Highly satisfactory.
   e. Outstanding.

Figure B. Critique forms used at different computer testing centers may vary. This sample form contains typical questions.

RETESTING AFTER FAILURE

The applicant shall surrender the previous test report to the test proctor prior to retesting. The original test report shall be destroyed by the test proctor after administering the retest. The latest test taken will reflect the official score.

As stated in 14 CFR section 61.49, an applicant may apply for retesting after receiving additional training and an endorsement from an authorized instructor who has determined the applicant has been found competent to pass the test.

WHERE TO TAKE THE FAA TEST

Almost all testing is now administered via computer at FAA-designated test centers. As indicated, these CTDs are located throughout the U.S. You can expect to pay a fee and the cost varies at different locations. The following is a listing of the approved computer testing designees at the time of publication of this test guide. You might check with your local FSDO for changes.

Computer Assisted Testing Service (CATS)
www.catstest.com/
1-800-947-4228
Outside U.S. (650) 259-8550

PSI Testing
www.psiexams.com
1-800-211-2754

BUILDING PROFESSIONAL EXPERIENCE

This textbook chapter introduces some of the training requirements and the opportunities for pilots with instrument ratings and commercial certificates. It presents highlights of aviation history as well.

Each chapter and section in the Instrument Rating FAA Airman Knowledge Test Guide directly corresponds to the same chapter and section in the Guided Flight Discovery (GFD) Instrument/Commercial textbook. The textbook explores in depth each topic presented in this guide, and covers many areas not tested in the computer exam. This additional information is vital to your instrument rating preparation, and we strongly encourage you to study the textbook, in addition to this guide.

SECTION A — INSTRUMENT/COMMERCIAL TRAINING AND OPPORTUNITIES

INSTRUMENT PILOT PRIVILEGES

The addition of an instrument rating to your private pilot certificate allows you to fly under instrument flight rules (IFR). These regulations govern flight operations in weather conditions below VFR weather minimums.

OPERATING UNDER IFR

- When referring to weather conditions, the terms IFR and IMC (instrument meteorological conditions) are often used interchangeably, as are the terms VFR and VMC (visual meteorological conditions). In addition, the terms IFR and VFR can define the type of flight plan under which you are operating.

- Instrument and visual flight rules are contained in the Federal Aviation Regulations (FARs), which are part of the Code of Federal Regulations, Aeronautics and Space, Title 14 (14 CFR). Some of the FARs are contained in 14 CFR Part 1, 61, and 91).

- Instrument training enhances your skill at precisely controlling the aircraft, improves your ability to operate in the complex ATC system, and increases your confidence level. Statistics have shown the risk of a weather-related accident declines as pilots gain instrument flying experience.

REQUIREMENTS FOR INSTRUMENT RATING

- To be eligible for an instrument rating, you must hold a private pilot certificate, be able to read, write, speak, and understand the English language, and complete specific training and flight time requirements described in 14 CFR 61, as well as pass a knowledge and practical test.

- You must have at least 50 hours of cross-country time as pilot in command (PIC) and 40 hours of actual or simulated instrument time, including at least 15 hours of instrument flight training from an authorized instructor in the airplane.

- Some of your instrument time may be conducted with a safety pilot who is appropriately rated for the airplane. Part of your instrument training may be provided by an authorized instructor in a flight simulator, flight training device. or a personal computer-based aviation training device (PCATD).

MAINTAINING INSTRUMENT PROFICIENCY

- To meet recency of experience requirements for instrument flight, you must have intercepted and tracked courses through the use of navigation systems, performed holding procedures, and flown at least six instrument approaches within the preceding six calendar months.

- If you do not meet the instrument currency requirements within six calendar months or within six calendar months after that, you must pass an instrument proficiency check.

There are no Instrument FAA questions assigned to this section.

SECTION B — ADVANCED HUMAN FACTORS CONCEPTS

AERONAUTICAL DECISION MAKING

- Aeronautical decision making is a systematic approach to the mental process used by aircraft pilots to consistently determine the best course of action in response to a given set of circumstances.

- Approximately 75% of all aviation accidents are attributed to human factors-related causes. Studies have identified five hazardous attitudes which can interfere with a pilot's ability to make sound decisions and exercise authority properly.

PILOT-IN-COMMAND RESPONSIBILITY

As pilot in command, you are the final authority in the airplane you are flying. When only one pilot is in the cockpit, the PIC is obvious, but when two pilots are present, each pilot's responsibilities must be defined before the flight. Within the cockpit, one person is pilot in command, and the other serves to assist the PIC.

RESOURCE USE

- Resource use is an important part of human factors training. Cockpit resources increase as you fly more complex aircraft with advanced systems. If you are not thoroughly familiar with the equipment in your aircraft or you rely on it so much that you become complacent, flight safety is compromised.

- The focus of crew resource management (CRM) programs is the effective use of all available resources: human resources, hardware, and information. CRM training helps flight crews understand the limitations of human performance, especially under stressful situations, and makes them aware of the importance of crew coordination to combat error.

COMMUNICATION

- Readback of ATC clearances is crucial in the IFR environment. Do not assume controller silence after a readback is verification of your transmission. Ask for a verbal confirmation.

- When flying with another pilot, it is important to use standard terminology and verify that your meaning is understood. A breakdown in communication can cause friction and frustration, detracting from important tasks, or lead to a hazardous situation where one pilot believes the other is controlling the airplane, but in reality, neither pilot has control.

WORKLOAD MANAGEMENT

Effective workload management directly impacts safety by ensuring that you are prepared for the busiest segments of the flight through proper use of down time. Organizing charts in the order of use, setting radio frequencies, and writing down expected altitudes and route clearances will help you visualize and mentally prepare for what comes next.

SITUATIONAL AWARENESS

Controlled flight into terrain (CFIT) occurs when an aircraft is flown into terrain or water with no prior awareness on the part of the crew that the crash is imminent.

AVIATION PHYSIOLOGY

The study of aviation physiology is an important part of human factors training. How you feel, physically, has a direct impact on how well you fly.

DISORIENTATION

- When there is a conflict between the information relayed by your central vision and your peripheral vision, you may suffer from spatial disorientation. When subjected to the various forces of flight, the vestibular system can send misleading signals to the brain resulting in vestibular disorientation.

- A rapid acceleration during a missed approach can create the illusion of being in a nose-up attitude, and an abrupt change from climb to straight-and-level flight can create the illusion of tumbling backwards. To prevent or overcome spatial disorientation, you must rely on and properly interpret the indications of the flight instruments.

MOTION SICKNESS

Nausea, sweating, dizziness, and vomiting are some of the symptoms of motion sickness. To overcome motion sickness without outside visual references, you should focus on the instrument panel, since it is your only source of accurate position information.

HYPOXIA

- Hypoxia occurs when the tissues in the body do not receive enough oxygen. It can be caused by an insufficient supply of oxygen, inadequate transportation of oxygen, or the inability of the body tissues to use oxygen. Hypoxic hypoxia occurs when there are not enough molecules of oxygen available at sufficient pressure to pass between the membranes in your respiratory system.

- If you are planning a flight with a cruise altitude over 12,500 feet MSL, you should review FAR Part 91 for the requirements regarding supplemental oxygen. Prior to operating a pressurized aircraft with a service ceiling or maximum operating altitude higher than 25,000 feet MSL, you must complete high-altitude training.

- Hypemic hypoxia occurs when your blood is not able to carry a sufficient amount of oxygen to your body's cells. Since it attaches itself to the hemoglobin about 200 times more easily than does oxygen, carbon monoxide (CO) prevents the hemoglobin from carrying sufficient oxygen. Even without considering the dangers of incapacitating the flight crew, carbon monoxide poisoning can be fatal. Frequent inspections should be made of aircraft exhaust manifold-type heating systems to minimize the possibility of exhaust gases leaking into the cockpit.

- Stagnant hypoxia is an oxygen deficiency in the body due to the poor circulation of the blood. It can result from pulling excessive positive Gs. The inability of the cells to effectively use oxygen is defined as histotoxic hypoxia. This can be caused by alcohol and other drugs such as narcotics and poisons.

HYPERVENTILATION

Hyperventilation is a physiological disorder that develops when too much carbon dioxide (CO_2) has been eliminated from the body, usually caused by breathing too rapidly or too deeply. To overcome the symptoms of hyperventilation, you should slow your breathing rate.

DECOMPRESSION SICKNESS

Decompression sickness (DCS) is a painful condition that can occur if flying too soon after diving. It is very important that you allow enough time for the body to rid itself of excess nitrogen absorbed during diving.

FITNESS FOR FLIGHT

- Stress is the body's reaction to the physical and psychological demands placed upon it, and it can adversely affect your ability to fly safely. When you are fatigued, you are more prone to error in the cockpit. Getting adequate rest and improving your overall fitness will help you perform at your best.

- Preflight use of the I'm Safe Checklist will help ensure you are fit for flight. Consider illness, and medication that might affect your safety as a pilot. Factors such as rest, a good breakfast, and issues at work can interfere with your concentration level in the airplane. If you have any reservations about your ability to make the flight, save the trip for another time.

1-1   PLT280
Without visual aid, a pilot often interprets centrifugal force as a sensation of

A– rising or falling.
B– turning.
C– motion reversal.

1-1. Answer A. GFDIC 1B, IFH
A level turn that produces a load factor, such as 1.5 positive Gs, can give you the illusion of a climb.

1-2   PLT334
Abrupt head movement during a prolonged constant rate turn in IMC or simulated instrument conditions can cause

A– pilot disorientation.
B– false horizon.
C– elevator illusion

1-2. Answer A. GFDIC 1B, IFH
During prolonged constant-rate turns, abrupt head movements may set fluid in more than one semicircular canal in motion. This creates the strong sensation of turning or accelerating in an entirely different axis. The sensation, known as Coriolis illusion, causes serious disorientation.

1-3   PLT280
A sloping cloud formation, an obscured horizon, and a dark scene spread with ground lights and stars can create an illusion known as

A– elevator illusions.
B– autokinesis.
C– false horizons.

1-3. Answer C. GFDIC 1B, IFH
A sloping cloud formation, an obscured horizon, a dark scene spread with ground lights and stars, and certain geometric patterns of ground lights can provide inaccurate visual information for aligning the aircraft correctly with the actual horizon. This illusion is known as a false horizon.

1-4   PLT280
An abrupt change from climb to straight and level flight can create the illusion of

A– tumbling backwards.
B– a nose-up attitude.
C– a descent with the wings level.

1-4. Answer A. GFDIC 1B, IFH
The inversion illusion can occur when you abruptly change from a climb to straight-and-level flight. This abrupt change can create the feeling of tumbling backward.

1-5   PLT280

A rapid acceleration during takeoff can create the illusion of

A– spinning in the opposite direction.

B– being in a nose up attitude.

C– diving into the ground.

1-5. Answer B. GFDIC 1B, IFH

This somatographic illusion usually is associated with rapid acceleration such as that encountered on takeoff and gives you a feeling of being in a nose-up attitude.

1-6   PLT330

Why is hypoxia particularly dangerous during flights with one pilot?

A– Night vision may be so impaired that the pilot cannot see other aircraft.

B– Symptoms of hypoxia may be difficult to recognize before the pilot's reactions are affected.

C– The pilot may not be able to control the aircraft even if using oxygen.

1-6. Answer B. GFDIC 1B, IFH

An early symptom of hypoxia is impaired judgment. When the onset of hypoxia is rapid, your judgment may be so impaired that you will not recognize other symptoms.

1-7   PLT330

Tunnel vision and cyanosis are symptoms of

A– hypoxia.

B– hyperventilation.

C– carbon monoxide poisoning.

1-7. Answer A. GFDIC 1B, PHB

Hypoxia occurs when the tissues in the body do not receive enough oxygen. The symptoms of hypoxia include visual impairment (such as tunnel vision), cyanosis (blue fingernails and lips), headache, increased response time, impaired judgment, drowsiness, dizziness, tingling fingers and toes, numbness, and limp muscles.

1-8   PLT334

The sensations which lead to spatial disorientation during instrument flight conditions

A– are frequently encountered by beginning instrument pilots, but never by pilots with moderate instrument experience.

B– occur, in most instances, during the initial period of transition from visual to instrument flight.

C– must be suppressed and complete reliance placed on the indications of the flight instruments.

1-8. Answer C. GFDIC 1B IFH

Spatial disorientation can occur any time there is a lack of outside visual cues. In the absence of reliable visual information you become more aware of information provided by your body's motion and position sensing systems. These systems can be misleading and the only way to overcome spatial disorientation is to rely on the flight instruments.

1-9   PLT334
How can an instrument pilot best overcome spatial disorientation?

A– Rely on kinesthetic sense.

B– Use a very rapid cross-check.

C– Read and interpret the flight instruments, and act accordingly.

1-9. Answer C. GFDIC 1B, IFH
Spatial disorientation can occur any time there is a lack of outside visual cues. In the absence of reliable visual information referenced to the natural horizon, you must read and interpret the flight instruments, and act accordingly.

1-10   PLT334
How can an instrument pilot best overcome spatial disorientation?

A– Use a very rapid cross-check.

B– Properly interpret the flight instruments and act accordingly.

C– Avoid banking in excess of 30°.

1-10. Answer B. GFDIC 1B, IFH
In the absence of reliable visual information referenced to the natural horizon, you must read and interpret the flight instruments, and act accordingly.

1-11   PLT334
A pilot is more subject to spatial disorientation if

A– kinesthetic senses are ignored.

B– eyes are moved often in the process of cross-checking the flight instruments.

C– body signals are used to interpret flight attitude.

1-11. Answer C. GFDIC 1B, IFH
In the absence of reliable visual information, you become more aware of information provided by your body's motion and position sensing systems. Conflicting information is transmitted to the brain, creating spatial disorientation, especially when the body signals are used to interpret flight attitudes.

1-12   PLT334
Which procedure is recommended to prevent or overcome spatial disorientation?

A– Reduce head and eye movements to the extent possible.

B– Rely on the kinesthetic sense.

C– Rely on the indications of the flight instruments.

1-12. Answer C. GFDIC 1B, IFH
Spatial disorientation can occur anytime there is a lack of outside visual cues. In the absence of reliable visual information referenced to the natural horizon, you must read and interpret the flight instruments, and act accordingly.

1-13   **PLT332**

What action should be taken if hyperventilation is suspected?

A– Breathe at a slower rate by taking very deep breaths.

B– Consciously breathe at a slower rate than normal.

C– Consciously force yourself to take deep breaths and breathe at a faster rate than normal.

1-13. Answer B. GFDIC 1B, AFH

The treatment for hyperventilation involves restoring the proper carbon dioxide level to the body. Slowing the breathing rate down to a normal level is both the best prevention and the best cure. You also can breathe into a paper bag or talk aloud to overcome hyperventilation.

1-14   **PLT333**

Which statement is correct regarding the use of cockpit lighting for night flight?

A– Reducing the lighting intensity to a minimum level will eliminate blind spots.

B– The use of regular white light, such as a flashlight, will impair night adaptation.

C– Coloration shown on maps is least affected by the use of direct red lighting.

1-14. Answer B. GFDIC 1B, AFH

To maintain night vision, it is important to avoid bright lights before and during the flight. This includes sources of white light such as headlights, landing lights, strobe lights, or flashlights.

1-15   **PLT333**

Which use of cockpit lighting is correct for night flight?

A– Reducing the interior lighting intensity to a minimum level.

B– The use of regular white light, such as a flashlight, will not impair night adaptation.

C– Coloration shown on maps is least affected by the use of direct red lighting.

1-15. Answer A. GFDIC 1B, AFH

Reducing the interior lighting to a minimum level helps you to see outside visual references more clearly.

Principles of Instrument Flight

SECTION A — FLIGHT INSTRUMENT SYSTEMS

The instruments which provide information about the airplane's attitude, direction, altitude, and speed are collectively referred to as the flight instruments.

GYROSCOPIC INSTRUMENTS

- Gyroscopic instrument operation is based on rigidity in space and precession.
- The gyroscopic instruments are the attitude indicator, heading indicator, and turn coordinator.
- Prior to engine start, check the turn-and-slip indicator to determine if the needle is approximately centered and the tube is full of fluid. Turn on the master switch and listen for unusual noises from the electrically powered gyro. During taxi turns, the ball should move to the outside of the turn, and the needle should deflect in the direction of the turn.
- Give the vacuum-driven heading indicator and attitude indicator 5 minutes to spin up during taxi. Make sure that the horizon bar on the attitude indicator tilts no more than 5° during taxi turns, and that the heading indicator maintains proper alignment with the magnetic compass.

ATTITUDE INDICATOR

- The attitude indicator, or artificial horizon, is the only instrument that gives you an immediate and direct indication of the airplane's pitch and bank attitude.
- Pendulous vanes on vacuum-powered attitude indicators control the outflow of air from ports on the side of the gyro's shaft and near the bottom. Their purpose is to help erect the gyro.
- Errors in pitch and bank occur because the pendulous vanes act on the attitude indicator's gyro in an undesirable way during turns. These errors are minor; they are most noticeable as the aircraft rolls out of a 180° turn, and cancel after 360° of turn.
- Acceleration and deceleration also may induce precession errors. During acceleration, the horizon bar moves down, indicating a climb, and during deceleration, the instrument may indicate a slight descent.

HEADING INDICATOR

- When properly set, the heading indicator is your primary source of heading information.
- You must align the heading indicator with the magnetic compass before flight and recheck it periodically during flight.

TURN INDICATORS

- Turn indicators allow you to establish and maintain standard-rate turns of three degrees per second, or in the case of certain high performance aircraft, half-standard-rate turns.
- Both turn coordinators and turn-and-slip indicators indicate rate of turn, but because of the improved design of the turn coordinator, this instrument also indicates rate of roll as you enter a turn.
- One advantage of an electric turn coordinator is that it serves as a backup in case of vacuum system failure.
- During a constant-bank level turn, an increase in airspeed results in a decreased rate of turn, and an increased turn radius.
- The inclinometer is the part of the turn indicator that tells whether you are using the correct angle of bank for the rate of turn. Step on the ball to correct a slipping or skidding condition.

MAGNETIC COMPASS

- The magnetic compass is the only direction-seeking instrument in most light airplanes.
- Magnetic dip is responsible for the most significant compass errors, including northerly turning error.
- To compensate for northerly turning error in the northern hemisphere, you must roll out early on turns to the north, and turn past the compass-indicated heading on turns to the south. Remember the acronym, OSUN (Overshoot South, Undershoot North).
- If it is necessary to make turns without the aid of a gyroscopic heading indicator, the most accurate way is make a standard-rate timed turn.
- Another magnetic dip error, east-west acceleration error is described by the acronym, ANDS (Accelerate North, Decelerate South). When accelerating on an east-west heading the compass turns to the north and when decelerating, it turns to the south.
- Magnetic deviation is error due to magnetic interference with metal components in the aircraft, as well as magnetic fields from aircraft electrical equipment. It varies for different headings of the same aircraft.

PITOT-STATIC INSTRUMENTS

- The pitot-static instruments are the airspeed indicator, altimeter, and vertical speed indicator. Blockages in either the pitot or static systems affect the airspeed indicator, while the remaining instruments are affected only by static system blockage.
- The altimeter and static system, as well as the transponder, must have been inspected within the preceding 24 calendar months before flying IFR.

AIRSPEED INDICATOR

- The airspeed indicator operates by comparing ram air (pitot) pressure to ambient (static) pressure. Indicated airspeed is the result of this raw measurement.
- Calibrated airspeed (CAS) is indicated airspeed corrected for installation and instrument errors. Equivalent airspeed (EAS) is calibrated airspeed corrected for compressibility. True airspeed (TAS) is the actual speed your airplane moves through undisturbed air. Mach is the ratio of the aircraft's true airspeed to the speed of sound at the temperature and altitude in which the aircraft is flying.
- You should use the same indicated airspeed for takeoff, approach and landing at higher elevation airports, even though the corresponding groundspeed is faster.
- If, while maintaining a constant indicated altitude, you are able to maintain constant power as outside air temperature increases, true airspeed will increase.
- Design maneuvering speed (V_A) is one important value not shown by the color coding of an airspeed indicator. During operations in turbulence, you should slow the airplane below this speed.
- If you are flying in visible moisture and your airplane is equipped with pitot heat, it should be on to prevent pitot tube icing. Complete blockage of the pitot tube can cause the airspeed indicator to react opposite of normal, showing runaway airspeed as you climb, and extremely low airspeed in a descent.

ALTIMETER

- The most common altimeter error is failure to keep it set to the current barometric pressure.
- It indicates high when the actual pressure is lower than what is set in the window. The altimeter also indicates high when in colder than standard temperature conditions.
- Before an IFR flight, verify that the altimeter indicates within 75 feet of the actual field elevation when set to the current altimeter setting.
- Pressure altitude is displayed on the altimeter when it is set to the standard sea level pressure of 29.92 inches Hg. However, to provide for proper vertical separation of aircraft up to 17,999 feet MSL, all pilots should use the local altimeter setting so that their altimeters approximately indicate true altitude. At or above 18,000 feet MSL, all pilots must set their altimeters to 29.92 inches Hg.

VERTICAL SPEED INDICATOR

Although the VSI is a very useful instrument, it is not legally required for IFR flight. If this instrument erroneously indicates a climb or descent during taxi, you can simply use the observed value as a zero indication during flight.

2-1   PLT454

Your aircraft had the static pressure system and altimeter tested and inspected on January 5, of this year, and was found to comply with FAA standards. These systems must be reinspected and approved for use in controlled airspace under IFR by

A— January 5, next year.

B— January 5, 2 years hence.

C— January 31, 2 years hence.

2-1. Answer C. GFDIC 2A, FAR 91.411

The static pressure and altimeter systems must be tested and inspected every 24 calendar months. If the date of the last inspection was January 5, of this year, the systems must be reinspected by January 31, 2 years hence.

2-2   PLT454

An aircraft altimeter system test and inspection must be accomplished within

A— 12 calendar months.

B— 18 calendar months.

C— 24 calendar months.

2-2. Answer C. GFDIC 2A, FAR 91.411

The static pressure and altimeter systems must be tested and inspected every 24 calendar months. If the date of the last inspection was January 5, of this year, the systems must be reinspected by January 31, 2 years hence.

2-3   PLT405

An aircraft operated under 14 CFR part 91 IFR is required to have which of the following?

A— Radar altimeter.

B— Dual VOR system.

C— Gyroscopic direction indicator.

2-3. Answer C. GFDIC 2A, FAR 91.205

For operations under IFR, the required aircraft equipment includes the instruments and equipment required for visual flight rules plus a two-way radio, navigational equipment appropriate to the ground facilities to be used, a gyroscopic rate-of-turn indicator, a slip-skid indicator, a sensitive altimeter adjustable for barometric pressure, a clock displaying hours, minutes, and seconds with a sweep-second pointer or digital presentation, a generator or alternator of adequate capacity, a gyroscopic pitch and bank indicator, and a gyroscopic direction indicator (directional gyro or equivalent).

2-4   PLT445
You check the flight instruments while taxiing and find that the vertical speed indicator (VSI) indicates a descent of 100 feet per minute. In this case, you

A— must return to the parking area and have the instrument corrected by an authorized instrument repairman.

B— may take off and use 100 feet descent as the zero indication.

C— may not take off until the instrument is corrected by either the pilot or a mechanic.

2-4. Answer B. GFDIC 2A, IFH
If the vertical speed indicator (VSI) indicates a descent of 100 feet per minute while taxiing, you may use the 100-foot descent as the zero indication.

2-5   PLT345
Under what condition is pressure altitude and density altitude the same value?

A— At standard temperature.

B— When the altimeter setting is 29.92 inches Hg.

C— When indicated, and pressure altitudes are the samevalue on the altimeter.

2-5. Answer A. GFDIC 2A, IFH
Density altitude is pressure altitude corrected for non-standard temperature. Pressure altitude is read on your altimeter when it is set to standard sea level pressure (29.92 inches Hg). True altitude is the actual height of an object above mean sea level. When standard temperature and pressure exist at a given level, pressure altitude, density altitude, and true altitude will be equal.

2-6   PLT023
Under which condition will pressure altitude be equal to true altitude?

A— When the atmospheric pressure is 29.92 inches Hg.

B— When standard atmospheric conditions exist.

C— When indicated altitude is equal to the pressure altitude.

2-6. Answer B. GFDIC 2A (IFH)
Density altitude is pressure altitude corrected for non-standard temperature. Pressure altitude is read on your altimeter when it is set to standard sea level pressure (29.92 inches Hg). True altitude is the actual height of an object above mean sea level. When standard temperature and pressure exist at a given level, pressure altitude, density altitude, and true altitude will be equal.

2-7   PLT165
Which condition would cause the altimeter to indicate a lower altitude than actually flown (true altitude)?

A— Air temperature lower than standard.

B— Atmospheric pressure lower than standard.

C— Air temperature warmer than standard.

2-7. Answer C. GFDIC 2A, IFH
In temperatures that are warmer than standard, your true altitude will be higher than your indicated altitude. In contrast, colder than standard temperatures will result in true altitude being lower than indicated altitude.

2-8   PLT166

When an altimeter is changed from 30.11 inches Hg to 29.96 inches Hg, in which direction will the indicated altitude change and by what value?

A– Altimeter will indicate 15 feet lower.

B– Altimeter will indicate 150 feet lower.

C– Altimeter will indicate 150 feet higher.

2-8. Answer B. GFDIC 2A, IFH

In the lower atmosphere, pressure decreases approximately 1" Hg. for each 1,000-foot increase in altitude. In this case, the indicated altitude will decrease by 150 feet. You can compute this by taking the difference, in inches, between the two altimeter settings and multiplying it by 1,000 (30.11 - 29.96 = .15 × 1,000 = 150). Since the pressure has fallen, the altimeter will also indicate lower with the new setting.

2-9   PLT165

Under what condition will true altitude be lower than indicated altitude with an altimeter setting of 29.92 inches Hg?

A– In warmer than standard air temperature.

B– In colder than standard air temperature.

C– When density altitude is higher than indicated altitude.

2-9. Answer B. GFDIC 2A, IFH

The memory aid, "When flying from a high to a low or hot to cold, look out below," applies in this situation. In air temperatures below standard, true altitude is lower than indicated.

2-10   PLT166

Which of the following defines the type of altitude used when maintaining FL 210?

A– Indicated.

B– Pressure.

C– Calibrated.

2-10. Answer B. GFDIC 2A, FAR 91.121

When operating at or above 18,000 feet MSL, you must set the altimeter to 29.92. The altimeter then indicates pressure altitude.

2-11   PLT041

Altimeter setting is the value to which the scale of the pressure altimeter is set so the altimeter indicates

A– true altitude at field elevation.

B– pressure altitude at field elevation.

C– pressure altitude at sea level.

2-11. Answer A. GFDIC 2A, AW

Altimeter setting is the value to which the scale of the pressure altimeter is set so the altimeter indicates true altitude at field elevation. This is important because airport elevations, terrain, and obstructions are charted in true altitude.

2-12   PLT002
(Refer to figures 27 and 28.)

What CAS must be used to maintain the filed TAS at the flight planned altitude if the outside air temperature is -5°C?

A– 134 KCAS.

B– 139 KCAS.

C– 142 KCAS.

2-12. Answer B. GFDIC 2A, PHB
This question requires you to compute knots calibrated airspeed (KCAS). To do this, use the following steps.

1. Enter pressure altitude (8,000 feet).
2. Enter true airspeed (155 knots).
3. Enter outside air temperature (-5°C).
4. Compute CAS, 139 knots.

2-13   PLT002
(Refer to figure 32.)

What CAS must be used to maintain the filed TAS at the flight planned altitude if the outside air temperature is +8°C?

A– 154 KCAS.

B– 157 KCAS.

C– 163 KCAS.

2-13. Answer B. GFDIC 2A, PHB
This question requires you to compute knots calibrated airspeed (KCAS). To do this, use the following steps.

1. Enter pressure altitude (8,000 feet).
2. Enter true airspeed (180 knots).
3. Enter outside air temperature (+8°C).
4. Compute CAS, 157 knots.

2-14   PLT002
(Refer to figure 38.)

What CAS must be used to maintain the filed TAS at the flight planned altitude if the outside air temperature is +05°C?

A– 129 KCAS.

B– 133 KCAS.

C– 139 KCAS.

2-14. Answer A. GFDIC 2A, PHB
This question requires you to compute knots calibrated airspeed (KCAS). To do this, use the following steps.

1. Enter pressure altitude (11,000 feet).
2. Enter true airspeed (156 knots).
3. Enter outside air temperature (+5°C).
4. Compute CAS, 129 knots.

2-15   PLT002
(Refer to figure 44.)

What CAS must be used to maintain the filed TAS at the flight planned altitude if the outside air temperature is +5°C?

A– 147 KCAS.

B– 150 KCAS.

C– 154 KCAS.

2-15. Answer A. GFDIC 2A, PHB
This question requires you to compute knots calibrated airspeed (KCAS). To do this, use the following steps.

1. Enter pressure altitude (12,000 feet).
2. Enter true airspeed (180 knots).
3. Enter outside air temperature (+5°C).
4. Compute CAS, 147 knots.

2-16   PLT002
(Refer to figure 50.)

What CAS must be used to maintain the filed TAS at the flight planned altitude? (Temperature 0°C)

A— 136 KCAS.

B— 140 KCAS.

C— 147 KCAS.2-18

2-16. Answer B. GFDIC 2A, PHB
This question requires you to compute knots calibrated airspeed (KCAS). To do this use the following steps.

5. Enter pressure altitude (8,000 feet).

6. Enter true airspeed (158 knots).

7. Enter outside air temperature (0°C).

8. Compute CAS, 140 knots

2-17   PLT002
(Refer to figure 69.)

What CAS should be used to maintain the filed TAS if the outside air temperature is +05°C?

A— 119 KCAS.

B— 124 KCAS.

C— 126 KCAS.

2-17. Answer A. GFDIC 2A, PHB
This question requires you to compute knots calibrated airspeed (KCAS). To do this, use the following steps.

9. Enter pressure altitude (5,000 feet).

10. Enter true airspeed (128 knots).

11. Enter outside air temperature (+5°C).

12. Compute CAS, 119 knots.

2-18   PLT002
(Refer to figure 74.)

What CAS should be used to maintain the filed TAS at the flight planned altitude if the outside air temperature is +5°C?

A— 129 KCAS.

B— 133 KCAS.

C— 139 KCAS.

2-18. Answer B. GFDIC 2A, PHB
This question requires you to compute knots calibrated airspeed (KCAS). To do this, use the following steps.

13. Enter pressure altitude (11,000 feet).

14. Enter true airspeed (160 knots).

15. Enter outside air temperature (+5°C).

16. Computer CAS, 133 knots.

2-19   PLT300

How should you preflight check the altimeter prior to an IFR flight?

A– Set the altimeter to 29.92 inches Hg. With current temperature and the altimeter indication, determine the true altitude to compare with the field elevation.

B– Set the altimeter first with 29.92 inches Hg and then the current altimeter setting. The change in altitude should correspond to the change in setting.

C– Set the altimeter to the current altimeter setting. The indication should be within 75 feet of the actual elevation for acceptable accuracy.

2-19. Answer C. GFDIC 2A, IFH

Set the altimeter to the current altimeter setting. If it is within 75 feet of the actual elevation of your location, the altimeter is acceptable for use.

2-20   PLT166

What is the procedure for setting the altimeter when assigned an IFR altitude of 18,000 feet or higher on a direct flight off airways?

A– Set the altimeter to 29.92 inches Hg before take-off.

B– Set the altimeter to the current altimeter setting until reaching the assigned altitude, then set to 29.92 inches Hg.

C– Set the altimeter to the current reported setting for climbout and 29.92 inches Hg upon reaching 18,000 feet.

2-20. Answer C. GFDIC 2A, FAR 91.121

FAR Part 91.121 states that below 18,000 feet MSL, you must set your altimeter to the "... current reported altimeter setting of a station along the route and within 100 NM" or use the "... current reported altimeter setting available before departure." Above 18,000 feet MSL, you must set your altimeter to 29.92 inches Hg.

2-21   PLT166

En route at FL 290, the altimeter is set correctly, but not reset to the local altimeter setting of 30.57 inches Hg during descent. If the field elevation is 650 feet and the altimeter is functioning properly, what is the approximate indication upon landing?

A– 715 feet.

B– 1,300 feet.

C– Sea level.

2-21. Answer C. GFDIC 2A, IFH

One inch of pressure altitude equals 1,000 feet, and .65 (the difference between 30.57 and 29.92), equals 650 feet. Since your altimeter was not properly reset, you would be 650 feet lower then your actual altitude. For a landing at a field elevation of 650 feet, your indication would be zero (650 feet – 650 feet), or sea level.

2-22   PLT041

While you are flying at FL 250, you hear ATC give an altimeter setting of 28.92 inches Hg in your area. At what pressure altitude are you flying?

A– 24,000 feet.

B– 25,000 feet.

C– 26,000 feet

2-22. Answer B. GFDIC 2A, IFH

When above 18,000 feet MSL, your altimeter should be set to 29.92. In this case, 29.92 provides a pressure altitude of 25,000 feet which is FL 250.

2-23   PLT345

How can you obtain the pressure altitude on flights below 18,000 feet?

A– Set your altimeter to 29.92 inches Hg.

B– Use your computer to change the indicated altitude to pressure altitude.

C– Contact an FSS and ask for the pressure altitude.

2-23. Answer A. GFDIC 2A, IFH

Pressure altitude is displayed on your altimeter when it is set to the standard sea level atmospheric pressure of 29.92 inches Hg.

2-24   PLT345

How can you determine the pressure altitude at an airport without a tower or FSS?

A– Set the altimeter to 29.92 inches Hg and read the altitude indicated.

B– Set the altimeter to the current altimeter setting of a station within 100 miles and correct this indicated altitude with local temperature.

C– Use your computer and correct the field elevation for temperature.

2-24. Answer A. GFDIC 2A, IFH

Pressure altitude is displayed on your altimeter when it is set to the standard sea level atmospheric pressure of 29.92 inches Hg.

2-25   PLT345

Which altitude is indicated when the altimeter is set to 29.92 inches Hg?

A– Density.

B– Pressure.

C– Standard.

2-25. Answer B. GFDIC 2A, IFH

Pressure altitude is displayed on your altimeter when it is set to the standard sea level atmospheric pressure of 29.92 inches Hg. In this case, true altitude and pressure altitude are equal only when standard atmospheric conditions exist.

2-26   PLT166

If you are departing from an airport where you cannot obtain an altimeter setting, you should set your altimeter

A– on 29.92 inches Hg.

B– on the current airport barometric pressure, if known.

C– to the airport elevation.

2-26. Answer C. GFDIC 2A, IFH, FAR 91.121

Pressure altitude is displayed on your altimeter when it is set to the standard sea level atmospheric pressure of 29.92 inches Hg. At an airport where you cannot get the current altimeter setting, adjust your altimeter so it shows the field elevation.

2-27   PLT166

En route at FL 290, your altimeter is set correctly, but you fail to reset it to the local altimeter setting of 30.26 inches Hg during descent. If the field elevation is 134 feet and your altimeter is functioning properly, what will it indicate after landing?

A– 100 feet MSL.

B– 474 feet MSL.

C– 206 feet below MSL.

2-27. Answer C. GFDIC 2A, IFH

The question indicates your altimeter is set correctly at FL 290, meaning it was set at 29.92 inches Hg. The difference between 30.26 and 29.92 (30.26 – 29.92) equals 0.34. If one inch equals 1,000 feet, 0.34 equals 340 feet. Since you are still on 29.92, your altimeter would be showing 340 feet below field elevation, or 206 feet below mean sea level (MSL) (134 feet – 340 feet). Pressure altitude is what you read on your altimeter when it is set to the standard sea level setting, 29.92. Local altimeter settings adjust for field elevation above mean sea level.

2-28   PLT166

How does a pilot normally obtain the current altimeter setting during an IFR flight in Class E airspace below 18,000 feet?

A– The pilot should contact ARTCC at least every 100 NM and request the altimeter setting.

B– FSS's along the route broadcast the weather information at 15 minutes past the hour.

C– ATC periodically advises the pilot of the proper altimeter setting.

2-28. Answer C. GFDIC 2A, AIM

When an aircraft is enroute on an instrument flight plan, ATC will furnish this information to the pilot at least once while the aircraft is in each controller's airspace.

2-29   PLT041

(Refer to figure 83.)

Which altimeter depicts 12,000 feet?

A– 2.

B– 3.

C– 4.

2-29. Answer C. GFDIC 2A, IFH

The depicted altimeter has three hands. The longest has a triangular tip and it indicates 10,000-foot increments; the short, thick hand shows 1,000-foot increments; and the long, thin hand shows 100-foot increments. The 12,000-foot indication is displayed by altimeter 4.

2-30 PLT041
(Refer to figure 84.)

Which altimeter depicts 8,000 feet?

A– 1.

B– 2.

C– 3.

2-30. Answer B. GFDIC 2A, IFH
The depicted altimeter has three hands. The longest has a triangular tip and it indicates 10,000-foot increments; the short, thick hand shows 1,000-foot increments; and the long, thin hand shows 100-foot increments. The 8,000-foot indication is displayed by altimeter 2.

2-31 PLT118
What indication should be observed on a turn coordinator during a left turn while taxiing?

A– The miniature aircraft will show a turn to the left and the ball remains centered.

B– The miniature aircraft will show a turn to the right and the ball moves to the left.

C– Both the miniature aircraft and the ball will remain centered.

2-31. Answer B. GFDIC 2A, IFH
During taxi turns, the turn coordinator and heading indicator should display a turn in the correct direction. The ball in the inclinometer should swing to the outside of the turn. Therefore, in a right turn, the miniature aircraft shows a turn to the right and the ball moves to the left.

2-32 PLT215
On the taxi check, the magnetic compass should

A– swing opposite to the direction of turn when turning from north.

B– exhibit the same number of degrees of dip as the latitude.

C– swing freely and indicate known headings.

2-32. Answer C. GFDIC 2A, IFH
Prior to flight, make sure the compass is full of fluid. During taxi, the compass should swing freely and indicate known headings while taxiing straight or stopped.

2-33 PLT118
Which condition during taxi is an indication that an attitude indicator is unreliable?

A– The horizon bar tilts more than 5° while making taxi turns.

B– The horizon bar vibrates during warmup.

C– The horizon bar does not align itself with the miniature airplane after warmup.

2-33. Answer A. GFDIC 2A, IFH
After starting the engines the gyros normally reach full operating speed in approximately five minutes. During this time, it is common to see some vibration in the instruments. After warmup and during normal taxi turns, the attitude indicator should not tilt more than 5° while on level ground.

2-34   PLT187

What does the miniature aircraft of the turn coordinator directly display?

A– Rate of roll and rate of turn.

B– Angle of bank and rate of turn.

C– Angle of bank.

2-34. Answer A. GFDIC 2A, IFH

The gimbal in the turn coordinator is set at an angle, or canted. This allows gyro precession to sense both rate of roll and rate of turn.

2-35   PLT300

What pretakeoff check should be made of the attitude indicator in preparation for an IFR flight?

A– The horizon bar does not vibrate during warmup.

B– The miniature airplane should erect and become stable within 5 minutes.

C– The horizon bar should erect and become stable within 5 minutes.

2-35. Answer C. GFDIC 2A, IFH

After starting the engines the gyros normally reach full operating speed in approximately five minutes. During this time, it is common to see some vibration in the instruments. When the gyros have stabilized, the horizon bar in the attitude indicator should stop vibrating and remain level within 5° while the airplane is stopped or taxiing straight ahead on level ground.

2-36   PLT248

During a skidding turn to the right, what is the relationship between the component of lift, centrifugal force, and load factor?

A– Centrifugal force is less than horizontal lift and the load factor is increased.

B– Centrifugal force is greater than horizontal lift and the load factor is increased.

C– Centrifugal force and horizontal lift are equal and the load factor is decreased.

2-36. Answer B. GFDIC 2A, IFH)

During a skid, centrifugal force exceeds the horizontal component of lift. This will make the rate of turn too great for the angle of bank. As a result the ball of the inclinometer moves to the outside of the turn, and load factor increases.

2-37   PLT187

What indications are displayed by the miniature aircraft of a turn coordinator?

A– Rate of roll and rate of turn.

B– Direct indication of bank angle and pitch attitude.

C– Indirect indication of bank angle and pitch attitude.

2-37. Answer A. GFDIC 2A, IFH

The gimbal in the turn coordinator is set at an angle, or canted. This allows gyro precession to sense both rate of roll and rate of turn.

2-38   PLT337

If the pitot tube ram air pressure hole and drain hole become obstructed, the airspeed indicator will operate

A– like an altimeter as the aircraft climbs and descends.

B– like a very sluggish airspeed indicator lagging all changes by minutes.

C– normally due to the static port pressure changes..

2-38. Answer A. GFDIC 2A, PHB

If both the ram air input and the drain hole of a pitot tube become obstructed simultaneously, the airspeed indicator will operate like an altimeter as the airplane climbs and descends. In this case, a climb results in an increase in indicated airspeed, and a descent results in a decrease in indicated airspeed

2-39   PLT337

If both the ram air input and drain hole of the pitot system are blocked, what airspeed indication can be expected?

A– Increase of indicated airspeed during a climb.

B– Decrease of indicated airspeed during a climb.

C– Constant indicated airspeed during any change in altitude.

2-39. Answer A. GFDIC 2A, PHB

If both the ram air input and the drain hole of a pitot tube become obstructed simultaneously, the airspeed indicator will operate like an altimeter as the airplane climbs and descends. In this case, a climb results in an increase in indicated airspeed, and a descent results in a decrease in indicated airspeed.

2-40   PLT187

What indication is presented by the miniature aircraft of the turn coordinator?

A– Indirect indication of the bank attitude.

B– Direct indication of the bank attitude and the quality of the turn.

C– Quality of the turn.

2-40. Answer A. GFDIC 2A, IFH

The turn coordinator gives an indirect indication of the aircraft's bank attitude, while the miniature airplane of a turn coordinator provides a direct indication of an aircraft's rate of turn. When the miniature airplane is aligned with the turn index, you are in a standard-rate turn (3° per second).

2-41   PLT118

During normal operation of a vacuum-driven attitude indicator, what attitude indication should you see when rolling out from a 180° skidding turn to straight-and-level coordinated flight?

A– A straight-and-level coordinated flight indication.

B– A nose-high indication relative to level flight.

C– The miniature aircraft shows a turn in the direction opposite the skid.

2-41. Answer C. GFDIC 2A, IFH

In attitude indicators, a skidding turn precesses the gyro to the inside of the turn. When an aircraft returns to straight-and-level flight from a skidding turn, the miniature airplane will show a turn in the direction opposite the skid.

2-42   PLT118

During normal coordinated turns, what error due to precession should you observe when rolling out to straight-and-level flight from a 180° steep turn to the right?

A– A straight-and-level coordinated flight indication.

B– The miniature aircraft would show a slight turn indication to the left.

C– The miniature aircraft would show a slight descent and wings-level attitude.

2-42. Answer B. GFDIC 2A, IFH

Centrifugal force in a turn can cause some attitude indicators to precess, creating errors in both pitch and bank. The effect is greatest in a 180° steep turn. For example, when rolling out of a 180° steep turn to straight-and-level flight, the attitude indicator will show a slight climb and turn in the opposite direction.

2-43   PLT036

What information does a Mach meter present?

A– The ratio of aircraft true airspeed to the speed of sound.

B– The ratio of aircraft indicated airspeed to the speed of sound.

C– The ratio of aircraft equivalent airspeed, corrected for installation error, to the speed of sound.

2-43. Answer A. GFDIC 2A, IFH

In high performance aircraft, some limiting airspeeds are based on a relationship to the speed of sound. These aircraft usually have a Mach indicator or Mach meter in addition to an airspeed indicator. Mach indicators simply show the ratio of the aircraft's true airspeed to the speed of sound at the flight altitude.

2-44   PLT248

What is the relationship between centrifugal force and the horizontal lift component in a coordinated turn?

A– Horizontal lift exceeds centrifugal force.

B– Horizontal lift and centrifugal force are equal.

C– Centrifugal force exceeds horizontal lift.

2-44. Answer B. GFDIC 2A, IFH

During a turn lift can be divided into two components, a vertical component and a horizontal component. Weight opposes the vertical component of lift while centrifugal force opposes the horizontal component. Once established in the turn, the horizontal component of lift and centrifugal force will be equal.

2-45   PLT248

What force causes an airplane to turn?

A– Rudder pressure or force around the vertical axis.

B– Vertical lift component.

C– Horizontal lift component.

2-45. Answer C. GFDIC 2A, IFH

During a turn lift can be divided into two components, a vertical component and a horizontal component.

2-46   PLT215

What should be the indication on the magnetic compass as you roll into a standard rate turn to the left from an east heading in the Northern Hemisphere?

A– The compass will initially indicate a turn to the right.

B– The compass will remain on east for a short time, then gradually catch up to the magnetic heading of the aircraft.

C– The compass will indicate the approximate correct magnetic heading if the roll into the turn is smooth.

2-46. Answer C. GFDIC 2A, IFH

In the northern hemisphere, compass turning errors are most apparent when turning from a heading of north or south. For example, when making a turn from a northerly heading, the compass will give an initial indication of a turn in the opposite direction. When making a turn from a southerly heading, the compass will give an indication of a turn in the correct direction, but it will lead the actual heading. On headings of east or west, these turning errors are minimized.

2-47   PLT337

What would be the indication on the VSI during entry into a 500 FPM actual descent from level flight if the static ports were iced over?

A– The indication would be in reverse of the actual rate of descent (500 FPM climb).

B– The initial indication would be a climb, then descent at a rate in excess of 500 FPM.

C– The VSI pointer would remain at zero regardless of the actual rate of descent.

2-47. Answer C. GFDIC 2A, IFH

If the static port is iced over, the airspeed indicator will still indicate changes in airspeed, but they will not be correct. When operating above the altitude where the static port became clogged, the airspeed will read lower than it should. Conversely, when you are operating below that altitude, the indicator will read higher than the correct value. A blocked static port will also freeze the altimeter at the altitude the blockage occurred, and the vertical speed indicator (VSI) will freeze at zero showing no indication of a descent or a climb.

2-48   PLT300

How should you preflight check the altimeter prior to an IFR flight?

A– Set the altimeter to the current temperature. With current temperature and the altimeter indication, determine the calibrated altitude to compare with the field elevation.

B– Set the altimeter first with 29.92" Hg and then the current altimeter setting. The change in altitude should correspond to the change in setting.

C– Set the altimeter to the current altimeter setting. The indication should be within 75 feet of the actual elevation for acceptable accuracy.

2-48. Answer C. GFDIC 2A, IFH

Prior to taking off, you should check the altimeter for the proper reading. To do this, set the altimeter to the current altimeter setting and check to see that the indicated altitude is within 75 feet of the actual field elevation. If it is, the altimeter is generally considered acceptable for use, provided other required inspections have been accomplished.

2-49   PLT118
Which practical test should be made on the electric gyro instruments prior to starting an engine?

A– Check that the electrical connections are secure on the back of the instruments.

B– Check that the attitude of the miniature aircraft is wings level before turning on electrical power.

C– Turn on the electrical power and listen for any unusual or irregular mechanical noise.

2-49. Answer C. GFDIC 2A, IFH
Prior to starting an engine, turn on the electrical power and listen for any unusual noises from the electrical gyros.

2-50   PLT187
Prior to starting an engine, you should check the turn-and-slip indicator to determine if the

A– needle indication properly corresponds to the angle of the wings or rotors with the horizon.

B– needle is approximately centered and the tube is full of fluid.

C– ball will move freely from one end of the tube to the other when the aircraft is rocked.

2-50. Answer B. GFDIC 2A, IFH
Prior to starting an aircraft, check to make sure the needle of the turn-and-slip indicator is centered and the inclinometer is full of fluid.

2-51   PLT187
What indications should you observe on the turn-and-slip indicator during taxi?

A– The ball moves freely opposite the turn, and the needle deflects in the direction of the turn.

B– The needle deflects in the direction of the turn, but the ball remains centered.

C– The ball deflects opposite the turn, but the needle remains centered.

2-51. Answer A. GFDIC 2A, IFH
When turning during ground operations, centrifugal force will cause the gyro in a turn-and-slip indicator to precess and deflect the needle in the direction of the turn. In addition, the centrifugal force also will cause the ball in the inclinometer to move in the opposite direction of the turn.

2-52   PLT185
Which instrument indicates the quality of a turn?

A– Attitude indicator.

B– Heading indicator or magnetic compass.

C– Ball of the turn coordinator.

2-52. Answer C. GFDIC 2A, PHB
The inclinometer (ball of the turn coordinator) shows the relationship between the opposing horizontal forces in a turn. This provides an indication of the quality of a turn.

2-53   PLT300

What pretakeoff check should be made of a vacuum-driven heading indicator in preparation for an IFR flight?

A– After 5 minutes, set the indicator to the magnetic heading of the aircraft and check for proper alignment after taxi turns.

B– After 5 minutes, check that the heading indicator card aligns itself with the magnetic heading of the aircraft.

C– Determine that the heading indicator does not precess more than 2° in 5 minutes of ground operation.

2-53. Answer A. GFDIC 2A, IFH

Once the aircraft is started, the vacuum-driven gyros should reach full operating speed within 5 minutes. After this time, set the heading indicator to the magnetic heading as indicated on the compass. While taxiing, make sure the heading indicator maintains its proper alignment after each turn.

2-54   PLT215

What should be the indication on the magnetic compass as you roll into a standard rate turn to the right from an easterly heading in the Northern Hemisphere?

A– The compass will remain on east for a short time, then gradually catch up to the magnetic heading of the aircraft.

B– The compass will initially indicate a turn to the left.

C– The compass will indicate the approximate correct magnetic heading if the roll into the turn is smooth.

2-54. Answer C. GFDIC 2A, IFH

In the northern hemisphere, compass turning errors are most apparent when turning from a heading of north or south. For example, when making a turn from a northerly heading, the compass will give an initial indication of a turn in the opposite direction. When making a turn from a southerly heading, the compass will give an indication of a turn in the correct direction, but it will lead the actual heading. On headings of east or west, these turning errors are minimized.

2-55   PLT215

What should be the indication on the magnetic compass as you roll into a standard rate turn to the right from a south heading in the Northern Hemisphere?

A– The compass will initially indicate a turn to the left.

B– The compass will indicate a turn to the right, but at a faster rate than is actually occurring

C– The compass will remain on south for a short time, then gradually catch up to the magnetic heading of the aircraft.

2-55. Answer B. GFDIC 2A, IFH

In the northern hemisphere, compass turning errors are most apparent when turning from a heading of north or south. For example, when making a turn from a northerly heading, the compass will give an initial indication of a turn in the opposite direction. When making a turn from a southerly heading, the compass will give an indication of a turn in the correct direction, leading the actual heading. On headings of east or west, these turning errors are minimized. During turns from a heading of south, in the northern hemisphere the compass will lead the actual heading of the aircraft.

2-56   PLT215

On what headings will the magnetic compass read most accurately during a level 360° turn, with a bank of approximately 15°?

A– 135° through 225°.

B– 90° and 270°.

C– 180° and 0°.

2-56. Answer B. GFDIC 2A, IFH

In the northern hemisphere, compass turning errors are most apparent when turning from a heading of north or south. For example, when making a turn fro a northerly heading, the compass will give an initial indication of a turn in the opposite direction. When making a turn from a southerly heading, the compass will give an indication of a turn in the correct direction, but it will lead the actual heading. On headings of east or west, these turning errors are minimized.

2-57   PLT215

What causes the northerly turning error in a magnetic compass?

A– Coriolis force at the mid-latitudes.

B– Centrifugal force acting on the compass card.

C– The magnetic dip characteristic.

2-57. Answer C. GFDIC 2A, IFH

In the northern hemisphere, compass turning errors are most apparent when turning from a heading of north or south. This error increases as you near the poles due to magnetic dip and the vertical component of the earth's magnetic field.

2-58   PLT215

What should be the indication on the magnetic compass when you roll into a standard-rate turn to the left from a south heading in the Northern Hemisphere?

A– The compass will initially indicate a turn to the right.

B– The compass will indicate a turn to the left, but at a faster rate than is actually occurring.

C– The compass will remain on south for a short time, then gradually catch up to the magnetic heading of the aircraft.

2-58. Answer B. GFDIC 2A, IFH

In the northern hemisphere, compass turning errors are most apparent when turning from a heading of north or south. For example, when making a turn from a southerly heading, the compass will give an indication of a turn in the correct direction, but it will lead the actual heading. When making a turn from a northerly heading, the compass will give an initial indication of a turn in the opposite direction. On headings of east or west, these turning errors are minimized.

2-59   PLT215

What should be the indication on the magnetic compass as you roll into a standard rate turn to the right from a westerly heading in the Northern Hemisphere?

A– The compass will remain on a westerly heading for a short time, then gradually catch up to the actual heading of the aircraft.

B– The compass will initially show a turn in the opposite direction, then turn to a northerly indication but lagging behind the actual heading of the aircraft.

C– The compass will indicate the approximate correct magnetic heading if the roll into the turn is smooth.

2-59. Answer C. GFDIC 2A, IFH

In the northern hemisphere, compass turning errors are most apparent when turning from a heading of north or south. On easterly or westerly headings, compass turning errors are minimal.

2-60   PLT215

What should be the indication on the magnetic compass as you roll into a standard-rate turn to the right from a northerly heading in the Northern Hemisphere?

A– The compass will remain on north for a short time, then gradually catch up to the magnetic heading of the aircraft.

B– The compass will initially indicate a turn to the left

C– The compass will indicate a turn to the right, but at a faster rate than is actually occurring.

2-60. Answer B. GFDIC 2A, IFH

In the northern hemisphere, compass turning errors are most apparent when turning from a heading of north or south. For example, when making a turn from a northerly heading, the compass will give an initial indication of a turn in the opposite direction.

2-61   PLT215

What should be the indication on the magnetic compass as you roll into a standard rate turn to the left from a west heading in the Northern Hemisphere?

A– The compass will initially indicate a turn to the right.

B– The compass will remain on west for a short time, then gradually catch up to the magnetic heading of the aircraft.

C– The compass will indicate the approximate correct magnetic heading if the roll into the turn is smooth.

2-61. Answer C. GFDIC 2A, IFH

In the northern hemisphere, compass turning errors are most apparent when turning from a heading of north or south. On easterly or westerly headings, compass turning errors are minimal.

In the northern hemisphere, compass turning errors are most apparent when turning from a heading of north or south. For example, when making a turn from a northerly heading, the compass will give an initial indication of a turn in the opposite direction.

2-62   PLT215

What should be the indication on the magnetic compass as you roll into a standard-rate turn to the left from a north heading in the Northern Hemisphere?

A– The compass will remain on north for a short time, then gradually catch up to the magnetic heading of the aircraft.

B– The compass will indicate a turn to the left, but at a faster rate than is actually occurring.

C– The compass will initially indicate a turn to the right

2-62. Answer C. GFDIC 2A, IFH

In the northern hemisphere, compass turning errors are most apparent when turning from a heading of north or south. For example, when making a turn from a northerly heading, the compass will give an initial indication of a turn in the opposite direction.

2-63   PLT187

If a half-standard rate turn is maintained, how long would it take to turn 360°?

A– 1 minute.

B– 2 minutes.

C– 4 minutes.

2-63. Answer C. GFDIC 2A, IFH

A standard-rate turn is 3° per second. At this rate, you will complete a 180° turn in one minute and a 360° turn in two minutes. A half-standard-rate turn will result in a turn rate of one point five degrees (1.5°) per second.

2-64   PLT187

If a standard rate turn is maintained, how long would it take to turn 180°?

A– 1 minute.

B– 2 minutes.

C– 3 minutes.

2-64. Answer A. GFDIC 2A, IFH

A standard-rate turn is 3° per second. At this rate, you will complete a 180° turn in one minute and a 360° turn in two minutes. A half-standard-rate turn will result in a turn rate of one point five degrees (1.5°) per second.

2-65   PLT187

If a half-standard rate turn is maintained, how much time would be required to turn clockwise from a heading of 090° to a heading of 180°?

A– 30 seconds.

B– 1 minute.

C– 1 minute 30 seconds.

2-65. Answer B. GFDIC 2A, IFH

A standard-rate turn is 3° per second. At this rate, you will complete a 180° turn in one minute and a 360° turn in two minutes. A half-standard-rate turn will result in a turn rate of one point five degrees (1.5°) per second.

2-66   PLT278

Errors in both pitch and bank indication on an attitude indicator are usually at a maximum as the aircraft rolls out of a

A– 180° turn.

B– 270° turn.

C– 360° turn.

2-66. Answer A. GFDIC 2A, IFH

Centrifugal force in a turn can cause some attitude indicators to precess, creating errors in both pitch and bank. These errors are usually minor and result in deviations of no more than five degrees of bank and one bar-width of pitch. The effect is greatest in a 180° steep turn.

2-67   PLT278

If a 180° steep turn is made to the right and the aircraft is rolled out to straight-and-level flight by visual references, the attitude indicator

A– should immediately show straight-and-level flight.

B– will show a slight skid and climb to the right.

C– may show a slight climb and turn.

2-67. Answer C. GFDIC 2A, IFH

Centrifugal force in a turn can cause some attitude indicators to precess, creating errors in both pitch and bank. These errors are usually minor and result in deviations of no more than 5 degrees of bank and one bar-width of pitch. The effect is greatest in a 180° steep turn. For example, when you roll out of a 180° steep turn to straight-and-level flight. The attitude indicator may show a slight climb and turn.

2-68   PLT118

One characteristic that a properly functioning gyro depends upon for operation is the

A– ability to resist precession 90° to any applied force.

B– resistance to deflection of the spinning wheel or disc.

C– deflecting force developed from the angular velocity of the spinning wheel.

2-68. Answer B. GFDIC 2A, IFH

Gyros are affected by two principles — rigidity in space and precession. Rigidity in space means that once a gyro is spinning, it tends to remain in a fixed position and resists external forces applied to it. This principle allows a gyroscope to be used to measure changes in attitude or direction.

2-69   PLT187

If a standard rate turn is maintained, how much time would be required to turn to the right from a heading of 090° to a heading of 270°?

A– 1 minute.

B– 2 minutes.

C– 3 minutes.

2-69. Answer A. GFDIC 2A, AIM

A standard-rate turn is a turn at a rate of three degrees per second. At this rate, you will complete a 360° turn in two minutes. Since the heading change in this question is 180° (270 – 090 = 180), it will take one minute to complete the standard-rate turn.

2-70   PLT187
If a standard rate turn is maintained, how much time would be required to turn to the left from a heading of 090° to a heading of 300°?

A– 30 seconds.

B– 40 seconds.

C– 50 seconds.

2-70. Answer C. GFDIC 2A, AIM
The degree of heading change in this example is 150° (360 – 300 = 60 + 90 = 150). Since a standard-rate turn results in a turn rate of 3 degrees per second, the time to turn 150° is 50 seconds (150 ÷ 3 = 50).

2-71   PLT187
If a half-standard rate turn is maintained, how long would it take to turn 135°?

A– 1 minute.

B– 1 minute 20 seconds.

C– 1 minute 30 seconds.

2-71. Answer C. GFDIC 2A, AIM
If a standard-rate turn is 3 degrees per second, a half standard-rate turn results in a 1-1/2 degrees per second turn. At a half-standard-rate turn, it will take one minute thirty seconds to turn 135° (135 ÷ 1-1/2 = 90 seconds).

2-72   PLT337
If, while in level flight, it becomes necessary to use an alternate source of static pressure vented inside the airplane, which of the following should the pilot expect?

A– The gyroscopic instruments to become inoperative.

B– The altimeter and airspeed indicator to become inoperative.

C– The vertical speed to momentarily show a climb.

2-72. Answer C. GFDIC 2A, IFH
Due to slipstream, the pressure inside the cabin is less than that of the outside air. If an alternate static source is selected that is inside the aircraft, the altimeter will read a little high, the airspeed a little fast, and the vertical speed indicator (VSI) will initially indicate a climb.

2-73   PLT337
During flight, if the pitot-tube becomes clogged with ice, which of the following instruments would be affected?

A– The airspeed indicator only.

B– The airspeed indicator and the altimeter.

C– The airspeed indicator, altimeter, and vertical speed indicator.

2-73. Answer A. GFDIC 2A, IFH
The airspeed indicator is the only instrument affected by a pitot tube blockage. There are two ways the system can become blocked. First, the ram air inlet can clog, while the drain hole remains open. In this situation, the pressure in the line to the airspeed indicator will vent out the drain hole, causing the airspeed indicator to drop to zero. The second situation occurs when both the ram air inlet and drain hole become blocked. When this occurs, the air pressure in the line is trapped and, during level flight, the airspeed indicator no longer indicates changes in airspeed.

2-74   PLT166
The local altimeter setting should be used by all pilots in a particular area, primarily to provide for

A– the cancellation of altimeter error due to nonstandard temperatures aloft.

B– better vertical separation of aircraft.

C– more accurate terrain clearance in mountainous areas.

2-74. Answer B. GFDIC 2A, IFH
The altimeter setting system provides you with the means to correct your altimeter for pressure variations. The system is necessary to ensure safe terrain clearance for instrument approaches and landings, and to maintain vertical separation between aircraft during instrument weather.

2-75   PLT019
At an altitude of 6,500 feet MSL, the current altimeter setting is 30.42 inches Hg. The pressure altitude would be approximately

A– 7,500 feet.

B– 6,000 feet.

C– 6,500 feet.

2-75. Answer C. GFDIC 2A, IFH
To find the current pressure altitude, compute the difference between the current altimeter setting and 29.92. In this example it's .50 inches (30.42 – 29.92 = .50). Since the pressure decreases about one inch for every 1,000-foot increase in altitude, .50 inches is equivalent to about 500 feet. With a current altimeter setting above standard (30.42) you need to subtract 500 feet from the indicated altitude of 6,500 feet. The answer is 6,000 feet (6,500 – 500 = 6,000).

2-76   PLT345
The pressure altitude at a given location is indicated on the altimeter after the altimeter is set to

A– the field elevation.

B– 29.92 inches Hg.

C– the current altimeter setting.

2-76. Answer B. GFDIC 2A, AW
Pressure altitude is always referenced to the standard datum plane where the barometric pressure is 29.92 inches Hg.

2-77   PLT005
If the outside air temperature increases during a flight at constant power and at a constant indicated altitude, the true airspeed will

A– decrease and true altitude will increase.

B– increase and true altitude will decrease.

C– increase and true altitude will increase.

2-77. Answer C. GFDIC 2A, IFH
True airspeed compensates for nonstandard pressure and temperature and represents the true speed of your airplane through the air. As atmospheric pressure decreases or air temperature increases, the density of the air decreases. As the air density decreases at a given indicated airspeed, true airspeed increases. True altitude is the actual height of an object above mean sea level. Your altimeter displays true altitude only under standard conditions. As temperatures increase, true altitude also increases.

2-78   PLT132

When an aircraft is accelerated, some attitude indicators will precess and incorrectly indicate a

A– climb.

B– descent.

C– right turn.

2-78. Answer A. GFDIC 2A, IFH

In addition to centrifugal force, acceleration and deceleration also may induce precession errors in gyros. For example, while accelerating, the attitude indicator can precess down and indicate a climb. When this occurs, the normal tendency is to lower the pitch attitude. This can be hazardous during a low visibility, low ceiling take-off and climb.

2-79   PLT132

When an aircraft is decelerated, some attitude indicators will precess and incorrectly indicate a

A– left turn.

B– climb.

C– descent.

2-79. Answer C. GFDIC 2A, IFH

In addition to centrifugal force, acceleration and deceleration also may induce precession errors in gyros. For example, while accelerating, the attitude indicator can precess down and indicate a climb. When this occurs, the normal tendency is to lower the pitch attitude. This can be hazardous during a low visibility, low ceiling take-off and climb.

2-80   PLT187

The displacement of a turn coordinator during a coordinated turn will

A– indicate the angle of bank.

B– remain constant for a given bank regardless of airspeed.

C– increase as angle of bank increases.

2-80. Answer C. GFDIC 2A, IFH

The miniature airplane portion of the turn coordinator will be displaced when in a turn. The amount of displacement will vary with the angle of bank. As the angle of bank increases, the amount of displacement also increases. As the angle of bank decreases, the amount of displacement also decreases.

2-81   PLT166

Altimeter setting is the value to which the scale of the pressure altimeter is set so the altimeter indicates

A– pressure altitude at sea level.

B– true altitude at field elevation.

C– pressure altitude at field elevation.

2-81. Answer B. GFDIC 2A, AW

When the altimeter is set to the current altimeter setting prior to take off, it should indicate the true altitude at field elevation.

2-82   PLT023

Pressure altitude is the altitude read on your altimeter when the instrument is adjusted to indicate height above

A– sea level.

B– the standard datum plane.

C– ground level.

2-82. Answer B. GFDIC 2A, IFH

The altimeter senses the current atmospheric pressure, but it indicates height in feet above the barometric pressure level set in the altimeter setting window.

2-83   PLT337

If while in level flight, it becomes necessary to use an alternate source of static pressure vented inside the airplane, which of the following variations in instrument indications should the pilot expect?

A– The altimeter will read lower than normal, airspeed lower than normal, and the VSI will momentarily show a descent.

B– The altimeter will read higher than normal, airspeed greater than normal, and the VSI will momentarily show a climb.

C– The altimeter will read lower than normal, airspeed greater than normal, and the VSI will momentarily show a climb and then a descent.

2-83. Answer B. GFDIC 2A, IFH

Due to the slipstream around the cabin, the pressure inside the cabin is less than that of outside air. Therefore, when you select an alternate static source inside the cabin, the pressure differential is greater and the altimeter will read a little higher, the airspeed indicator will read a little fast, and the VSI will show a momentary climb.

2-84   PLT086

(Refer to figure 144.)

What changes in control displacement should be made so that "2" would result in a coordinated standard rate turn?

A– Increase left rudder and increase rate of turn.

B– Increase left rudder and decrease rate of turn.

C– Decrease left rudder and decrease angle of bank.

2-84. Answer A. GFDIC 2A, IFH

Refer to the second (#2) turn-and-slip indicator. The needle shows a turn to the left at a rate less than standard, while the ball in the inclinometer indicates that the aircraft is in a slip. To establish a coordinated standard-rate turn, you must increase left rudder pressure (step on the ball) and increase the rate of turn.

2-85   **PLT086**
(Refer to figure 144.)

Which illustration indicates a coordinated turn?

A– 3.

B– 1.

C– 2.

2-85. Answer A. GFDIC 2A, IFH
The turn-and-slip indicator supplies two types of information. First, the needle indicates a standard-rate turn when aligned with either of the turn indexes. Second, the inclinometer defines the quality of the turn. When the ball is centered, the opposing horizontal forces are in balance and the turn is coordinated.

2-86   **PLT086**
(Refer to figure 144.)

Which illustration indicates a skidding turn?

A– 2.

B– 1.

C– 3.

2-86. Answer B. GFDIC 2A, IFH
The turn-and-slip indicator supplies two types of information. First, the needle indicates a standard-rate turn when aligned with either of the turn indexes. Second, the inclinometer defines the quality of the turn. When the ball is centered, the opposing horizontal forces are in balance and the turn is coordinated.

A skidding turn is indicated when the ball of the inclinometer is forced to the outside of the turn. In this case, centrifugal force exceeds the horizontal component of lift.

2-87   **PLT086**
(Refer to figure 144.)

What changes in control displacement should be made so that "1" would result in a coordinated standard-rate turn?

A– Increase right rudder and increase rate of turn.

B– Decrease right rudder and increase angle of bank.

C– Increase right rudder and decrease rate of turn.

2-87. Answer A. GFDIC 2A, IFH
Refer to the first (#1) turn-and-slip indicator. The needle shows a left turn at a rate less than standard, while the ball in the inclinometer indicates that the aircraft is in a skid. To establish a coordinated standard-rate turn, you must increase right rudder pressure (step on the ball) and increase the rate of turn.

2-88   **PLT086**
(Refer to figure 144.)

Which illustration indicates a slipping turn?

A– 1.

B– 3.

C– 2.

2-88. Answer C. GFDIC 2A, IFH
The turn-and-slip indicator supplies two types of information. First, the needle indicates a standard-rate turn when aligned with either of the turn indexes. Second, the inclinometer defines the quality of the turn. When the ball is centered, the opposing horizontal forces are in balance and the turn is coordinated.

A slipping turn is indicated when the ball of the inclinometer falls to the inside of the turn. In this situation, the vertical component of lift exceeds centrifugal force.

SECTION B — ATTITUDE INSTRUMENT FLYING

FUNDAMENTAL SKILLS

- Attitude instrument flying consists three fundamental skills. These are instrument cross-check, instrument interpretation, and aircraft control.

- Instrument cross-check, or scan, requires logical and systematic observation of the instrument panel. The most common scanning errors are fixation, omission, and emphasis.

- Effective instrument interpretation requires a good working knowledge of how each instrument operates.

- Aircraft control is the result of instrument cross-check and interpretation. It requires that the airplane be kept properly trimmed so small flight control movements can achieve precise adjustments to pitch, bank, and power.

PRIMARY AND SUPPORTING INSTRUMENTS

- Primary instruments provide the most pertinent pitch, bank and power information for a given flight condition. Supporting instruments provide additional pitch, bank, and power information to help you maintain the desired indications on the primary instruments.

- Supporting instruments are no less important than primary instruments. The attitude indicator, although usually a supporting instrument, is essential and central to your scan.

- The attitude indicator is the primary pitch instrument during any change in pitch and the primary bank instrument during any change in bank. The altimeter is the primary pitch instrument any time your objective is to maintain altitude. The heading indicator is the primary bank instrument any time your objective is to maintain straight flight.

- The vertical speed indicator (VSI) is the primary pitch instrument any time your objective is to maintain a specific rate of climb or descent. The turn coordinator is the primary bank instrument any time your objective is to maintain a specific rate of turn. The airspeed indicator is the primary power instrument any time your objective is to maintain a constant airspeed during level flight. It is the primary pitch instrument during a constant airspeed climb or descent.

STRAIGHT-AND-LEVEL FLIGHT

- The three conditions which determine pitch attitude required to maintain level flight are airspeed, air density, and aircraft weight.

- For maintaining level flight at constant thrust, the attitude indicator would be the least appropriate pitch instrument for determining the need for a pitch change.

- The altimeter provides the most pertinent information for pitch control. As a rule of thumb, you should make altitude corrections of less than 100 feet using a half-bar width correction on the attitude indicator, and confirm the adjustment on the altimeter and VSI.

- The instrument which provides the most pertinent information for bank control is the heading indicator. Deviations in heading are not as eye-catching as altitude deviations, and for that reason, require more careful monitoring. When you see a heading deviation, use the attitude indicator to establish an angle of bank equal to the degrees deviation from heading.

- During level flight you normally adjust pitch to maintain altitude and power to get the desired airspeed. The airspeed indicator provides the most pertinent information for power control.

- During changes in power, the manifold pressure gauge or tachometer provides the most pertinent power information, since these instruments give you more instantaneous indications and help you make the required adjustments more precisely.

TURNS

- A standard-rate turn is 3 degrees per second. You should use this rate of turn or less for most IFR operations.

- You can quickly estimate the approximate angle of bank required for a standard-rate turn by dividing the true airspeed in knots by 10 and adding 5 to the result.

- At steeper banks, the rate of turn increases and the radius decreases. Lowering the airspeed also increases the rate and decreases the radius of turn for a given angle of bank.

- The primary reason the angle of attack must be increased to maintain a constant altitude during a coordinated turn, is because the vertical component of lift decreases as the result of the bank.
- When airspeed is increased during a level turn, additional vertical lift is generated. To avoid climbing, you must increase the angle of bank and/or decrease the angle of attack.
- When airspeed is decreased in a turn, the angle of bank must be decreased and/or the angle of attack must be increased to maintain level flight.

CLIMBS AND DESCENTS

- In a constant airspeed climb, you set climb power, pitch up to get a specific airspeed, and accept the resulting rate of climb. In a constant rate climb you maintain a specific vertical velocity in addition to controlling airspeed.
- The proper way to transition from cruise flight to a climb at a specific speed is to increase back elevator pressure until the attitude indicator shows the approximate pitch attitude for that speed climb.
- To enter a constant airspeed descent, reduce the power, pitch down to maintain airspeed using the attitude indicator as a reference, and accept the resulting rate of descent. In a constant rate descent you control the rate of descent with pitch and control airspeed with power.
- To level off from a descent maintaining the descending airspeed, lead the desired altitude by approximately 10 percent of the vertical velocity. To level off at an airspeed higher than the descent speed, add power at approximately 100 to 150 feet above the desired altitude.

COPING WITH INSTRUMENT FAILURE

- Although you will become proficient in partial panel instrument flying, loss of the attitude indicator in IFR conditions is a potential distress situation under which you should immediately advise ATC.
- Instrument failures can be subtle. When you suspect an instrument failure, look for corresponding indications among various instruments, and cover the instrument(s) that disagree with the rest.
- Use the VSI and airspeed indicator to make changes in pitch when flying with inoperative gyroscopic instruments. Use smooth, gradual control inputs and allow a few moments for the change in pitch to be reflected on these instruments.
- The magnetic compass is the primary bank instrument, during partial panel operations, but it is hard to control the airplane using this instrument. Keeping the wings level, with the ball centered on the turn coordinator, is your best means of maintaining your course without the attitude and heading indicators.
- Because it can be difficult to perform accurate compass turns, a timed turn is the most accurate way to turn to a heading without the heading indicator. In a timed turn, you use the clock instead of the heading indicator to determine when to roll out.

UNUSUAL ATTITUDE RECOVERY

- When recovering from a nose-high unusual attitude, your objective is to avert a stall. The correct sequence is to add power, lower the nose, level the wings, and return to the original attitude and heading.
- When recovering from a nose-low, increasing airspeed, unusual attitude, your objective is to avoid overstressing the airplane structure, as well as an excessive loss of altitude. The correct sequence is to reduce power, correct the bank attitude, and raise the nose to a level attitude.
- When recovering partial panel, use the turn coordinator to stop a turn, and the pitot-static instruments to arrest an unintended climb or descent. An approximate level pitch attitude is first attained when the airspeed and altimeter stop their movement and the VSI reverses its trend

CONTROL AND PERFORMANCE METHOD

In the control and performance method, you use the control instruments, such as the manifold pressure gauge and the attitude indicator, to set up power/attitude combinations for specific maneuvers. Then, you check the performance instruments for the desired effect.

2-89   **PLT185**
As a rule of thumb, altitude corrections of less than 100 feet should be corrected by using

A– full bar width on the attitude indicator.

B– two bar width on the attitude indicator.

C– half bar width on the attitude indicator.

2-89. Answer C. GFDIC 2B, IFH
As a rule of thumb use a one-half bar width correction on the attitude indicator for deviations of 100 feet or less. You should use an initial, full-bar width correction for larger altitude deviations.

2-90   **PLT215**
The gyroscopic heading indicator is inoperative. What is the primary bank instrument in unaccelerated straight-and-level flight?

A– Magnetic compass.

B– Attitude indicator.

C– Miniature aircraft of turn coordinator.

2-90 Answer A. GFDIC 2B, IFH
In straight-and-level flight, the heading indicator is normally the primary instrument for bank. It indirectly provides bank information, since banking results in a turn and a changing heading. The only other instrument that provides heading information is the magnetic compass and it should be considered the primary bank instrument when the heading indicator fails.

2-91   **PLT185**
When airspeed is decreased in a turn, what must be done to maintain level flight?

A– Decrease the angle of bank and/or increase the angle of attack.

B– Increase the angle of bank and/or decrease the angle of attack.

C– Increase the angle of attack.

2-91. Answer A. GFDIC 2B, IFH
If you decrease airspeed in a level turn your vertical component of lift will be reduced. To maintain the same vertical lift component required to maintain altitude, you must compensate by either decreasing the angle of bank and/or by increasing the angle of attack.

2-92   **PLT278**
What instruments are considered supporting bank instruments during a straight, stabilized climb at a constant rate?

A– Attitude indicator and turn coordinator.

B– Heading indicator and attitude indicator.

C– Heading indicator and turn coordinator.

2-92. Answer A. GFDIC 2B, IFH
The heading indicator is your primary bank instrument during both transition to, and when established in, a straight, constant rate climb. Your supporting bank instruments for an established straight, constant rate climb are the attitude indicator and turn coordinator.

2-93   PLT187

What instruments are primary for pitch, bank, and power, respectively, when transitioning into a constant airspeed climb from straight-and-level flight?

A— Attitude indicator, heading indicator, and manifold pressure gauge or tachometer.

B— Attitude indicator for both pitch and bank; airspeed indicator for power.

C— Vertical speed, attitude indicator, and manifold pressure or tachometer.

2-93. Answer A. GFDIC 2B, IFH

When transitioning from straight-and-level flight to a constant airspeed climb, the attitude indicator, heading indicator, and tachometer or manifold pressure gauge (MP) are the primary instruments for pitch, bank, and power, respectively.

2-94   PLT187

What is the primary bank instrument once a standard-rate turn is established?

A— Heading indicator.

B— Turn coordinator.

C— Attitude indicator.

2-94. Answer B. GFDIC 2B, IFH

After the turn is established, the turn coordinator is primary for bank, and the altimeter is primary for pitch control.

2-95   PLT185

What is the correct sequence in which to use the three skills used in instrument flying?

A— Aircraft control, cross-check, and instrument interpretation.

B— Instrument interpretation, cross-check, and aircraft control.

C— Cross-check, instrument interpretation, and aircraft control.

2-95. Answer C. GFDIC 2B, IFH

Three fundamental skills for instrument flying are instrument cross-check, instrument interpretation, and aircraft control in that order. You must first cross-check your instruments, then interpret them correctly so that you can apply the proper control inputs.

2-96   PLT237

The rate of turn at any airspeed is dependent upon

A— the horizontal lift component.

B— centrifugal force.

C— the vertical lift component.

2-96. Answer A. GFDIC 2B, IFH

The rate of turn at any given airspeed actually depends on the horizontal component of lift, which is directly proportional to the angle of bank.

2-97   PLT278

As power is increased to enter a 500 feet per minute rate of climb in straight flight, which instruments are primary for pitch, bank, and power respectively?

A– Attitude indicator, heading indicator, and manifold pressure gauge or tachometer.

B– Airspeed indicator, attitude indicator, and manifold pressure gauge or tachometer.

C– VSI, attitude indicator, and airspeed indicator

2-97. Answer A. GFDIC 2B, IFH

As power is increased during the transition to a constant rate climb, the attitude indicator is the primary for pitch.

2-98   PLT186

What is the primary pitch instrument during a stabilized climbing left turn at cruise climb airspeed?

A– Attitude indicator.

B– VSI.

C– Airspeed indicator.

2-98. Answer C. GFDIC 2B, IFH

A stabilized climbing left turn at cruise climb airspeed is a stabilized constant airspeed climb. As with straight-and-level constant airspeed climbs, the primary instruments are the airspeed indicator for pitch and the turn coordinator for bank.

2-99   PLT186

What is the primary pitch instrument when establishing a constant altitude standard-rate turn?

A– Airspeed indicator.

B– VSI.

C– Altimeter.

2-99. Answer C. GFDIC 2B, IFH

During the roll-in to a constant altitude standard-rate turn, check the altimeter, vertical speed indicator (VSI), and attitude indicator for the pitch adjustments necessary as the vertical lift component decreases with increased bank. The altimeter is the primary pitch instrument while the VSI and attitude indicator are supporting pitch.

2-100   PLT185

What is the initial primary bank instrument when establishing a level standard rate turn?

A– Turn coordinator.

B– Heading indicator.

C– Attitude indicator.

2-100. Answer C. GFDIC 2B, IFH

When entering a level turn, your primary reference for bank is the bank index on the attitude indicator.

2-101   PLT185

What instrument(s) is(are) supporting bank instrument when entering a constant airspeed climb from straight-and-level flight?

A— Heading indicator.

B— Turn coordinator and heading indicator.

C— Attitude indicator and turn coordinator.

2-101. Answer C. GFDIC 2B, IFH

When transitioning from straight-and-level flight to a constant airspeed climb, the attitude indicator, heading indicator, and tachometer or manifold pressure gauge are the primary instruments for pitch, bank, and power, respectively. The supporting instrument for pitch is the vertical speed indicator, while the supporting bank instruments include the attitude indicator and turn coordinator.

2-102   PLT185

What are the three fundamental skills involved in attitude instrument flying?

A— Instrument interpretation, trim application, and aircraft control.

B— Cross-check, instrument interpretation, and aircraft control.

C— Cross-check, emphasis, and aircraft control.

2-102. Answer B. GFDIC 2B, IFH

To achieve smooth, positive control of the aircraft during instrument flight maneuvers, you need to develop three fundamental skills. They are instrument cross-check, instrument interpretation, and aircraft control.

2-103   PLT185

What is the primary bank instrument while transitioning from straight-and-level flight to a standard rate turn to the left?

A— Heading indicator.

B— Turn coordinator (miniature aircraft).

C— Attitude indicator.

2-103. Answer C. GFDIC 2B, IFH

When transitioning from straight-and-level flight to a level turn to the left, the altimeter and attitude indicator are the primary instruments for determining pitch and bank, respectively. After the turn is established, the turn coordinator will be primary for bank.

2-104   PLT185

What is the third fundamental skill in attitude instrument flying?

A— Instrument cross-check.

B— Power control.

C— Aircraft control.

2-104. Answer C. GFDIC 2B, IFH

There are three fundamental skills in attitude instrument flying. The final fundamental skill, aircraft control, is the result of cross-check and accurate interpretation of the instruments.

2-105 PLT187

During standard-rate turns, which instrument is considered "primary" for bank?

A– Heading indicator.

B– Turn and slip indicator or turn coordinator.

C– Attitude indicator.

2-105. Answer B. GFDIC 2A, IFH

For standard–rate turns, the turn and slip indicator or turn coordinator is the primary bank instrument. In this case, the attitude indicator is a supporting instrument, and is essential and central to the scan. It is the only instrument that provides instant and direct aircraft attitude information, and is primary for pitch and bank information.

2-106 PLT185

What is the first fundamental skill in attitude instrument flying?

A– Aircraft control.

B– Instrument cross-check.

C– Instrument interpretation.

2-106. Answer B. GFDIC 2B, IFH

There are three fundamental skills in attitude instrument flying. The first is instrument cross-check which requires the logical and systematic observation of the instrument panel.

2-107 PLT185

As power is reduced to change airspeed from high to low cruise in level flight, which instruments are primary for pitch, bank, and power, respectively?

A– Attitude indicator, heading indicator, and manifold pressure gauge or tachometer.

B– Altimeter, attitude indicator, and airspeed indicator.

C– Altimeter, heading indicator, and manifold pressure gauge or tachometer.

2-107. Answer C. GFDIC 2B, IFH

When making adjustments in speed, your primary instruments for pitch, bank, and power are the altimeter, heading indicator, and tachometer or manifold pressure gauge, respectively. Supporting pitch instruments include the attitude indicator and VSI, while supporting bank instruments are the attitude indicator and turn coordinator. The supporting power instrument is the airspeed indicator.

2-108 PLT185

Which instrument provides the most pertinent information (primary) for bank control in straight-and-level flight?

A– Attitude indicator.

B– Heading indicator.

C– Turn-and-slip indicator.

2-108. Answer B. GFDIC 2B, IFH

In straight-and-level flight, the altimeter is the primary instrument for determining pitch, the heading indicator is primary for determining bank, and the airspeed indicator is primary for determining power.

2-109   PLT185

Which instruments are considered primary and supporting for bank, respectively, when establishing a level standard rate turn?

A– Turn coordinator and heading indicator.

B– Turn coordinator and attitude indicator.

C– Attitude indicator and turn coordinator.

2-109. Answer C. GFDIC 2B, IFH

When establishing a level standard-rate turn, the primary in instruments for determining pitch, bank, and power are the altimeter, attitude indicator, and airspeed indicator respectively. The supporting instruments for determining pitch include the attitude indicator and VSI. The supporting instrument for determining bank is the turn coordinator. The tachometer or manifold pressure gauge is the supporting power instrument.

2-110   PLT297

While recovering from an unusual flight attitude without the aid of the attitude indicator, approximate level pitch attitude is reached when the

A– airspeed and altimeter stop their movement and the VSI reverses its trend.

B– airspeed arrives at cruising speed, the altimeter reverses its trend, and the vertical speed stops its movement.

C– altimeter and vertical speed reverse their trend and the airspeed stops its movement.

2-110. Answer A. GFDIC 2B, IFH

Recovery from unusual attitudes by partial panel is basically the same as with a full panel, except the turn coordinator is used to stop any turn and the altimeter, airspeed, and vertical speed indicators are used for pitch information. For example, when recovering from a nose-low unusual attitude, an approximate level pitch attitude is indicated when the airspeed indicator and altimeter stop their movement. The VSI will reverse its trend when you begin the initial recovery and will then indicate zero after a few seconds of level flight.

2-111   PLT186

Which instruments, in addition to the attitude indicator, are pitch instruments?

A– Altimeter and airspeed only.

B–Altimeter and VSI only.

C–Altimeter, airspeed indicator, and vertical speed indicator.

2-111. Answer C. GFDIC 2B, IFH

In addition to the attitude indicator, the altimeter, airspeed indicator, and vertical speed indicator all give pitch information.

2-112   PLT186

Which instrument provides the most pertinent information (primary) for pitch control in straight-and-level flight?

A– Attitude indicator.

B–Airspeed indicator.

C–Altimeter.

2-112. Answer C. GFDIC 2B, IFH

In straight-and-level flight, the primary instruments for pitch, bank, and power are the altimeter, heading indicator, and airspeed indicator respectively.

2-113   PLT186
Which instruments are considered to be supporting instruments for pitch during change of airspeed in a level turn?

A– Airspeed indicator and VSI.

B– Altimeter and attitude indicator.

C– Attitude indicator and VSI.

2-113. Answer C. GFDIC 2B, IFH
Anytime you make a change in airspeed, your primary instruments for pitch and bank are the altimeter and the turn coordinator. The supporting instruments for determining pitch are the attitude indicator and vertical speed indicator. The supporting instrument for bank is the attitude indicator.

2-114   PLT297
If an airplane is in an unusual flight attitude and the attitude indicator has exceeded its limits, which instruments should be relied on to determine pitch attitude before starting recovery?

A– Turn indicator and VSI.

B–Airspeed and altimeter.

C–VSI and airspeed to detect approaching VSI or V_{MO}.

2-114. Answer B. GFDIC 2B, IFH
If the attitude indicator is unusable, you can determine pitch attitude by referencing the airspeed indicator and altimeter. A nose-down attitude will be indicated by an increasing airspeed and decreasing altimeter. A nose-up attitude will be indicated by a decreasing airspeed and an increasing altimeter.

2-115   PLT185
Which instrument is considered primary for power as the airspeed reaches the desired value during change of airspeed in a level turn?

A– Airspeed indicator.

B– Attitude indicator.

C– Altimeter.

2-115. Answer A. GFDIC 2B, IFH
During the period when airspeed is changing, the tachometer or manifold pressure gauge is your primary instrument for determining power. However, as the airspeed reaches the desired reading, the airspeed indicator becomes the primary instrument for determining power.

2-116   PLT297
Which is the correct sequence for recovery from a spiraling, nose-low, increasing airspeed, unusual flight attitude?

A– Increase pitch attitude, reduce power, and level wings.

B– Reduce power, correct the bank attitude, and raise the nose to a level attitude.

C– Reduce power, raise the nose to level attitude, and correct the bank attitude.

2-116. Answer B. GFDIC 2B, IFH
When recovering from a spiraling, nose-down unusual attitude, the first thing you should do is reduce power to prevent excessive airspeed and loss of altitude. Then, correct the bank attitude with coordinated aileron and rudder pressure to straight flight by referring to the turn coordinator. After this is done, raise the nose to a level flight attitude by applying smooth back elevator pressure.

2-117   PLT186

Which instruments should be used to make a pitch correction when you have deviated from your assigned altitude?

A– Altimeter and VSI.

B– Manifold pressure gauge and VSI.

C– Attitude indicator, altimeter, and VSI.

2-117. Answer C. GFDIC 2B, IFH

In level flight, the altimeter is the primary instrument for pitch information. The supporting instruments are the attitude indicator, airspeed indicator, and vertical speed indicator (VSI). If you deviate from an assigned altitude, you should use the attitude indicator, altimeter, and VSI to correct the deviation. As a guide, adjust the pitch attitude to produce a rate of change which is double the amount of altitude deviation and use power as necessary.

2-118   PLT185

When airspeed is increased in a turn, what must be done to maintain a constant altitude?

A– Decrease the angle of bank.

B– Increase the angle of bank and/or decrease the angle of attack.

C– Decrease the angle of attack.

2-118. Answer B. GFDIC 2B, IFH

If all other variables remain constant, and your airspeed increases, additional lift will be produced and the aircraft will climb. To prevent this from happening, you must decrease the amount of vertical lift being produced. You can do this by increasing the angle of bank and/or by decreasing the angle of attack.

2-119   PLT311

During a constant-bank level turn, what effect would an increase in airspeed have on the rate and radius of turn?

A– Rate of turn would increase, and radius of turn would increase.

B– Rate of turn would decrease, and radius of turn would decrease.

C– Rate of turn would decrease, and radius of turn would increase.

2-119. Answer C. GFDIC 2B, IFH

A specific angle of bank and true airspeed will always produce the same rate and radius of turn, regardless of aircraft type. If you increase the angle of bank in a turn, the rate of turn will increase and the radius will decrease. If you increase the true airspeed in a turn, radius will increase and the rate will decrease.

2-120   PLT237

Conditions that determine the pitch attitude required to maintain level flight are

A– airspeed, air density, wing design, and angle of attack.

B– flight path, wind velocity, and angle of attack.

C– relative wind, pressure altitude, and vertical lift component.

2-120. Answer A. GFDIC 2B, IFH

Lift is directly proportional to the density of the air, the area of the wings (wing design), and airspeed. Lift is pilot controlled, by modifying the angle of attack.

2-121   PLT185

Approximately what percent of the indicated vertical speed should be used to determine the number of feet to lead the level-off from a climb to a specific altitude?

A– 10 percent.

B– 20 percent.

C– 25 percent.

2-121. Answer A. GFDIC 2B, IFH

A rule of thumb for determining the amount of lead to use when leveling off is to lead your level-off point by 10% of the vertical speed. For example, if you are climbing at 1,000 feet per minute, you would begin leveling off 100 feet (1,000 × .1 = 100) prior to the desired altitude.

2-122   PLT185

To level off from a descent to a specific altitude, the pilot should lead the level-off by approximately

A– 10 percent of the vertical speed.

B– 30 percent of the vertical speed.

C– 50 percent of the vertical speed.

2-122. Answer A. GFDIC 2B, IFH

A rule of thumb for determining the amount of lead to use when leveling off is to lead your level-off point by 10% of the vertical speed. For example, if you are climbing at 1,000 feet per minute, you would begin leveling off 100 feet (1,000 × .1 = 100) prior to the desired altitude.

The same rule of thumb used for leveling off in a climb can be used for a descent. Lead your desired level-off altitude by 10% of the descent rate.

2-123   PLT311

Rate of turn can be increased and radius of turn decreased by

A– decreasing airspeed and shallowing the bank.

B– decreasing airspeed and increasing the bank.

C– increasing airspeed and increasing the bank.

2-123. Answer B. GFDIC 2B, IFH

A specific angle of bank and true airspeed will always produce the same rate and radius of turn, regardless of aircraft type. If you increase your angle of bank, the rate of turn will increase and the radius of the turn will decrease. If you increase your true airspeed, the rate of turn will decrease and the radius of turn will increase.

2-124   PLT168

The primary reason the angle of attack must be increased, to maintain a constant altitude during a coordinated turn, is because the

A– thrust is acting in a different direction, causing a reduction in airspeed and loss of lift.

B– vertical component of lift has decreased as the result of the bank.

C– use of ailerons has increased the drag.

2-124. Answer B. GFDIC 2B, IFH

In a turn, lift can be broken down into two components: a vertical component of lift and a horizontal component of lift. The vertical component of lift supports the weight of the aircraft while the horizontal component causes the aircraft to turn. When you initiate a turn or increase your bank angle, the vertical component of lift decreases and the aircraft tends to descend. Therefore, you must increase the angle of attack, increase the airspeed, or decrease the angle of bank in order to maintain level flight.

2-125   PLT186

For maintaining level flight at constant thrust, which instrument would be the least appropriate for determining the need for a pitch change?

A– Altimeter.

B– VSI.

C–Attitude indicator.

2-125. Answer C. GFDIC 2B, IFH

According to the primary/support concept of attitude instrument flying, the attitude indicator is the least appropriate instrument for determining the need for a pitch change under these conditions. In straight-and-level flight, the altimeter is the primary pitch instrument since it provides the most pertinent altitude information.

2-126   PLT125

To enter a constant-airspeed descent from level-cruising flight, and maintain cruising airspeed, the pilot should

A– first adjust the pitch attitude to a descent using the attitude indicator as a reference, then adjust the power to maintain the cruising airspeed.

B– first reduce power, then adjust the pitch using the attitude indicator as a reference to establish a specific rate on the VSI.

C– simultaneously reduce power and adjust the pitch using the attitude indicator as a reference to maintain the cruising airspeed.

2-126. Answer C. GFDIC 2B, IFH

To enter a constant-airspeed descent, simultaneously reduce the power and pitch the nose of the aircraft down. The primary pitch instrument while transitioning to the descent is the attitude indicator.

2-127   PLT125

To level off at an airspeed higher than the descent speed, the addition of power should be made, assuming a 500 FPM rate of descent, at approximately

A– 50 to 100 feet above the desired altitude.

B– 100 to 150 feet above the desired altitude.

C– 150 to 200 feet above the desired altitude.

2-127. Answer B. GFDIC 2B, IFH

The level-off from a descent must be started before you reach the desired altitude. The amount of lead depends upon the rate of descent and the desired level-off airspeed. When descending at 500 f.p.m. and leveling off at an airspeed higher than the descent airspeed, begin adding power when you are 100 to 150 feet above the desired altitude.

2-128   PLT185

To level off from a descent maintaining the descending airspeed, the pilot should lead the desired altitude by approximately

A– 20 feet.

B– 50 feet.

C– 60 feet.

2-128. Answer B. GFDIC 2B, IFH

The level-off from a descent must be started before you reach the desired altitude. The amount of lead depends upon the rate of descent and the desired level-off airspeed. When descending at 500 f.p.m. and leveling off at an airspeed higher than the descent airspeed, begin adding power when you are 100 to 150 feet above the desired altitude.

2-129   PLT297

During recoveries from unusual attitudes, level flight is attained the instant

A— the horizon bar on the attitude indicator is exactly overlapped with the miniature airplane.

B— a zero rate of climb is indicated on the VSI.

C— the altimeter and airspeed needles stop prior to reversing their direction of movement.

2-129. Answer C. GFDIC 2B, IFH

During recoveries from unusual attitudes, the attitude indicator may become unusable. In this situation, you will know you are passing through level flight when the altimeter and airspeed needles stop and begin to reverse direction.

2-130   PLT185

While cruising at 160 knots, you wish to establish a climb at 130 knots. When entering the climb (full panel), it is proper to make the initial pitch change by increasing back elevator pressure until the

A— attitude indicator, airspeed, and vertical speed indicate a climb.

B— vertical speed indication reaches the predetermined rate of climb.

C— attitude indicator shows the approximate pitch attitude appropriate for the 130-knot climb.

2-130. Answer C. GFDIC 2B, IFH

When transitioning from straight-and-level flight to a climb, the attitude indicator is primary for pitch and should be used to establish the appropriate pitch attitude for 130 knots.

2-131   PLT185

While cruising at 190 knots, you wish to establish a climb at 160 knots. When entering the climb (full panel), it would be proper to make the initial pitch change by increasing back elevator pressure until the

A— attitude indicator shows the approximate pitch attitude appropriate for the 160-knot climb.

B— attitude indicator, airspeed, and vertical speed indicate a climb.

C— airspeed indication reaches 160 knots.

2-131. Answer A. GFDIC 2B, IFH

When transitioning from straight-and-level flight to a climb, the attitude indicator is primary for pitch and should be used to establish the appropriate pitch attitude for 130 knots.

2-132   PLT297

(Refer to figure 145.)

What is the correct sequence for recovery from the unusual attitude indicated?

A– Reduce power, increase back elevator pressure, and level the wings.

B– Reduce power, level the wings, bring pitch attitude to level flight.

C– Level the wings, raise the nose of the aircraft to level flight attitude, and obtain desired airspeed.

2-132. Answer B. GFDIC 2B, IFH

A cross check of the instruments shows that you are in a descending right turn. To recover, immediately reduce power to minimize the loss of altitude and the build up of airspeed. Next, use the turn coordinator and attitude indicator to level the wings. Then increase the pitch attitude to bring the aircraft back to level flight.

2-133   PLT297

(Refer to figure 146.)

Identify the system that has failed and determine a corrective action to return the airplane to straight-and-level flight.

A– Static/pitot system is blocked; lower the nose and level the wings to level-flight attitude by use of attitude indicator.

B– Vacuum system has failed; reduce power, roll left to level wings, and pitch up to reduce airspeed.

C– Electrical system has failed; reduce power, roll left to level wings, and raise the nose to reduce airspeed.

2-133. Answer A. GFDIC 2A, IFH

An increasing airspeed and altitude, plus a moderate climb, indicates that the pitot static instruments are unreliable. Based on the gyroscopic instruments, you are in a nose high attitude and turning right. To recover, lower the nose and level the wings to a level flight attitude.

2-134   PLT297

(Refer to figure 147.)

Which is the correct sequence for recovery from the unusual attitude indicated?

A– Level wings, add power, lower nose, descend to original attitude, and heading.

B– Add power, lower nose, level wings, return to original attitude and heading.

C– Stop turn by raising right wing and add power at the same time, lower the nose, and return to original attitude and heading.

2-134. Answer B. GFDIC 2B, IFH

Based on the indications, the aircraft is in a nose-high turn to the right. To recover, add power, lower the nose, and level the wings to return to a level-flight attitude.

2-135   PLT297

(Refer to figure 148.)

What is the flight attitude? One system which transmits information to the instruments has malfunctioned.

A– Climbing turn to left.

B– Climbing turn to right.

C– Level turn to left.

2-135. Answer B. GFDIC 2B, IFH

The combination of the altimeter, VSI, attitude indicator, and heading indicator show you in a climbing, right turn. Since the turn coordinator shows wings level, it appears to have failed.

2-136   PLT297

(Refer to figure 149.)

What is the flight attitude? One system which transmits information to the instruments has malfunctioned.

A– Level turn to the right.

B– Level turn to the left.

C– Straight-and-level flight.

2-136. Answer C. GFDIC 2B, IFH

The combination of airspeed indicator, altimeter, turn coordinator, and VSI indicate level flight. The attitude indicator and heading indicator disagree with each other, which implies that the vacuum system has failed.

2-137   PLT297

(Refer to figure 150.)

What is the flight attitude? One instrument has malfunctioned.

A– Climbing turn to the right.

B– Climbing turn to the left.

C– Descending turn to the right.

2-137. Answer A. GFDIC 2B, IFH

The combination of airspeed indicator, altimeter, turn coordinator, heading indicator, and VSI indicate that the aircraft is in a climbing right turn. Both the turn coordinator and heading indicator display a turn to the right. This implies that the attitude indicator has failed.

2-138   PLT297

(Refer to figure 151.)

What is the flight attitude? One instrument has malfunctioned.

A– Climbing turn to the right.

B– Level turn to the right.

C– Level turn to the left.

2-138. Answer B. GFDIC 2B, IFH

The combination of attitude indicator, altimeter, turn coordinator, heading indicator, and VSI show the aircraft in a level turn to the right. Since the attitude indicator, altimeter, and VSI indicate a level pitch attitude, you can assume the airspeed indicator is inoperative.

SECTION C — INSTRUMENT NAVIGATION

VOR NAVIGATION

- There are various types of indicators for VOR navigation, including the basic VOR indicator, the horizontal situation indicator (HSI) and the radio magnetic indicator (RMI).

- Flying a heading that is reciprocal to the bearing selected on the OBS would result in reverse sensing on a conventional VOR indicator.

- An HSI solves nearly all reverse sensing and other visualization problems associated with a conventional VOR indicator. The HSI display combines the VOR indicator with a heading indicator, so the display is automatically rotated to the correct position for you.

- Each dot on an HSI or conventional VOR course deviation scale is 2° deviation, or 200 feet per nautical mile, when tuned to a VOR. Station passage is indicated by the first positive, complete reversal of the TO/FROM indicator. Unlike a conventional VOR indicator, an HSI gives information about your aircraft heading and its relationship to your intended course.

- Although two VOR receivers makes it easier to identify a fix defined by the intersection of radials from two VOR ground stations, one VOR receiver is the minimum equipment needed. If you have only one VOR receiver, then carefully hold the heading that tracks your course from the first VOR while you tune to the second station whose radial intersects your course.

TIME AND DISTANCE TO A STATION

- You can calculate the time and distance to a station by turning perpendicular to the direct course to the station and measuring the time to move a specific number of degrees to a new radial. [Time to the station] = [Time to move to the new radial x 60] ÷ [Degrees to the new radial]. This formula also works when timing the degrees of change in the magnetic bearing to or from an NDB.

- Example: If it takes 3 minutes to traverse 10 degrees of DME arc, the time to the station is 3 minutes x 60 ÷ 10 = 18 minutes. If your speed is 120 knots (2 NM per minute), the distance to the station is 18 x 2 = 36 NM

- To determine time to a station using the isosceles triangle method, turn 10° (or any angle) to the side of your course and twist your course selector the same amount in the opposite direction. Time to station is the same as the time it takes for your CDI to center (assuming no wind).

ADF NAVIGATION

- To determine time to a station using the isosceles triangle method with an ADF, simply measure the time it takes for the relative bearing (left or right of the aircraft nose) to double while holding a constant heading. This is the time to the station.

- As you know from your private pilot course, the angle between the nose of the aircraft and an NDB is the relative bearing. Magnetic heading (MH) plus relative bearing (RB) equals magnetic bearing to the station (MB).

- Because a radio magnetic indicator (RMI) has a slaved compass card that automatically rotates to the correct heading, it always displays the bearing to a station at the head of the arrow, and the bearing from a station at the tail of the arrow.

- A movable card ADF also directly indicates bearing to a station when its compass card is adjusted to agree with the aircraft's actual heading.

- Most RMIs have two bearing pointer needles, either one of which can be set to point to an NDB or VOR station. The tail of an RMI needle set to a VOR station indicates the radial you are on FROM the station, and the arrowhead indicates the course TO the station.

- Intercepting a bearing to an NDB is easiest if you choose an angle, such as 45°, that is easy to read on the compass card. To establish a 45° intercept, turn so that the bearing to be intercepted appears over the heading indicator reference mark 45° to the left or right of the aircraft nose. Precisely maintain this heading and look for the ADF needle to also point 45° to the left or right of the aircraft's nose.

- When turned parallel to the course to the station, the needle indicates any deviation by pointing left or right toward the course. If you simply home to the station with a crosswind, you will fly a curved path to the station.

- If tracking on course to a station and holding a wind correction, the needle indicates the amount of wind correction, but in the opposite direction. If correcting 10° left, the needle points 10° right of the nose.

- NDB station passage occurs when the needle passes behind the wingtip position and settles at or near the 180° position.

- When on the desired track outbound with the proper drift correction established, the ADF pointer will be deflected to the windward side of the tail position.

DISTANCE MEASURING EQUIPMENT

- DME is accurate to within 1/2 mile or 3% (whichever is greater).

- DME indicates slant-range distance, resulting in greatest error at high altitudes close to a VORTAC. The indication should be 1 NM when you are directly over a VORTAC site at approximately 6,000 feet AGL. Slant range error is negligible when you are at least 1 mile from the DME facility for every 1,000 feet of altitude above the station

- It is easiest to fly a DME arc procedure using an RMI, although it is possible using a conventional VOR indicator. As you turn toward the VOR to compensate for a crosswind, the bearing pointer moves ahead of the wingtip reference. When correcting away from the VOR, the bearing pointer moves behind the wingtip.

- Use 10° to 20° of correction if you drift 1/2 nautical mile outside a DME arc.

RADIO NAVIGATION OPERATIONAL CONSIDERATIONS

- VOR facilities are classified according to their usable range and altitude, or **standard service volume** (SSV). You can find the SSV which applies to a particular VOR in the *Airport/Facility Directory.*

- At altitudes between 14,500 and 18,000 feet MSL, an (H) Class VORTAC has a usable signal range of 100 nautical miles. Therefore, for direct routes off established airways at these altitudes, the facilities should be no farther apart than 200 nautical miles

- A VOR receiver check is required within 30 days prior to an IFR flight. Written documentation of this check is required.

- When checking your VOR using a VOT, the CDI should be centered and the OBS should indicate that the aircraft is on the 360° radial, ±4°.

- When using a VOR ground checkpoint, the CDI must center within ±4°. The allowable error using an airborne checkpoint is ±6°. When you conduct a dual system check, the difference between VOR systems should not exceed 4°.

- VOR and DME facilities transmit their identifiers on a time sharing basis, with the VOR transmitting several identifiers for each one from the DME. If, when tuning to a VORTAC, you receive a single coded identification approximately once every 30 seconds, it means the DME component is operative and the VOR component is inoperative. The reverse is true if you hear the 1,020 Hz VOR signal several times and the 1,350 Hz DME tone is missing over a 30-second interval.

- If a station is not transmitting an identifier, it means the station is undergoing maintenance and is unreliable, even if you are receiving navigation indications from that station.

AREA NAVIGATION

- Area Navigation (RNAV) allows you to fly direct to your destination without the need to overfly VORs or other ground facilities. These systems include VOR/DME RNAV, inertial navigation system (INS), LORAN, and the global positioning system (GPS).

- GPS provides a 95% probability of horizontal accuracy within 100 meters (328 feet), and a 99.99% probability of accuracy within 300 meters (984 feet)

- You can determine whether a GPS installation is approved for IFR by checking the appropriate supplement to the airplane flight manual.

- Aircraft using GPS navigation equipment under IFR must be equipped with an alternate means of navigation appropriate to the flight. You do not have to actively monitor the alternative navigation equipment if the GPS receiver uses RAIM for integrity monitoring. However, if RAIM capability of the GPS equipment is lost, active monitoring of an alternate means of navigation is required.

2-139   PLT508

When must an operational check on the aircraft VOR equipment be accomplished when used to operate under IFR?

A– Within the preceding 10 days or 10 hours of flight time.

B– Within the preceding 30 days or 30 hours of flight time.

C– Within the preceding 30 days.

2-139. Answer C. GFDIC 2C, FAR 91.171

In order to operate an aircraft under IFR using the VOR system, the VOR equipment must be operationally checked within the preceding 30 days.

2-140   PLT508

Which data must be recorded in the aircraft log or other appropriate log by a pilot making a VOR operational check for IFR operations?

A– VOR name or identification, date of check, amount of bearing error, and signature.

B– Place of operational check, amount of bearing error, date of check, and signature.

C– Date of check, VOR name or identification, place of operational check, and amount of bearing error.

2-140. Answer B. GFDIC 2C, FAR 91.171

When conducting a VOR check, you must record the date and place where the check was done, as well as the bearing error indicated. In addition, you must sign the record indicating that you have completed the check.

2-141   PLT508

What record shall be made in the aircraft log or other permanent record by the pilot making the VOR operational check?

A– The date, place, bearing error, and signature.

B– The date, frequency of VOR or VOT, number of flight hours since last check, and signature.

C– The date, place, bearing error, aircraft total time, and signature.

2-141. Answer A. GFDIC 2C, FAR 91.171

When conducting a VOR check, you must record the date and place where the check was done, as well as the bearing error indicated. In addition, you must sign the record indicating that you have completed the check.

2-142   PLT508

Which checks and inspections of flight instruments or instrument systems must be accomplished before an aircraft can be flown under IFR?

A— VOR within 30 days, altimeter systems within 24 calendar months, and transponder within 24 calendar months.

B— ELT test within 30 days, altimeter systems within 12 calendar months, and transponder within 24 calendar months.

C— VOR within 24 calendar months, transponder within 24 calendar months, and altimeter system within 12 calendar months.

2-142. Answer A. GFDIC 2C, FAR 91.171, FAR 91.171, FAR 91.413

The VOR system must be checked within 30 days, and the altimeter system and transponder must be inspected within 24 calendar months. None of the systems mentioned except an ELT require an inspection every 12 calendar months.

2-143   PLT508

When making an airborne VOR check, what is the maximum allowable tolerance between the two indicators of a dual VOR system (units independent of each other except the antenna)?

A— 4° between the two indicated bearings of a VOR.

B— Plus or minus 4° when set to identical radials of a VOR.

C— 6° between the two indicated radials of a VOR.

2-143. Answer A. GFDIC 2C, FAR 91.171

If a dual VOR system is installed in an aircraft, you may check one system against the other. When doing this, both systems must be tuned to the same VOR facility and the maximum permissible variation between the two indicated bearings is 4°.

2-144   PLT405

What minimum navigation equipment is required for IFR flight?

A— VOR/LOC receiver, transponder, and DME.

B— VOR receiver and, if in ARTS III environment, a coded transponder equipped for altitude reporting.

C— Navigation equipment appropriate to the ground facilities to be used.

2-144. Answer C. GFDIC 2C, FAR 91.205, FAR 91.215

For operations under IFR, the required aircraft equipment includes the instruments and equipment required for visual flight rules plus a two-way radio, navigational equipment appropriate to the ground facilities to be used, a gyroscopic rate-of-turn indicator, a slip-skid indicator, a sensitive altimeter adjustable for barometric pressure, a clock displaying hours, minutes, and seconds with a sweep-second pointer or digital presentation, a generator or alternator of adequate capacity, a gyroscopic pitch and bank indicator, and a gyroscopic direction indicator (directional gyro or equivalent).

2-145   **PLT202**
(Refer to figure 108.)

Where should the bearing pointer be located relative to the wing-tip reference to maintain the 16 DME range in a left hand arc with a left crosswind component?

A– Ahead of the left wing-tip reference for the VOR 2.

B– Ahead of the right wing-tip reference for the VOR 1.

C– Behind the left wing-tip reference for the VOR 2.

2-145. Answer A. GFDIC 2C
The RMI needle points directly toward the station, so in a left hand DME arc with no wind, it would point to the left wing-tip reference. To compensate for a left crosswind component, the aircraft must turn slightly into the wind, so the RMI needle would point slightly ahead of the wing-tip reference.

2-146   **PLT202**
(Refer to figure 163.)

During the arc portion of the instrument departure procedure (GNATS6.GNATS), a left crosswind is encountered. Where should the bearing pointer of an RMI be referenced relative to the wingtip to compensate for wind drift and maintain the 15 DME arc?

A– Behind the right wingtip reference point.

B– On the right wingtip reference point.

C– Behind the left wingtip reference point.

2-146. Answer A. GFDIC 2C, AFH
In order to compensate for the left crosswind, you must turn the aircraft to the left. Since an RMI always points directly at the station, the bearing pointer will be slightly behind the right wingtip.

2-147   **PLT091**
(Refer to figure 163.) What is your position relative to GNATS intersection and the instrument departure routing?

A– On departure course and past GNATS.

B– Right of departure course and past GNATS.

C– Left of departure course and have not passed GNATS

2-147. Answer B. GFDIC 2C, IFH
Your heading is 280° and the ADF bearing pointer indicates that MEDFORD NDB is directly behind you. This means you are on the 280° bearing FROM MEDFORD NDB, which is right of course. On this heading and bearing from the NDB, you would have been at the 216° radial of OED VORTAC when the big needle was 26° behind the right wing. In this example, the needle is 36° behind the right wing indicating that you have passed the 216° radial, or GNATS Intersection. Another way to visualize your position is to note that the tail of the VOR needle indicates 226° which means you have passed the 216° radial.

2-148 **PLT078**

(Refer to figures 27 and 165.)

To which maximum service volume distance from the OED VORTAC should you expect to receive adequate signal coverage for navigation at the flight planned altitude?

A– 100 NM.

B– 80 NM.

C– 40 NM.

2-148. Answer C. GFDIC 2C, AIM

The *Airport/Facility Directory* contains the notation (H) next to the OED VORTAC. According to Legend 27 in Appendix 1, this indicates a high altitude service volume. This service volume is usable out to 40 NM from 1,000 to 14,500 feet MSL, out to 100 NM from 14,500 to 18,000 feet MSL, out to 130 NM from 18,000 to 45,000 feet MSL, and out to 100 NM from 45,000 to 60,000 feet MSL. With a cruising altitude of 8,000 feet, you should expect to receive adequate signal coverage out to 40 NM

2-149 **PLT091**

(Refer to figures 35 and 37.)

What is your position relative to the CONNY intersection on the BUJ.BUJ3 transition?

A– Left of the TXK R-272 and approaching the BUJ R-059°.

B– Left of the TXK R-266 and past the BUJ R-065.

C– Right of the R-270 and approaching the BUJ R-245.

2-149. Answer A. GFDIC 2C, IFH

The HSI and RMI in the figure have different headings. If you interpret each instrument independently, the RMI indicates you are on the 270° radial of TXK which places the aircraft slightly left, or south, of the 272° radial. The HSI shows a fly right which means you are approaching the BUJ 059° radial.

2-150 **PLT091**

(Refer to figures 42A and 43.)

What is your position relative to CHARR intersection? The aircraft is level at 3,000 feet MSL.

A– Right of the localizer course approaching CHARR intersection and approaching the glide slope.

B– Left of the localizer course approaching CHARR intersection and below the glide slope.

C– Right of the localizer course, past CHARR intersection and above the glide slope.

2-150. Answer A. GFDIC 2C, IFH

Your CDI is set to the inbound course (353°) for the ILS-1 RWY 36L approach and the course deviation needle is indicating that you are right of course. The DME also indicates that you are 7.5 NM from the localizer antenna. Since CHAAR Int. is located 7.2 NM from the localizer antenna, you have not reached CHAAR yet.

2-151   PLT202

(Refer to figures 48 and 182.)

What is your position relative to the 9 DME ARC and the 206° radial of the instrument departure procedure?

A– On the 9 DME arc and approaching R-206.

B– Outside the 9 DME arc and past R-206.

C– Inside the 9 DME arc and approaching R-206.

2-151. Answer A. GFDIC 2C, IFH

The HSI in the figure shows that you are 9.0 nautical miles from the VORTAC. Therefore you are on the 9 DME arc. The 206° radial is dialed in the bearing selector and the CDI deflected to the left. This means that you are approaching the 206° radial.

2-152   PLT091

(Refer to figure 189.)

What is the aircraft's position relative to the HABUT intersection? (The VOR 2 is tuned to 113.8.)

A– South of the localizer and past the GVO R-163.

B– North of the localizer and approaching the GVO R-163.

C– South of the localizer and approaching the GVO R-163.

2-152. Answer B. GFDIC 2C, IFH

The aircraft is on a heading of 240° tracking the localizer course outbound, which means the CDI has reverse sensing. The right deflection of the CDI indicates the localizer course is to the left, so you are north of the localizer. The tail of the larger needle on the RMI indicates you are on the 130° radial of the GVO VORTAC. Your heading is taking you toward the GVO R-163.

2-153   PLT202

(Refer to figure 192.)

As a guide in making range corrections, how many degrees of relative bearing change should be used for each one half mile deviation from the desired arc?

A– to 3°.

B– 5° maximum.

C– 10 to 20°.

2-153. Answer C. GFDIC 2C, IFH

The standard rule of thumb recommends that you change the relative bearing 10° to 20° for each 1/2-mile deviation from the desired arc. In a crosswind it may be necessary to keep the bearing pointer ahead or behind the wingtip position to remain on the arc.

2-154   PLT300

(Refer to figure 58.)

Which indications on the VOR receivers and DME at the Easterwood Field VOR receiver checkpoint would meet the regulatory requirement for this flight?

A– VOR #1...097° FROM; VOR #2...101° FROM; DME...3.3

B– VOR #1...097° TO; VOR #2...096° TO; DME...3.2

C– VOR #1...277° FROM; VOR #2...280° FROM; DME...3.3

2-154. Answer A. GFDIC 2C, FAR 91.171

The Airport/Facility Directory (A/FD) excerpt in the referenced figure lists the details on specific VOR receiver check points, including Easterwood Field at College Station. Included is G for ground check, 097° as the exact radial FROM the station, 3.2 NM as the distance from the navaid to the check point, and a description to visually identify the check point. FAR 91.171(b)(2) lists the maximum permissible bearing error of ± 4° for a ground check.

2-155　　PLT091

(Refer to figures 61 and 196.) What is your position relative to the CARCO intersection, glide slope, and the localizer course?

A– Past CARCO, below the glide slope, and right of the localizer course.

B– Approaching CARCO, above the glide slope, and left of the localizer course.

C– Past CARCO, above the glide slope, and right of the localizer course.

2-155. Answer C. GFDIC 2C, IFH

The tail of the large RMI needle is past 285°. It indicates you are on the 300° radial FROM VUH VOR. The glide slope indicator is deflected down, showing that you are one dot above the glide slope. The localizer CDI is deflected to the left, showing you are one dot right of course.

2-156　　PLT300

(Refer to figure 64.)

The course deviation indicators (CDI) are centered. Which indications on the No. 1 and No. 2 VOR receivers over the Lafayette Regional Airport would meet the requirements for the VOR receiver check?

A– VOR #1...162° TO; VOR #2...346° FROM

B– VOR #1...160° FROM; VOR #2...162° FROM

C– VOR #1...341° FROM; VOR #2...330° FROM

2-156. Answer A. GFDIC 2C, FAR 91.171

The Airport/Facility Directory (A/FD) excerpt in the referenced figure lists the details on specific VOR receiver check points, including Lafayette Regional Airport. The A/1000 means this is an airborne check at 1,000 feet, 340° is the exact radial FROM the station, the distance is 25 NM from the station, and the check point visual description over the rotating beacon is given. FAR 91.171 lists the maximum permissible bearing error of ± 6° when using a designated airborne check point. Centered CDIs must be within 6° of 340° or the reciprocal, 160°. Indications of centered on 162° with TO and centered on 346° with FROM comply with the regulations.

2-157　　PLT091

(Refer to figures 65 and 66.)

What is your position relative to GRICE intersection?

A– Right of V552 and approaching GRICE intersection.

B– Right of V552 and past GRICE intersection.

C– Left of V552 and approaching GRICE intersection.

2-157. Answer A. GFDIC 2C, IFH

The VOR indicator on the left is tuned to the frequency for TBD VORTAC. The bearing selector is set to 116° and the CDI is deflected to the left. This indicates you are right, or south, of V552. The VOR indicator on the right is tuned to the frequency for the ILS that establishes the intersection. The bearing selector is set to the inbound course of 236° and the CDI is also deflected to the left. This indicates that you are approaching GRICE intersection.

2-158   PLT091
(Refer to figures 71 and 71A.)

What is your position relative to the FLOSI intersection Northbound on V213?

A– West of V213 and approaching the FLOSI intersection.

B– East of V213 and approaching the FLOSI intersection.

C– West of V213 and past the FLOSI intersection.

2-158. Answer A. GFDIC 2C, IFH
The VOR indicator on the left is tuned to IGN VORTAC and the bearing selector is set to 265° which is the radial that establishes Flosi intersection. The CDI is deflected to the right which indicates that you are south of and approaching Flosi intersection. The VOR indicator on the right is tuned to SAX VORTAC, the bearing selector is set to 029° and the CDI is deflected to the right. This indicates that you are left or west of the 029° radial.

2-159   PLT300
(Refer to figure 76.)

Which indication would be an acceptable accuracy check of both VOR receivers when the aircraft is located on the VOR receiver checkpoint at the Helena Regional Airport?

A– A.

B– B.

C– C.

2-159. Answer C. GFDIC 2C, A/FD Legend, FAR 91.171
The VOR receiver check at Helena is a ground checkpoint based on the 237° radial FROM the HLN VORTAC. FAR 91.171 states that a designated VOR check point on the surface has a maximum permissible bearing error of ± 4°. The tails of the two RMI bearing pointers in illustration C are on 235°, well within the ± 4° tolerance.

2-160   PLT091
(Refer to figures 78 and 79.)

What is your position relative to the VOR COP southeast bound on V86 between the BOZEMAN and LIVINGSTON VORTACs? The No. 1 VOR is tuned to 116.1 and the No. 2 VOR is tuned to 112.2.

A– Past the LVM R-246 and west of the BZN R-110.

B– Approaching the LVM R-246 and west of the BZN R-110.

C– Past the LVM R-246 and east of the BZN R-110.

2-160. Answer C. GFDIC 2C, IFH
Figure 2-40 indicates an eastbound heading of 130°. The tail of the thin bearing pointer (VOR-1) is on 239°, indicating that you are past the 246° radial of LVM VORTAC. The tail of the thick bearing pointer (VOR-2) is on 102°, indicating that you are east of the 110° radial of BZN VORTAC.

2-161   PLT300
What is the maximum tolerance allowed for an operational VOR equipment check when using a VOT?

A– Plus or minus 4°.

B– Plus or minus 6°.

C– Plus or minus 8°.

2-161. Answer A. GFDIC 2C, AIM, FAR 91.171
The maximum tolerance for a VOR equipment check using a VOT is ± 4°.

2-162   PLT363
When using VOT to make a VOR receiver check, the CDI should be centered and the OBS should indicate that the aircraft is on the

A– 090 radial.

B– 180 radial.

C– 360 radial.

2-162. Answer C. GFDIC 2C, AIM, FAR 91.171
To use a VOT, tune in the VOT frequency and center the CDI. The OBS should read 360° with the ambiguity indicator showing FROM, meaning you are on the 360° radial.

2-163   PLT300
How should the pilot make a VOR receiver check when the aircraft is located on the designated checkpoint on the airport surface?

A– Set the OBS on 180° plus or minus 4°; the CDI should center with a FROM indication.

B– Set the OBS on the designated radial. The CDI must center within plus or minus 4° of that radial with a FROM indication.

C– With the aircraft headed directly toward the VOR and the OBS set to 000°, the CDI should center within plus or minus 4° of that radial with a TO indication.

2-163. Answer B. GFDIC 2C, AIM, FAR 91.171
A ground checkpoint is a designated point on the surface of an airport where you can use a VOR radial to check your VOR receiver. You must first set the OBS to the designated radial and the CDI must center within ± 4° of that radial with the ambiguity indicator showing FROM.

2-164   PLT300
When the CDI needle is centered during an airborne VOR check, the omnibearing selector and TO/FROM indicator should read

A– within 4° of the selected radial.

B– within 6° of the selected radial.

C– 0° TO, only if you are due south of the VOR.

2-164. Answer B. GFDIC 2C, AIM, FAR 91.171
All airborne checkpoints are based on centering the CDI within 6° of a selected radial.

2-165   PLT507
(Refer to figure 81.)

When checking a dual VOR system by use of a VOT, which illustration indicates the VOR's are satisfactory?

A– 1.

B– 2.

C– 4.

2-165. Answer A. GFDIC 2C, AIM
For a VOT check with dual VORs and an RMI, the head of each needle should point toward 180°. In addition, both needles must be within 4° of each other.

2-166   PLT300
While airborne, what is the maximum permissible variation between the two indicated bearings when checking one VOR system against the other?

A– Plus or minus 4° when set to identical radials of a VOR.

B– 4° between the two indicated bearings to a VOR.

C– Plus or minus 6° when set to identical radials of a VOR.

2-166. Answer B. GFDIC 2C, AIM, FAR 91.171
The maximum permissible error between two VOR receivers is 4° between the indicators.

2-167   PLT300
How should the pilot make a VOR receiver check when the aircraft is located on the designated

checkpoint on the airport surface?

A– With the aircraft headed directly toward the VOR and the OBS set to 000°, the CDI should center within plus or minus 4° of that radial with a TO indication.

B– Set the OBS on the designated radial. The CDI must center within plus or minus 4° of that radial with a FROM indication.

C– Set the OBS on 180° plus or minus 4°; the CDI should center with a FROM indication.

2-167. Answer B. GFDIC 2C, AIM, FAR 91.171
A ground checkpoint is a designated point on the surface of an airport where you can use a VOR radial to check your VOR receiver. You must first set the OBS to the designated radial and the CDI must center within ± 4° of that radial with the ambiguity indicator showing FROM.

2-168   PLT300
(Refer to figure 82.)

Which is an acceptable range of accuracy when performing an operational check of dual VOR's using one system against the other?

A– 1.

B– 2.

C– 4.

2-168. Answer C. GFDIC 2C, AIM, FAR 91.171
When using a dual VOR system to complete a VOR accuracy check, tune both VORs to the same frequency and note the bearings to the station. The needles should be within 4° of each other.

2-169   **PLT281**

Where can the VOT frequency for a particular airport be found?

A– On the IAP Chart and in the Airport/Facility Directory.

B– Only in the Airport/Facility Directory.

C– In the Airport/Facility Directory and on the A/G Voice Communication Panel of the En Route Low Altitude Chart.

2-169. Answer C. GFDIC 2C, A/FD Legend, AIM

The location and frequency of VOTs are listed near the back of each Airport/Facility Directory (A/FD). This information is also in the A/G voice communication panel of NOS enroute low altitude charts.

2-170   **PLT300**

Which indications are acceptable tolerances when checking both VOR receivers by use of the VOT?

A– 360° TO and 003° TO, respectively.

B– 001° FROM and 005° FROM, respectively.

C– 176° TO and 003° FROM, respectively.

2-170. Answer C. GFDIC 2C, AIM

To use a VOT, tune in the VOT frequency and center the CDI. The OBS should read either 360° with a FROM indication or 180° with a TO indication. When conducting a VOT the permissible bearing error is ± 4°.

2-171   **PLT281**

In which publication can the VOR receiver ground checkpoint(s) for a particular airport be found?

A– Airman's Information Manual.

B– En Route Low Altitude Chart.

C– Airport/Facility Directory.

2-171. Answer C. GFDIC 2C, AIM

Information on VOR receiver checkpoints can be found in the back of the Airport/Facility Directory.

2-172   **PLT200**

Which is the maximum tolerance for the VOR indication when the CDI is centered and the aircraft is directly over the airborne checkpoint?

A– Plus or minus 6° of the designated radial.

B– Plus 6° or minus 4° of the designated radial.

C– Plus or minus 4° of the designated radial.

2-172. Answer A. GFDIC 2C, AIM, FAR 91.171

Single VOR checks using an airborne checkpoint allow a maximum error +/- 6°.

2-172   PLT300
When making an airborne VOR check, what is the maximum allowable tolerance between the two indicators of a dual VOR system (units independent of each other except the antenna)?

A– 4° between the two indicated radials of a VOR.

B– Plus or minus 4° when set to identical radials of a VOR.

C– 6° between the two indicated radials of a VOR.

2-172. Answer A. GFDIC 2C, AIM, FAR 91.171
The maximum permissible error between two VOR receivers is 4° between the indicator. When using a dual VOR system to complete a VOR accuracy check, both VORs should be tuned to the same frequency and the CDIs should be centered with no more than 4° difference between the indicated radials.

2-173   PLT202
Which distance is displayed by the DME indicator?

A– Slant range distance in NM.

B– Slant range distance in SM.

C– Line-of-sight direct distance from aircraft to VORTAC in SM.

2-173. Answer A. GFDIC 2C, IFH
Since the airborne interrogator is at altitude, DME distance is the slant range distance in nautical miles between the aircraft and the ground station rather than the actual horizontal distance measured on the earth's surface.

2-174   PLT202
Where does the DME indicator have the greatest error between ground distance to the VORTAC and displayed distance?

A– High altitudes far from the VORTAC.

B– High altitudes close to the VORTAC.

C– Low altitudes far from the VORTAC.

2-174. Answer B. GFDIC 2C, IFH
DME displays slant range distance in nautical miles between the aircraft and the ground station, rather than the actual horizontal distance measured on the earth's surface. The higher your altitude and the closer to the station you are, the greater the error.

2-175   PLT322
For operations off established airways at 17,000 feet MSL in the contiguous U.S., (H) Class VORTAC facilities used to define a direct route of flight should be no farther apart than

A– 75 NM.

B– 100 NM.

C– 200 NM.

2-175. Answer C. GFDIC 2C, AIM
The service volume of an (H) class VOR between 14,500 feet AGL up to and including 60,000 feet is 100 NM For flights between these altitudes, (H) Class VORs forming an unpublished direct route should be no more than 200 NM apart.

2-176   PLT300

What indication should a pilot receive when a VOR station is undergoing maintenance and may be considered unreliable?

A– No coded identification, but possible navigation indications.

B– Coded identification, but no navigation indications.

C– A voice recording on the VOR frequency announcing that the VOR is out of service for maintenance.

2-176. Answer A. GFDIC 2C, AIM

The only positive method for identifying a VOR is by its Morse code identification or by a recorded automatic voice identification. During periods of maintenance, the facility may radiate a T-E-S-T code (Morse code), or the code may be removed.

2-177   PLT300

A particular VOR station is undergoing routine maintenance. This is evidenced by

A– removal of the navigational feature.

B– broadcasting a maintenance alert signal on the voice channel.

C– removal of the identification feature.

2-177. Answer C. GFDIC 2C, AIM

The only positive method for identifying a VOR is by its Morse code identification or by a recorded automatic voice identification. During periods of maintenance, the facility may radiate a T-E-S-T code (Morse code), or the code may be removed.

2-178   PLT300

What is the meaning of a single coded identification received only once approximately every 30 seconds from a VORTAC?

A– The VOR and DME components are operative.

B– VOR and DME components are both operative, but voice identification is out of service.

C– The DME component is operative and the VOR component is inoperative.

2-178. Answer C. GFDIC 2C, AIM

A single, coded identification with a repetition interval of approximately 30 seconds indicates the DME is operative. If the DME is inoperative, the coded identification will be removed even though the distance indications may appear normal.

2-179   PLT202

Which DME indication should you receive when you are directly over a VORTAC site at approximately 6,000 feet AGL?

A– 0.

B– 1.

C– 1.3.

2-179. Answer B. GFDIC 2C, IFH

DME indicates slant range, not horizontal range. The difference between slant range distance and horizontal distance is slant range error, which is smallest at low altitudes and long range. Slant range error is greatest when the aircraft is directly over the navigational facility. In this case, the DME receiver will display altitude in nautical miles above the facility. One nautical mile is approximately 6,000 feet above the facility (AGL).

2-180   PLT161

Which of the following is required equipment for operating an aircraft within Class B airspace?

A– A 4096 code transponder with automatic pressure altitude reporting equipment.

B– A VOR receiver with DME.

C– A 4096 code transponder.

2-180. Answer A. GFDIC 3A, AIM, FAR 91.131d

For all operations in Class B airspace, a Mode S or a 4096-code transponder with Mode C automatic altitude reporting is required.

2-181   PLT202

As a rule of thumb, to minimize DME slant range error, how far from the facility should you be to consider the reading as accurate?

A– Two miles or more for each 1,000 feet of altitude above the facility.

B– One or more miles for each 1,000 feet of altitude above the facility.

C– No specific distance is specified since the reception is line-of-sight.

2-181. Answer B. GFDIC 2C, IFH

Slant range error is negligible if the aircraft is one mile or more from the ground facility for each 1,000 feet of altitude above the elevation of the facility.

2-182 PLT090

(Refer to figures 87 and 88.)

What is your position with reference to FALSE intersection (V222) if your VOR receivers indicate as shown?

A– South of V222 and east of FALSE intersection.

B– North of V222 and east of FALSE intersection.

C– South of V222 and west of FALSE intersection.

2-182. Answer A. GFDIC 2C, Enroute Chart Lesson

The No. 1 VOR indicates that you have tuned the Beaumont VORTAC (BPT, 114.5), the 264° radial is dialed in, and the CDI is deflected to the right. Since you have a FROM indication, the 264° radial (V222) is to the right of your position. In other words, you are to the left or south of V222. The No. 2 VOR indicates that you have Daisetta VORTAC (DAS, 116.9) tuned, the 139° radial dialed in, and the CDI is deflected to the right. As figure 2-44 shows, you have a FROM indication, the 139° radial is to your right, and you are to the left (east) of the radial. This puts you east of FALSE intersection which is defined by the 142° radial from DAS VORTAC (116.9) and the 264° radial from BPT VORTAC (114.5).

2-183   PLT090
(Refer to figures 89 and 90.)

What is your relationship to the airway while en route from BCE VORTAC to HVE VORTAC on V8?

A– Left of course on V8.

B– Left of course on V382.

C– Right of course on V8.

2-183. Answer A. GFDIC 2C, IFH
VOR No. 1 indicates you are slightly right of the 033° radial of BCE VORTAC, placing you to the right of V382. VOR No. 2 indicates that you are slightly left of the 046° radial of HVE VORTAC, or left of course on V8.

2-184   PLT276
What angular deviation from a VOR course centerline is represented by a full-scale deflection of the CDI?

A– 4°.

B– 5°.

C– 10°.

2-184. Answer C. GFDIC 2C, IFH
Full-scale deflection for VOR on the course deviation indicator (CDI) is usually 10° on either side of the course centerline. This may very slightly, depending on instrument calibration.

2-185   PLT507
When using VOR for navigation, which of the following should be considered as station passage?

A– The first movement of the CDI as the airplane enters the zone of confusion.

B– The moment the TO-FROM indicator becomes blank.

C– The first positive, complete reversal of the TO-FROM indicator.

2-185. Answer C. GFDIC 2C, IFH
Station passage is indicated by a complete and positive reversal of the TO-FROM indicator.

2-186   PLT507
Which of the following should be considered as station passage when using VOR?

A– The first flickering of the TO-FROM indicator and CDI as the station is approached.

B– The first full-scale deflection of the CDI.

C– The first complete reversal of the TO-FROM indicator.

2-186. Answer C. GFDIC 2C, IFH
Station passage is indicated by a complete and positive reversal of the TO-FROM indicator.

2-187   PLT091
When checking the sensitivity of a VOR receiver, the number of degrees in course change as the OBS is rotated to move the CDI from center to the last dot on either side should be between

A– 5° and 6°.

B– 8° and 10°.

C– 10° and 12°.

2-187. Answer C. GFDIC 2C, IFH
You can verify the course sensitivity of your VOR by rotating the bearing selector knob until the course deviation indicator (CDI) moves to full deflection. Then note the number of degrees the course changed. This figure should be between 10° and 12°.

2-188   PLT090
A VOR receiver with normal five-dot course sensitivity shows a three-dot deflection at 30 NM from the station. The aircraft would be displaced approximately how far from the course centerline?

A– 2 NM.

B– 3 NM.

C– 5 NM.

2-188. Answer B. GFDIC 2C, IFH
For VOR, each dot of deflection means you are about 200 feet off centerline for each mile away from the station. For example, at 30 miles, one dot equals about one mile from the course centerline (200' × 30 = 6,000'). You can determine your distance from a specific radial if you know how far you are from the station and the number of dots your CDI is deflected. Multiply the number of dots times the distance from the station times 200 feet. In this case, 3 dots × 30 NM × 200 feet = 18,000 feet ÷ 6,000 ft./NM = 3 NM.

2-189   PLT090
An aircraft which is located 30 miles from a VOR station and shows a 1/2-scale deflection on the CDI would be how far from the selected course centerline?

A– 1 1/2 miles.

B– 2 1/2 miles.

C– 3 1/2 miles.

2-189. Answer B. GFDIC 2C, IFH
Each dot of deflection means you are 200 feet off centerline for each mile away from the station. You can determine your distance from a specific radial by multiplying the number of dots times the distance from the station times 200 feet. Half scale deflection, or 2-1/2 dots×30 NM × 200 feet = 15,000 feet ÷ 6,000 ft./NM = 2-1/2 NM

2-190   PLT090
An aircraft which is located 30 miles from a VOR station and shows a 1/2-scale deflection on the CDI would be how far from the selected course centerline?

A– 2°.

B– 4°.

C– 5°.

2-190. Answer C. GFDIC 2C, IFH
For VOR, full scale deflection is between 10° and 12°, therefore, a 1/2 scale deflection is approximately 5°.

2-191   PLT090
After passing a VORTAC, the CDI shows 1/2 scale deflection to the right. What is indicated if the deflection remains constant for a period of time?

A– The airplane is getting closer to the radial.

B– The OBS is erroneously set on the reciprocal heading.

C– The airplane is flying away from the radial.

2-191. Answer C. GFDIC 2C, IFH
As you travel further from the VOR, the distance between the radials becomes greater since they diverge. At 5 miles from the station, you would be 2,500 feet from the radial, and at 10 miles, you would be displaced about 5,000 feet.

2-192   PLT056
(Refer to figure 95.)

What is the lateral displacement of the aircraft in NM from the radial selected on the No. 1 NAV?

A– 5.0 NM.

B– 7.5 NM.

C– 10.0 NM.

2-192. Answer A. GFDIC 2C, IFH
Each dot of deflection means you are about 200 feet off centerline for each mile away from the station. You can determine your distance from a specific radial if you know how far you are from the station and the number of dots your CDI is deflected. Multiply the number of dots times distance from the station times 200 feet. The referenced figure shows a 2-1/2 dot deflection and 60 NM on the No. 1 NAV (2-1/2 dots×60 NM×200 ft = 30,000 ft ÷ 6,000 ft./NM = 5.0 NM).

2-193   PLT056
(Refer to figure 95.)

On which radial is the aircraft as indicated by the No.1 NAV?

A– R-175.

B– R-165.

C– R-345.

2-193. Answer C. GFDIC 2C
The TO/FROM indicator (triangular pointer) is showing FROM and with the bearing selector set on 350°; however, the aircraft is flying a heading of 140°. The CDI shows that you are about 5° to the left, or west, of the 350° radial, on the 345° radial..

2-194   PLT056
(Refer to figure 95.)

Which OBS selection on the No. 1 NAV would center the CDI and change the TO/FROM indication to a TO?

A– 175°.

B– 165°.

C– 345°.

2-194. Answer B. GFDIC 2C, IFH
The TO/FROM indicator is showing a FROM indication, with the bearing selector set on 350°; however, the aircraft is flying a heading of 140°. The 1/2-scale deflection shows a position about 5° to the left or west of the 350° radial. If the bearing selector were set to the reciprocal, 170°, the TO/FROM indicator would switch to a TO indication and the CDI would show that you are 5° right, or west, of the 170° course to the station. A 5° adjustment of the bearing selector to 165° would center the CDI.

2-195   PLT056
(Refer to figure 95.)

What is the lateral displacement in degrees from the desired radial on the No. 2 NAV?

A– 1°.

B– 2°.

C– 4°.

2-195. Answer C. GFDIC 2C, IFH
Each dot represents a 2° displacement. A two dot deflection would indicate a 4° lateral displacement.

2-196   PLT056
(Refer to figure 95.)

Which OBS selection on the No. 2 NAV would center the CDI?

A– 174°.

B– 166°.

C– 335°.

2-196. Answer A. GFDIC 2C, IFH
The bearing selector is set to 170° with a two dot deflection to the left. With VOR, this indicates that the 170° radial is 4° to the left. Rotating the bearing selector 4° to 174° would center the CDI.

2-197   PLT056
(Refer to figure 95.)

Which OBS selection on the No. 2 NAV would center the CDI and change the TO/FROM indication to a TO?

A– 166°.

B– 346°.

C– 354°.

2-197. Answer C. GFDIC 2C, IFH
The bearing selector is set to 170° with a two dot deflection to the left and FROM on the TO/FROM indicator. This indicates that the 170° radial is 4° to the left. Rotating the bearing selector 4° to 174° would center the CDI without changing the FROM indication. The reciprocal of 174°, or 354° would center the CDI with a TO indication.

2-198   PLT056
(Refer to figures 98 and 99.)

To which aircraft position does HSI presentation "D" correspond?

A– 4.

B– 15.

C– 17.

2-198. Answer C. GFDIC 2C, IFH
The aircraft in position 17 is on a heading of south with the course selector set on 180°. As shown, the CDI would be deflected to the left, and the ambiguity indicator would display FROM.

2-199   **PLT056**
(Refer to figures 98 and 99.)

To which aircraft position does HSI presentation "E" correspond?

A– 5.

B– 6.

C– 15.

2-199. Answer B. GFDIC 2C, IFH
The aircraft in position 6 is on a heading of north with the course selector set to 360°. The ambiguity indicator shows FROM with the CDI deflected to the left.

2-200   **PLT056**
(Refer to figures 98 and 99.)

To which aircraft position does HSI presentation "F" correspond?

A– 10.

B– 14.

C– 16.

2-200. Answer C. GFDIC 2C, IFH
The aircraft in position 16 is on a northeast heading on the 180° radial. With the bearing selector set to 180°, the CDI should be centered and the ambiguity indicator correctly displays FROM.

2-201   **PLT056**
(Refer to figures 98 and 99.)

To which aircraft position does HSI presentation "A" correspond?

A– 1.

B– 8.

C– 11.

2-201. Answer A. GFDIC 2C, IFH
The aircraft in position 1 is northwest of the station on a southwest heading of 205°. With 090° dialed in the course selector, the ambiguity indicator would show TO, and the CDI would be deflected to the left.

2-202   **PLT056**
(Refer to figures 98 and 99.)

To which aircraft position does HSI presentation "B" correspond?

A– 9.

B– 13.

C– 19

2-202. Answer C. GFDIC 2C, IFH
The aircraft in position 19 is southwest of the station. With the 270° radial dialed in the course selector, the ambiguity indicator would show FROM, and the CDI would be deflected to the left.

2-203   PLT056
(Refer to figures 98 and 99.)

To which aircraft position does HSI presentation "C" correspond?

A– 6.

B– 7

C– 12.

2-203. Answer C. GFDIC 2C, IFH
The aircraft in position 12 is southeast of the station. With 360° dialed in the bearing selector, the ambiguity indicator would show TO and the CDI would be deflected to the left.

2-204   PLT014
(Refer to figure 101.)

What is the magnetic bearing TO the station?

A– 60°.

B– 260°.

C– 270°.

2-204. Answer B. GFDIC 2C, IFH
With a magnetic heading of 350°, plus a relative bearing of 270°, you get a 260° magnetic bearing TO the station (620° – 360° = 260°).

2-205   PLT014
(Refer to figure 100.)

Which RMI illustration indicates the aircraft to be flying outbound on the magnetic bearing of 235°

FROM the station? (Wind 050° at 20 knots.)

A– 2.

B– 3.

C– 4.

2-205. Answer B. GFDIC 2C, IFH
With an RMI, the tail of the bearing pointer indicates your magnetic bearing FROM the station. The number 3 RMI indicates the aircraft is on a heading of 235° and shows the tail of the bearing pointer on 235°.

2-206   PLT014
(Refer to figure 100.)

What is the magnetic bearing TO the station as indicated by illustration 4?

A– 285°.

B– 055°.

C– 235°.

2-206. Answer B. GFDIC 2C, IFH
The bearing pointer indicates the magnetic bearing TO the station. In illustration number 4, the bearing pointer indicates 055°..

2-207   PLT091
(Refer to figure 100.)

Which RMI illustration indicates the aircraft is southwest of the station and moving closer TO the station?

A– 1.

B– 2.

C– 3.

2-207. Answer A. GFDIC 2C, IFH
The tail of the bearing pointer indicates your position FROM the station, and the head indicates the direction to the station. Illustration 1 indicates the aircraft is southwest moving toward the station.

2-208   PLT091
(Refer to figure 100.)

Which RMI illustration indicates the aircraft is located on the 055° radial of the station and heading away from the station?

A– 1.

B– 2.

C– 3.

2-208. Answer B. GFDIC 2C, IFH
The tail of the bearing pointer indicates the magnetic bearing FROM the station. Illustration 2 indicates the aircraft is on the 055° bearing FROM the station moving away.

2-209   PLT091
(Refer to figure 103.)

On the basis of this information, the magnetic bearing TO the station would be

A– 175°.

B– 255°.

C– 355°.

2-209. Answer C. GFDIC 2C, IFH
With a fixed-card ADF indicator, the magnetic bearing (MB) TO the station equals the magnetic heading (MH) plus the relative bearing (RB) TO the station.

MH + RB = MB

215° + 140° = 355°

2-210   PLT091
(Refer to figure 102.)

On the basis of this information, the magnetic bearing FROM the station would be

A– 175°.

B– 255°.

C– 355°.

2-210. Answer A. GFDIC 2C, IFH
With a fixed-card ADF indicator, the magnetic bearing TO the station equals your magnetic heading plus your relative bearing TO the station. An easy way to figure this relationship in this question is to use the standard formula for magnetic bearing to the station and then subtract 180°.

MH + RB = MB

215° + 140° = 355° − 180° = 175°.

2-211   PLT091

(Refer to figure 103.)

On the basis of this information, the magnetic bearing FROM the station would be

A– 030°.

B– 060°.

C– 240°.

2-211. Answer B. GFDIC 2C, IFH

With a fixed-card ADF indicator, the magnetic bearing TO the station equals your magnetic heading plus your relative bearing TO the station. An easy way to figure this relationship in this question is to use the standard formula for magnetic bearing to the station and then subtract 180°.

MH + RB = MB

330° + 270° = 600° − 180° = 420°

In this case, you must subtract 360°, since 420° is greater than 360°.

420° − 360° = 060°

2-212   PLT091

(Refer to figure 103.)

On the basis of this information, the magnetic bearing TO the station would be

A– 060°.

B– 240°.

C– 270°.

2-212. Answer B. GFDIC 2C, IFH

With a fixed-card ADF indicator, the magnetic bearing TO the station equals your magnetic heading plus your relative bearing TO the station. If the result is greater than 360°, subtract 360°.

MH + RB = MB

330° + 270° = 600° − 360° = 240°

2-213   PLT091

(Refer to figure 104.)

If the radio magnetic indicator is tuned to a VOR, which illustration indicates the aircraft is on the 115° radial?

A– 1.

B– 2.

C– 3.

2-213. Answer A. GFDIC 2C, IFH

The tail of the RMI shows the radial that you are on FROM the VOR. Illustration 1 indicates that you are on the 115° radial.

2-214   PLT091

(Refer to figure 104.)

If the radio magnetic indicator is tuned to a VOR, which illustration indicates the aircraft is on the 335° radial?

A– 2.

B– 3.

C– 4.

2-214. Answer C. GFDIC 2C, IFH

The tail of the RMI shows the VOR radial that you are on. Illustration 4 indicates that you are on the 335° radial.

2-215　　PLT091
(Refer to figure 104.)

If the radio magnetic indicator is tuned to a VOR, which illustration indicates the aircraft is on the 315° radial?

A– 2.

B– 3.

C– 4.

2-215. Answer A. GFDIC 2C, IFH
The tail of the RMI shows the radial that you are on. Illustration 2 indicates that you are on the 315° radial.

2-216　　PLT091
(Refer to figure 104.)

If the radio magnetic indicator is tuned to a VOR, which illustration indicates the aircraft is on the 010° radial?

A– 1.

B– 2.

C– 3.

2-216. Answer C. GFDIC 2C, IFH
The tail of the RMI shows the radial you are on FROM the VOR. Illustration 3 indicates that you are on the 010° radial.

2-217　　PLT091
(Refer to figure 105.)

If the magnetic heading shown for aircraft 7 is maintained, which ADF illustration would indicate the aircraft is on the 120° magnetic bearing FROM the station?

A– 2.

B– 4.

C– 5.

2-217. Answer C. GFDIC 2C, IFH
Even with the fixed-card ADF installation, the ADF bearing pointer always points to the station. Since you're looking for a magnetic bearing of 120° FROM the station, first compute the magnetic bearing TO the station by using the basic formula and add 180°:

MH + RB = MB + 180°

270° + (unknown) = 300°

RB = 30°

2-218　　PLT091
(Refer to figure 105.)

If the magnetic heading shown for aircraft 5 is maintained, which ADF illustration would indicate the aircraft is on the 210° magnetic bearing FROM the station?

A– 2.

B– 3.

C– 4.

2-218. Answer C. GFDIC 2C, IFH
Even with the fixed-card ADF installation, the ADF bearing pointer always points to the station. Since you're looking for a magnetic bearing of 210° FROM the station, first compute the magnetic bearing TO the station by using the basic formula and add 180°:

MH + RB = MB + 180°

180° + (unknown) = 30°

RB = 210°

2-219   **PLT091**
(Refer to figure 105.)

If the magnetic heading shown for aircraft 3 is maintained, which ADF illustration would indicate the aircraft is on the 120° magnetic bearing TO the station?

A– 4.

B– 5.

C– 8.

2-219. Answer B. GFDIC 2C, IFH
Even with the fixed-card ADF installation, the ADF bearing pointer always points to the station. Since you're looking for a magnetic bearing of 120° TO the station, first determine the missing information. In this question, it is the relative bearing (RB). Then, use the basic formula:

MH + RB = MB

090° + (unknown) = 120°

RB = 030°

2-220   **PLT091**
(Refer to figure 105.)

If the magnetic heading shown for aircraft 1 is maintained, which ADF illustration would indicate the aircraft is on the 060° magnetic bearing TO the station?

A– 2.

B– 4.

C– 5.

2-220. Answer A. GFDIC 2C, IFH
Even with the fixed-card ADF installation, the ADF bearing pointer always points to the station. Since you're looking for a magnetic bearing of 060° TO the station, determine what information is missing — in this case the relative bearing (RB). Then, use the basic formula:

MH + RB = MB

360° + (unknown) = 060°

RB = 060°.

2-221   **PLT091**
(Refer to figure 105.)

If the magnetic heading shown for aircraft 2 is maintained, which ADF illustration would indicate the aircraft is on the 255° magnetic bearing TO the station?

A– 2.

B– 4.

C– 5.

2-221. Answer B. GFDIC 2C, IFH
Even with the fixed-card ADF installation, the ADF bearing pointer always points to the station. Since you're looking for a magnetic bearing of 255° TO the station, determine what information, if any, is needed. In this question, you must compute the relative bearing (RB). Use the basic formula:

MH + RB = MB

045° + (unknown) = 255°

RB = 210°.

2-222   **PLT091**
(Refer to figure 105.)

If the magnetic heading shown for aircraft 4 is maintained, which ADF illustration would indicate the aircraft is on the 135° magnetic bearing TO the station?

A– 1.

B– 4.

C– 8.

2-222. Answer A. GFDIC 2C, IFH
Even with the fixed-card ADF installation, the ADF bearing pointer always points to the station. Since you're looking for a magnetic bearing of 135° TO the station, determine what information is needed. In this case, you'll need to find the relative bearing (RB). Use the basic formula:

MH + RB = MB

135° + (unknown) = 135°

RB = 0°.

2-223 PLT091
(Refer to figure 105.)

If the magnetic heading shown for aircraft 6 is maintained, which ADF illustration would indicate the aircraft is on the 255° magnetic bearing FROM the station?

A– 2.

B– 4.

C– 5.

2-223. Answer B. GFDIC 2C, IFH
Even with the fixed-card ADF installation, the ADF bearing pointer always points to the station. Since you're looking for a magnetic bearing of 255° FROM the station, first compute the magnetic bearing TO the station and subtract 180° (255° – 180° = 075°). Then find RB by using the basic formula:

MH + RB = MB

225° + (unknown) = 075°

RB = 210°

2-224 PLT091
(Refer to figure 105.)

If the magnetic heading shown for aircraft 8 is maintained, which ADF illustration would indicate the aircraft is on the 090° magnetic bearing FROM the station?

A– 3.

B– 4.

C– 6.

2-224. Answer C. GFDIC 2C, IFH
Even with the fixed-card ADF installation, the ADF bearing pointer always points to the station. Since you're looking for a magnetic bearing of 090° FROM the station, first compute the magnetic bearing TO the station and subtract 180° (090° – 180° = 270°). Then find RB by using the basic formula:

MH + RB = MB

315° + (unknown) – 360° = 270°

RB = 315°

2-225 PLT091
(Refer to figure 105.)

If the magnetic heading shown for aircraft 5 is maintained, which ADF illustration would indicate the aircraft is on the 240° magnetic bearing TO the station?

A– 2.

B– 3.

C– 4.

2-225. Answer A. GFDIC 2C, IFH
Even with the fixed-card ADF installation, the ADF bearing pointer always points to the station. Since you're looking for a magnetic bearing of 240° TO the station, determine what information, if any, is needed. In this question, you must compute the relative bearing (RB). Use the basic formula:

MH + RB = MB

180° + (unknown) = 240°

RB = 060°.

2-226 PLT091
(Refer to figure 105.)

If the magnetic heading shown for aircraft 8 is maintained, which ADF illustration would indicate the aircraft is on the 315° magnetic bearing TO the station?

A– 3.

B– 4.

C– 1.

2-226. Answer C. GFDIC 2C, IFH
Even with the fixed-card ADF installation, the ADF bearing pointer always points to the station. Since you're looking for a magnetic bearing of 315° TO the station, determine what information, if any, is needed. In this question, you must compute the relative bearing (RB). Use the basic formula:

MH + RB = MB

315° + (unknown) = 315°

RB = 0°.

2-227   PLT090
(Refer to figure 106)

The course selector of each aircraft is set on 360 degrees. Which aircraft would have a FROM indication on the TO/FROM indicator and the CDI pointing to left of center?

A– 1.

B– 2.

C– 3.

2-227. Answer B. GFDIC 2C, IFH
The TO/FROM indicator shows whether the aircraft would fly toward or away from the station if the selected course is intercepted and flown. A FROM indication places the aircraft north of the VOR. When the CDI is left of center, the aircraft is to the right of course, regardless of the aircraft heading.

2-228   PLT091
(Refer to figure 107.)

Where should the bearing pointer be located relative to the wingtip reference to maintain the 16 DME range in a right-hand arc with a right crosswind component?

A– Behind the right wingtip reference for VOR-2.

B– Ahead of the right wingtip reference for VOR-2.

C– Behind the right wingtip reference for VOR-1.

2-228. Answer B. GFDIC 2C, IFH
The crosswind would cause you to drift away from the station, so you would need to correct toward the station, placing the VOR-2 needle ahead of the right wingtip.

2-229   PLT202
(Refer to figure 108.)

Where should the bearing pointer be located relative to the wingtip reference to maintain the 16 DME range in a left-hand arc with a left crosswind component?

A– Ahead of the left wingtip reference for the VOR-2.

B– Ahead of the right wingtip reference for the VOR 1.

C– Behind the left wingtip reference for the VOR-2.

2-229. Answer A. GFDIC 2C, IFH
To prevent the left crosswind from blowing you away from VOR-2, turn toward the station so that the bearing pointer is ahead of the left wingtip reference.

2-230   PLT056
(Refer to figure 109.)

In which general direction from the VORTAC is the aircraft located?

A– Northeast.

B– Southeast.

C– Southwest.

2-230. Answer A. GFDIC 2C, IFH
The diagram shows a selected course of 180° with a TO indication (shown by the head of the triangular arrowhead). This places the aircraft north of the station. Since the aircraft is shown left of the 180° course, it is in the northeast quadrant.

2-231   PLT056

(Refer to figure 110.)

In which general direction from the VORTAC is the aircraft located?

A– Southwest.

B– Northwest.

C– Northeast.

2-231. Answer C. GFDIC 2C, IFH

The HSI shows a selected course of 060° with a FROM indication. When on course, the aircraft would be northeast of the VORTAC. The course deviation bar shows the aircraft about 6° left of course, or on the 054° radial.

2-232   PLT056

(Refer to figure 111.)

In which general direction from the VORTAC is the aircraft located?

A– Northeast.

B– Southeast.

C– Northwest.

2-232. Answer C. GFDIC 2C, IFH

The HSI shows a selected course of 360° with a FROM indication. The aircraft is generally north of the VORTAC. It is left of the 360° course by about 8°, so it is northwest of the VORTAC.

2-233   PLT322

For IFR operations off of established airways below 18,000 feet, VOR navigational aids used to describe the "route of flight" should be no more than

A– 80 NM apart.

B– 40 NM apart.

C– 70 NM apart.

2-233. Answer A. GFDIC 2C, AIM

Air navigation radio aids provide positive course guidance within the standard service volume for the given NAVAID, which is usable for random/unpublished route navigation. In this case, the standard service volume for a low altitude VOR is 40 nautical miles. So, on an off airway flight below 18,000 feet, the VORs used to define a route of flight should be no more than 80 nautical miles apart to insure adequate course guidance.

2-234   PLT322

(Refer to figure 47.)

When en route on V448 from YKM VORTAC to BTG VORTAC, what minimum navigation equipment is required to identify ANGOO intersection?

A– One VOR receiver.

B– One VOR receiver and DME.

C– Two VOR receivers.

2-234. Answer A. GFDIC 2C, IFH

Using one VOR receiver, you can establish yourself on V448 by tuning it to YKM VORTAC. Maintaining your heading, you can periodically tune the VOR receiver to DLS VORTAC to determine your progress along the airway. As you near ANGOO, select the 330° radial, and when the CDI centers, you are at the intersection.

2-235   PLT202

When a VOR/DME is collocated under frequency pairings and the VOR portion is inoperative, the DME identifier will repeat at an interval of

A– 20 second intervals at 1020 Hz.

B– 30 second intervals at 1350 Hz.

C– 60 second intervals at 1350 Hz.

2-235. Answer B. GFDIC 2C, AIM

The DME is operative when it transmits an identifier at an interval of approximately 30 seconds. The DME tone is modulated at 1350 Hz, and the VOR or localizer portion is at 1020 Hz.

2-236   PLT507

Full scale deflection of a CDI occurs when the course deviation bar or needle

A– deflects from left side of the scale to right side of the scale.

B– deflects from the center of the scale to either far side of the scale.

C– deflects from half scale left to half scale right.

2-236. Answer B. GFDIC 2C, IFH

Full scale deflection of a CDI is defined as the deflection from the center to one side of the scale. This indicates 10° or more off course.

2-237   PLT202

(Refer to figure 240.)

How should a pilot determine when the DME at PUC airport is inoperative?

A– The airborne DME will always indicate '0' mileage.

B– The airborne DME will 'search,' but will not 'lock on.'

C– The airborne DME may appear normal, but there will be no code tone.

2-237. Answer C. GFDIC 2C, AIM

Regardless of the DME indication, if there is no coded tone identification, the DME is inoperative. Keep in mind that when it is functioning properly, the coded DME identification is transmitted one time for each three or four times that the VOR or localizer coded identification is transmitted. A single coded identification, repeated at approximately 30-second intervals, indicates the DME is operating, and the VOR is inoperative.

2-238   **PLT118**

(Refer to figure 143.)

When the system is in the free gyro mode, depressing the clockwise manual heading drive button will rotate the remote indicating compass card to the

A– right to eliminate left compass card error.

B– right to eliminate right compass card error.

C– left to eliminate left compass card error.

2-238. Answer A. GFDIC 2C, IFH

HSI units utilize a remote indicating compass, which includes a slaving control and compensator unit. The slaving meter deflects from zero when there is a difference between the magnetic heading and the remote indicating compass heading. If your compass card had rotated counterclockwise (to the left), you would have a left compass card error. To correct it, you would need to depress the clockwise button, which would rotate the card to the right.

2-239   **PLT118**

(Refer to figure 143.)

The heading on a remote indicating compass is 5° to the left of that desired. What action is required to move the desired heading under the heading reference?

A– Select the free gyro mode and depress the clockwise heading drive button.

B– Select the slaved gyro mode and depress the clockwise heading drive button.

C– Select the free gyro mode and depress the counterclockwise heading drive button.

2-239. Answer C. GFDIC 2C, IFH

HSI units utilize a remote indicating compass, which includes a slaving control and compensator unit. The slaving meter deflects from zero when there is a difference between the magnetic heading and the remote indicating compass heading. When making an adjustment to correct a compass card that is indicating a heading 5° to the left (a right compass card error), you select the free gyro mode and then depress the counterclockwise manual heading drive button. This will rotate the remote indicating compass card to the left (increasing heading) and eliminate the error.

2-240   **PLT354**

During IFR en route operations using an approved TSO-C129() or TSO-C196() GPS system for navigation,

A– the aircraft must have an approved and operational alternate navigation system appropriate for the route.

B– active monitoring of an alternate navigation system is always required.

C– no other navigation system is required.

2-240. Answer C. GFDIC 2C, AIM

Aircraft using a GPS system approved by TSO-C129 or TSO-C196 during IFR enroute operations must be equipped with an approved and operational alternate means of navigation appropriate to the flight. You are not required to actively monitor alternate systems unless your GPS equipment loses RAIM capability.

THE FLIGHT ENVIRONMENT

SECTION A — AIRPORTS, AIRSPACE, AND FLIGHT INFORMATION

RUNWAY MARKINGS

Precision instrument runways provide distance information in 500 foot increments. Aiming point markings are located approximately 1,000 feet from the landing threshold.

TAXIWAY MARKINGS

- Mandatory instruction signs, such as those marking hold lines, consist of white lettering on a red background. A hold line painted on the pavement consists of four yellow lines, with the two dashed lines nearest the runway.
- When you exit the runway after landing, be sure to cross the hold line before stopping to ensure that you are clear of the runway.
- Remain outside of the ILS hold line if asked to hold

APPROACH LIGHT SYSTEMS

- Normally, approach lights extend outward from the landing threshold to a distance of 2,400 to 3,000 feet from precision instrument runways and 1,400 to 1,500 feet from nonprecision instrument runways.
- Some approach light systems incorporate sequenced flashing lights (SFL) or runway alignment indicator lights (RAIL), which are moving strobe lights pointing the way to the runway.
- High intensity white strobe lights on each side of the runway threshold are called runway end identifier lights (REIL), and provide a means of rapidly identifying the approach end of the runway during reduced visibility.

VISUAL GLIDE SLOPE INDICATORS

- A two-bar visual approach slope indicator (VASI) normally has an approach angle of 3°, is visible from 3 to 5 miles during the day and up to 20 miles at night. The near and middle bars of a three-bar VASI provide the same glide path as a standard two-bar VASI installation. The middle and far bars are for high-cockpit aircraft, and provide an upper glide path that is usually .25° steeper than the lower glide path. Remaining on or above the proper glide path of a VASI assures safe obstruction clearance in the approach area.
- Pulsating approach slope indicators (PLASIs) and tri-color VASIs provide glide path guidance from a single light box. The precision approach path indicator (PAPI) uses a single row of normally four lights similar to VASI and can indicate the degree of deviation from the glide path by the number of red and white lights.

RUNWAY LIGHTING

- Runway edge lights include high intensity runway lights (HIRL), medium intensity runway lights (MIRL), and low intensity runway lights (LIRL). HIRL and MIRL intensity can be adjusted from the control tower or by the pilot using the CTAF frequency. Runway edge lights are white, except on instrument runways where amber replaces white on the last 2,000 feet or half the runway length, whichever is less, as a caution zone.
- Threshold lights mark the ends of the each runway. They appear green when landing and red when departing the end of the runway. Displaced threshold lights are located on each side of the runway. If the displaced runway area is usable for taxi, takeoff, or rollout, the area short of the displaced threshold will have runway 3-2 Chapter 3 - The Flight Environment edge lights, which appear red taking off toward the displaced threshold and white or amber when rolling out after landing.

- Touchdown zone lighting (TDZL) is a series of white lights flush-mounted in the runway, which help identify the touchdown area during low visibility. Runway centerline lights (RCLS), flush-mounted in the runway, initially appear white, changing to alternating red and white when 3,000 feet remain, and all red for the last 1,000 feet of runway.
- Land and hold short lights are a row of five flush-mounted flashing white lights at the hold short point, and are normally on during land and hold short operations.
- Taxiway lead-off lights are flush-mounted alternating green and yellow lights that define the curved path of an aircraft from turning from the runway centerline onto a taxiway. When installed, taxiway centerline lights are green and taxiway edge lights are blue.

AIRSPACE

CONTROLLED AIRSPACE

- Controlled airspace includes Class A, B, C, D, and Class E airspace. It is where air traffic control service is available to pilots. When you are operating under IFR, you must comply with ATC clearances.
- You must have an operating transponder with Mode C (or Mode S) capability in Class A and B airspace and within 30 nautical miles of Class B primary airports. This equipment is also required in and above Class C airspace, and at or above 10,000 feet MSL, except at and below 2,500 feet AGL.
- Below 10,000 feet MSL, basic VFR visibility is 3 statute miles in controlled airspace and 1 mile in uncontrolled airspace. Cloud clearance requirements within 1,200 feet of the surface in uncontrolled airspace, and in Class B airspace, is simply clear of clouds. Otherwise, you must maintain 1,000 feet above, 500 feet below, and 2,000 feet horizontal distance from clouds. Above 10,000 feet MSL and more than 1,200 feet above the surface, required flight visibility increases to 5 miles in both controlled and uncontrolled airspace with 1 mile horizontal and 1,000-foot vertical separation required from clouds.

CLASS A AIRSPACE

Most Class A airspace extends from 18,000 feet MSL up to and including FL600. You are required to use an altimeter setting of 29.92 inches Hg, you must be rated and current for instrument flight, your aircraft must be equipped for IFR and you must be operating on an IFR clearance at an altitude assigned by ATC. DME is required at or above FL 240 where VOR is required, with exceptions for in-flight failure.

CLASS B AIRSPACE

Most Class B airspace is from the surface to 10,000 feet MSL. You must be at least a private pilot, or a student pilot with the appropriate endorsement, and must receive an ATC clearance before you entering this airspace. Some Class B areas completely prohibit student pilot operations.

CLASS C AIRSPACE

- Class C airspace normally resides in 5 and 10 nautical mile circles extending outward from a primary airport. An outer area with radar coverage outside Class C airspace extends to 20 NM From 5 to 10 NM from the airport, Class C airspace generally begins at about 1,200 feet above the primary airport surface and extends to approximately 4,000 feet above the airport. Within 5 NM of the primary airport, Class C airspace is from the surface to about 4,000 feet AGL.
- Radio contact is encouraged within the 20 NM outer area and required prior to entering Class C airspace. If you depart a satellite airport within Class C airspace, you must establish two-way communication with ATC as soon as practicable after takeoff.

CLASS D AIRSPACE

- Class D airspace exists at airports with operating control towers which are not associated with Class B or C airspace. Normally, the upper limit of Class D airspace is about 2,500 feet above the surface of the primary airport and the lateral limits are approximately 4 nautical miles from the primary airport.

- Two-way radio communication with the control tower must be established prior to entering this airspace or taking off from the primary airport. Pilots taking off from satellite airports within Class D airspace must check in with the tower as soon as practicable.
- At part-time tower locations, Class D airspace normally becomes Class E airspace when the tower is closed, or Class G if weather observations and reporting are not available.

CLASS E AIRSPACE

- The remaining controlled airspace includes Federal airways, which are normally 8 nautical miles wide, begin at 1,200 feet AGL, and extend up to 17,999 feet MSL. Transition areas are depicted with magenta shading on sectional charts, for certain airports with approved instrument approach procedures. These areas of Class E airspace typically begin at 700 feet AGL and extend to the overlying controlled airspace.
- At some nontower airports, Class E airspace extends upward from the surface, and typically encompasses a 4 NM circle around the airport, in addition to extensions to accommodate arrivals and departures. These are depicted with dashed magenta lines on VFR charts.
- At almost all remaining U.S. locations where Class E airspace is not designated at a lower altitude, it begins at 14,500 feet MSL (except within 1,500 feet of the surface) and extends up to 17,999 feet MSL.

SPECIAL VFR

When the weather is below basic VFR minimums, as indicated by daytime operation of a rotating beacon, you may obtain a special VFR (SVFR) clearance from the ATC facility controlling the airspace at selected airports. Ground (or flight) visibility must be at least 1 statute mile and you must remain clear of clouds. An instrument rating and IFR equipped airplane are required for SVFR after sunset and it is not allowed at airports indicating "No SVFR" on aeronautical charts.

CLASS G AIRSPACE

Class G airspace is that area which has not been designated as Class A, B, C, D, or E airspace. It is uncontrolled by ATC. For example, the airspace below a Class E airspace area or below a Victor airway is normally uncontrolled. Most Class G airspace terminates at the base of Class E airspace at 700 or 1,200 feet AGL, or at 14,500 feet MSL.

AIRCRAFT SPEED LIMITS

The speed limit is 250 knots indicated airspeed (KIAS) below 10,000 feet MSL and 200 KIAS within 4 nautical miles of the primary airport of Class C or Class D airspace within 2,500 feet of the surface. The 200 KIAS limit also applies to the airspace underlying Class B airspace or in a VFR corridor through such airspace. Aircraft that cannot safely operate at these speeds are exempt.

SPECIAL USE AIRSPACE

- An IFR clearance through a restricted area is authorization to penetrate that airspace.
- Military operations areas (MOAs) separate certain military training activities from IFR traffic. You may be cleared IFR through an active MOA only if ATC can provide separation.

OTHER AIRSPACE AREAS

An airport advisory area is within 10 statute miles of an airport with an FSS but no control tower. At these locations, the FSS provides local airport advisory (LAA) service.

FLIGHT INFORMATION

AIRPORT/FACILITY DIRECTORY

The *Airport/Facility Directory* (A/FD) is a series of regional books with FAA information for public-use civil airports, associated terminal control facilities, air route traffic control centers, and radio aids to navigation.

AERONAUTICAL INFORMATION MANUAL

The *Aeronautical Information Manual* (AIM) contains fundamental information required for both VFR and IFR flight operations within the National Airspace System. It is a major reference for this Study Guide.

NOTICES TO AIRMEN

NOTAM information is disseminated for all navigational facilities that are part of the National Airspace System, all public use airports, seaplane bases, and heliports listed in the *Airport/Facility Directory*. NOTAM information also includes items such as taxiway closures, construction activities near runways, snow conditions, and changes in the status of airport lighting, such as VASI, that do not affect instrument approach criteria. FDC NOTAMs are used to disseminate information that is regulatory in nature. Examples are amendments to aeronautical charts, changes to instrument approach procedures, and temporary flight restrictions.

3-1   PLT405
Where is DME required under IFR?

A– Above 18,000 feet MSL.

B– At or above 24,000 feet MSL if VOR navigational equipment is required.

C– In positive control airspace.

3-1. Answer B. GFDIC 3A, FAR 91.205
DME is required when flying above 24,000 feet MSL when VOR navigational equipment is required.

3-2   PLT323
What is the purpose of FDC NOTAMs?

A– To provide the latest information on the status of navigation facilities to all FSS facilities for scheduled broadcasts.

B– To issue notices for all airports and navigation facilities in the shortest possible time.

C– To advise of changes in flight data which affect instrument approach procedure (IAP), aeronautical charts, and flight restrictions prior to normal publication.

3-2. Answer C. GFDIC 3A, AIM
FDC NOTAMs are used to disseminate information that is regulatory in nature. Examples include: amendments to aeronautical charts, changes to instrument approach procedures, and temporary flight restrictions. FDC NOTAMs are kept on file at the FSS until published in the Notices to Airmen publication or canceled. FDC NOTAM information is provided to a pilot by an FSS only upon request.

3-3   PLT052
(Refer to figure 30.)

Which restriction to the use of the OED VORTAC would be applicable to the (GNATS1.MOURN) departure?

A– R 333 beyond 30 NM below 6,500 feet.

B– R 210 beyond 35 NM below 8,500 feet.

C– R 251 within 15 NM below 6,100 feet.

3-3. Answer A. GFDIC 3A, A/FD Legend
The excerpt from the *Airport/Facility Directory* indicates that the VORTAC is unusable in several areas, including between the 280° and 345° radials beyond 30 NM and below 6,500 feet. The R-333 falls within this area.

3-4   PLT081
(Refer to figure 162.)

What are the hours of operation (local standard time) of the control tower at Eugene/Mahlon Sweet Field?

A– 0800 to 2330.

B– 0600 to 2330.

C– 0700 to 0130.

3-4. Answer B. GFDIC 3A, A/FD Legend
The excerpt from the *Airport/Facility Directory* indicates that the tower is open from 1400 to 0730 Zulu time. To convert this to local time subtract 8 hours (shown in the line after the airport name). The answer is 0600 to 2330 local time.

3-5   PLT281
(Refer to figure 184.)

What are the hours of operation (local time) of the control tower for the Yakima Air Terminal when daylight savings time is in effect?

A– 0500 to 2100.

B– 0600 to 2200.

C– 0700 to 2300.

3-5. Answer B. GFDIC 3A, A/FD Legend
The A/FD excerpt notes that the control tower is operated from 1400Z through 0600Z. The symbol indicates that effective times will be one hour earlier during periods of daylight savings time (1300Z to 0500Z). To convert to local time, subtract 7 hours (during daylight savings time). The answer is 0600 to 2200 local time.

3-6   PLT078
(Refer to figure 193.)

On which frequencies could you communicate with the Montgomery County FSS while on the ground at College Station?

A– 122.65, 122.2, 122.1, 113.3.

B– 122.65, 122.2.

C– 118.5, 122.65, 122.2.

3-6. Answer B. GFDIC 3A, A/FD Legend
Easterwood Field at College Station has a remote communications outlet (RCO) for Montgomery County Radio. The frequencies of 122.65 and 122. 2 are in the Communications section of the A/FD entry.

3-7   PLT281
(Refer to figures 59 and 60.)

What are the operating hours (local standard time) of the Houston EFAS?

A– 0600 to 2200.

B– 0700 to 2300.

C– 1800 to 1000.

3-7. Answer A. GFDIC 3A, AIM
The figure includes a communications outlet for Houston, but no FSS. This area is now covered by the Montgomery County automated FSS. If flying in the Houston area, you would contact Montgomery County between 1200Z and 0400Z (0600 to 2200 local) for enroute flight advisory service.

3-8   PLT076
(Refer to figure 166.)

The landing distance available on Runway 05 at Memorial Field is

A– 4,100 feet.

B– 6,595 feet.

C– 4,098 feet.

3-8. Answer B. AF/D Legend
The landing distance available (LDA) appears under Runway Declared Distance Information. For Runway 05, it is 6,595 feet.

3-9   PLT196
When are ATIS broadcasts updated?

A– Every 30 minutes if weather conditions are below basic VFR; otherwise, hourly.

B– Upon receipt of any official weather, regardless of content change or reported values.

C– Only when the ceiling and/or visibility changes by a reportable value.

3-9. Answer B. GFDIC 3B, AIM
The ATIS broadcast is updated upon the receipt of any official hourly and special weather. A new recording will also be made when there is a change in other pertinent data, such as a change of runway or the instrument approach in use.

3-10   PLT196
Absence of the sky condition and visibility on an ATIS broadcast specifically implies that

A– the ceiling is more than 5,000 feet and visibility is 5 miles or more.

B– the sky condition is clear and visibility is unrestricted.

C– the ceiling is at least 3,000 feet and visibility is 5 miles or more.

3-10. Answer A. GFDIC 3B, AIM
The ceiling/sky condition, visibility, and obstructions to vision may be omitted from the ATIS broadcast if the ceiling is 5,000 feet or higher, and the visibility is 5 miles or more.

3-11   PLT323
From what source can you obtain the latest FDC NOTAM's?

A– Notices to Airmen publications.

B– FAA AFSS/FSS.

C– *Airport/Facility Directory.*

3-11. Answer B. GFDIC 3A, AIM
National Flight Data Center (FDC) NOTAMs are only transmitted once, and then kept on file at the FSS or AFSS until published or cancelled. Therefore, the most current FDC NOTAMs should be on file.

3-12   PLT141

The operation of an airport rotating beacon during daylight hours may indicate that

A– the in-flight visibility is less than 3 miles and the ceiling is less than 1,500 feet within Class E airspace.

B– the ground visibility is less than 3 miles and/or the ceiling is less than 1,000 feet in Class B, C, or D airspace.

C– an IFR clearance is required to operate within the airport traffic area.

3-12. Answer B. GFDIC 3A, AIM

The operation of an airport beacon during daylight hours indicates that the ground visibility is less than 3 miles and/or the ceiling is less than 1,000 feet within the surface areas of Class B, C, D, and E airspace. However, you should not rely solely on the beacon as an indication of actual weather conditions. At many airports the beacon is turned on by a photoelectric cell or a time clock. In addition, there is no regulatory requirement for the daylight operation of the airport beacon.

3-13   PLT161

MOAs are established to

A– prohibit all civil aircraft because of hazardous or secret activities.

B– separate certain military activities from IFR traffic.

C– restrict civil aircraft during periods of high-density training activities.

3-13. Answer B. GFDIC 3A, AIM

MOAs consist of airspace of defined vertical and lateral limits that are established to separate certain military training activities from IFR traffic. If an MOA is not being used, ATC may clear civil IFR traffic through the airspace, as long as IFR separation can be provided. Otherwise, ATC will reroute or restrict nonparticipating IFR traffic.

3-14   PLT406

What action should you take if your DME fails at FL 240?

A– Advise ATC of the failure and land at the nearest available airport where repairs can be made.

B– Notify ATC that it will be necessary for you to go to a lower altitude, since your DME has failed.

C– Notify ATC of the failure and continue to the next airport of intended landing where repairs can be made.

3-14. Answer C. GFDIC 3A, FAR 91.205

FAR Part 91.205(e) states that when DME fails at or above FL 240, "...the pilot in command of the aircraft shall notify ATC immediately, and then may continue operations at and above FL 240 to the next airport of intended landing at which repairs or replacements of the equipment can be made".

3-15   PLT406

What is the procedure when the DME malfunctions at or above 24,000 feet MSL?

A– Notify ATC immediately and request an altitude below 24,000 feet.

B– Continue to your destination in VFR conditions and report the malfunction.

C– After immediately notifying ATC, you may continue to the next airport of intended landing where repairs can be made.

3-15. Answer C. GFDIC 3A, FAR 91.205

FAR Part 91.205(e) states that when DME fails at or above FL 240, "...the pilot in command of the aircraft shall notify ATC immediately, and then may continue operations at and above FL 240 to the next airport of intended landing at which repairs or replacements of the equipment can be made".

3-16   PLT161

When are you required to establish communications with the tower, (Class D airspace) if you cancel your IFR flight plan 10 miles from the destination?

A– Immediately after canceling the flight plan.

B– When advised by ARTCC.

C– Before entering Class D airspace.

3-16. Answer C. GFDIC 3A, FAR 91.129

Class D airspace areas are designated at airports with operating control towers not associated with Class B or C airspace. Before you enter Class D airspace, you must establish and maintain two-way radio communications with the control tower.

3-17   PLT162

Which airspace is defined as a transition area when designated in conjunction with an airport which has a prescribed IAP?

A– The Class E airspace extending upward from 700 feet or more above the surface and terminating at the base of the overlying controlled airspace.

B– That Class D airspace extending from the surface and terminating at the base of the continental control area.

C– The Class C airspace extending from the surface to 700 or 1,200 feet AGL, where designated.

3-17. Answer A. GFDIC 3A, AIM

Several types of airspace may be designated as Class E. One example is domestic airspace areas which extend upward from 700 feet or more above the surface when designated in conjunction with an airport which has an approved instrument approach procedure (IAP).

3-18   PLT161
The vertical extent of the Class A airspace throughout the conterminous U.S. extends from

A– 18,000 feet to and including FL 450.

B– 18,000 feet to and including FL 600.

C– 12,500 feet to and including FL 600.

3-18. Answer B. GFDIC 3A, AIM
Within the conterminous U.S., and within 12 NM of the coast, Class A airspace extends from 18,000 feet MSL up to and including FL 600.

3-19   PLT161
Class G airspace is that airspace where

A– ATC does not control air traffic.

B– ATC controls only IFR flights.

C– the minimum visibility for VFR flight is 3 miles.

3-19. Answer A. GFDIC 3A, AIM
In the United States, uncontrolled airspace is designated Class G airspace. It is that area which has not been designated as Class A, B, C, D, or E airspace and within which ATC has neither the authority nor the responsibility to exercise control over air traffic.

3-20   PLT161
What are the vertical limits of a transition area that is designated in conjunction with an airport having a prescribed IAP?

A– Surface to 700 feet AGL.

B– 1,200 feet AGL to the base of the overlying controlled airspace.

C– 700 feet AGL or more to the base of the overlying controlled airspace.

3-20. Answer C. GFDIC 3A, AIM
Several types of airspace may be designated as Class E. One example is domestic airspace areas which extend upward from 700 feet or more above the surface when designated in conjunction with an airport which has an approved instrument approach procedure (IAP).

3-21   PLT298
What is the minimum flight visibility and distance from clouds for flight at 10,500 feet with a VFR-on-Top clearance during daylight hours (Class E airspace)?

A– 3 SM, 1,000 feet above, 500 feet below, and 2,000 feet horizontal.

B– 5 SM, 1,000 feet above, 1,000 feet below, and 1 mile horizontal.

C– 5 SM, 1,000 feet above, 500 feet below, and 1 mile horizontal.

3-21. Answer B. GFDIC 3A, AIM, FAR 91.155
A VFR-on-Top clearance requires you to follow visual flight rules, including cloud clearance and visibility requirements. Above 10,000 feet MSL, and more than 1,200 feet AGL, you must have 5 miles visibility and remain at least one mile horizontally and at least 1,000 feet above or below the clouds in Class E (controlled) and in Class G (uncontrolled) airspace.

3-22   PLT298

What is the required flight visibility and distance from clouds if you are operating in Class E airspace at 9,500 feet MSL with a VFR-on-Top clearance during daylight hours?

A– 3 SM, 1,000 feet above, 500 feet below, and 2,000 feet horizontal.

B– 5 SM, 500 feet above, 1,000 feet below, and 2,000 feet horizontal.

C– 3 SM, 500 feet above, 1,000 feet below, and 2,000 feet horizontal.

3-22. Answer A. GFDIC 3A, AIM, FAR 91.155
A VFR-on-Top clearance requires you to follow visual flight rules, including cloud clearance and visibility requirements. Flights in Class E (controlled) airspace above 1,200 feet AGL, but less than 10,000 feet MSL, require a minimum flight visibility of 3 miles and 1,000 feet above the clouds, 500 feet below, and 2,000 feet horizontal.

3-23   PLT163

(Refer to figure 92.)

What is the minimum in flight visibility and distance from clouds required for a VFR-on-Top flight at 9,500 feet MSL (above 1,200 feet AGL) during daylight hours for area 3?

A– 2,000 feet; (E) 1,000 feet; (F) 2,000 feet; (H) 500 feet.

B– 5 miles; (E) 1,000 feet; (F) 2,000 feet; (H) 500 feet.

C– 3 miles; (E) 1,000 feet; (F) 2,000 feet; (H) 500 feet.

3-23. Answer C. GFDIC 3A, FAR 91.155, AIM
A VFR-on-Top clearance requires you to follow visual flight rules, including cloud clearance and visibility requirements. Flights in controlled airspace above 1,200 feet AGL, but less than 10,000 feet MSL, require a minimum flight visibility of 3 miles, 1,000 feet above the clouds, 500 feet below, and 2,000 feet horizontal.

3-24   PLT298

(Refer to figure 92.)

A flight is to be conducted in VFR-on-Top conditions at 12,500 feet MSL (above 1200 feet AGL). What is the in-flight visibility and distance from clouds required for operation in Class E airspace during daylight hours for area 1?

A– 5 miles; (A) 1,000 feet; (B) 2,000 feet; (D) 500 feet.

B– 5 miles; (A) 1,000 feet; (B) 1 mile; (D) 1,000 feet.

C– 3 miles; (A) 1,000 feet; (B) 2,000 feet; (D) 1,000 feet.

3-24. Answer B. GFDIC 3A, AIM, FAR 91.155
A VFR-on-Top clearance requires you to follow visual flight rules, including cloud clearance and visibility requirements. When more than 1,200 feet above the surface and at or above 10,000 feet MSL, you must have 5 miles visibility and remain at least one mile horizontally and at least 1,000 feet vertically from any clouds.

3-25   PLT163
(Refer to figure 92.)

What is the minimum in-flight visibility and distance from clouds required in VFR conditions above clouds at 13,500 feet MSL (above 1,200 feet AGL) in Class G airspace during daylight hours for area 2?

A– 5 miles; (A) 1,000 feet; (C) 2,000 feet; (D) 500 feet.

B– 3 miles; (A) 1,000 feet; (C) 1 mile; (D) 1,000 feet.

C– 5 miles; (A) 1,000 feet; (C) 1 mile; (D) 1,000 feet.

3-25. Answer C. GFDIC 3A, AIM, FAR 91.155
In Class G (uncontrolled) airspace at or above 10,000 feet MSL and more than 1,200 feet AGL, you must have 5 miles flight visibility and remain at least one mile horizontally and at least 1,000 feet vertically from the clouds.

3-26   PLT163
(Refer to figure 92.)

What in flight visibility and distance from clouds is required for a flight at 8,500 feet MSL (above 1,200 feet AGL) in Class G airspace in VFR conditions during daylight hours in area 4?

A– 1 mile; (E) 1,000 feet; (G) 2,000 feet; (H) 500 feet.

B– 3 miles; (E) 1,000 feet; (G) 2,000 feet; (H) 500 feet.

C– 5 miles; (E) 1,000 feet; (G) 1 mile; (H) 1,000 feet.

3-26. Answer A. GFDIC 3A, AIM, FAR 91.155
In Class G (uncontrolled) airspace above 1,200 feet AGL and below 10,000 feet MSL, you must have 1 mile visibility and remain 1,000 feet above, 2,000 feet horizontal, and 500 feet below any clouds.

3-27   PLT163
(Refer to figure 92.)

What is the minimum in flight visibility and distance from clouds required for an airplane operating less than 1,200 feet AGL during daylight hours in area 6?

A– 3 miles; (I) 1,000 feet; (K) 2,000 feet: (L) 500 feet.

B– 1 mile; (I) clear of clouds; (K) clear of clouds; (L) clear of clouds.

C– 1 mile; (I) 500 feet; (K) 1,000 feet; (L) 500 feet.

3-27. Answer B. GFDIC 3A, AIM, FAR 91.155
In uncontrolled airspace below 1,200 feet AGL during the day, you must have 1 mile visibility and remain clear of clouds. Answer (B) is wrong because the in flight visibility must be 5 SM.

3-28   PLT163
(Refer to figure 92.)

What is the minimum in flight visibility and distance from clouds required for an airplane operating less than 1,200 feet AGL under special VFR during daylight hours in area 5?

A– 1 mile; (I) 2,000 feet; (J) 2,000 feet; (L) 500 feet.

B– 3 miles; (I) clear of clouds; (J) clear of clouds; (L) 500 feet.

C– 1 mile; (I) clear of clouds; (J) clear of clouds; (L) clear of clouds.

3-28. Answer C. GFDIC 3A, AIM, FAR 91.155
When operating under a special VFR clearance, you must have 1 mile visibility and remain clear of clouds.

3-29   PLT161
(Refer to figure 93.)

What is the floor of Class E airspace when designated in conjunction with an airway?

A– 700 feet AGL.

B– 1,200 feet AGL.

C– 1,500 feet AGL.

3-29. Answer B. GFDIC 3A, AIM
Class E airspace designated as Federal Airways begin at 1,200 feet AGL or higher unless otherwise specified.

3-30   PLT161
(Refer to figure 93.)

Which altitude is the normal upper limit for Class D airspace?

A– 1,000 feet AGL.

B– 2,500 feet AGL.

C– 4,000 feet AGL.

3-30. Answer B. GFDIC 3A, AIM
Class D airspace extends upward to and includes approximately 2,500 feet AGL.

3-31   PLT161
(Refer to figure 93.)

What is the floor of Class E airspace when designated in conjunction with an airport which has an approved IAP?

A– 500 feet AGL.

B– 700 feet AGL.

C– 1,200 feet AGL.

3-31. Answer B. GFDIC 3A, AIM
The Class E airspace surrounding an airport with an instrument approach procedure usually begins at 700 feet AGL.

3-32   PLT161
(Refer to figure 93.)

Which altitude is the upper limit for Class A airspace?

A– 14,500 feet MSL.

B– 18,000 feet MSL.

C– 60,000 feet MSL.

3-32. Answer C. GFDIC 3A, AIM
The upper limit of Class A airspace is 60,000 feet MSL.

3-33   PLT161
(Refer to figure 93.)

What is generally the maximum altitude for Class B airspace?

A– 18,000 feet MSL.

B– 14,500 feet MSL.

C– 14,000 feet MSL.

3-33. Answer B. GFDIC 3A, AIM
The upper limit of Class G airspace (the base of Class E airspace) in some areas is 14,500 feet MSL.

3-34   PLT161
(Refer to figure 93.)

What is generally the maximum altitude for Class B airspace?

A– 14,500 feet MSL.

B– 18,000 feet MSL.

C– 60,000 feet MSL.

3-34. Answer B. GFDIC 3A, AIM
Generally, the maximum altitude for Class B airspace is 10,000 feet MSL, although the configuration of each area is tailored to the specific airport.

3-35   PLT161
(Refer to figure 93.)

What is the floor of Class A airspace?

A– 10,000 feet MSL.

B– 14,500 feet MSL.

C– 18,000 feet MSL.

3-35. Answer C. GFDIC 3A, AIM
Class A airspace begins at 18,000 feet MSL and extends upward to FL 600.

3-36   PLT222

When should pilots state their position on the airport when calling the tower for takeoff?

A– When visibility is less than 1 mile.

B– When parallel runways are in use.

C– When departing from a runway intersection.

3-36. Answer C. GFDIC 3A, AIM

According to the AIM, pilots are required to state their position when ready to depart from a runway intersection.

3-37   PLT161

What minimum aircraft equipment is required for operation within Class C airspace?

A– Two-way communications and Mode C transponder.

B– Two-way communications.

C– Transponder and DME.

3-37. Answer A. GFDIC 3A, AIM

The minimum equipment required to operate in Class airspace is a two-way radio and a Mode C transponder.

3-38   PLT161

The aircraft's transponder fails during flight within Class D airspace.

A– The pilot should immediately request clearance to depart the Class D airspace.

B– No deviation is required because a transponder is not required in Class D airspace.

C– The pilot must immediately request priority handling to proceed to destination.

3-38. Answer B. GFDIC 3A, AIM

A transponder is not required in Class D airspace. If your transponder fails while you are flying in Class D airspace, you are not required to deviate from your flight path.

3-39   PLT141

(Refer to figure 134.)

Unless a higher angle is necessary for obstacle clearance, what is the normal glide path angle for a 2-bar VASI?

A– 2.75°.

B– 3.00°.

C– 3.25°.

3-39. Answer B. GFDIC 3A, AIM

The normal glide path angle for a 2-bar visual approach slope indicator (VASI) is 3°. At some locations, the angle may be higher for obstacle clearance.

3-40   PLT141

Which of the following indications would a pilot see while approaching to land on a runway served by a 2-bar VASI?

A– If on the glide path, the near bars will appear red, and the far bars will appear white.

B– If departing to the high side of the glide path, the far bars will change from red to white.

C– If on the glide path, both near bars and far bars will appear white.

3-40. Answer B. GFDIC 3A, AIM

The on glide path indication for a 2-bar VASI is red over white (far bar red, near bar white). If departing to the high side of the glide path, the far bar will change from red to white.

3-41   PLT141

The middle and far bars of a 3-bar VASI will

A– both appear white to the pilot when on the upper glide path.

B– constitute a 2-bar VASI for using the lower glide path.

C– constitute a 2-bar VASI for using the upper glide path.

3-41. Answer C. GFDIC 3A, AIM

Pilots of high-cockpit aircraft use the middle and far bars of a 3-bar VASI to fly the upper glide path. In effect, these two bars constitute a 2-bar VASI for the upper glide path.

3-42   PLT141

Tricolor Visual Approach Indicators normally consist of

A– a single unit, projecting a three-color visual approach path.

B– three separate light units, each projecting a different color approach path.

C– three separate light projecting units of very high candle power with a daytime range of approximately 5 miles.

3-42. Answer A. GFDIC 3A, AIM

Tri-color VASIs typically are made up of a single light which projects red, green, and amber. Red indicates you are below the glide path, green indicates you are on the glide path, and amber indicates you are above the glide path. If you descend below the proper glide path you may see a dark amber color.

3-43   PLT141

When on the proper glide path of a 2-bar VASI, the pilot will see the near bar as

A– white and the far bar as red.

B– red and the far bar as white.

C– white and the far bar as white.

3-43. Answer A. GFDIC 3A, AIM

The on glide path indication for a 2-bar VASI is red over white (far bar red, near bar white).

3-44   PLT141

If an approach is being made to a runway that has an operating 3-bar VASI and all the VASI lights appear red as the aircraft reaches the MDA, the pilot should

A– start a climb to reach the proper glide path.

B– continue at the same rate of descent if the runway is in sight.

C– level off momentarily to intercept the proper approach path.

3-44. Answer C. GFDIC 3A, AIM

If all three bars are red, it means you are below both the upper and lower glide paths. You should level off until you see the indications for the appropriate glide path, and intercept it.

3-45   PLT141

Which is a feature of the tricolor VASI?

A– One light projector with three colors: red, green, and amber.

B– Two visual glide paths for the runway.

C– Three glide paths, with the center path indicated by a white light.

3-45. Answer A. GFDIC 3A, AIM

A tri-color VASI consists of a single light projector with three colors, red, green, and amber. It projects a single glide path.

3-46   PLT141

Which approach and landing objective is assured when the pilot remains on the proper glide path of the VASI?

A– Continuation of course guidance after transition to VFR.

B– Safe obstruction clearance in the approach area.

C– Course guidance from the visual descent point to touchdown.

3-46. Answer B. GFDIC 3A (AIM)

VASI systems are designed to help pilots maintain a safe descent path and to ensure obstruction clearance within ± 10° of the extended centerline and out to 4 NM from the runway threshold.

3-47   **PLT141**
(Refer to figure 135.)

Unless a higher angle is required for obstacle clearance, what is the normal glide path for a 3-bar VASI?

A– 2.3°.

B– 2.75°.

C– 3.0°.

3-47. Answer C. GFDIC 3A, AIM
Assuming the normal glide path is the lower one, it is typically 3.0°. It may be higher for obstacle clearance, but not lower. It may help to remember that the second (upper) glide path is about 0.25° steeper than the first.

3-48   **PLT141**
(Refer to figure 135.)

Which illustration would a pilot observe when on the lower glide path?

A– 4.

B– 5.

C– 6.

3-48. Answer B. GFDIC 3A, AIM
On the lower glide path, you would use the near and middle bars. Illustration 5 shows these two bars as red over white, which is on glide path.

3-49   **PLT141**
(Refer to figure 135.)

Which illustration would a pilot observe if the aircraft is above both glide paths?

A– 5.

B– 6.

C– 7.

3-49. Answer C. GFDIC 3A, AIM
When above both glide paths, all three bars will be white.

3-50   **PLT141**
(Refer to figure 135.)

Which illustration would a pilot observe if the aircraft is below both glide paths?

A– 4.

B– 5.

C– 6.

3-50. Answer A. GFDIC 3A, AIM
All three bars will be red if you are below both glide paths.

3-51   **PLT141**
(Refer to figure 136.)

Which illustration depicts an "on glide path" indication?

A– 8.

B– 10.

C– 11.

3-51. Answer B. GFDIC 3A, AIM
"On glide path" for a PAPI shows two white lights and two red lights.

3-52   **PLT141**
(Refer to figure 136.)

Which illustration depicts a "slightly low" (2.8°) indication?

A– 9.

B– 10.

C– 11.

3-52. Answer C. GFDIC 3A, AIM
Three red lights and one white light shows "slightly low."

3-53   **PLT141**
(Refer to figure 136.)

Which illustration would a pilot observe if the aircraft is on a glide path higher than 3.5°?

A– 8.

B– 9.

C– 11.

3-53. Answer A. GFDIC 3A, AIM
Assuming the glide path is set at the normal 3° angle, the indication, if you were higher than a 3.5° glide path, would be all white lights.

3-54   **PLT141**
(Refer to figure 136.)

Which illustration would a pilot observe if the aircraft is "slightly high" (3.2°) on the glide path?

A– 8.

B– 9.

C– 11.

3-54. Answer B. GFDIC 3A, AIM
Three white lights and one red light indicates you are "slightly high."

3-55   PLT141
(Refer to figure 136.)

Which illustration would a pilot observe if the aircraft is less than 2.5°?

A– 10.

B– 11.

C– 12.

3-55. Answer C. GFDIC 3A, AIM
On a PAPI set to a normal 3° approach angle, you would see all red lights if below a 2.5° glide path.

3-56   PLT141
(Refer to figure 137.)

What is the distance (A) from the beginning of the runway to the fixed distance marker?

A– 500 feet.

B– 1,000 feet.

C– 1,500 feet.

3-56. Answer B. GFDIC 3A, AIM
The solid bold stripes of the fixed distance marker begin 1,000 feet from the threshold. (The current term for the fixed distance marker is "aiming point marking.")

3-57   PLT141
(Refer to figure 137.)

What is the distance (B) from the beginning of the runway to the touchdown zone marker?

A– 250 feet.

B– 500 feet.

C– 750 feet.

3-57. Answer B. GFDIC 3A, AIM
The touchdown zone marker begins 500 feet from the threshold.

3-58   PLT141
(Refer to figure 137.)

What is the distance (C) from the beginning of the touchdown zone marker to the beginning of the fixed distance marker?

A– 1,000 feet.

B– 500 feet.

C– 250 feet.

3-58. Answer B. GFDIC 3A, AIM
The distance between the beginning of the touchdown zone marker and the beginning of the fixed distance marker is 500 feet. (The current term for the fixed distance marker is "aiming point marking.")

3-59   PLT141
Which runway marking indicates a displaced threshold on an instrument runway?

A– Arrows leading to the threshold mark.

B– Centerline dashes starting at the threshold.

C– Red chevron marks in the nonlanding portion of the runway.

3-59. Answer A. GFDIC 3A, AIM
A series of arrows along the runway centerline leading up to a threshold bar indicates a displaced threshold.

3-60   PLT145
Which type of runway lighting consists of a pair of synchronized flashing lights, one on each side of the runway threshold?

A– RAIL.

B– HIRL.

C– REIL.

3-60. Answer C. GFDIC 3A, AIM
These lights identify the runway threshold, and are called runway end identifier lights (REIL).

3-61   PLT141
The primary purpose of runway end identifier lights, installed at many airfields, is to provide

A– rapid identification of the approach end of the runway during reduced visibility.

B– a warning of the final 3,000 feet of runway remaining as viewed from the takeoff or approach position.

C– rapid identification of the primary runway during reduced visibility.

3-61. Answer A. GFDIC 3A, AIM
Runway end identifier lights (REILs) help you identify the approach end of the runway during darkness and conditions of low visibility.

3-62   PLT141

(Refer to figure 138.)

What night operations, if any, are authorized between the approach end of the runway and the threshold lights?

A– No aircraft operations are permitted short of the threshold lights.

B– Only taxi operations are permitted in the area short of the threshold lights.

C– Taxi and takeoff operations are permitted, providing the takeoff operations are toward the visible green threshold lights.

3-62. Answer C. GFDIC 3A, AC 150/5340-24

In the area behind the displaced threshold, taxi, takeoff, and rollout operations are permitted, as long as take-offs are toward the green lights.

3-63   PLT141

The 'runway hold position' sign denotes

A– intersecting runways.

B– an entrance to runway from a taxiway

C– an area protected for an aircraft approaching a runway.

3-63. Answer A. GFDIC 3A, AIM

Runway hold position markings identify the locations on a taxiway where an aircraft is supposed to stop when it does not have clearance to proceed onto the runway.

3-64   PLT141

'Runway hold position' markings on the taxiway

A– identifies where aircraft hold short of the runway.

B– identifies area where aircraft are prohibited.

C– allows an aircraft permission onto the runway

3-64. Answer A. GFDIC 3A, AIM

Runway hold position markings identify the locations on a taxiway where an aircraft is supposed to stop when it does not have clearance to proceed onto the runway

3-65   PLT141

The 'No Entry' sign identifies

A– the exit boundary for the runway protected area.

B– an area that does not continue beyond intersection.

C– paved area where aircraft entry is prohibited.

3-65. Answer C. GFDIC 3A, AIM

The 'no entry' sign prohibits an aircraft from entering an area. Typically, this sign would be located on a taxiway intended to be used in only one direction or at the intersection of vehicle roadways with runway, taxiways, or aprons where the roadway may be mistaken as a taxiway or other aircraft movement surface.

3-66   PLT141

When turning onto a taxiway from another taxiway, the 'taxiway directional sign' indicates

A– direction to the take-off runway.

B– designation and direction of taxiway leading out of an intersection.

C– designation and direction of exit taxiway from runway.

3-66. Answer B. GFDIC 3A, AIM

The taxiway directional sign designates the intersecting taxiway or taxiways leading out of the intersection that a pilot would normally be expected to turn onto or hold short of. Each designation is accompanied by an arrow indicating the direction of the turn.

3-67   PLT140

What is the rule for a pilot receiving a "Land and Hold Short Operation (LAHSO) clearance?"

A– The pilot is required to accept the controller's clearance in visual meteorological conditions.

B– The pilot must accept the clearance if the pavement is dry and the stopping distance is adequate.

C– The pilot has the option to accept or reject all LAHSO clearances regardless of the meteorological conditions

3-67. Answer C. GFDIC 3A, IPH

The pilot in command has final authority to accept or decline any LAHSO clearances. The safety and operation of the aircraft remain the responsibility of the pilot. You are expected to decline a LAHSO clearance if you think it may compromise safety.

3-68   PLT077

(Refer to figures 202 and 203.)

What are the hours of operation (local time) of the control tower for the Acadiana Tower when daylight savings time is in effect?

A– The tower operates full time.

B– 1300 to 0300.

C– 0600 to 2100.

3-68. Answer C. GFDIC 3A, 7A, Airport Diagram Legend, A/FD Legend

The asterisk next to the tower frequency on the airport diagram indicates that the tower operates part time. The A/FD excerpt notes that the control tower is operated from 1200Z to 0300Z. The symbol indicates that effective times are one hour earlier during periods of daylight savings time (1100Z to 0200Z). To convert to local time, subtract 5 hours during daylight savings time. The answer is 0600 to 2100 local time.

3-69   PLT077

(Refer to figures 203A and 204.)

What is the landing distance available (LDA) for Runway 18R?

A– 6,680 feet

B– 5,510 feet

C– 6,879 feet

3-69. Answer B. GFDIC 3A, 7A, Airport Diagram Legend, A/FD Legend

The symbol of the white letter D on the black square below the communications section of the airport diagram indicates that runway declared distance information can be found in the A/FD. The A/FD excerpt shows that Runway 18R has 5,510 feet of landing distance available (LDA–5510). This is due to the displaced threshold (indicated on the airport diagram by a symbol over the runway.)

3-70   PLT077

(Refer to figures 205 and 206.)

What is the available landing distance when performing LAHSO on Runway 04L?

A– 3,700 feet.

B– 6,250 feet.

C– 6,952 feet.

3-70. Answer A. GFDIC 3A, 7A, Airport Diagram Legend, A/FD Legend

The airport diagram shows LAHSO hold short points with a line over the runway and a callout. Under the heading Land and Hold Short Operations, the A/FD indicates that the available landing distance is 3,700 feet when landing on Runway 4L and holding short of to Runway 08L/26R.

3-71   PLT141

(Refer to figure 132.)

While clearing an active runway, you are clear of the ILS critical area when you pass which sign?

A– Top red.

B– Middle yellow.

C– Bottom yellow.

3-71. Answer C. GFDIC 3A, AIM, PHB

ILS critical areas are established near each localizer and glide slope antenna. An ILS holding position marking on the pavement consists of two yellow solid lines spaced two feet apart connected by pairs of solid lines spaced ten feet apart. The ILS critical area boundary sign has a yellow background with a black graphic depicting the ILS pavement holding position marking.

3-72   PLT281

(Refer to figure 231.)

What is true about the restrictions to navigation that apply to the White Cloud VOR/DME near Baldwin Municipal Airport?

A– White Cloud VOR/DME is unusable for navigation on the 030° radial beyond 30 NM below 3,000 feet MSL.

B– White Cloud VOR/DME is unusable for navigation on the 165° radial beyond 30 NM below 3,000 feet MSL.

C– White Cloud DME is unusable on the 165° radial beyond 30 NM below 3,000 feet MSL.

3-72. Answer A. GFDIC 3A, A/FD Legend

The A/FD indicates that White Cloud VOR/DME is unusable for navigation from the 020° to 090° radials beyond 30 NM below 3,000 feet MSL. The 030° radial is within this area. The White Cloud DME is also unusable from the 270° to 290° radials. The 165° radial is not within either area.

SECTION B — AIR TRAFFIC CONTROL SYSTEM

ATC FACILITIES

The air traffic control (ATC) system consists of enroute and terminal facilities. The main enroute facility is air route traffic control center (ARTCC), while approach and departure control, the control tower, ground control, and clearance delivery are terminal facilities.

ARTCC TRAFFIC SEPARATION

- You must file an IFR flight plan and receive an ATC clearance prior to entering controlled airspace in IFR conditions. IFR flight plans should be filed at least 30 minutes before departure.

- ATC's first priorities are separating IFR traffic and issuing safety alerts. A safety alert is issued when, in the controller's judgment, an aircraft is in unsafe proximity to terrain, an obstruction, or another aircraft.

- ATC is not obligated to advise an IFR pilot of conflicting VFR traffic, and may not be aware of all VFR traffic. Whether VFR or IFR, it is your responsibility to see and avoid other aircraft whenever weather conditions permit.

- Flight plans are processed by the ARTCC in which the flight originates.

- IFR flight plans are usually deleted from the ARTCC computer if they are not activated within one hour of the proposed departure time. To ensure your flight plan remains active, advise ATC of your revised departure time if you will be delayed one hour or more.

- Due to weather, unplanned pilot requests, flow control restrictions, etc., controllers may alter your clearance to maintain proper aircraft separation. An ATC request for a speed reduction means you should maintain the new indicated airspeed within 10 knots.

- If you have a transponder and it has been inspected within the previous 24 months, it must be turned on and squawking Mode C, if available, anywhere in controlled airspace.

ATC WEATHER SERVICES

- If adverse weather exists or is forecast, an on-site meteorologist at the ARTCC may issue a center weather advisory (CWA).

- ATC may be able to provide vectors around hazardous weather. However, you should be aware that ATC radar limitations and frequency congestion may limit a controller's capability to provide in-flight weather avoidance assistance.

PROCEDURES AT TOWER-CONTROLLED AIRPORTS

- Automatic terminal information service (ATIS) broadcasts are updated upon receipt of any official weather information. The absence of the sky condition and visibility on an ATIS broadcast specifically implies the ceiling is more than 5,000 feet AGL and the visibility is more than 5 statute miles.

- To relieve congestion on ground control frequencies, clearance delivery is used for ATC clearances at busier airports.

- At airports with an operating control tower, you are required to obtain a clearance before operating in a movement area, which is an area on the airport, other than a parking area and loading ramp, used for taxiing, takeoff, and landing. When departing from a runway intersection, always state your position when calling the tower for takeoff.

- During a takeoff on an IFR flight plan, contact departure control only after you are advised to do so by the tower controller.

TERMINAL PROCEDURES

- Terminal radar service for VFR aircraft includes basic radar service, terminal radar service area (TRSA) service, Class C service, and Class B service.

- Basic radar service for VFR aircraft includes safety alerts, traffic advisories, and limited radar vectoring. Sequencing also is available at certain terminal locations.

- Departure control provides separation of all aircraft within Class B and Class C airspace.
- When calling out traffic, controllers describe the position of the traffic in terms of the 12-hour clock. For example, "traffic at 3 o'clock" indicates the aircraft lies off your right wing. Traffic advisories from ATC are based on your aircraft's actual ground track, not on your aircraft's heading.
- A local airport advisory (LAA) is provided by flight service at FSS airports not served by an operating control tower, or when the tower is closed. Although VFR participation LAA service is not mandatory, it is strongly encouraged that you report your position, aircraft type, and intentions when 10 miles from the airport, and request an airport advisory from the FSS

3-73 PLT405
When should your transponder be on Mode C while on an IFR flight?

A– Only when ATC requests Mode C.

B– At all times if the equipment has been calibrated, unless requested otherwise by ATC.

C– When passing 12,500 feet MSL.

3-73. Answer A. GFDIC 3A (AIM)
When operating in controlled airspace, transponders must be on, including Mode C if installed, and set to the appropriate code or as assigned by ATC. In uncontrolled airspace, the transponder should be operating while airborne unless otherwise requested by ATC.

3-74 PLT161
What service is provided by departure control to an IFR flight when operating within the outerarea of Class C airspace?

A– Separation from all aircraft.

B– Position and altitude of all traffic within 2 miles of the IFR pilot's line of flight and altitude.

C– Separation from all IFR aircraft and participating VFR aircraft.

3-74. Answer C. GFDIC 3B, AIM
VFR aircraft are separated from IFR aircraft within the Class C airspace by any of the following:

1. Visual separation.

2. 500 feet vertical; except when operating beneath a heavy jet.

3. Target resolution.

3-75 PLT435
If a control tower and an FSS are located on the same airport, which function is provided by the FSS during those periods when the tower is closed?

A– Automatic closing of the IFR flight plan.

B– Approach control services.

C– Airport Advisory Service.

3-75. Answer C. GFDIC 3B, AIM
Local airport advisory (LAA) is a service provided by an FSS physically located on an airport which does not have a control tower or where the tower is operated part-time.

3-76   PLT435

Which service is provided for IFR arrivals by a FSS located on an airport without a control tower?

A– Automatic closing of the IFR flight plan.

B– Airport advisories.

C– All functions of approach control.

3-76. Answer B. GFDIC 3B, AIM

Local airport advisory (LAA) is a service provided by an FSS physically located on an airport which does not have a control tower or where the tower is operated part-time.

3-77   PLT390

During a takeoff into IFR conditions with low ceilings, when should the pilot contact departure control?

A– Before penetrating the clouds.

B– When advised by the tower.

C– Upon completing the first turn after takeoff or upon establishing cruise climb on a straight-out departure.

3-77. Answer B. GFDIC 3B, AIM

As a general rule, you should not change to the departure control frequency until instructed to do so.

3-78   PLT044

During a flight, the controller advises "traffic 2 o'clock 5 miles southbound." The pilot is holding 20° correction for a crosswind from the right. Where should the pilot look for the traffic?

A– 40° to the right of the aircraft's nose.

B– 20° to the right of the aircraft's nose.

C– Straight ahead.

3-78. Answer A. GFDIC 3B, AIM

Traffic advisories are based on the observation of your ground track on the radar. Radar cannot tell which way the nose of your aircraft is pointed. Position of traffic is called in terms of the 12-hour clock. In this example, the aircraft's nose is pointed 20° right of its ground track to compensate for a strong crosswind. In a nowind situation, the 2 o'clock position would be 60° to the right of the nose. Since the nose is already pointed toward the 2 o'clock position by 20°, you would only have to look further right by 40° to see the controller's advisory. Remember, the controller only sees your ground track on the radar display, not the aircraft's nose position.

3-79   PLT172

Pilots on IFR flights seeking ATC in flight weather avoidance assistance should keep in mind that

A– ATC radar limitations and frequency congestion may limit the controllers capability to provide this service.

B– circumnavigating severe weather can only be accommodated in the en route areas away from terminals because of congestion.

C– ATC Narrow Band Radar does not provide the controller with weather intensity capability.

3-79. Answer A. GFDIC 3B, AIM

While ATC's primary function is to provide safe separation between aircraft, center controllers will issue pertinent information on weather and assist pilots in avoiding areas of threatening weather to the extent possible. Keep in mind, the controller's workload is generally heavier than normal when weather disrupts the normal traffic flow.

3-80   PLT370

What is the pilot-in-command's responsibility when flying a propeller aircraft within 20 miles of the airport of intended landing and ATC requests the pilot to reduce speed to 160? (Pilot complies with speed adjustment.)

A— Reduce TAS to 160 knots and maintain until advised by ATC.

B— Reduce IAS to 160 MPH and maintain until advised by ATC.

C— Reduce IAS to 160 knots and maintain that speed within 10 knots.

3-80. Answer C. GFDIC 3B, AIM

You should comply with the requested speed, if able, and reduce your indicated airspeed to 160 kts. When within 20 miles of your destination airport, ATC must obtain pilot concurrence to reduce propeller aircraft speed below 150 knots. You should maintain the assigned airspeed within 10 knots.

SECTION C — ATC CLEARANCES

An ATC clearance is an authorization for you to proceed under a specified set of conditions within controlled airspace.

PILOT RESPONSIBILITIES

- You may not deviate from an ATC clearance unless you experience an emergency or the clearance will cause you to violate a rule or regulation. If you deviate from an ATC clearance, you must notify ATC as soon as possible. If you are given priority over other aircraft you may be requested to submit a written report to the manager of the ATC facility within 48 hours.

- While operating under VFR, if ATC assigns an altitude or heading that will cause you to enter clouds, you should avoid the clouds and inform ATC that the altitude or heading will not permit VFR.

- Anytime you are in VFR conditions, it is your responsibility to see and avoid all other traffic, even if you have filed an IFR flight plan and are operating under an IFR clearance.

IFR CLIMB CONSIDERATIONS

- Unless ATC advises "At pilot's discretion," you are expected to climb at an optimum rate consistent with your airplane's performance to within 1,000 feet of your assigned altitude. Then attempt to climb at a rate of between 500 and 1,500 f.p.m. for the last 1,000 feet of climb. You should notify ATC if you are unable to maintain a 500 f.p.m. climb rate.

- While climbing on an airway, you are required by regulation to maintain the centerline except when maneuvering in VFR conditions to detect and/or avoid other air traffic.

IFR FLIGHT PLAN AND ATC CLEARANCE

- An IFR flight plan is required before flying into Class A airspace or any other controlled airspace when the weather is below VFR minimums.

- You must receive an ATC clearance before entering Class A or B airspace regardless of the weather, and in Class C, D, and E airspace when the weather is below VFR minimums.

- You may cancel an IFR flight plan anytime you are operating under VFR conditions outside of Class A airspace. However, once you cancel IFR, the flight must be conducted strictly in VFR conditions from that point on. If you were to encounter additional IFR weather, it would be necessary to file a new flight plan and again obtain an IFR clearance prior to entering IFR conditions.

TYPES OF IFR CLEARANCES

- The elements of an ATC clearance are: aircraft identification, clearance limit, departure procedure, route of flight, altitudes/flight levels in the order to be flown, holding instructions, any special information, and frequency and transponder code information.

- A cruise clearance authorizes you to operate at any altitude from the minimum IFR altitude up to and including the altitude specified in the clearance without reporting changes in altitude to ATC. A cruise clearance also authorizes you to proceed to and execute an approach at the destination airport.

- An abbreviated clearance can be issued when your route of flight has not changed substantially from that filed in your flight plan. An abbreviated always contains the words "cleared as filed" as well as the name of the destination airport or clearance limit; any applicable SID name, number and transition; the assigned enroute altitude; and any additional instructions such as departure control frequency or transponder code assignment.

- A VFR-on-top clearance can be issued upon request when suitable weather conditions exist. It allows you to fly in VFR conditions and at the appropriate VFR cruising altitudes of your choice. You must remain above the minimum IFR altitude and comply with all instrument flight rules while also maintaining VFR cloud clearances. VFR-on-top is prohibited in Class A airspace.

- A climb-to-VFR-on-top clearance should be requested in order to climb through a cloud layer or an area of reduced visibility and then continue the flight VFR.

APPROACH CLEARANCES

- A contact approach must be initiated by the pilot; it cannot be initiated by ATC. In order to fly a contact approach, the reported ground visibility must be at least one statute mile, and you must be able to remain clear of clouds with at least one statute mile flight visibility.

- A visual approach may be initiated by the controller or the pilot when the ceiling is at least 1,000 feet and the visibility is at least 3 statute miles and the pilot has the airport or the aircraft to follow in sight. During a visual approach, radar service is terminated when ATC tells you to contact the tower.

VFR RESTRICTIONS TO AN IFR CLEARANCE

VFR restrictions can be included in an IFR clearance if requested by the pilot. If weather conditions permit, you might request a VFR climb or descent to avoid a complicated departure or arrival procedure.

COMPOSITE FLIGHT PLAN

A composite flight plan should be filled when you wish to operate IFR on one portion of a flight and VFR on another portion. Check both the VFR and IFR boxes on the flight plan form, and if the IFR portion of the trip is first, contact the nearest FSS while still in VFR conditions to close the VFR portion, then contact ATC and request a clearance.

TOWER ENROUTE CONTROL

A tower enroute control clearance (TEC) is intended to be used by nonturbojet aircraft at altitudes less than 10,000 feet MSL where the duration of the flight is less than 2 hours. It is available in certain, more densely populated areas of the United States where it is possible to conduct a flight in continuous contact with local towers and approach control facilities.

DEPARTURE RESTRICTIONS

Departure restrictions, such as release time, hold for release time, and a clearance void time, may be imposed to separate IFR departure traffic from other traffic in the area or to regulate the flow of IFR traffic. When departing from a non-tower airport, and receiving a clearance containing a void time, you must advise ATC as soon as possible, and no later than 30 minutes, of your intentions if not airborne by the void time.

CLEARANCE COPYING AND READBACK

- Shorthand should be used to quickly copy IFR clearances. The type of shorthand you use is not as important as whether you can read the clearance at a later time.

- You should read back those parts of a clearance which contain altitude assignments, radar vectors, or any instructions requiring clarification.

3-81   **PLT224**

When may a pilot file a composite flight plan?

A– When requested or advised by ATC.

B– Any time a portion of the flight will be VFR.

C– Any time a landing is planned at an intermediate airport.

3-81. Answer B. GFDIC 3C, AIM

A composite flight plan is a request to operate under both IFR and VFR on one flight. You can file a composite flight plan anytime a portion of the flight will be in VFR weather conditions.

3-82   PLT224

When filing a composite flight plan where the first portion of the flight is IFR, which fix(es) should be indicated on the flight plan form?

A— All points of transition from one airway to another, fixes defining direct route segments, and the clearance limit fix.

B— Only the fix where you plan to terminate the IFR portion of the flight.

C— Only those compulsory reporting points on the IFR route segment

3-82. Answer A. GFDIC 3C, AIM

When a composite flight plan is filed, the IFR portion must include all fixes indicating transitions from one airway to another, those defining direct route segments, and the clearance limit.

3-83   PLT390

What is the recommended procedure for transitioning from VFR to IFR on a composite flight plan?

A— Prior to transitioning to IFR, contact the nearest FSS, close the VFR portion, and request ATC clearance.

B— Upon reaching the proposed point for change to IFR, contact the nearest FSS and cancel your VFR flight plan, then contact ARTCC and request an IFR clearance.

C— Prior to reaching the proposed point for change to IFR, contact ARTCC, request your IFR clearance, and instruct them to cancel the VFR flight plan.

3-83. Answer A. GFDIC 3C, AIM

When transitioning from VFR to IFR on a composite flight plan, you must contact the flight service station nearest the VFR to IFR change point, close your VFR flight plan, and then request your IFR clearance. When doing this, keep in mind that you must remain in VFR conditions until you receive an IFR clearance.

3-84   PLT393

Prior to which operation must an IFR flight plan be filed and an appropriate ATC clearance received?

A— Flying by reference to instruments in controlled airspace.

B— Entering controlled airspace when IMC exists.

C— Takeoff when IFR weather conditions exist

3-84. Answer B. GFDIC 3C, FAR 91.173

An IFR flight plan must be filed prior to flying in Class E airspace in instrument meteorological conditions (IMC). An IFR flight plan is also required prior to flying in Class A airspace.

3-85   PLT393

To operate under IFR below 18,000 feet, a pilot must file an IFR flight plan and receive an appropriate ATC clearance prior to

A– entering controlled airspace.

B– entering weather conditions below VFR minimums.

C– takeoff.

3-85. Answer A. GFDIC 3C, FAR 91.173

An IFR flight plan must be filed prior to flying in Class E airspace in instrument meteorological conditions (IMC). An IFR flight plan is also required prior to flying in Class A airspace.

3-86   PLT393

To operate an aircraft under IFR, a flight plan must have been filed and an ATC clearance received prior to

A– controlling the aircraft solely by use of instruments.

B– entering weather conditions in any airspace.

C– entering controlled airspace.

3-86. Answer C. GFDIC 3C, FAR 91.173

An IFR flight plan must be filed prior to flying in Class E airspace in instrument meteorological conditions (IMC). An IFR flight plan is also required prior to flying in Class A airspace.

3-87   PLT393

When is an IFR clearance required during VFR weather conditions?

A– When operating in the Class E airspace.

B– When operating in a Class A airspace.

C– When operating in airspace above 14,500 feet.

3-87. Answer B. GFDIC 3C, FAR 91.135

An IFR flight plan must be filed prior to flying in Class E airspace in instrument meteorological conditions (IMC). An IFR flight plan is also required prior to flying in Class A airspace. Anytime you operate in Class A airspace you must first receive an IFR clearance.

3-88   PLT393

Operation in which airspace requires filing an IFR flight plan?

A– Any airspace when the visibility is less than 1 mile.

B– Class E airspace with IMC and class A airspace.

C– Positive control area, Continental Control Area, and all other airspace, if the visibility is less than 1 mile.

3-88. Answer B. GFDIC 3C, FAR 91.173, FAR 91.135

An IFR flight plan must be filed prior to flying in controlled airspace when instrument meteorological conditions (IMC) exist and prior to flying in Class A airspace.

3-89   PLT161

When departing from an airport located outside controlled airspace during IMC, you must file an IFR flight plan and receive a clearance before

A– takeoff.

B– entering IFR conditions.

C– entering Class E airspace.

3-89. Answer C. GFDIC 3C, FAR 91.173

An IFR flight plan must be filed prior to flying in controlled airspace when instrument meteorological conditions (IMC) exist and prior to flying in Class A airspace.

3-90   PLT225

(Refer to figure 1.)

Which item(s) should be checked in block 1 for a composite flight plan?

A– VFR with an explanation in block 11.

B– IFR with an explanation in block 11.

C– VFR and IFR.

3-90. Answer C. GFDIC 3C, AIM

When filing a composite flight plan, check both the VFR and IFR boxes in block 1 of the flight plan.

3-91   PLT161

When may a pilot cancel the IFR flight plan prior to completing the flight?

A– Any time.

B– Only if an emergency occurs.

C– Only in VFR conditions when not in Class A airspace

3-91. Answer C. GFDIC 3C, AIM

You may cancel an IFR flight plan when in Class G (uncontrolled) airspace, and in VFR conditions in controlled airspace which is outside Class A airspace (formerly the positive control area).

3-92   PLT044

When departing from an airport not served by a control tower, the issuance of a clearance containing a void time indicates that

A– ATC will assume the pilot has not departed if no transmission is received before the void time.

B– the pilot must advise ATC as soon as possible, but no later than 30 minutes, of their intentions if not off by the void time.

C– ATC will protect the airspace only to the void time.

3-92. Answer B. GFDIC 3C, AIM

The wording, "clearance void if not off by ...," indicates that ATC expects you to be airborne by a certain time. In the event you do not depart by the void time, you must advise ATC of your intentions as soon as possible, but no later than 30 minutes after the void time.

3-93   **PLT044**

What response is expected when ATC issues an IFR clearance to pilots of airborne aircraft?

A– Read back the entire clearance as required by regulation.

B– Read back those parts containing altitude assignments or vectors and any part requiring verification.

C– Read back should be unsolicited and spontaneous to confirm that the pilot understands all instructions.

3-93. Answer B. GFDIC 3C, AIM

Although there is no requirement to read back an ATC clearance, you are expected to read back those parts of any clearance which contain altitude assignments, radar vectors, or any other instructions requiring verification.

3-94   **PLT044**

Which clearance items are always given in an abbreviated IFR departure clearance? (Assume radar environment.)

A– Altitude, destination airport, and one or more fixes which identify the initial route of flight.

B– Destination airport, altitude, SID Name, Number, and/or Transition, if appropriate.

C– Clearance limit, SID Name, Number, and/or Transition, if appropriate.

3-94. Answer B. GFDIC 3C, AIM

ATC may issue an abbreviated clearance by using the phrase "cleared as filed." This clearance will contain the name of your destination airport or clearance limit, the assigned enroute altitude, and SID information if appropriate.

3-95   **PLT044**

On the runup pad, you receive the following clearance from ground control:

CLEARED TO THE DALLAS LOVE AIRPORT AS FILED-MAINTAIN SIX THOUSAND - SQUAWK ZERO SEVEN ZERO FOUR JUST BEFORE DEPARTURE-DEPARTURE CONTROL WILL BE ONE TWO FOUR POINT NINER.

An abbreviated clearance, such as this, will always contain the

A– departure control frequency.

B– requested enroute altitude.

C– destination airport and route.

3-95. Answer C. GFDIC 3C, AIM

An abbreviated clearance contains the name of your destination airport or clearance limit; the assigned enroute altitude or altitude to expect; SID information, and route as appropriate; and it may include a departure frequency or transponder code assignment.

3-96   PLT044

Which information is always given in an abbreviated departure clearance?

A– SID or transition name and altitude to maintain.

B– Name of destination airport or specific fix and altitude.

C– Altitude to maintain and code to squawk.

3-96. Answer B. GFDIC 3C, AIM

An abbreviated clearance will always contain the name of the destination airport or a clearance limit, any applicable SID, and the assigned enroute altitude.

3-97   PLT298

What altitude may a pilot on an IFR flight plan select upon receiving a VFR-on-Top clearance?

A– Any altitude at least 1,000 feet above or 1,000 feet below the meteorological condition.

B– Any appropriate VFR altitude at or above the MEA in VFR weather conditions.

C– Any VFR altitude appropriate for the direction of flight at least 500 feet above the meteorological condition.

3-97. Answer B. GFDIC 3C, AIM

When flying with a VFR-on-Top clearance, you must fly at an appropriate VFR altitude as defined in FAR 91.159. This type of clearance may be issued to a pilot on an IFR flight plan. In this case, you must comply with VFR visibility and cloud clearance requirements, as well as minimum IFR altitude rules. When flying below 18,000 feet MSL, and more than 3,000 feet AGL, you must maintain an odd thousand foot MSL altitude plus 500 feet for easterly magnetic courses (0° through 179°), for example 3,500, 5,500, or 7,500 feet MSL. For westerly magnetic courses (180° through 359°), maintain even thousand foot MSL altitudes plus 500 feet, for example 4,500, 6,500, or 8,500 feet MSL. Refer to the regulation for applicable flight levels above 18,000 feet MSL.

3-98   PLT298

When must a pilot fly at a cardinal altitude plus 500 feet on an IFR flight plan?

A– When flying above 18,000 feet in VFR conditions.

B– When flying in VFR conditions above clouds.

C– When assigned a VFR-on-Top clearance.

3-98. Answer C. GFDIC 3C, FAR 91.159, AIM

When flying with a VFR-on-Top clearance, you must fly at an appropriate VFR altitude as defined in FAR 91.159. This type of clearance may be issued to a pilot on an IFR flight plan. In this case, you must comply with VFR visibility and cloud clearance requirements, as well as minimum IFR altitude rules. When flying below 18,000 feet MSL, and more than 3,000 feet AGL, you must maintain an odd thousand foot MSL altitude plus 500 feet for easterly magnetic courses (0° through 179°), for example 3,500, 5,500, or 7,500 feet MSL. For westerly magnetic courses (180° through 359°), maintain even thousand foot MSL altitudes plus 500 feet, for example 4,500, 6,500, or 8,500 feet MSL. Refer to the regulation for applicable flight levels above 18,000 feet MSL.

3-99   PLT298

You have filed an IFR flight plan with a VFR-on-Top clearance in lieu of an assigned altitude. If you receive this clearance and fly a course of 180°, at what altitude should you fly? (Assume VFR conditions.)

A– Any IFR altitude which will enable you to remain in VFR conditions.

B– An odd thousand-foot MSL altitude plus 500 feet.

C– An even thousand-foot MSL altitude plus 500 feet.

3-99. Answer C. GFDIC 3C, FAR 91.159, AIM

Assuming that your flight is below FL 180, and above 3,000 feet AGL, FAR 91.159 specifies that for any magnetic course, 180° through 359°, you will operate at an even thousand foot MSL altitude plus 500 feet, for example 4,500, 6,500, or 8,500 feet MSL.

3-100   PLT044

Which clearance procedures may be issued by ATC without prior pilot request?

A– SIDs, STARs, and contact approaches.

B– Contact and visual approaches.

C– SIDs, STARs, and visual approaches.

3-100. Answer C. GFDIC 3C, AIM

SIDs, STARs, and visual approaches can be initiated by either the pilot or ATC. A contact approach request must be initiated by the pilot.

3-101   PLT370

What is the significance of an ATC clearance which reads "...CRUISE SIX THOUSAND..."?

A– The pilot must maintain 6,000 until reaching the IAF serving the destination airport, then execute the published approach procedure.

B– It authorizes a pilot to conduct flight at any altitude from minimum IFR altitude up to and including 6,000.

C– The pilot is authorized to conduct flight at any altitude from minimum IFR altitude up to and including 6,000, but each change in altitude must be reported to ATC.

3-101. Answer B. GFDIC 3C, AIM

A cruise clearance is an authorization by ATC to conduct flight at any altitude from the minimum IFR altitude up to and including the altitude specified, in this case 6,000 feet MSL.

3-102   PLT298

Where are VFR-on-Top operations prohibited?

A– In Class A airspace.

B– During off-airways direct flights.

C– When flying through Class B airspace.

3-102. Answer A. GFDIC 3C, FAR 91.135, AIM

ATC will not authorize VFR or VFR-on-Top operations in Class A airspace, and you must operate under an IFR flight plan

3-103   PLT298

Which rules apply to the pilot-in-command when operating on a VFR-on-Top clearance?

A– VFR only.

B– VFR and IFR.

C– VFR when "in the clear" and IFR when "in the clouds."

3-103. Answer B. GFDIC 3C, AIM

VFR-on-Top allows you to fly in VFR conditions and at appropriate VFR cruising altitudes while on an IFR flight plan. In addition to compliance with VFR visibility, cloud clearance, and cruising altitude requirements, you also must observe minimum IFR altitudes.

3-104   PLT298

When can a VFR-on-Top clearance be assigned by ATC?

A– Only upon request of the pilot when conditions are indicated to be suitable.

B– Any time suitable conditions exist and ATC wishes to expedite traffic flow.

C– When VFR conditions exist, but there is a layer of clouds below the MEA.

3-104. Answer A. GFDIC 3C, AIM

Only the pilot can initiate a VFR-on-Top clearance. In addition, you must maintain VFR flight conditions at all times. Altitude selection must comply with the VFR cruising altitude rules. You may not select an altitude that is less than the minimum IFR altitude prescribed for the route segment.

3-105   PLT298

Which ATC clearance should instrument-rated pilots request in order to climb through a cloud layer or an area of reduced visibility and then continue the flight VFR?

A– To VFR on Top.

B– Special VFR to VFR Over-the-Top.

C– VFR Over-the-Top.

3-105. Answer A. GFDIC 3C, AIM

Pilots desiring to climb through a cloud, haze, smoke, or other meteorological formation and then either cancel their IFR flight plan or operate VFR-on-Top may request a climb to VFR-on-Top.

3-106   PLT298
When on a VFR-on-Top clearance, the cruising altitude is based on

A– true course.

B– magnetic course.

C– magnetic heading.

3-106. Answer B. GFDIC 3C, AIM
Altitude selection must comply with the VFR cruising altitude rules which are based on the magnetic course of the aircraft.

3-107   PLT298
In which airspace is VFR-on-Top operation prohibited?

A– Class B airspace.

B– Class E airspace.

C– Class A airspace.

3-107. Answer C. GFDIC 3C, AIM
ATC will not authorize VFR or VFR-on-Top operations in Class A airspace, and you must operate under an IFR flight plan.

3-108   PLT298
What cruising altitude is appropriate for VFR on Top on a westbound flight below 18,000 feet?

A– Even thousand-foot levels.

B– Even thousand-foot levels plus 500 feet, but not below MEA.

C– Odd thousand-foot levels plus 500 feet, but not below MEA.

3-108. Answer B. GFDIC 3C, AIM, FAR 91.159
When flying on a VFR-on-Top clearance, VFR cruising altitude rules must be followed. On westbound flights (magnetic courses 180° through 359°) above 3,000 feet AGL and below 18,000 feet MSL, you must maintain an even thousand-foot MSL altitude plus 500 feet. The selected altitude must not be less then the applicable MEA.

3-109   PLT298
What minimums must be considered in selecting an altitude when operating with a VFR-on-Top clearance?

A– At least 500 feet above the lowest MEA, or appropriate MOCA, and at least 1,000 feet above the existing meteorological condition.

B– At least 1,000 feet above the lowest MEA, appropriate MOCA, or existing meteorological condition.

C– Minimum IFR altitude, minimum distance from clouds, and visibility appropriate to altitude selected.

3-109. Answer C. GFDIC 3C, AIM, FAR 91.155, FAR 91.159
Minimums are set according to the existing weather conditions and follow the appropriate VFR cruising altitude, visibility, and distance from cloud criteria specified in FAR Parts 91.159 and 91.155, respectively

3-110   **PLT370**
A "CRUISE FOUR THOUSAND FEET" clearance would mean that the pilot is authorized to

A– vacate 4,000 feet without notifying ATC.

B– climb to, but not descend from 4,000 feet, without further ATC clearance.

C– use any altitude from minimum IFR to 4,000 feet, but must report leaving each altitude.

3-110. Answer A. GFDIC 3C, AIM
The term "cruise" is used by ATC to assign a block of airspace to a pilot from the minimum IFR altitude up to and including the altitude specified in the cruise clearance. You may level off at any intermediate altitude or climb/descend within the block at your discretion. However, once you start descent and verbally report leaving an altitude in the block, you may not return to that altitude without additional ATC clearance.

3-111   **PLT403**
While on an IFR flight, a pilot has an emergency which causes a deviation from an ATC clearance. What action must be taken?

A– Notify ATC of the deviation as soon as possible.

B– Squawk 7700 for the duration of the emergency.

C– Submit a detailed report to the chief of the ATC facility within 48 hours.

3-111. Answer A. GFDIC 3C, FAR 91.123
FAR Part 91.123(c) states that, "Each pilot in command who, in an emergency, deviates from an ATC clearance or instruction shall notify ATC of that deviation as soon as possible."

3-112   **PLT444**
What responsibility does the pilot-in-command of an IFR flight assume upon entering VFR conditions?

A– Report VFR conditions to ARTCC so that an amended clearance may be issued.

B– Use VFR operating procedures.

C– To see and avoid other traffic.

3-112. Answer C. GFDIC 3C, FAR 91.113
FAR Part 91.113(b) states, "When weather conditions permit, regardless of whether an operation is conducted under instrument flight rules or visual flight rules, vigilance shall be maintained by each person operating an aircraft so as to see and avoid other aircraft."

3-113   **PLT044**
An abbreviated departure clearance "...CLEARED AS FILED..." will always contain the name

A– and number of the STAR to be flown when filed in the flight plan.

B– of the destination airport filed in the flight plan.

C– of the first compulsory reporting point if not in a radar environment.

3-113. Answer B. GFDIC 3C, AIM 5-2-3f
An abbreviated clearance will always contain the name of the destination airport or a clearance limit; any applicable SID name, number, and transition; and your assigned enroute altitude

3-114 **PLT298**

If, while in Class E airspace, a clearance is received to "maintain VFR conditions on top," the pilot should maintain a VFR cruising altitude based on the direction of the

A— true course.

B— magnetic heading.

C— magnetic course.

3-114. Answer C. GFDIC 3C, AIM, FAR 91.159, FAR 91.179a

With a VFR-on-Top clearance, you must maintain an appropriate VFR cruising altitude. VFR cruising altitudes are based on magnetic course. Magnetic course is true course corrected for magnetic variation. It does not take into consideration any wind drift correction.

3-115 **PLT298**

When operating under IFR with a VFR-On-Top clearance, what altitude should be maintained?

A— An IFR cruising altitude appropriate to the magnetic course being flown.

B— A VFR cruising altitude appropriate to the magnetic course being flown and as restricted by ATC.

C— The last IFR altitude assigned by ATC.

3-115. Answer B. GFDIC 3C, AIM

When flying on an IFR flight plan operating in VFR weather conditions, you may request VFR-ON-TOP in lieu of an assigned altitude. This permits you to select an appropriate VFR cruising altitude or flight level (subject to any ATC restrictions).

3-116 **PLT292**

What are the main differences between a visual approach and a contact approach?

A— The pilot must request a contact approach; the pilot may be assigned a visual approach and higher weather minimums must exist.

B— The pilot must request a visual approach and report having the field in sight; ATC may assign a contact approach if VFR conditions exist.

C— Any time the pilot reports the field in sight, ATC may clear the pilot for a contact approach; for a visual approach, the pilot must advise that the approach can be made under VFR conditions.

3-116. Answer A. GFDIC 3C, AIM

A contact approach cannot be initiated by ATC; it must be requested by the pilot. Weather minimums need only be one mile flight visibility and clear of clouds. A visual approach may be assigned by ATC if VFR conditions exist.

3-117   PLT292

What are the requirements for a contact approach to an airport that has an approved IAP, if the pilot is on an instrument flight plan and clear of clouds?

A– The controller must determine that the pilot can see the airport at the altitude flown and can remain clear of clouds.

B– The pilot must agree to the approach when given by ATC and the controller must have determined that the visibility was at least 1 mile and be reasonably sure the pilot can remain clear of clouds.

C– The pilot must request the approach, have at least 1 mile visibility, and be reasonably sure of remaining clear of clouds.

3-117. Answer C. GFDIC 3C, AIM

Only the pilot can initiate a contact approach with a request. You must have 1 mile flight visibility and be able to remain clear of clouds. In addition, you must reasonably expect to be able to remain in these conditions.

3-118   PLT292

When is radar service terminated during a visual approach?

A– Automatically when ATC instructs the pilot to contact the tower.

B– Immediately upon acceptance of the approach by the pilot.

C– When ATC advises, "Radar service terminated; resume own navigation."

3-118. Answer A. GFDIC 3C, AIM

On a visual approach, radar service is automatically terminated, without advising the pilot, when advised by ATC to change to the tower or an advisory frequency.

3-119   PLT420

When may you obtain a contact approach?

A– ATC may assign a contact approach if VFR conditions exist or you report the runway in sight and are clear of clouds.

B– ATC may assign a contact approach if you are below the clouds and the visibility is at least 1 mile.

C– ATC will assign a contact approach only upon request if the reported visibility is at least 1 mile

3-119. Answer C. GFDIC 3C, AIM

The pilot must request the approach, and the visibility must be at least 1 mile.

3-120   PLT420

What conditions are necessary before ATC can authorize a visual approach?

A– You must have the preceding aircraft in sight, and be able to remain in VFR weather conditions.

B– You must have the airport in sight or the preceding aircraft in sight, and be able to proceed to, and land in IFR conditions.

C– You must have the airport in sight or a preceding aircraft to be followed, and be able to proceed to the airport in VFR conditions.

3-120. Answer C. GFDIC 3C, AIM
The controller may issue a visual approach clearance if you have either the airport or a preceding aircraft in sight. You must also be able to maintain VFR conditions to the airport.

3-121   PLT292

A contact approach is an approach procedure that may be used

A– in lieu of conducting a SIAP.

B– if assigned by ATC and will facilitate the approach.

C– in lieu of a visual approach.

3-121. Answer A. GFDIC 3C, AIM
A contact approach may be used instead of the published standard instrument approach procedure (SIAP).

3-122   PLT370

If during a VFR practice instrument approach, Radar Approach Control assigns an altitude or heading that will cause you to enter the clouds, what action should be taken?

A– Enter the clouds, since ATC authorization for practice approaches is considered an IFR clearance.

B– Avoid the clouds and inform ATC that altitude/ heading will not permit VFR.

C– Abandon the approach.

3-122. Answer B. GFDIC 3C, AIM
You should not accept a clearance that would cause you to violate an FAR such as entering clouds while operating under VFR. Take the necessary action to avoid the clouds and notify ATC of your situation.

3-123   PLT194

Which technique should a pilot use to scan for traffic to the right and left during straight-and-level flight?

A– Systematically focus on different segments of the sky for short intervals.

B– Concentrate on relative movement detected in the peripheral vision area.

C– Continuous sweeping of the windshield from right to left

3-123. Answer A. GFDIC 3C, AIM

Only a very small area in the back of the eye can send clear, sharply focused images to the brain. Since the eyes require time to focus on this narrow viewing area, scanning is most effective when using a series of short, regularly spaced eye movements. This will help to bring successive areas of the sky into the central visual field.

DEPARTURE

SECTION A — DEPARTURE CHARTS

DEPARTURE PROCEDURES OVERVIEW

- Charted departure procedures help simplify complex clearances, reduce frequency congestion, ensure obstacle clearance, and control the flow of traffic around an airport. They help reduce fuel consumption, and may include noise abatement procedures.
- The two types of procedures are obstacle departure procedures (ODPs) and standard instrument departures (SIDs).
- Departure charts list the airport served by the procedure, the name, and the word OBSTACLE (if the procedure is an ODP) at the top of the chart. The applicable enroute charts are listed below the navaid information boxes.
- Initial takeoff procedures may apply to all runways, or apply only to the specific runway identified.
- The departure route is shown by a bold black line and transition routes are shown with light lines.

FLIGHT PLANS AND CLEARANCES

- When you accept a SID in a clearance, or file one in your flight plan, you must possess the SID chart or the textual description.
- To avoid being issued SIDs, enter the phrase "NO SID" in the remarks section of your flight plan.
- The computer identification code for a transition in your flight plan informs ATC you intend to fly both the SID and the appropriate transition. For example, the DAWNN ONE DEPARTURE (DAWNN1), Louisville transition (IIU), is entered as "DAWNN1.IIU." You will find these abbreviations on the charts.

PERFORMANCE REQUIREMENTS

- Departure procedures DPs require minimum climb gradients of at least 200 feet per nautical mile to ensure you can clear departure path obstacles.
- Departure procedures may specify a minimum ceiling and visibility to allow you to see and avoid obstacles, a climb gradient greater than 200 feet per mile, detailed flight maneuvers, or a combination of these procedures.
- When you are cleared for SID, you must ensure your aircraft is capable of achieving the performance requirements. Minimum climb gradients are given in feet per nautical mile and must be converted to feet per minute for use during departure.

PILOT NAV AND VECTOR SIDS

- Pilot nav SIDs allow you to navigate along a route with minimal ATC communications. They usually contain instructions to all aircraft, followed by transition routes to navigate to an enroute fix, and may include radar vectors that help you join the SID.
- Vector SIDs exist where ATC provides radar navigation guidance. They usually contain a heading to fly, and an altitude for initial climb. When ATC establishes radar contact, they provide vectors to help you reach fixes portrayed on the chart. When special lost communication procedures are necessary for a SID, they are included on the chart.
- If you are instructed to maintain runway heading, it means you should maintain the magnetic heading of the runway centerline.

4-1   PLT052

(Refer to figure 211.)

At which point does the basic SID terminate?

A– When Helena Departure Control establishes radar contact.

B– At STAKK.

C– Over the BOZEMAN VOR.

4-1. Answer B. GFDIC 4A, AIM, STAR/DP Legend
The STAKK THREE DEPARTURE ends at STAKK as indicated by the end of the bold black line. From STAKK, a DME arc provides a transition route to five departure routes.

4-2   PLT052

(Refer to figure 211.)

At which minimum altitude should you cross STAKK?

A– 11,800 feet MSL.

B– 10,800 feet MSL.

C– 10,200 feet MSL.

4-2. Answer C. GFDIC 4A, STAR/DP Legend
You must cross STAKK at or above 10,200 feet MSL. This is listed in the departure route descriptions for Runways 9 and 27, as well as in the plan view by the callout 10200.

4-3   PLT004

(Refer to figure 211.)

Using an average groundspeed of 140 knots, what minimum rate of climb would meet the required minimum climb rate per NM as specified on the SID for takeoff on Runway 27?

A– 340 feet per minute.

B– 816 feet per minute.

C– 793 feet per minute.

4-3. Answer C. GFDIC 4A, STAR/DP Legend, Rate of Climb Table
The STAKK THREE DEPARTURE requires a minimum climb of 340 feet per NM if you are taking off on Runway 27 as indicated in the TAKEOFF MINIMUMS on the chart plan view. To determine the feet per minute climb rate, use the Rate of Climb Table in Appendix 1. Use the climb rates of 300 and 350 ft/NM and read across to the groundspeed of 140 knots. Interpolate between 700 ft/min and 816 ft/min to determine a climb rate of 793 ft/min. A second way to calculate the climb rate is to divide the groundspeed of 140 knots by 60 to convert to NM per minute. Then multiply by the required climb rate of 340 feet per NM. The result is approximately 793 feet per minute ($140 \div 60 = 2.33 \times 340 = 793.3$).

4-4   **PLT100**
(Refer to figures 172 and 211.)

Which enroute low altitude navigation chart would cover the proposed routing at the BOZEMAN VORTAC?

A– H-1.

B– L-S4.

C– L-13.

4-4. Answer C. GFDIC 4A, STAR/DP, A/FD Legend
On the STAKK THREE DEPARTURE chart for Helena Regional Airport, the appropriate low altitude enroute chart of L-13 is indicated below the navaid information boxes and fixes identifying each transition. The A/FD excerpt for Helena Regional Airport lists chart L-13 in the upper right-hand corner. The letter C indicates the appropriate section of the chart.

4-5   **PLT052**
(Refer to figure 85.)

What route should you take if cleared for the WASHOE TWO DEPARTURE and your assigned route is V6?

A– Climb on the LOC south course to WAGGE where you will be vectored to V6.

B– Climb on the LOC south course to cross WAGGE at 9,000, turn left and fly direct to FMG VORTAC and cross at or above 10,000, and proceed on FMG R-241.

C– Climb on the LOC south course to WAGGE, turn left and fly direct to FMG VORTAC. If at 10,000 turn left and proceed on FMG R-241; if not at 10,000 enter depicted holding pattern and climb to 10,000 before proceeding on FMG R-241.

4-5. Answer A. GFDIC 4A, STAR/DP Legend
The WASHOE TWO DEPARTURE requires all flights taking off on RWYS 16 L/R to climb via the I-RNO Localizer south course to WAGGE, then via radar vectors to the assigned route.

4-6   **PLT052**
(Refer to figure 85.)

What procedure should be followed if communications are lost before reaching 9,000 feet?

A– At 9,000 turn left direct to FMG VORTAC, then via assigned route if at proper altitude; if not, climb in holding pattern until reaching the proper altitude.

B– Continue climb to WAGGE INT, turn left direct to FMG VORTAC, then if at or above MCA, proceed on assigned route; if not, continue climb in holding pattern until at the proper altitude.

C– Continue climb on LOC course to cross WAGGE at or above 9,000, turn left direct to FMG VORTAC to cross at 10,000 or above, and continue on assigned course.

4-6. Answer B. GFDIC 4A, STAR/DP Legend
Lost communications procedures before reaching 9,000 feet are to continue the climb via I-RNO localizer south course to WAGGE, turn left, and proceed direct to FMG VORTAC. Cross the FMG VORTAC at or above the published minimum crossing altitude (MCA), then via the assigned route or climb in a holding pattern northeast on the FMG 041° radial, left turns to cross FMG VORTAC at or above the MCA, for the assigned route.

Chapter 4 — Departure

4-7   PLT 052

(Refer to figure 155.)

What initial procedure should be followed when taking off on Runway 29 and climbing at a groundspeed of 120 knots?

A— Climb at a rate of 600 feet per minute on a heading of 112° to 6,000 feet MSL and then perform a climbing right turn direct to JNC VOR/DME.

B— Climb at a rate of 300 feet per minute on a heading of 292° to 6,000 feet MSL and then perform a climbing left turn direct to JNC VOR/DME.

C— Climb at a rate of 600 feet per minute on a heading of 292° to 6,000 feet MSL and then perform a climbing left turn direct to JNC VOR/DME.

4-7. Answer C. GFDIC 4A, STAR/DP Legend, Rate of Climb Table

The GRAND JUNCTION SIX DEPARTURE requires a minimum climb of 300 feet per NM if you are taking off on Runway 29 as indicated in the TAKEOFF MINIMUMS on the chart plan view. To determine the feet per minute climb rate, use the Rate of Climb Table in Appendix 1. At 120 knots, a climb rate of 600 feet per minute is required. You can also calculate the climb rate by dividing the groundspeed of 120 knots by 60 to convert to NM per minute. Then multiply by the required climb rate of 300 feet per NM. (120 ÷ 60 = 2 × 300 = 600) The departure route is described textually after the heading TAKEOFF RUNWAY 29. The initial route prior to the transition requires you to climb on a heading of 292° to 6,000 feet MSL and then perform a climbing left turn direct to JNC VOR/DME before flying the appropriate transition.

4-8   PLT 133

When instrument procedures are designed, unless otherwise stated or declared, the procedures use a standard IFR climb gradient of

A— 500 feet per minute.

B— 400 feet per nautical mile.

C— 200 feet per nautical mile.

4-8. Answer C. GFDIC 4A, AIM

IFR procedures are designed according to the criteria established in the *U.S. Standard for Terminal Instrument Procedures* (TERPs). In part, TERPs sets standards for a specific clearance from obstacles at a given distance from the runway based on an aircraft climbing at least 200 feet per nautical mile.

SECTION B — DEPARTURE PROCEDURES

TAKEOFF MINIMUMS

- IFR takeoff minimums do not apply to private aircraft under IFR and Part 91, but good judgment should dictate compliance.
- Standard takeoff weather minimums are usually based on visibility. Greater than standard takeoff minimums may be due to terrain, obstructions, or departure procedures.
- Runway visibility value (RVV) is the distance down the runway you can see unlighted objects or unfocused lights of moderate intensity; it is reported in statute miles or fractions of miles.
- Runway visual range (RVR) represents the horizontal distance a pilot will see when looking down the runway from a moving aircraft at the approach end. It is always a transmissometer value.
- When RVR is out of service, convert published RVR values to visibility in statute miles.
- Prevailing visibility or RVR in the aviation routine weather report should normally be used only for informational purposes. The current visibility at the time of departure is the value you should use for determining compliance with takeoff minimums.

IFR DEPARTURE OPTIONS

- To accept a clearance with a SID, you must possess the charted procedure or at least the textual description. Otherwise, you should file NO SID in your flight plan.
- Obstacle departure procedures (ODPs) are not assigned as a portion of your IFR clearance unless required for separation purposes. In general, it is your responsibility to determine if one has been established, then comply with it.
- Radar departures are often assigned at radar-equipped approach control facilities and require close coordination with the tower.

GENERAL PROCEDURES

- During the IFR departure, you should not contact departure control until advised to do so by the tower.
- During departure, terrain and obstruction clearance remains your responsibility until the controller begins to provide navigational guidance in the form of radar vectors.
- The term *". . . radar contact"* means your aircraft has been identified and radar flight following will be provided until radar identification has been terminated.
- *"Resume own navigation"* is a phrase used by ATC to advise you to assume responsibility for your own navigation. It generally cancels assigned vectors or other restrictions previously imposed by ATC.

4-9   PLT004
(Refer to figure 163.)

Using an average groundspeed of 120 knots, what minimum rate of climb must be maintained after takeoff from Runway 32 to meet the required climb rate (feet per NM) to 6,800 feet as specified in the SID?

A– 400 feet per minute.

B– 500 feet per minute.

C– 800 feet per minute.

4-9. Answer C. GFDIC 4A, STAR/DP Legend, Rate of Climb Table
The GNATS SIX DEPARTURE requires a minimum climb rate of 400 feet per NM to 6,800 feet MSL if you are taking off from Runway 32 as indicated in the TAKEOFF MINIMUMS on the plan view. To determine the feet per minute climb rate, use the Rate of Climb Table in Appendix 1. At 120 knots, a climb rate of 800 feet per minute is required. You also can compute the climb rate in feet per minute. Divide the groundspeed (120 knots) by 60 (to convert to NM per minute). Then, multiply by the required rate per nautical mile, 400 feet, $(120 \div 60 = 2 \times 400 = 800$ ft/min$)$.

4-10   PLT004
(Refer to figure 182.)

Using an average groundspeed of 140 knots, what minimum indicated rate of climb must be maintained to meet the required climb rate (feet per NM) to 6,300 feet after taking off on Runway 27?

A– 350 feet per minute.

B– 583 feet per minute.

C– 886 feet per minute.

4-10. Answer C. GFDIC 4A, STAR/DP Legend, Rate of Climb Table
The GROMO THREE DEPARTURE requires a minimum climb rate of 380 feet per NM to 6,300 feet MSL if you are taking off on Runway 27 as indicated in the TAKEOFF MINIMUMS on the plan view. To determine the rate of climb needed, refer to the Rate of Climb Table in Appendix 1. At 140 knots, you must interpolate between the climb rate for 350 ft/NM and 400 ft/NM to find the answer of 886 feet per minute. You also can compute the climb rate in feet per minute. Divide the groundspeed (140 knots) by 60 (to convert to NM per minute). Then, multiply by the required rate per NM, 380 feet, (140 ÷ 60 = 2.3 × 380 = 886 ft/min).

4-11   PLT004
(Refer to figure 52.)

Using an average groundspeed of 100 knots, what minimum rate of climb would meet the required minimum climb rate per NM as specified by the SID?

A– 425 feet per minute.

B– 580 feet per minute.

C– 642 feet per minute.

4-11. Answer C. GFDIC 4A, STAR/DP Legend, Rate of Climb Table
The HABUT ONE DEPARTURE requires a minimum climb rate of 385 feet per NM to 6,000 feet as indicated in the note on the plan view. To determine the rate of climb needed, refer to the Rate of Climb Table in Appendix 1. At an airspeed of 100 knots, you must interpolate between the climb rate for 350 ft/NM and 400 ft/NM to find the answer of 642 feet per minute. You also can compute the climb rate in feet per minute. Divide the groundspeed (100 knots) by 60 (to convert to NM per minute). Then, multiply by the required rate per NM, 380 feet, (100 ÷ 60 × 385 = 641.6 ft/min).

4-12   PLT133
When ATC has not imposed any climb or descent restrictions and aircraft are within 1,000 feet of assigned altitude, pilots should attempt to both climb and descend at a rate of between

A– 500 feet per minute and 1,000 feet per minute.

B– 500 feet per minute and 1,500 feet per minute.

C– 1000 feet per minute and 2,000 feet per minute.

4-12. Answer B. GFDIC 4B, AIM
When ATC has not used the term "at pilot's discretion" nor imposed any climb or descent restrictions, you should climb or descend at an optimum rate to within 1,000 feet of the assigned altitude. Then, you should attempt to maintain a rate between 500 and 1,500 feet per minute.

4-13   PLT201

What action is recommended if a pilot does not wish to use a SID?

A– Advise clearance delivery or ground control before departure.

B– Advise departure control upon initial contact.

C– Enter "No SID" in the REMARKS section of the IFR flight plan.

4-13. Answer C. GFDIC 4B, AIM

If you do not possess a charted SID or a preprinted SID description or, for any other reason, do not wish to use a SID, you are expected to notify ATC. Notification may be accomplished by filing "NO SID" in the REMARKS section of the filed flight plan. You may notify ATC verbally, but this is the less desirable method.

4-14   PLT004

A particular instrument departure procedure requires a minimum climb rate of 210 feet per NM to 8,000 feet. If you climb with a groundspeed of 140 knots, what is the rate of climb required in feet per minute?

A– 210.

B– 450.

C– 490.

4-14. Answer C. GFDIC 4A, PHB

Use the rate-of-climb table, Appendix 1, and interpolate between 200 feet per mile and 250 feet per mile at a groundspeed of 140 knots. Since 210 is one fifth of the way between 200 and 250 feet per minute, (583 − 467 = 116 × 1/5 = 23.2). Add 23.2 to 467 and the result is 490.2, rounded to 490.

You can also find the answer with a simple conversion; A groundspeed of 140 knots is 140 ÷ 60, or 2.33 NM per minute. Then, 2.33 NM per minute × 210 feet per nautical mile equals 490 feet per minute.

4-15   PLT201

Which procedure applies to SIDs?

A– SIDs will not be issued unless requested by the pilot.

B– The pilot in command must accept a SID when issued by ATC.

C– If a SID is accepted, the pilot must possess a textual or graphic description.

4-15. Answer C. GFDIC 4B, AIM

Use of a SID requires you to possess a textual or graphic description of the departure procedure.

4-16   PLT370

What is meant when departure control instructs you to "resume own navigation" after you have been vectored to a Victor airway?

A– You should maintain the airway by use of your navigation equipment.

B– Radar service is terminated.

C– You are still in radar contact, but must make position reports.

4-16. Answer A. GFDIC 4B, AIM

This phrase is used by ATC to advise you to resume your own navigational responsibility. It is issued after completion of a radar vector, or when radar contact is lost while your aircraft is being radar vectored.

4-17   **PLT044**

What does the ATC term "Radar Contact" signify?

A– Your aircraft has been identified and you will receive separation from all aircraft while in contact with this radar facility.

B– Your aircraft has been identified on the radar display and radar flight following will be provided until radar identification is terminated.

C– You will be given traffic advisories until advised the service has been terminated or that radar contact has been lost.

4-17. Answer B. GFDIC 4B, AIM

This term is used by ATC to inform you that your aircraft is identified on the radar display and radar flight following will be provided until radar identification is terminated. Position reports are not required while in radar contact.

4-18   **PLT370**

Upon intercepting the assigned radial, the controller advises you that you are on the airway and to "RESUME OWN NAVIGATION." This phrase means that

A– you are still in radar contact, but must make position reports.

B– radar services are terminated and you will be responsible for position reports.

C– you are to assume responsibility for your own navigation.

4-18. Answer C. GFDIC 4B, AIM

This phrase is used by ATC to advise you to resume your own navigational responsibility. It is issued after completion of a radar vector, or when radar contact is lost while your aircraft is being radar vectored.

4-19   **PLT102**

What does the symbol T within a black triangle in the minimums section of the IAP for a particular airport indicate?

A– Takeoff minimums are 1 mile for aircraft having two engines or less and 1/2 mile for those with more than two engines.

B– Instrument takeoffs are not authorized.

C– Takeoff minimums are not standard and/or departure procedures are published.

4-19. Answer C. GFDIC 4B, Approach Chart Legend

On NOS charts, the symbol T within a black triangle indicates takeoff minimums are nonstandard and/or IFR departure procedures are published.

4-20   **PLT052**
(Refer to figure 85.)

What is the minimum rate climb per nautical mile to 9,000 feet required for the WASH2 WAGGE Departure?

A– 400 feet.

B– 750 feet.

C– 875 feet.

4-20. Answer A. GFDIC 4A, STAR/DP Legend
The short note (lower right side of the departure sketch) specifies a minimum climb rate of 400 feet per NM to 9,000 feet. This climb gradient is required for the WASH2.WAGGE Departure.

4-21   **PLT004**
(Refer to figure 85.)

Of the following, which is the minimum acceptable rate of climb (feet per minute) to 9,000 feet required for the WASH2 WAGGE departure at a GS of 150 knots?

A– 750 feet per minute.

B– 825 feet per minute.

C– 1,000 feet per minute.

4-21. Answer C. GFDIC 4A, STAR/DP Legend, Rate of Climb Table
If you know the groundspeed, there are two easy ways to find the feet per minute climb rate. One way is to use the Rate of Climb Table in Appendix 1. Enter the table with the required climb rate (400 ft/NM) and read across to the known groundspeed (150 knots) to find 1,000 feet per minute. The second way is the computational method. Divide the 150-knot groundspeed by 60 (to convert to NM per minute). Then, multiply by the required climb rate of 400 feet per NM The result is 1,000 feet per minute.

4-22   **PLT370**
To comply with ATC instructions for altitude changes of more than 1,000 feet, what rate of climb or descent should be used?

A– As rapidly as practicable to 500 feet above/below the assigned altitude, and then at 500 feet per minute until the assigned altitude is reached.

B– 1,000 feet per minute during climb and 500 feet per minute during descents until reaching the assigned altitude.

C– As rapidly as practicable to 1,000 feet above/below the assigned altitude, and then between 500 and 1,500 feet per minute until reaching the assigned altitude.

4-22. Answer C. GFDIC 4B, AIM
Unless ATC advises "At pilot's discretion," you are expected to climb at an optimum rate consistent with your airplane's performance to within 1,000 feet of your assigned altitude. Then attempt to climb at a rate between 500 and 1,500 f.p.m. for the last 1,000 feet of climb.

4-23   PLT194
What is expected of you as pilot on an IFR flight plan if you are descending or climbing in VFR conditions?

A– If on an airway, climb or descend to the right of the centerline.

B– Advise ATC you are in visual conditions and will remain a short distance to the right of the centerline while climbing.

C– Execute gentle banks, left and right, at a frequency which permits continuous visual scanning of the airspace about you.

4-23. Answer C. GFDIC 4B, AIM
When climbing or descending in VFR conditions, pilots should make gentle turns in both directions in order to scan for other traffic.

4-24   PLT201
Which is true regarding the use of a SID chart?

A– The use of SIDs is mandatory.

B– To use a SID, the pilot must possess at least the textual description of the approved standard departure.

C– To use a SID, the pilot must possess both the textual and graphic form of the approved procedure.

4-24. Answer B. GFDIC 4B, AIM
In order to fly a SID, the pilot must have either the charted procedure or at least the textual description.

4-25   PLT004
(Refer to figure 220.)

What is the initial obstacle departure procedure in instrument conditions for takeoff from Runway 6 at Flabob Airport at Riverside/Rubidoux, California?

A– Climb at 670 feet per minute and proceed direct to PDZ VORTAC. Hold as depicted at PDZ while climbing to 4,000 feet MSL.

B– Climb on a heading of 244° and intercept the PDZ 031° radial to PDZ VORTAC.

C– Climb on a heading of 064° to 4,000 feet MSL and then turn right and proceed direct to PDZ VORTAC.

4-25. Answer C. GFDIC 6B, IFH
Obstacle departure procedures are listed in the Takeoff Minimums and (Obstacle) Departure Procedures section of the Terminal Procedures Publication. The initial departure procedure for Runway 6 is listed as: climb via heading 064° to 4000 then right turn direct PDZ VORTAC.

4-26   **PLT083**
(Refer to figures 224 and 225.)

What does the "T" symbol in the notes and limitations section indicate for Leadville/Lake County Airport?

A– Takeoffs in IFR conditions are not authorized at the airport due to terrain.

B– Obstacle departure procedures are published for IFR takeoffs from Runway 16.

C– Standard takeoff minimums apply to departing from the airport.

4-26. Answer B. GFDICM 4B, Approach Chart Legend
The "T" symbol in the notes and limitations box of the pilot briefing information section of the approach chart indicates that you should look for nonstandard takeoff minimums and/or obstacle departure procedures in the Terminal Procedures Publication. The TPP excerpt states that you should use LOZUL and DAVVY (RNAV) DEPARTURE procedures for Runways 16 and 34, respectively. These obstacle departure procedures are published on separate charts.

ENROUTE

SECTION A — ENROUTE AND AREA CHARTS

AIRWAYS

- Airways below 18,000 feet MSL are called Victor airways. Airways at and above 18,000 feet MSL are jet routes
- Airways are 8 nautical miles wide within 51 nautical miles of a navaid. At distances greater than 51 miles, the airway widens, and is defined by lines diverging at 4.5° from the center of each navaid.

IFR ALTITUDES

- Since Class A airspace begins at 18,000 feet MSL, it is not shown on low altitude enroute charts. High altitude enroute charts must be used for operations at and above 18,000 feet MSL.
- The minimum enroute altitude (MEA) generally guarantees both obstruction clearance and navigation signal coverage for the length of the airway segment. It is normally the lowest altitude you can use on an airway.
- To provide obstruction clearance when flying outside of established airways, the FAA enroute charts provide off-route obstruction clearance altitudes (OROCAs) on enroute low altitude charts.
- The minimum obstruction clearance altitude (MOCA) has the same terrain and obstruction clearance specifications as MEA and OROCA/MORA, but only promises reliable navigation signal coverage within 22 nautical miles of the facility. A MOCA is preceded by an asterisk on an FAA chart.
- The maximum authorized altitude (MAA) keeps you from receiving more than one VOR station at a time.
- The minimum reception altitude (MRA) ensures reception of an off-course navaid that helps define a fix. Below the MRA and above the MEA you still have course guidance, but may not be able to receive the off-course navaid.
- When an MEA changes to a higher altitude, you normally begin your climb upon reaching the fix where the change occurs. When rising terrain does not permit a safe climb after passing the fix, a minimum crossing altitude (MCA) is published. A flag with an X signifies the MCA on FAA charts. The altitude and applicable flight direction appear near the symbol. Plan your climb so that you will reach the MCA before crossing the fix.
- In mountainous areas where no other minimum altitude is prescribed, IFR operations must remain 2,000 feet above the highest obstacle within a horizontal distance of 4 nautical miles from the intended course.
- The MEA along jet routes is 18,000 feet MSL, unless otherwise specified.

SPECIAL IFR POSITIONS

- Intersections are defined by two navaids, or by a navaid and a DME distance. All intersections can be used as reporting points. Compulsory reporting points are charted as filled triangles.
- You normally change frequencies midway between navaids, unless a changeover point (COP) is designated. A COP is established where the navigation signal coverage from a navaid is not usable to the midpoint of an airway segment.
- ARTCC boundaries are shown with distinctive lines on FAA charts.

COMMUNICATIONS

- Most FSSs are able to use 122.2 MHz, as well as the emergency frequency, 121.5. Additional frequencies are shown above navaid boxes.
- HIWAS is indicated by a small square in the communications box on FAA charts.
- Look for ARTCC discrete frequencies in boxes with the name of the controlling center. A remote communications outlet (RCO) for an FSS will have the name of the FSS and the frequency in a communication box.

AIRPORTS, AIRSPACE, AND OTHER INFORMATION

- Colors are used to differentiate between airports with approach procedures and airports without instrument approaches.

- Basic information about each airport is portrayed on enroute charts using symbols from the chart legend. Additional information about airports with instrument approaches is found on the end panels of the chart.

- Class G airspace is uncontrolled and shown with brown shading on FAA charts. Additionally, airspace below 1,200 feet AGL is uncontrolled, unless designated as Class B, C, D, or E.

- Area charts are usually larger-scale depictions of major terminal areas. They should be referred to whenever you are in their coverage area, since they may show details that have been omitted from enroute charts.

- On FAA enroute charts, localizers and back courses are shown only when they serve an enroute ATC function, such as establishing a fix or intersection.

- The FAA uses blue hatching around the edges of all special use airspace (prohibited, restricted, warning, and alert areas) except military operations areas, which are shown with brown hatched edges.

5-1   PLT100

Which types of airspace are depicted on the En Route Low Altitude Chart?

A– Limits of controlled airspace, military training routes and special use airspace.

B– Special use airspace, Class E, Class D, Class A, Class B and Class C.

C– Class A, special use airspace, Class D and Class E.

5-1. Answer A. GFDIC 5A, Enroute Chart Legend
Enroute Low Altitude Charts depict the limits of Controlled airspace, military training routes, and special use airspace.

5-2   PLT100
(Refer to figure 24.)

Proceeding southbound on V187, (vicinity of Cortez VOR) contact is lost with Denver Center. You should attempt to reestablish contact with Denver Center on:

A– 133.425 MHz.

B– 122.1 MHz and receive on 108.4 MHz.

C– 122.35 MHz.

5-2. Answer A. GFDIC 5A, Enroute Chart Legend
There is a communications box just to the west of Cortez VOR indicating that Denver Center should be contacted on 133.425.

5-3   PLT100
(Refer to figures 22 and 24.)

For planning purposes, what would be the highest MEA on V187 between Grand Junction, Walker Airport and Durango, La Plata Co. Airport?

A– 12,000 feet.

B– 15,000 feet.

C– 16,000 feet.

5-3. Answer B. GFDIC 5A, Enroute Chart Legend
The highest MEA is 15,000 feet, located on V187 between HERRM and MANCA Intersections.

5-4   **PLT100**
(Refer to figure 24.)

At what point should a VOR changeover be made from JNC VOR to MANCA intersection southbound on V187?

A– 36 NM south of JNC.

B– 52 NM south of JNC.

C– 74 NM south of JNC.

5-4. Answer B. GFDIC 5A, Enroute Chart Legend
The changeover point is 52 miles south of the JNC VOR as indicated by the changeover symbol and callout.

5-5   **PLT100**
(Refer to figure 24.)

What is the MOCA between JNC and MANCA intersection on V187?

A– 10,900 feet MSL.

B– 12,000 feet MSL.

C– 13,700 feet MSL.

5-5. Answer C. GFDIC 5A, Enroute Chart Legend
The minimum obstruction clearance altitude (MOCA) is identified with an "*" in front of the altitude callout. The MOCA between JNC and MANCA Intersection is 13,700 feet MSL.

5-6   **PLT100**
(Refer to figure 34.)

At which altitude and location on V573 would you expect the navigational signal of the HOT VOR/DME to be unreliable?

A– 3,000 feet at APINE intersection.

B– 2,600 feet at MARKI intersection.

C– 4,000 feet at ELMMO intersection.

5-6. Answer A. GFDIC 5A, Enroute Chart Legend
The MEA normally provides reliable navigation signals.

5-7   **PLT100**
(Refer to figure 53.)

Where is the VOR COP on V27 between the GVO and MQO VORTACs?

A– 20 DME from GVO VORTAC.

B– 20 DME from MQO VORTAC.

C– 30 DME from SBA VORTAC.

5-7. Answer A. GFDIC 5A, Enroute Chart Legend
The changeover point (COP) between GVO and MQO VORTACs is 20 NM from GVO VORTAC and 34 NM from MQO VORTAC. The COP symbol is designed so the mileage on top of the airway refers to the VOR on the right, and the mileage on the bottom of the airway refers to the VOR on the left.

5-8   **PLT058**

(Refer to figure 53.)

What service is indicated by the inverse `H` symbol in the radio aids to navigation box for SAN MARCUS VORTAC?

A– VOR with TACAN compatible DME.

B– Availability of HIWAS.

C– The VOR has an "H" (high altitude) SSV Class Designator.

5-8. Answer B. GFDIC 5A, AIM, Enroute Chart Legend

If hazardous inflight weather advisory service (HIWAS) is available on the associated NAVAID frequency, it is indicated by an inverse "H" in the upper corner of the facility box.

5-9   **PLT091**

(Refer to figure 65.)

Which point would be the appropriate VOR COP on V552 from the LFT to the TBD VORTACs?

A– CLYNT intersection.

B– HATCH intersection.

C– 34 DME from the LFT VORTAC.

5-9. Answer C. GFDIC 5A, Enroute Chart Legend

If there is no designated changeover point along an airway, you change to the next frequency at the halfway point. In this case, it is 34 DME from LFT VORTAC.

5-10   **PLT100**

(Refer to figures 65 and 67.)

What is the significance of the symbol at GRICE intersection?

A– It signifies a localizer only approach is available at Harry P. Williams Memorial.

B– The localizer has an additional navigation function.

C– GRICE intersection also serves as the FAF for the ILS approach procedure to Harry P. Williams Memorial.

5-10. Answer B. GFDIC 5A, Approach Chart Legend

When the localizer symbol showing the inbound course appears on an enroute chart, it means the facility serves a navigation function. The navaid information box will also be printed near the intersection.

5-11   PLT100
(Refer to figures 70 and 71.)

Which VORTAC along the proposed route of flight could provide HIWAS information?

A– SPARTA VORTAC.

B– HUGUENOT VORTAC.

C– KINGSTON VORTAC.

5-11. Answer C. GFDIC 5A, Enroute Chart Legend
When hazardous inflight weather advisory service (HIWAS) is transmitted over a VOR, the FAA places a small square in the upper left corner of the facility box on enroute charts.

5-12   PLT100
(Refer to figure 78.)

What is the maximum altitude that you may flight plan an IFR flight on V 86 eastbound between BOZEMAN and BILLINGS VORTACs?

A– 14,500 feet MSL.

B– 17,000 feet MSL.

C– 18,000 feet MSL.

5-12. Answer B. GFDIC 5A, AIM
Victor airways extend from 1,200 feet AGL up to but not including 18,000 feet MSL; therefore, the highest IFR cruising altitude is 17,000 feet MSL for an eastbound flight. Also, IFR cruising altitudes are based on even thousands for westbound flights and odd thousands for eastbound flights.

5-13   PLT100
(Refer to figure 78.)

What is the minimum crossing altitude over the BOZEMAN VORTAC for a flight southeast bound on V86?

A– 8,500 feet MSL.

B– 9,300 feet MSL.

C– 9,700 feet MSL.

5-13. Answer B. GFDIC 5A, Enroute Chart Legend
A flag with an "X" marks the VOR or the intersection where a minimum crossing altitude (MCA) is required. The MCA at BZN VOR, listed above the navaid information box is 9,300 feet MSL for flights southeast bound on V86-365.

5-14   PLT430
Unless otherwise prescribed, what is the rule regarding altitude and course to be maintained during an off airways IFR flight over nonmountainous terrain?

A– 1,000 feet above the highest obstacle within 3 NM of course.

B– 2,000 feet above the highest obstacle within 5 SM of course.

C– 1,000 feet above the highest obstacle within 4 NM of course.

5-14. Answer C. GFDCM 5A, FAR 91.177
Normally you must fly the applicable minimum altitude prescribed in 14 CFR Part 95 or Part 97. However when no minimum altitude is prescribed you may fly an off airways IFR flight over nonmountainous terrain no lower than 1,000 feet above the highest obstacle within a horizontal distance of 4 nautical miles from the course line.

5-15   PLT430
Unless otherwise prescribed, what is the rule regarding altitude and course to be maintained during an IFR off airways flight over mountainous terrain?

A– 2,000 feet above the highest obstacle within 4 NM of course.

B– 1,000 feet above the highest obstacle within a horizontal distance of 4 NM of course.

C– 2,000 feet above the highest obstacle within a horizontal distance of 5 NM of course.

5-15. Answer A. GFDCM 5A, FAR 91.177
Normally you must fly the applicable minimum altitude prescribed in 14 CFR Part 95 or Part 97. However when no minimum altitude is prescribed you may fly an off airways IFR flight over mountainous terrain no lower than 2,000 feet above the highest obstacle within a horizontal distance of 4 nautical miles from the course line.

5-16   PLT033
What is the definition of MEA?

A– The lowest published altitude which meets obstacle clearance requirements and assures acceptable navigational signal coverage.

B– The lowest published altitude which meets obstacle requirements, assures acceptable navigational signal coverage, two-way radio communications, and provides adequate radar coverage.

C– An altitude which meets obstacle clearance requirements, assures acceptable navigation signal coverage, two-way radio communications, adequate radar coverage, and accurate DME mileage.

5-16. Answer A. GFDIC 5A, AIM
MEA is defined as the lowest published altitude between radio fixes which ensures acceptable navigational signal coverage and meets obstacle clearance requirements between those fixes. Two-way radio, radar coverage, and accurate DME reception are not requirements for an MEA.

5-17   PLT033
The altitude that provides acceptable navigational signal coverage for the route, and meets obstacle clearance requirements, is the minimum:

A– enroute altitude.

B– reception altitude.

C– obstacle clearance altitude.

5-17. Answer A. GFDIC 5A, AIM
The Minimum Enroute Altitude (MEA) guarantees obstacle clearance, reception of navigational signals (but not necessarily DME), and two-way communications. It does not guarantee radar coverage.

5-18   PLT033
Reception of signals from an off-airway radio facility may be inadequate to identify the fix at the designated MEA. In this case, which altitude is designated for the fix?

A– MRA.

B– MCA.

C– MOCA.

5-18. Answer A. GFDIC 5A, AIM
A minimum reception altitude (MRA) is established to ensure adequate reception of the navigation signals forming an intersection.

5-19 PLT033
Which condition is guaranteed for all of the following altitude limits: MAA, MCA, MRA, MOCA and MEA? (Non-mountainous area.)

A– Adequate navigation signals.

B– Adequate communications.

C– 1,000 foot obstacle clearance.

5-19. Answer C. GFDIC 5A, AIM
Minimum altitudes for IFR operations are discussed in Part 91.177. Except for takeoff and landing, the minimum IFR altitudes prescribed for operations in non-mountainous areas are 1,000 feet above the highest obstacle within 4 NM of the course to be flown. This is the only condition guaranteed for all of the altitude limits, including MAA, MCA, MRA, MOCA, and MEA.

5-20 PLT033
If no MCA is specified, what is the lowest altitude for crossing a radio fix, beyond which a higher minimum applies?

A– The MEA at which the fix is approached.

B– The MRA at which the fix is approached.

C– The MOCA for the route segment beyond the fix.

5-20. Answer A. GFDIC 5A, AIM
The minimum altitude at which you can cross a fix, where a higher altitude is subsequently established, is the MEA. Remember, the MEA ensures acceptable navigational signal coverage and meets obstacle clearance requirements.

5-21 PLT220
Unless otherwise specified on the chart, the minimum en route altitude along a jet route is

A– 18,000 feet MSL.

B– 24,000 feet MSL.

C– 10,000 feet MSL.

5-21. Answer A. GFDIC 5A, AIM
The jet route system is designed for aircraft operating from 18,000 feet MSL to FL 450, inclusive. These routes are depicted on enroute high altitude charts and are identified by the letter "J."

5-22 PLT100
(Refer to figure 87.)

Where is the VOR COP when flying east on V306 from Daisetta to Lake Charles?

A– 50 NM east of DAS.

B– 40 NM east of DAS.

C– 30 NM east of DAS.

5-22. Answer C. GFDIC 5A, Enroute Chart Legend
The changeover point (COP), shown by a perpendicular symbol on V306, indicates that it is 30 NM east of Daisetta, or 50 NM west of Lake Charles. As a double-check, the two changeover distances should add up to the total distance between these VORs — 80 NM

5-23   PLT100
(Refer to figure 87.)

What is indicated by the localizer course symbol at Jefferson County Airport?

A– A published ILS localizer course, which has an additional navigation function.

B– A published LDA localizer course.

C– A published SDF localizer course.

5-23. Answer A. GFDIC 5A, Enroute Chart Legend
The symbol shown on the chart at Jefferson Co. Field indicates the availability of an ILS localizer course with an ATC function, such as identifying a fix or intersection. When the localizer serves an ATC function, the facility identifier, frequency, and inbound course are shown.

5-24   PLT100
(Refer to figure 87.)

Which VHF frequencies, other than 121.5, can be used to receive De Ridder FSS in the Lake Charles area?

A– 122.1, 126.4.

B– 123.6, 122.65.

C– 122.2, 122.3.

5-24. Answer C. GFDIC 5A, Enroute Chart Legend
The frequency 122.2 is a standard FSS frequency available even when not indicated. The frequency 122.3 is listed above the Lake Charles VOR facility box, and is another frequency available at this FSS.

5-25   PLT100
(Refer to figure 87.)

Why is the localizer back course at Jefferson County Airport depicted?

A– The back course has a glide slope.

B– The back course is not aligned with a runway.

C– The back course has an additional navigation function.

5-25. Answer C. GFDIC 5A, Enroute Chart Legend
The large feathered arrow symbol indicates Jefferson County Airport has a back course approach. This portrayal means the localizer provides an ATC function. In this case, the back course is used to form PORTZ intersection.

5-26   PLT100
(Refer to figure 87.)

Where is the VOR changeover point on V20 between Beaumont and Hobby?

A– Halfway point.

B– MOCKS intersection.

C– Anahuac Beacon.

5-26. Answer A. GFDIC 5A, Enroute Chart Legend
Since there is no changeover point established on V20, the changeover point will be the halfway point between Hobby and Beaumont VORTACs.

5-27   **PLT100**
(Refer to figure 89.)

When flying from Milford Municipal to Bryce Canyon via V235 and V293, what minimum altitude should you be at when crossing Cedar City VOR?

A– 11,400 feet.

B– 12,000 feet.

C– 13,000 feet.

5-27. Answer B. GFDIC 5A, Enroute Chart Legend, FAR 91.177
The flag marking Cedar City VOR/DME (near the center of the left side of the figure) has an "X" in it, meaning there is a minimum crossing altitude (MCA). An MCA of 12,000 feet is noted above the CDC VOR information box for aircraft traveling eastbound on V293.

5-28   **PLT100**
(Refer to figure 89.)

What VHF frequencies are available for communications with Cedar City FSS?

A– 123.6, 121.5, 108.6, and 112.8.

B– 122.2, 121.5, 122.6, and 112.1.

C– 122.2, 121.5, 122.0, and 123.6.

5-28. Answer B. GFDIC 5A, Enroute Chart Legend
The frequency 122.6 is indicated above the heavy-line Cedar City VOR-DME information box. You can also communicate with Cedar City FSS over the Milford VORTAC frequency by transmitting on 122.1 and receiving on 112.1. These frequencies are in addition to the standard frequency of 122.2, and the emergency frequency of 121.5.

5-29   **PLT438**
(Refer to figure 89.)

What are the oxygen requirements for an IFR flight northeast bound from Bryce Canyon on V382 at the lowest appropriate altitude in an unpressurized aircraft?

A– The required minimum crew must be provided and use supplemental oxygen for that part of the flight of more than 30 minutes.

B– The required minimum crew must be provided and use supplemental oxygen for that part of the flight of more than 30 minutes, and the passengers must be provided supplemental oxygen.

C– The required minimum crew must be provided and use supplemental oxygen, and all occupants must be provided supplemental oxygen for the entire flight above 15,000 feet.

5-29. Answer C. GFDIC 5A, Enroute Chart Legend, FAR 91.211a
At cabin pressure altitudes above 14,000 feet MSL, the required minimum flight crew must use supplemental oxygen. All passengers must be supplied with oxygen for the entire flight above 15,000 feet MSL.

5-30   **PLT100**
(Refer to figure 89.)

What is the ARTCC discrete frequency at the COP on V208 southwest bound from HVE to PGA VOR/DME?

A– 122.1.

B– 122.4.

C– 133.6.

5-30. Answer C. GFDIC 5A, Enroute Chart Legend
You are located in the Salt Lake City ARTCC sector. There is an ARTCC remote site with the discrete frequency 133.6 to the east of HVE VORTAC.

5-31   **PLT100**
(Refer to figure 89.)

What type airspace exists above Bryce Canyon Airport from the surface to 1,200 feet AGL?

A– Class D.

B– Class E.

C– Class G.

5-31. Answer C. GFDIC 5A, Enroute Chart Legend
The surface area at Bryce Canyon Airport is in Class G airspace. The brown lettering indicates that no approved instrument approach procedure exists. The base of the Federal airway (Class E airspace) is 1,200 AGL. Class G (uncontrolled) airspace exists from the surface to 1,200 feet AGL.

5-32   **PLT100**
(Refer to figure 91.)

What is the minimum crossing altitude at DBS VORTAC for a northbound IFR flight on V257?

A– 7,500 feet.

B– 8,600 feet.

C– 11,100 feet.

5-32. Answer B. GFDIC 5A, Enroute Chart Legend
An altitude of 8,600 feet is the MCA northbound on V257 crossing DBS VORTAC.

5-33   **PLT100**
(Refer to figure 91.)

What lighting is indicated on the chart for Jackson Hole Airport?

A– Lights on prior request.

B– No lighting available.

C– Pilot controlled lighting.

5-33. Answer C. GFDIC 5A, Enroute Chart Legend
The circle around the "L" in the airport information block indicates Pilot Controlled Lighting (PCL).

5-34   PLT100

(Refer to figure 91.)

What is the function of the Great Falls RCO (Yellowstone vicinity)?

A– Long range communications outlet for Great Falls Center.

B– Remote communications outlet for Great Falls FSS.

C– Satellite remote controlled by Salt Lake Center with limited service.

5-34. Answer B. GFDIC 5A, Enroute Chart Legend
The Great Falls remote communications outlet (RCO) is depicted by a circle symbol above the communications box (near the center of the referenced figure). The circle symbol for an FSS remote communications outlet is depicted in the chart legend (see Appendix B). This RCO is used by the Great Falls FSS, as indicated by the communications box.

5-35   PLT100

(Refer to figure 91.)

Where should you change VOR frequencies when en route from DBS VORTAC to JAC VOR/DME on V520?

A– 35 NM from DBS VORTAC.

B– 60 NM from DBS VORTAC.

C– 60 NM from JAC VOR/DME.

5-35. Answer B. GFDIC 5A, AIM
Along V520 between DBS VORTAC and JAC VOR/DME, there is a changeover point (COP) close to the JAC VOR/DME at 60 NM from DBS VORTAC.

5-36   PLT100

(Refer to figure 91.)

What is the minimum crossing altitude at SABAT intersection when eastbound from DBS VORTAC on V298?

A– 8,300 feet.

B– 11,100 feet.

C– 13,000 feet.

5-36. Answer B. GFDIC 5A, Enroute Chart Legend
Under the intersection name "SABAT" is the MCA for V298 eastbound, 11,100 feet.

5-37   PLT430

In the case of operations over an area designated as a mountainous area where no other minimum altitude is prescribed, no person may operate an aircraft under IFR below an altitude of

A– 500 feet above the highest obstacle.

B– 1,000 feet above the highest obstacle.

C– 2,000 feet above the highest obstacle.

5-37. Answer C. GFDIC 5A, FAR 91.177
In mountainous terrain, the minimum altitude for any IFR operation is 2,000 feet above the highest obstacle within a horizontal distance of 4 NM of the route to be flown.

5-38   PLT033
MEA is an altitude which assures

A– obstacle clearance, accurate navigational signals from more than one VORTAC, and accurate DME mileage.

B– a 1,000-foot obstacle clearance within 2 miles of an airway and assures accurate DME mileage.

C– acceptable navigational signal coverage and meets obstruction clearance requirements.

5-38. Answer C. GFDIC 5A, AIM
The minimum enroute altitude (MEA) guarantees adequate obstruction clearance and navigation signal reception.

5-39   PLT033
Reception of signals from a radio facility, located off the airway being flown, may be inadequate at the designated MEA to identify the fix. In this case, which altitude is designated for the fix?

A– MOCA.

B– MRA.

C– MCA.

5-39. Answer B. GFDIC 5A, AIM
The minimum reception altitude (MRA) is the minimum altitude that guarantees adequate reception of the navaids that form an intersection or other fix.

5-40   PLT033
ATC may assign the MOCA when certain special conditions exist, and when within

A– 22 NM of a VOR.

B– 25 NM of a VOR.

C– 30 NM of a VOR.

5-40. Answer A. GFDIC 5A, AIM
The minimum obstruction clearance altitude (MOCA) provides adequate navaid reception only with 22 NM of the VOR.

5-41   PLT100
Which aeronautical chart depicts Military Training Routes (MTR) above 1500 feet?

A– IFR Planning Chart.

B– IFR Low Altitude En Route Chart.

C– IFR High Altitude En Route Chart.

5-41. Answer B. GFDIC 5A, AIM
Military Training Routes (MTRs) are depicted on FAA IFR low altitude enroute charts.

5-42   **PLT033**

Acceptable navigational signal coverage at the MOCA is assured for a distance from the VOR of only

A– 12 NM.

B– 22 NM.

C– 25 NM.

5-42. Answer B. GFDIC 5A, AIM

The minimum obstruction clearance altitude (MOCA) provides adequate navaid reception only with 22 NM of the VOR. The minimum obstruction clearance altitude (MOCA) ensures navaid reception within 22 NM of the navaid.

5-43   **PLT100**

(Refer to figure 78.)

When eastbound on V86 between Whitehall and Livingston, the minimum altitude that you should cross BZN is

A– 9,300 feet.

B– 10,400 feet.

C– 8,500 feet.

5-43. Answer A. GFDIC 5A, IFH

A flag with an "X" marks the VOR or the intersection where a minimum crossing altitude (MCA) is required. The MCA at BZN VOR, listed above the navaid information box is 9,300 feet MSL for flights southeast bound on V86-365.

5-44   **PLT100**

(Refer to figure 47.)

En route on V112 from BTG VORTAC to LTJ VORTAC, the minimum altitude crossing GYMME intersection is

A– 6,400 feet.

B– 6,500 feet.

C– 7,000 feet.

5-44. Answer C. GFDIC 5A, IFH

The MEA for eastbound flights on V112 is depicted as 7,000 feet, both before and after Gymme Intersection.

5-45   **PLT100**

(Refer to figure 47.)

En route on V468 from BTG VORTAC to YKM VORTAC, the minimum altitude at TROTS intersection is

A– 7,100 feet.

B– 10,000 feet.

C– 11,500 feet.

5-45. Answer C. GFDIC 5A, IFH

The flag symbol with an "X" denotes a minimum crossing altitude at TROTS. The restriction "V448 11500 NE" means that flights northeast bound on V448 must be at (or above) 11,500 feet when crossing TROTS.

SECTION B — ENROUTE PROCEDURES

GENERAL COMMUNICATION PROCEDURES

- During a radar handoff, the controller may advise you to give the next controller certain information, such as a heading or altitude.
- If you cannot establish contact using a newly assigned frequency, return to the one previously used and request an alternate frequency.

REQUIRED REPORTS

- You should make the following reports to ATC whether or not you are in radar contact: leaving an altitude, an altitude change if VFR-on-top, time and altitude upon reaching a holding fix or clearance limit, leaving a holding fix or clearance limit, missed approach, inability to climb or descend at a rate of at least 500 feet per minute, and change in true airspeed by 5% or 10 knots (whichever is greater).
- You are required by regulation to report a loss of airplane navigational capability, unforecast or hazardous weather conditions, and any other information relating to the safety of flight.
- If radar contact has been lost or radar service terminated, the FARs require you to provide ATC with position reports over compulsory reporting points.
- The compulsory reporting points on a direct route are those fixes that define the route.
- A standard position report includes your identification, current position, time, altitude, ETA over the next reporting fix, the following reporting point, and any pertinent remarks.
- When flying on a VFR-on-top clearance, you should make the same position reports as on any IFR flight, and you should fly at an appropriate VFR cruising altitude.
- In a nonradar environment, you should report when you reach the final approach fix inbound on a nonprecision approach, and when you leave the outer marker inbound on a precision approach. In addition, a report is necessary when it becomes apparent that an estimated time that you previously submitted to ATC will be in error in excess of 3 minutes.

GPS NAVIGATION

- To use panel-mounted, IFR enroute-approved GPS as your primary means of point-to-point navigation, your aircraft must be equipped with an alternate means of navigation, such as VOR-based equipment, appropriate to the flight.
- Active monitoring of alternate navigation equipment is not required if the GPS receiver uses receiver autonomous integrity monitoring (RAIM).

CLEARANCES THROUGH RESTRICTED AREAS

ATC usually does not issue an IFR route clearance that crosses an active restricted area, but inactive areas are often released for use.

IFR ALTITUDES

- Though you may request and be assigned any altitude in controlled airspace, most pilots file flight plan altitudes that correspond to the hemispheric rule.
- Lowest usable altitudes are specified for use above 18,000 feet MSL when the barometric pressure is below certain values.
- When you are given a descent clearance "...at pilot's discretion," you are authorized to begin the descent whenever you choose, and level off temporarily during the descent, but you cannot return to an altitude once you vacate it.

5-46　　PLT390

For which speed variation should you notify ATC?

A– When the groundspeed changes more than 5 knots.

B– When the average true airspeed changes 5 percent or 10 knots, whichever is greater.

C– Any time the groundspeed changes 10 MPH.

5-46. Answer B. GFDIC 5B, AIM

You must notify ATC if a change in your flight plan occurs or is expected. In addition to changes in altitude, destination, and/or routing, increasing or decreasing the aircraft's true airspeed constitutes a change in your flight plan. Therefore, whenever your average true airspeed at cruising altitude between reporting points changes, or is expected to change by 5% or 10 knots, whichever is greater, ATC should be advised.

5-47　　PLT224

For IFR planning purposes, what are the compulsory reporting points when using VOR/DME or VORTAC fixes to define a direct route not on established airways?

A– Fixes selected to define the route.

B– At the changeover points.

C– There are no compulsory reporting points unless advised by ATC.

5-47. Answer A. GFDIC 5B, AIM

Any portion of a route which is not flown on radials or courses of established airways, such as a direct route flight, must be defined by indicating the radio fixes over which the flight will pass. Fixes selected must represent a point where your aircraft's position can be accurately determined. These points automatically become compulsory reporting points for your flight, unless advised otherwise by ATC.

5-48　　PLT100

(Refer to figure 34.)

For planning purposes, what is the highest useable altitude for an IFR flight on V573 from the HOT VORTAC to the TXK VORTAC?

A– 16,000 feet MSL.

B– 14,500 feet MSL.

C– 13,999 feet MSL.

5-48. Answer A. GFDIC 5B, AIM

Low altitude enroute charts portray the enroute structure from the surface up to, but not including 18,000 feet MSL. In controlled airspace, IFR cruising altitudes are specified by ATC. IFR cruising altitudes in uncontrolled airspace are as prescribed by FAR 91.179. When flying on a heading from 360° to 179°, you must fly at odd thousand-foot altitudes. When on a heading of 180° to 359°, you must fly at even thousand-foot altitudes. While the flight on V573 from HOT VORTAC to TXK VORTAC is in controlled airspace, application of FAR 91.179 would result in a cruising altitude of 16,000 feet MSL.

5-49　　PLT100

(Refer to figure 40.)

For planning purposes, what is the highest useable altitude for an IFR flight on V16 from BGS VORTAC to ABI VORTAC?

A– 6,500 feet MSL.

B– 17,000 feet MSL.

C– 18,000 feet MSL.

5-49. Answer B. GFDIC 5B, AIM

Low altitude enroute charts depict the enroute structure from the surface up to, but not including, 18,000 feet MSL. In controlled airspace IFR cruising altitudes are specified by ATC. In uncontrolled airspace, IFR cruising altitudes are as prescribed in FAR 91.179. When flying on a heading of 360° to 179°, you must fly at odd thousand-foot altitudes. When on a heading of 180° to 359°, you must fly at even thousand-foot altitudes. While the flight on V16 on a heading of 075° from HOT VORTAC to TXK VORTAC is in controlled airspace, application of FAR 91.179 would result in a cruising altitude of 17,000 feet MSL.

5-50   PLT370

What is the recommended climb procedure when a non-radar departure control instructs a pilot to climb to the assigned altitude?

A– Maintain a continuous optimum climb until reaching assigned altitude and report passing each 1,000-foot level.

B– Climb at a maximum angle of climb to within 1,000 feet of the assigned altitude, then 500 feet per minute the last 1,000 feet.

C– Maintain an optimum climb on the centerline of the airway without intermediate level offs until 1,000 feet below assigned altitude, then 500 to 1500 feet per minute.

5-50. Answer C. GFDIC 5B, AIM

Unless ATC advises "At pilot's discretion," you are expected to climb at an optimum rate to within 1,000 feet of any assigned altitude. Then, attempt to climb at a rate of between 500 and 1,500 feet per minute for the last 1,000 feet of climb.

5-51   PLT390

What reports are required of a flight operating on an IFR clearance specifying VFR on Top in a nonradar environment?

A– The same reports that are required for any IFR flight.

B– All normal IFR reports except vacating altitudes.

C– Only the reporting of any unforecast weather.

5-51. Answer A. GFDIC 5B, AIM, AIM

When operating in VFR conditions with an ATC authorization to "MAINTAIN VFR-ON-TOP/ MAINTAIN VFR CONDITIONS," pilots on IFR flight plans must:

1. Fly at the appropriate VFR altitude.

2. Comply with the VFR visibility and distance from clouds criteria.

3. Comply with instrument flight rules that are applicable, including minimum IFR altitudes, position reporting, radio communications, course to be flown, and adherence to ATC clearances.

5-52   PLT390

Which report should be made to ATC without a specific request when not in radar contact?

A– Entering instrument meteorological conditions.

B– When leaving final approach fix inbound on final approach.

C– Correcting an ETA any time a previous ETA is in error in excess of 2 minutes.

5-52. Answer B. GFDIC 5B, AIM

The AIM contains specific guidance on required reports to ATC. This includes reports to be made at all times, as well as reports when not in radar contact. When not in radar contact, you should report leaving a final approach fix inbound on final approach (nonprecision approach).

5-53 **PLT100**

(Refer to figure 91.)

What are the two limiting cruising altitudes useable on V343 for a VFR-on-Top flight from DBS VORTAC to RANEY intersection?

A– 14,500 and 16,500 feet.

B– 15,000 and 17,000 feet.

C– 15,500 and 17,500 feet.

5-53. Answer C. GFDIC 5B, AIM, FAR 91.159

When flying VFR-on-Top you must fly by both visual and instrument flight rules. This requires you to fly at or above the MEA yet below 18,000 feet MSL. You must also follow the VFR cruising altitudes, odd thousand plus 500 feet eastbound, and even thousand plus 500 feet for westbound flights. With this in mind the 15,000 feet MEA along V343 on a heading of 008° between DBS VORTAC and RANEY intersection restricts you to between 15,500 and 17,500 feet.

5-54 **PLT390**

During the en route phase of an IFR flight, the pilot is advised "Radar service terminated." What action is appropriate?

A– Set transponder to code 1200.

B– Resume normal position reporting.

C– Activate the IDENT feature of the transponder to re-establish radar contact.

5-54. Answer B. GFDIC 5B, AIM

While in radar contact, pilots should discontinue position reports. When ATC advises "Radar service terminated," you should resume normal position reporting.

5-55 **PLT430**

In the case of operations over an area designated as a mountainous area, no person may operate an aircraft under IFR below 2,000 feet above the highest obstacle within a horizontal distance of

A– 3 SM from the course flown.

B– 4 SM from the course flown.

C– 4 NM from the course flown.

5-55. Answer C. GFDIC 5B, FAR 91.177

In designated mountainous areas, you must remain at least 2,000 feet above the highest obstacle within a horizontal distance of 4 NM from the course to be flown.

SECTION C — HOLDING PROCEDURES

PURPOSE OF HOLDING

- A holding pattern is a time delay used by ATC to help maintain separation and smooth out the traffic flow.

- You may request a hold, for example, to wait for weather conditions to improve.

FLYING A HOLDING PATTERN

- Holding pattern size is directly proportional to aircraft speed; doubling your speed doubles the size of your holding pattern.

- Turns are to the right in standard holding patterns, and to the left in nonstandard holding patterns.

- Each circuit of the holding pattern begins and ends at the holding fix.

- Timing for the outbound leg of either a standard or nonstandard holding pattern should begin abeam the holding fix. If the abeam position cannot be identified, start timing the outbound leg at the completion of the turn outbound.

- Adjust the timing of your outbound leg to make your inbound leg one minute long.

- When DME is used, the same holding procedures apply, but the turns are initiated at specified DME distances from the station.

- To correct for crosswind drift in the holding pattern, triple your inbound wind correction angle on the outbound leg.

HOLDING SPEEDS

To keep the volume of the protected airspace for a holding pattern within reasonable limits, maximum holding airspeeds are designated according to altitude. The maximum holding speeds for civil aircraft are 200 KIAS up to 6,000 feet MSL, 230 KIAS from 6,001 to 14,000 feet, and 265 KIAS above 14,000 feet.

HOLDING PATTERN ENTRIES

The entry procedure for a holding pattern depends on your heading relative to the holding course. The three recommended procedures are direct, teardrop, and parallel.

HOLDING CLEARANCES

A holding clearance should always contain the holding direction, the holding fix, and an expect further clearance (EFC) time. If the holding pattern is not published, the clearance also contains the holding course. For nonstandard patterns, left turns are specified. For patterns using DME, the clearance gives the outbound leg length in nautical miles.

5-56   **PLT296**
(Refer to figure 87.)

At STRUT intersection headed eastbound, ATC instructs you to hold west on the 10 DME fix west of LCH on V306, standard turns, what entry procedure is recommended?

A– Direct.

B– Teardrop.

C– Parallel.

5-56. Answer A. GFDIC 5C, Enroute Chart Legend
It appears that you are to hold on the 265° radial at the 10 DME fix west of LCH. Since you are inbound to the holding fix, on the holding course, you are aligned for a direct entry to the pattern.

5-57   **PLT296**

(Refer to figure 112.)

You arrive at the 15 DME fix on a heading of 350°. Which holding pattern correctly complies with the ATC clearance below, and what is the recommended entry procedure? "...HOLD WEST OF THE ONE FIVE DME FIX ON THE ZERO NINE ZERO RADIAL OF THE ABC VORTAC, FIVE MILE LEGS, LEFT TURNS..."

A– 1; teardrop entry.

B– 1; direct entry.

C– 2; direct entry.

5-57. Answer B. GFDIC 5C, AIM

To answer this question you need to be familiar with holding pattern terminology. (See accompanying illustrations for nonstandard and standard patterns.) Then, you need to have a clear understanding of holding pattern instructions. An ATC clearance with holding instructions at a fix where the pattern is not charted will include the following information:

1. Direction of holding from the fix in terms of the eight cardinal compass points (N, NE, E, SE, etc.).

2. Holding fix (the fix may be omitted if included at the beginning of the transmission as the clearance limit).

3. Radial, course, bearing, airway, or route on which the aircraft is to hold.

4. Leg length in miles if DME or RNAV is to be used (leg length will be specified in minutes on pilot request or if the controller considers it necessary).

5. Direction of turn if left turns are to be made, the pilot requests, or the controller considers it necessary. If the direction of turn is not included, the pattern is standard with right turns.

6. Time to expect further clearance and any pertinent additional delay information.

For entry maneuvering, a key is to visualize your position and heading when you first approach the holding fix. You also have to know where the pattern is in relation to the holding fix. As a general rule, you turn in the shortest direction to get into a position where you can intercept the course of the inbound leg of the holding pattern. Your heading when you initially cross the holding fix determines the type of entry — parallel, teardrop, or direct.

For this question, you first must determine that pattern 1 properly depicts the holding instructions. With an initial heading of 350°, you are approaching the fix within the direct entry sector (340° clockwise to 160°). See accompanying illustration.

5-58   PLT296

You receive this ATC clearance

"...HOLD EAST OF THE ABC VORTAC ON THE ZERO NINER RADIAL, LEFT TURNS..."

What is the recommended procedure to enter the holding pattern?

A– Parallel only.

B– Direct only.

C– Teardrop only.

5-58. Answer A. GFDIC 5C, AIM

Note that the clearance is for a nonstandard (left turns) pattern. The HSI depicts the aircraft on a course of 060°, heading 055°, inbound TO the station, which places it southwest of the VORTAC. An inbound heading between 340° clockwise to 090° will place the airplane in the sector for a parallel entry (answer A). A direct entry (answer B) is wrong because your inbound heading would have to be between 160° clockwise to 340°. The teardrop (answer C) heading would apply in the inbound heading was between 090° clockwise to 160°.

5-59   PLT296

(Refer to figure 113.)

You receive this ATC clearance: "...CLEARED TO THE ABC VORTAC. HOLD SOUTH ON THE ONE

EIGHT ZERO RADIAL..." What is the recommended procedure to enter the holding pattern?

A– Teardrop only.

B– Direct only.

C– Parallel only.

5-59. Answer B. GFDIC 5C, AIM

The HSI depicts the aircraft on a 060° course inbound TO the VORTAC (on the 240° radial). The holding pattern is on the 180° radial, right turns implied. As shown in the accompanying illustration, the aircraft is within the 180° of azimuth which requires a direct entry.

5-60   PLT296

(Refer to figure 113.)

You receive this ATC clearance: "...CLEARED TO THE XYZ VORTAC. HOLD NORTH ON THE THREE SIX ZERO RADIAL, LEFT TURNS..." What is the recommended procedure to enter the holding pattern.

A– Parallel only.

B– Direct only.

C– Teardrop only.

5-60. Answer C. GFDIC 5C, AIM

The HSI depicts the aircraft on a course of 060° inbound TO the VORTAC, on the 240° radial. Since the aircraft is on the nonholding side of the pattern and its heading is within 70° of the outbound course, a teardrop entry is recommended.

5-61   PLT296

(Refer to figure 113.)

You receive this ATC clearance: "...CLEARED TO THE ABC VORTAC. HOLD WEST ON THE TWO SEVEN ZERO RADIAL..." What is the recommended procedure to enter the holding pattern?

A– Parallel only.

B– Direct only.

C– Teardrop only.

5-61. Answer B. GFDIC 5C, AIM

The HSI depicts the aircraft on a 060° course inbound TO the VORTAC (on the 240° radial), with a heading of 055°. The holding pattern is on the 270° radial, right turns implied. The aircraft heading is within 70° of the inbound holding course of 090°, so a direct entry is recommended.

5-62   PLT296

(Refer to figure 114.)

A pilot receives this ATC clearance: "...CLEARED TO THE ABC VORTAC. HOLD WEST ON THE TWO SEVEN ZERO RADIAL..." What is the recommended procedure to enter the holding pattern?

A– Parallel or teardrop.

B– Parallel only.

C– Direct only.

5-62. Answer C. GFDIC 5C, AIM

The HSI depicts the aircraft on the 330° radial on the 150° course TO the VORTAC, heading 155°. The holding course is on the 270° radial, with standard right turns implied. The aircraft heading is within 110° of the inbound course on the nonholding side, so a direct entry is recommended.

5-63   PLT296

(Refer to figure 114.)

A pilot receives this ATC clearance: "...CLEARED TO THE XYZ VORTAC. HOLD NORTH ON THE THREE SIX ZERO RADIAL, LEFT TURNS..." What is the recommended procedure to enter the holding pattern?

A– Teardrop only.

B– Parallel only.

C– Direct only.

5-63. Answer C. GFDIC 5C, AIM

The HSI depicts the aircraft on the 150° course TO the VORTAC on the 330° radial. The inbound heading of 155° is within the 180° sector where a direct entry is recommended.

5-64   **PLT296**

(Refer to figure 114.)

A pilot receives this ATC clearance: "...CLEARED TO THE ABC VORTAC. HOLD SOUTH ON THE ONE EIGHT ZERO RADIAL..." What is the recommended procedure to enter the holding pattern?

A– Teardrop only.

B– Parallel only.

C– Direct only.

5-64. Answer A. GFDIC 5C, AIM

The HSI depicts the aircraft on the 330° radial, on the 150° course TO the VORTAC. Since the aircraft is on the nonholding side of the pattern and the heading of 155° is within 70° of the outbound leg, a teardrop entry is recommended.

5-65   **PLT296**

To ensure proper airspace protection while in a holding pattern, what is the maximum indicated airspeed above 14,000 feet?

A– 220 knots.

B– 265 knots.

C– 200 knots.

5-65. Answer B. GFDIC 5C, AIM

The maximum airspeed for all aircraft holding above 14,000 feet MSL is 265 knots. Below 6,000 feet MSL the speed is 200 knots, and above 6,000 through 14,000 feet MSL the maximum holding speed is 230 knots.

5-66   **PLT296**

(Refer to figure 115.)

You receive this ATC clearance: "...HOLD WEST OF THE ONE FIVE DME FIX ON THE ZERO NINE ZERO RADIAL OF ABC VORTAC, FIVE MILE LEGS, LEFT TURNS..." You arrive at the 15 DME fix on a heading of 350°. Which holding pattern correctly complies with these instructions, and what is the recommended entry procedure?

A– 1; teardrop.

B– 2; direct.

C– 1; direct.

5-66. Answer C. GFDIC 5C, AIM

Since the inbound leg of the holding pattern will always take you to the holding fix, pattern 1 is the only one correctly depicted. The aircraft heading of 350° on the nonholding side places it within 110° of the holding course. A direct entry is recommended.

5-67   PLT296
(Refer to figure 116.)

You arrive over the 15 DME fix on a heading of 350°. Which holding pattern correctly complies with the ATC clearance below, and what is the recommended entry procedure? "...HOLD WEST OF THE ONE FIVE DME FIX ON THE TWO SIX EIGHT RADIAL OF THE ABC VORTAC , FIVE MILE LEGS, LEFT TURNS..."

A– 1; teardrop entry.

B– 2; direct entry.

C– 1; direct entry.

5-67. Answer B. GFDIC 5C, AIM
Since the inbound leg of the holding pattern will always take you to the holding fix, pattern 2 is the only one correctly depicted. The aircraft heading of 350° on the non-holding side places it within 110° of the holding course.

5-68   PLT296
At what point should the timing begin for the first leg outbound in a nonstandard holding pattern?

A– Abeam the holding fix, or wings level, whichever occurs last.

B– When the wings are level at the completion of the 180° turn outbound.

C– When over or abeam the holding fix, whichever occurs later.

5-68. Answer C. GFDIC 5C, AIM
Outbound leg timing begins over or abeam the holding fix, whichever occurs later.

5-69   PLT296
(Refer to figure 117.)

You receive this ATC clearance: "...CLEARED TO THE ABC NDB. HOLD SOUTHEAST ON THE ONE FOUR ZERO DEGREE BEARING FROM THE NDB. LEFT TURNS..." At station passage you note the indications in the referenced figure.

What is the recommended procedure to enter the holding pattern?

A– Direct only.

B– Teardrop only.

C– Parallel only

5-69. Answer C. GFDIC 5C, AIM
You are crossing the NDB on a heading of 055°. The holding pattern is southeast on the 140° bearing from the station, or 320° inbound. The aircraft is entering on the holding side with a heading greater than 70° from the inbound bearing.

5-70   PLT296

(Refer to figure 117.)

You receive this ATC clearance: "...CLEARED TO THE XYZ NDB. HOLD NORTHEAST ON THE ZERO FOUR ZERO DEGREE BEARING FROM THE NDB. LEFT TURNS..." At station passage you note the indications in the referenced figure.

What is the recommended procedure to enter the holding pattern?

A– Direct only.

B– Teardrop only.

C– Parallel only.

5-70. Answer B. GFDIC 5C, AIM

You are crossing the NDB on a heading of 055°. The holding pattern is northeast on the 040° bearing from the station, or 220° inbound. The aircraft is entering on the nonholding side, within the 70° arc for a teardrop entry.

5-71   PLT296

(Refer to figure 117.)

You receive this ATC clearance: "...CLEARED TO THE ABC NDB. HOLD SOUTHWEST ON THE TWO THREE ZERO DEGREE BEARING FROM THE NDB..." At station passage you note the indications in the referenced figure.

What is the recommended procedure to enter the holding pattern?

A– Direct only

B– Teardrop only.

C– Parallel only.

5-71. Answer A. GFDIC 5C, AIM

You are crossing the NDB on a heading of 055°. The holding pattern is southwest on the 230° bearing from the station, or 050° inbound. The aircraft heading is within the 180° sector for a direct entry.

5-72   PLT296

What timing procedure should be used when performing a holding pattern at a VOR?

A– Timing for the outbound leg begins over or abeam the VOR, whichever occurs later.

B– Timing for the inbound leg begins when initiating the turn inbound.

C– Adjustments in timing of each pattern should be made on the inbound leg.

5-72. Answer A. GFDIC 5C, AIM

Timing for the outbound leg begins over or abeam the holding fix, whichever occurs later.

5-73 PLT296

When holding at an NDB, at what point should the timing begin for the second leg outbound?

A— When the wings are level and the wind drift correction angle is established after completing the turn to the outbound heading.

B— When the wings are level after completing the turn to the outbound heading, or abeam the fix, whichever occurs first.

C— When abeam the holding fix.

5-73. Answer C. GFDIC 5C, AIM
Start timing on the outbound leg when abeam the VOR. If you can't determine the abeam position, then start timing when wings level after completing the outbound turn.

5-74 PLT296

To ensure proper airspace protection while holding at 5,000 feet in a civil aircraft, what is the maximum indicated airspeed a pilot should use?

A— 200 knots.

B— 210 knots.

C— 230 knots.

5-74. Answer A. GFDIC 5C, AIM
The maximum holding speed for civil aircraft (piston and jet) is 200 KIAS up to 6,000 feet MSL, 230 KIAS from 6,001 to 14,000 feet, and 265 KIAS above 14,000 feet.

5-75 PLT296

(Refer to figure 240.)

What type entry is recommended for the missed approach holding pattern depicted on the VOR/DME RWY 36 approach chart for PUC Airport?

A— Direct only

B— Teardrop only

C— Parallel or teardrop

5-75. Answer C. GFDIC 5C, AIM
If you arrive at FOSOV on the PUC R-164, you could perform either a parallel or teardrop entry to the holding pattern.

5-76 PLT083

(Refer to figure 242.)

What indication should you get when it is time to turn inbound while in the holding pattern course reversal at FAHXE?

A— 4 NM from FAHXE.

B— 4 NM from KAGBE.

C— Timer at 1 minute.

5-76. Answer A. GFDIC 5C, AIM
The RNAV (GPS) approach procedure depicts a holding pattern course reversal with a 4 NM leg length from FEHXE. The leg length is indicated on the holding pattern outbound leg in the plan view and on the profile view.

5-77   **PLT296**

(Refer to figure 242.)

What type of entry is recommended to the missed approach holding pattern if the inbound heading is 050°?

A– Direct.

B– Parallel.

C– Teardrop.

.

5-77. Answer C. GFDIC 5C, AIM

The missed approach holding pattern is at HIGHS waypoint. Note, this is a nonstandard (left turns) holding pattern. When you initially approach the fix from the southwest, heading 050°, you are within the sector where a teardrop entry is recommended. This applies to inbound headings between 042° and 112°

5-78   **PLT296**

(Refer to figure 247.)

What type of entry is recommended for the missed approach holding pattern at Riverside Municipal?

A– Parallel or teardrop

B– Direct.

C– Teardrop only.

5-78 PLT296 5-80. Answer A. GFDIC 5C, AIM

According to the missed approach instructions, you arrive at the missed approach holding point of WISUP on the 256° radial. On this course, you have the option of using a parallel or teardrop entry.

5-79   **PLT296**

(Refer to figure 238.)

What is the procedure for flying the holding pattern course reversal when proceeding from TARTO to FAIRF?

A– Use a parallel entry and fly 4-NM legs.

B– Use a teardrop entry and fly 1-minute legs.

C– Use a teardrop entry and fly 4-NM legs.

5-79. Answer C. GFDICM 5C, AIM

The recommended entry on a course of 044° is a teardrop entry. The RNAV (GPS) approach procedure depicts a holding pattern course reversal with a 4-NM leg length from FAIRF. The leg length is indicated on the holding pattern outbound leg in the plan view and on the profile view.

5-80   **PLT296**

To ensure proper airspace protection while in a holding pattern, what is the maximum indicated airspeed above 14,000 feet?

A– 220 knots.

B– 265 knots.

C– 200 knots.

5-80. Answer B. GFDIC 5C, AIM

The maximum indicated airspeed for all aircraft holding above 14,000 feet MSL is 265 knots. For 6,000 feet MSL and below, the speed is 200 knots. For 6,001 feet MSL through 14,000 feet MSL the maximum holding speed is 230 knots.

5-81   **PLT420**

Where a holding pattern is specified in lieu of a procedure turn, the holding maneuver must be executed within

A– 10 knots of the specified holding speed.

B– a radius of 5 miles from the holding fix.

C– the 1-minute time limitation or DME distance as specified in the profile view.

5-81. Answer C. GFDIC 5C, AIM

The airspace set aside for the holding pattern is based on the published leg length (for DME use) or on an inbound time of 1 minute.

ARRIVAL

CHAPTER 6

SECTION A — ARRIVAL CHARTS

STANDARD TERMINAL ARRIVAL ROUTES

- Standard terminal arrival routes (STARs) provide a standard method for leaving the enroute structure and entering a busy terminal area.
- STARs are established to simplify clearance delivery procedures.

STARS IN CLEARANCES

- If you accept a STAR, you must have at least a textual description of the procedure in your possession. A graphic description is preferable.
- Writing "No STAR" in the remarks section of your flight plan will alert ATC that you do not wish to use these procedures during your flight. You also may refuse a clearance containing a STAR, but avoid this practice if possible.

STAR CHARTS

- STARs use symbology that is similar to that on SIDs. Altitudes are given in reference to mean sea level, and distances are in nautical miles.
- A STAR begins at a navaid or intersection where all arrival transitions join.
- STARs are named according to the point where a procedure begins. They are revised in numerical sequence.
- Arrival route headings on an FAA STAR chart are depicted by large numerals within a heavyweight line.
- Frequencies on which to contact the proper approach controller are found in the corner of an FAA chart.
- Vertical navigation planning information is given for pilots of turboprop and jet traffic, to aid them in making efficient descents from the enroute structure to approach fixes.

6-1   PLT102

(Refer to figures 167 and 168.)

At which point does the BYP.BYP6 arrival begin?

A– At the LIT VORTAC.

B– At GLOVE.

C– At the BYP VORTAC.

6-1. Answer C. GFDIC 6A, STAR/DP Legend

The BONHAM SIX ARRIVAL (BYP.BYP6) consists of two charts. Figure 167 shows the transition routes to the arrival procedure. The arrival routes, which begin at BYP VORTAC, are depicted on the chart in by bold lines as opposed to transition routes that are shown with lighter line weights. The arrival routes also are described textually following the transition descriptions.

6-2   **PLT102**
(Refer to figures 41 and 41A.)

At which point does the AQN.AQN2 arrival begin?

A– ABI VORTAC.

B– ACTON VORTAC.

C– CREEK intersection.

6-2. Answer B. GFDIC 6A, STAR/DP Legend
The ACTON TWO ARRIVAL (AQN.AQN2) begins at the ACTON VORTAC. This is apparent on the graphic depiction. Arrival routes originating at AQN are shown with bold lines as opposed to transition routes which are shown with lighter line weights. The arrival routes also are specified in the textual description following the transitions.

6-3   **PLT102**
(Refer to figures 41 and 41A.)

Which frequency would you anticipate using to contact Regional Approach Control? (ACTON TWO ARRIVAL).

A– 119.05.

B– 124.15.

C– 125.8.

6-3. Answer C. GFDIC 6A, STAR/DP Legend
There is a listing of frequencies pertinent to the arrival procedure in the upper left hand corner of the ACTON TWO ARRIVAL. The first frequency listed is for the Regional Approach Control. When arriving from the west, as in this example, contact approach on 125.8.

6-4   **PLT102**
(Refer to figures 41 and 41A.)

On which heading should you plan to depart CREEK intersection?

A– 010°.

B– 040°.

C– 350°.

6-4. Answer C. GFDIC 6A, STAR/DP Legend
As you depart CREEK Intersection, you should be on a heading of 350°. This is indicated by the bold line and 350° callout in the upper right portion of the chart. It is also specified in the textual description of the procedure.

6-5   **PLT102**
(Refer to figures 208 and 209.)

At which location does the STELA. STELA1 arrival begin?

A– Albany VORTAC.

B– CANAN.

C– STELA.

6-5. Answer B. GFDIC 6A, STAR/DP Legend
The STELA ONE ARRIVAL (STELA.STELA1) begins over CANAN, which is indicated by the bold course line starting at this fix.

6-6   **PLT102**
(Refer to figures 174 and 175.)

When DFW is landing to the north, at CURLE expect

A– to be instructed to maintain 200 knots.

B– to fly a course of 010°.

C– radar vectors.

6-6. Answer C. GFDIC 6A, STAR/DP Legend
The arrival routes for GLEN ROSE NINE ARRIVAL are described textually following the transition descriptions on the chart in Figure 175. Following the heading, ALL AIRCRAFT LANDING NORTH, the description specifies that after flying to CURLE, you should expect vectors to the final approach course.

SECTION B — ARRIVAL PROCEDURES

- ATC will issue a STAR when they deem one appropriate, unless you request "No STAR" in your flight plan. It is up to you whether to accept or refuse the procedure.

- Altitudes and airspeeds published on the STAR are not considered restrictions until verbally given by ATC as part of a clearance.

- After receiving the arrival clearance, certain tasks can be completed before starting your approach, including gathering weather information and accomplishing the descent and approach checklists.

- After you determine the approach in use, review the appropriate chart and create a plan of action.

- A descend via clearance instructs you to follow the altitudes published on the STAR, with descent at your discretion.

- ATC may issue a descent clearance which includes a crossing altitude. Comply by estimating the distance and rate of descent required.

6-7   PLT004
(Refer to figure 192.)

Using an average groundspeed of 90 knots, what constant rate of descent from 3,100 feet MSL at CFIVO would enable the aircraft to arrive at 2,400 feet MSL at the FAF of ILSIC?

A– 300 feet per minute.

B– 350 feet per minute.

C– 700 feet per minute.

6-7. Answer B. GFDIC 6B, STAR/DP Legend, Rate of Descent Table

CFIVO is three miles from ILSIC. To solve this problem you first need to compute the time required to travel 3 miles at 90 knots, (2 minutes). Simple arithmetic will tell you that in order to descend 700 feet in 2 minutes you must descend at a minimum of 350 feet per minute

6-8   PLT080
Which is true regarding STARs?

A– STARs are used to separate IFR and VFR traffic.

B– STARs are established to simplify clearance delivery procedures.

C– STARs are used at certain airports to decrease traffic congestion.

6-8. Answer B. GFDIC 6B, AIM

STARs are primarily used to simplify clearance delivery procedures for pilots and controllers.

6-9   **PLT420**
How is ATC radar used for instrument approaches when the facility is approved for approach control service?

A– Precision approaches, weather surveillance, and as a substitute for any inoperative component of a navigation aid used for approaches.

B– ASR approaches, weather surveillance, and course guidance by approach control.

C– Course guidance to the final approach course, ASR and PAR approaches, and the monitoring of nonradar approaches.

6-8. Answer C. GFDIC 6B, AIM
Approach control radar is used for vectors, or course guidance, to the final approach course, for any established instrument approach procedure (IAP). It also may be used to provide guidance to the traffic pattern for a visual approach, or for ASR and PAR approaches, and to monitor nonradar approaches.

6-10   **PLT370**
Under which condition does ATC issue a STAR?

A– To all pilots wherever STARs are available.

B– Only if the pilot requests a STAR in the "Remarks" section of the flight plan.

C– When ATC deems it appropriate, unless the pilot requests "NO STAR."

6-10. Answer C. GFDIC 6B, AIM
When appropriate, ATC issues standard terminal arrival routes (STARs) to simplify clearance delivery procedures. If you do not wish to use a STAR, you should include the words "No STAR" in the remarks section of the flight plan.

APPROACH

SECTION A — APPROACH CHARTS

OVERVIEW

- The standard instrument approach procedure (IAP) allows you to descend safely by reference to instruments from the enroute altitude to a point near the runway at your destination from which a landing may be made visually. An IAP may be divided into as many as four segments: initial, intermediate, final, and missed approach.

- The procedure title indicates the type of approach system used and the equipment required to fly the approach.

PRECISION AND NONPRECISION APPROACHES

- A precision approach, such as an ILS or Precision Approach Radar (PAR) procedure provides vertical guidance through means of an electronic glide slope, as well as horizontal course guidance. A nonprecision approach, such as a VOR or NDB approach, provides horizontal course guidance with no glide slope information.

- If the glide slope becomes inoperative during an ILS procedure, it becomes a nonprecision approach, and higher localizer minimums are used.

APPROACH SEGMENTS

- Feeder routes, also referred to as approach transitions or terminal routes, provide a link between the enroute and approach structures. Flyable routes are indicated with a heavy line arrow on FAA charts. Each flyable route lists the radial or bearing, the distance, and the minimum altitude.

- The letters IAF indicate the location of an initial approach fix. The purpose of the initial approach segment which follows the IAF, is to provide a method for aligning your aircraft with the approach course. The intermediate segment primarily is designed to position your aircraft for the final descent to the airport.

- The final approach segment allows you to navigate safely to a point at which, if the required visual references are available, you can continue the approach to a landing.

- The final approach segment for a precision approach begins where the glide slope is intercepted at the minimum glide slope intercept altitude shown on the approach chart. For a nonprecision approach, the final approach segment begins either at a designated final approach fix (FAF) or at the point where you are aligned with the final approach course.

- If you know the glide slope angle (normally 3°), and if you maintain an average groundspeed on the final approach segment, you can determine the rate of descent to initially establish the airplane on the glidepath for an ILS approach procedure.

- The missed approach segment takes you from the missed approach point (MAP) to a point for another approach or to another airport.

GENERAL CHART INFORMATION

- FAA charts are published in regional volumes referred to as Terminal Procedures Publications, with each airport filed alphabetically by the name of the associated city. Generally, both charts present the same information; however, the symbology and chart layout vary.

- Approach charts present communications frequencies in the normal sequence used by arriving aircraft and use index numbers for chart identification.

- The plan view is an overhead presentation of the entire approach procedure, including navaid facility boxes and reference points, such as natural or man-made objects.

COURSE REVERSALS

- A procedure turn is a standard method of reversing your course. When a holding or teardrop pattern is shown instead of a procedure turn, it is the only approved method of course reversal. If a procedure turn, holding or teardrop pattern is not shown, a course reversal is not authorized.

- The procedure turn, as depicted on the profile view, must be completed within the prescribed distance from the facility.

ALTITUDE INFORMATION

- Minimum altitudes on approach procedures provide clearance of terrain and obstructions along the depicted flight tracks.

- The minimum safe altitude, or MSA, provides 1,000 feet of obstruction clearance within 25 nautical miles of the indicated facility, unless some other distance is specified.

- The touchdown zone elevation (TDZE) is the highest centerline altitude for the first 3,000 feet of the landing runway. FAA charts depict the TDZE in the pilot briefing information and on the airport sketch.

- The profile view shows the approach from the side and displays flight path, facilities, and minimum altitudes. Height above touchdown (HAT) is measured from the touchdown zone elevation of the runway. Height above airport (HAA) is measured above the official airport elevation, which is the highest point of an airport's usable runways.

- Distances between fixes along the approach path and the runway threshold are also shown on the profile view.

- The threshold crossing height (TCH) is the altitude at which you cross the runway threshold when established on the glide slope.

STEPDOWN FIXES

- Many approaches incorporate one or more stepdown fixes, used along approach segments to allow you to descend to a lower altitude as you overfly various obstacles. Your ability to identify selected stepdown fixes may permit lower landing minimums in some cases. When you cannot identify a stepdown fix, you must use the minimum altitude given just prior to the fix.

- A visual descent point (VDP) represents the point from which you can make a normal descent to a landing, assuming you have the runway in sight and you are starting from the minimum descent altitude.

CIRCLING AND SIDESTEP MANEUVERS

- An approach procedure to one runway with a landing on another is a circling approach, with circle-to-land minimums. Restrictions may apply to circle-to-land procedure. For example, a circle-to-land procedure might not be authorized in a specific area.

- During a sidestep maneuver, you are cleared for an approach to one runway with a clearance to land on a parallel runway.

AIRPORT INFORMATION

The airport diagram plan view portrays an overhead view of the airport, including runways and lighting systems. The airport reference point, or ARP, is where the official latitude and longitude coordinates are derived.

ALTERNATE AIRPORT

- If the forecast weather at your estimated time of arrival, plus or minus 1 hour, indicates a ceiling of less than 2,000 feet or a visibility of less than 3 miles, you must list an alternate airport on your IFR flight plan.

- Standard alternate minimums when a precision approach is available are a 600-foot ceiling and 2 statute miles visibility. When only nonprecision approaches are available, an 800-foot ceiling and 2 statute miles apply.

WHEN TO CONDUCT A MISSED APPROACH

- During a precision approach, the height where you must make the decision to continue the approach or execute a missed approach is referred to as the decision altitude (DA). FAA charts show the decision altitude as an MSL altitude with the height above touchdown (HAT) listed after the visibility requirement.

- When on the glide slope during a precision approach, the missed approach point is the decision altitude.

- Aircraft approach categories used to determine landing minimums are based on approach speed. This speed is 130% of the aircraft's power-off stall speed in the landing configuration at the maximum certificated landing weight ($1.3V_{SO}$). Landing minimums published on instrument approach charts consist of both minimum visibility and minimum altitude requirements for aircraft in various approach categories (A, B, C and D).

- Visibility is listed on approach charts in statute miles, usually as a prevailing visibility reported by an accredited observer such as tower or weather personnel, or in hundreds of feet determined through the use of runway visual range (RVR) equipment.

- If Runway Visual Range (RVR) minimums for landing are prescribed for an instrument approach procedure, but RVR is inoperative and cannot be reported for the intended runway at the time, RVR minimums should be converted and applied as ground visibility. For example, RVR 24 translates to 1/2 statute mile visibility.

- Landing minimums usually increase when a required component or visual aid becomes inoperative. Regulations permit you to make substitutions for certain components when the component is inoperative or is not utilized during an approach.

- The minimum altitude to which you can descend during a nonprecision approach is shown as a minimum descent altitude (MDA).

- For timed approaches, a conversion table provide various elapsed times to the MAP based on the aircraft's groundspeed.

7-1   PLT083
(Refer to figure 160.)

What is the TDZE for RWY 16L at Eugene/Mahlon Sweet Field?

A– 369 feet MSL.

B– 374 feet MSL.

C– 440 feet MSL

7-1. Answer A. GFDIC 7A, Approach Chart Legend
The touchdown zone elevation (TDZE) of 369 feet MSL can be found in the airport information box of the pilot briefing information and at the top of the airport sketch.

7-2   PLT083
(Refer to figure 160.)

Using a groundspeed of 90 knots on the ILS final approach course, what rate of descent should be used as a reference to maintain the ILS glide slope?

A– 415 feet per minute.

B– 480 feet per minute.

C– 555 feet per minute.

7-2. Answer B. GFDIC 7A, Approach Chart Legend, Rate of Descent Table
The glide slope is 3°, as indicated on the profile view by "GS 3.00°". To determine the appropriate rate of descent, refer to the Rate of Descent Table in Appendix 1. At a speed of 90 knots, you must descend at a rate of approximately 480 feet per minute to maintain the glide slope.

7-3   PLT083
(Refer to figure 171.)

What are the MDA and visibility criteria respectively for a category A airplane flying the RNAV (GPS) RWY 33 approach using the local altimeter setting?

A– 1,240 feet MSL; 1 SM.

B– 1,240 feet MSL; 1½ SM.

C– 1,280 feet MSL; 1 SM.

7-3. Answer A. GFDIC 7A, Approach Chart Legend
Using the referenced figure, the MDA and visibility criteria for the straight-in landing procedure are 1,240 feet MSL and 1 SM, respectively. These minimums apply to category A and B aircraft.

7-4   PLT102
(Refer to figures 174, 175, 176, 176A, and 177.)

Approaching DFW from Abilene, which frequencies should you expect to use for regional approach control, control tower, and ground control respectively?

A– 125.025; 118.425; 124.15; 121.85.

B– 119.87; 118.425; 126.55; 121.8.

C– 119.87; 118.425; 124.15; 121.85.

7-4. Answer C. GFDIC 7A, Approach Chart Legend, A/FD Legend
Regional approach control frequencies (119.87 and 133.62) for the GLEN ROSE NINE ARRIVAL are listed in the upper right-hand corner. If you are flying from Abilene on this arrival, you are approaching DFW from the west. The regional approach frequencies on the arrival chart are confirmed in the A/FD as frequencies to use when arriving from the west. If you are flying the Converging ILS Runway 36L approach, you most likely will be assigned the approach control frequency of 118.425 as indicated on the approach chart. The tower and ground control frequencies typically assigned when approaching from the west are indicated on the approach chart and are confirmed in the A/FD.

7-5   PLT083
(Refer to figure 177.)

Which navigational information and services would be available to the pilot when using the localizer frequency?

A– Localizer and glide slope, DME, TACAN with no voice capability.

B– Localizer information only, ATIS and DME are available.

C– Localizer and glide slope, DME, and no voice capability.

7-5. Answer C. GFDIC 7A, Approach Chart Legend
The title ILS RWY 36L means both localizer and glide slope are available. The figure shows a DME channel in the localizer identifier box, and DME fixes are shown on the profile view. No voice capability is indicated by the underlined localizer frequency.

7-6 **PLT083**
(Refer to figures 42 and 42A.)

What is the difference in elevation (in feet MSL) between the airport elevation and the TDZE for RWY 36L?

A– 15 feet.

B– 18 feet.

C– 22 feet.

7-6. Answer A. GFDIC 7A, Approach Chart Legend
The touchdown zone elevation (TDZE) is 588 feet. This is indicated on the airport diagram in the figure. The airport elevation is 603 feet and is indicated on the airport diagram. The difference between the airport elevation and the TDZE for RWY/36L is 15 feet.

7-7 **PLT083**
(Refer to figure 177.)

What rate of descent should you plan to use initially to establish the glide path for the CONVERGING ILS RWY/36L approach? (Use 120 knots groundspeed.)

A– 425 feet per minute.

B– 530 feet per minute.

C– 637 feet per minute.

7-7. Answer C. GFDIC 7A, Approach Chart Legend, Rate of Descent Table
The glide slope is 3.0°. This is indicated by the "GS 3.00°" on the profile view of the figure. To determine the rate of descent required to maintain the glide slope, refer to the Rate of Descent Table in Appendix 1. At 120 knots, you must descend at 637 feet per minute to maintain the glide slope.

7-8 **PLT083**
(Refer to figure 196.)

What is the TDZE for RWY 4?

A– 57 feet MSL.

B– 46 feet MSL.

C– 44 feet MSL.

7-8. Answer C. GFDIC 7A, Approach Chart Legend
The touchdown zone elevation (TDZE) of 44 feet MSL can be found in the airport information box of the pilot briefing information and at the top of the airport sketch.

7-9 **PLT083**
(Refer to figure 73.)

What is the minimum altitude at which you should intercept the glide slope on the ILS RWY 6 approach procedure?

A– 3,000 feet MSL.

B– 1,800 feet MSL.

C– 1,690 feet MSL.

7-9. Answer B. GFDIC 7A, Approach Chart Legend
The published glide slope intercept altitude is the lowest altitude at which you may intercept the ILS glide slope. This minimum altitude is shown on the approach chart profile view near the glide slope, prior to the non-precision FAF. It is indicated on FAA charts by a lightning bolt symbol.

7-10   PLT083
(Refer to figure 73.)

At which indication or occurrence should you initiate the published missed approach procedure for the ILS RWY 6 approach provided the runway environment is not in sight?

A– When reaching 374 feet MSL indicated altitude.

B– When 3 minutes (at 90 knots groundspeed) have expired or reaching 374 feet MSL, whichever occurs first.

C– Upon reaching 374 feet AGL.

7-10. Answer A. GFDIC 7A, Approach Chart Legend
Your missed approach point on an ILS approach is at the decision altitude (DA) on the glide slope.

7-11   PLT083
(Refer to figure 73.)

Using an average groundspeed of 90 knots on the final approach segment, what rate of descent should be used initially to establish the glidepath for the ILS RWY 6 approach procedure?

A– 395 feet per minute.

B– 480 feet per minute.

C– 555 feet per minute.

7-11. Answer B. GFDIC 7A, Approach Chart Legend, Rate of Descent Table
The chart indicates a glide slope angle of 3.0°. The FAA publishes a Rate of Descent Table in the Terminal Procedures Publication. (See Appendix 1.) To use this table, find the 3.0° glide path angle in the left column, then move right to the 90 knots. groundspeed column to find 480 feet per minute.

7-12   PLT083
(Refer to figure 73.)

What is the touchdown zone elevation for RWY 6?

A– 174 feet MSL.

B– 200 feet AGL.

C– 270 feet MSL.

7-12. Answer A. GFDIC 7A, Approach Chart Legend
The touchdown zone elevation (TDZE), 174 feet MSL, is shown on the airport sketch of FAA approach charts.

7-13 **PLT083**
(Refer to figure 73.)

Which runway and landing environment lighting
is available for approach and landing on RWY 6 at
Bradley International?

A– HIRL, REIL, and VASI.

B– HIRL and VASI.

C– ALSF2 and HIRL.

7-13. Answer C. GFDIC 7A, Approach Chart Legend
The FAA indicates the available approach light systems
on the airport diagram with an encircled alphanumeric
character. To determine the type of lighting installed,
you must refer to the Approach Lighting Systems legend in the front of each booklet. The circled A symbol
indicates ALSF-2 approach lighting and high intensity
runway lighting (HIRL).

7-14 **PLT382**
(Refer to figures 74 and 213.)

Which aircraft approach category should be used to
determine circling minimums for the VOR/DME RWY
28 approach?

A– A.

B– B.

C– C.

7-14. Answer B. GFDIC 7A, Approach Chart Legend
The approach category is based on 1.3 times the aircraft's stall speed in the landing configuration at maximum gross landing weight ($1.3 \times V_{S0}$). The stalling
speed for this aircraft is 72 knots, which suggests an
approach speed of 93.6 knots ($72 \times 1.3 = 93.6$). The
approach speed range for category B is 91 to 120
knots. (See the approach chart legend in Appendix 1).

7-15 **PLT083**
(Refer to figure 213.)

How many initial approach fixes serve the VOR/DME
RWY 28R (Billings Logan) approach procedure?

A– Two.

B– Three.

C– Four.

7-15. Answer B. GFDIC 7A, Approach Chart Legend
There are three initial approach fixes (IAFs) for the VOR/
DME RWY 28R approach, as indicated by the "IAF"
notations. These fixes are MUSTY along the approach
course and POCOV and NELWN at the beginning of
each DME arc.

7-16 **PLT083**
(Refer to figures 213 and 214.)

What lighting is available for RWY 28R?

A– Runway end identifier lights, high intensity runway
lights, and PAPI

B– Runway end identifier lights, medium intensity runway lights, and VASI.

C– Medium intensity runway lights and PAPI.

7-16. Answer A. GFDIC 7A, Approach Chart Legend
Runway end identifier lights (REIL) and high intensity
runway lights (HIRL) are listed at the bottom of the airport sketch and in the A/FD runway description. The
PAPI is shown by the letter P in a circle in the airport sketch and is also indicated in the A/FD runway
description.

7-17   PLT083
(Refer to figure 210.)

What is the THRE for RWY 6?

A– 173 feet MSL.

B– 200 feet AGL.

C– 270 feet MSL.

7-17. Answer A. GFDIC 7A, Approach Chart Legend
The threshold elevation (THRE) for RWY 6 at Windsor Locks/Bradley International Airport is identified as 173 feet MSL in the runway information box in the pilot briefing information section of the approach chart and at the top of the airport sketch. Typically you will find the touchdown zone elevation (TDZE) in place of the threshold elevation.

7-18   PLT292
What obstacle clearance and navigation signal coverage is a pilot assured with the Minimum Sector Altitudes depicted on the IAP charts?

A– 1,000 feet and acceptable navigation signal coverage within a 25-NM radius of the navigation facility.

B– 1,000 feet within a 25-NM radius of the navigation facility but not acceptable navigation signal coverage.

C– 500 feet and acceptable navigation signal coverage within a 10-NM radius of the navigation facility.

7-18. Answer B. GFDIC 7A, AIM
The minimum sector altitudes depicted on instrument approach procedure charts guarantee 1,000 feet clearance within a 25 NM radius of the navigational facility shown, but do not guarantee navigational signal or communications coverage at that altitude throughout the 25 NM radius area.

7-19   PLT292
What does the absence of the procedure turn barb on the plan view on an approach chart indicate?

A– A procedure turn is not authorized.

B– Teardrop-type procedure turn is authorized.

C– Racetrack-type procedure turn is authorized.

7-19. Answer A. GFDIC 7A, AIM
When a procedure turn barb is not depicted, the pilot is expected to fly a straight-in approach, and a procedure turn is not authorized.

7-20   **PLT083**

(Refer to figure 221.)

The final approach fix for the precision approach is located at

A– SKOLL.

B– Glide slope intercept (lightning bolt).

C– ARBIE.

7-20. Answer B. GFDIC 7A, Approach Chart Legend

On a precision (ILS) approach, the final approach fix is defined as the glide slope intercept point, which is depicted by a lightning bolt on the profile view of FAA charts.

7-21   **PLT083**

(Refer to figure 227.)

Refer to the APA ILS RWY 35R procedure. The FAF intercept altitude is

A– 7,977 feet MSL.

B– 8,000 feet MSL.

C– 7,080 feet MSL.

7-21. Answer B. GFDIC 7A, Approach Chart Legend

The FAF for an ILS is the glide slope intercept point, designated by a lightning bolt symbol on the profile view of FAA charts. The FAF intercept altitude is the minimum glide slope intercept altitude, which is shown as 8,000 feet MSL.

7-22   **PLT083**

(Refer to figure 227.)

The symbol on the plan view of the ILS RWY 35R procedure at APA represents a minimum safe/sector altitude within 25 NM of

A– Casse LOM.

B– FIRPI.

C– Denver/Centennial Airport.

7-22. Answer A. GFDIC 7A, AIM

The minimum safe/sector altitude (MSA) is shown in the upper left corner of this plan view and is referenced from Casse locator outer marker (LOM) (note the AP identifier above the circle).

7-23   **PLT083**

(Refer to figure 223.)

During the ILS RWY 31 procedure at DSM, the minimum altitude for glide slope interception is

A– 2,365 feet MSL.

B– 2,400 feet MSL.

C– 3,000 feet MSL.

7-23. Answer B. GFDICM 7A, Approach Chart Legend

The glide intercept altitude of 2,400 feet MSL is designated by the lightning bolt symbol. Since it is underlined, it is a minimum altitude.

7-24   PLT083
(Refer to figure 223.)

During the ILS RWY 31 procedure at DSM, what MDA applies for a straight-in landing should the glide slope becomes inoperative?

A– 1,158 feet MSL.

B– 1,320 feet MSL.

C– 1,420 feet MSL.

7-24. Answer B. GFDIC 7A, Approach Chart Legend
When the glide slope becomes inoperative, localizer minimums can be used. The S-LOC MDA is 1,320 for all categories of aircraft.

7-25   PLT083
(Refer to figure 122.)

The missed approach point of the ATL S-LOC 8L procedure is located how far from the LOM?

A– 4.8 NM.

B– 5.1 NM.

C– 5.2 NM.

7-25. Answer C. GFDIC 7A, Approach Chart Legend
The conversion table at the bottom of the chart shows the distance from the nonprecision (LOC) FAF to the MAP. The distance is listed as 5.2 NM

7-26   PLT083
(Refer to figure 228.)

When flying the approach at 90 knots, what is the missed approach point for the S-LOC 31 approach?

A– 1 DME based on the localizer (1-FFC) or timing of 3:24 from PECAT.

B– 5.1 DME from PECAT.

C– Reaching the DA of 1,200 feet MSL.

7-26. Answer A. GFDICM 7A, Approach Chart Legend
The profile view shows the MAP at 1 DME from 1-FFC. The conversion table at the bottom of the chart also shows that you can use timing from the FAF of 3:24 from PECAT at 90 knots. Because the localizer approach is a nonprecision approach, the missed approach point (MAP) is not a decision altitude (DA).

7-27   PLT083
(Refer to figure 123.)

What minimum navigation equipment is required to complete the VOR/DME-A procedure?

A– One VOR receiver.

B– One VOR receiver and DME.

C– Two VOR receivers and DME.

7-27. Answer B. GFDIC 7A, IFH
VOR/DME on the chart means that both VOR and DME are required for the approach. The -A alphabetic suffix indicates the procedure does not meet criteria for straight-in landing minimums.

7-28   **PLT083**
(Refer to figure 123.)

The symbol on the plan view of the VOR/DME-A procedure at 7D3 represents a minimum safe sector altitude within 25 NM of

A– DEANI intersection.

B– White Cloud VORTAC.

C– Baldwin Municipal Airport.

7-28. Answer B. GFDIC 7A, AIM
The letters HIC, above the minimum safe altitude (MSA) circle, identify the White Cloud VORTAC. The MSA is always based upon an NDB or a VOR.

7-29   **PLT083**
(Refer to figure 236.)

What landing minimums apply for a 14 CFR part 91 operator at Dothan, AL using a category C aircraft during a circling LOC 32 approach at 120 knots? (dual VOR receivers or radar available).

A– MDA 860 feet MSL and visibility 1 SM.

B– MDA 860 feet MSL and visibility 1½ SM.

C– MDA 820 feet MSL and visibility 24 RVR.

7-29. Answer B. GFDIC 7A, Approach Chart Legend
If you are able to identify FEKRA (dual VOR receivers or radar required), you may descend to 860 feet MSL for a circling approach. Even if flown at a slower airspeed, aircraft category C minimums must be used so 1½ SM visibility applies.

7-30   **PLT083**
(Refer to figure 236.)

What is the ability to identify the FEKRA stepdown fix worth in terms of localizer circle-to-land minimums for a category C aircraft?

A– Decreases the MDA by 360 feet.

B– Decreases the visibility by 1/2 SM.

C– Without the stepdown fix, a circling approach is not available.

7-30. Answer A. GFDIC 7A, Approach Chart Legend
When the FEKRA stepdown fix can be identified, the circling MDA for a category C aircraft is 860 feet MSL and the required visibility is 1½ SM. Without FEKRA, you are limited to published circling minimums of 1,220 feet MSL and a visibility of 2½ SM. Therefore, using FEKRA decreases the MDA by 360 feet and decreases the visibility by 1 SM.

7-31   PLT083

(Refer to figure 240.)

What is the purpose of the 10,300 MSA on the Price/
Carbon County Airport approach chart?

A— It provides safe clearance above the highest obstacle
in the defined sector out to 25 NM.

B— It provides an altitude above which navigational
course guidance is assured.

C— It is the minimum vector altitude for radar vectors in
the sector southeast of PUC between 020° and 290°
magnetic bearing to PUC VOR.

**7-31. Answer A. GFDIC 7A, Approach Chart Legend,
AIM**

The minimum safe/sector altitude (MSA) provides at
least 1,000 feet of clearance above the highest obstacle in that sector (25 NM from the navigation facility
unless some other distance is specified).

7-32   PLT083

(Refer to figure 230.)

The symbol on the plan view of the VOR/DME or
GPS-A procedure at Baldwin (7D3) represents a minimum safe/sector altitude within 25 NM of

A— DEANI intersection.

B— Baldwin Municipal Airport.

C— White Cloud VOR/DME.

**7-32. Answer C. GFDIC 7A, Approach Chart Legend,
AIM**

The minimum safe/sector altitude (MSA) provides at
least 1,000 feet of clearance above the highest obstacle
in that sector (25 NM from the navigation facility unless
some other distance is specified). The MSA is shown in
a circle on the plan view – in this case in the lower right
corner. At Baldwin Municipal Airport the MSA is valid
for within 25 nautical miles of White Cloud VOR/DME
(HIC) as indicated in text above the circle and shown as
a VOR/DME symbol in the center of the circle.

7-33   PLT083

(Refer to figure 188.)

When conducting a missed approach from the LOC/
DME RWY 21 approach at PDX, what is the minimum
safe/sector altitude (MSA) while maneuvering between
the runway and BTG VORTAC?

A— 4,400 feet MSL.

B— 3,500 feet MSL.

C— 6,200 feet MSL.

7-33. Answer B. GFDIC 7A, AIM

When performing a missed approach, you should climb
to the altitude indicated in the missed approach procedure (in this case, 4,200 feet). The minimum safe/
sector altitude (MSA) is designed only for use in an
emergency or during VFR flight, such as during a VFR
approach at night. The MSA for the sector between the
runway and BTG VORTAC is 3,500 feet MSL as indicated by the MSA circle in the upper left corner of the
plan view.

7-34   **PLT083**

(Refer to figure 244.)

What are the course reversal restrictions on the LDA RWY 6 approach at Roanoke Regional?

A– The proper entry procedure must be used and the holding pattern course reversal must be flown as depicted with one minute legs.

B– The type of turn is optional but the airplane must remain within 10 NM of EXUNE and on the south side of the approach course.

C– The holding pattern course reversal must be flown with optional leg length as long as the airplane remains within 15.4 NM of EXUNE.

7-34. Answer A. GFDIC 7A, Approach Chart Legend
When a holding pattern is published as a course reversal, you must make the proper entry and follow the depicted pattern to establish the airplane on the inbound course. One minute legs are specified in both the chart plan and profile views.

7-35   **PLT083**

(Refer to figure 244.)

What is a restriction regarding circle-to-land procedures for LDA RWY 6 approach at Roanoke Regional?

A– Circling to Runway 24 not authorized.

B– Circling not authorized NW of RWY 6-24.

C– Visibility increased 1 mile for circling approach.

7-35. Answer B. GFDIC 7A, Approach Chart Legend
The notes and limitations box of the pilot briefing information states that circling is not authorized NW of Runway 6-24 and circling to land on Runway 16 is also not authorized.

7-36   **PLT083**

(Refer to figure 244.)

What are the landing minimums for a category A airplane flying the LDA RWY 6 approach without the glide slope at Roanoke Regional/Woodrum Field? SKIRT can be identified.

A– 2,720 feet MSL and 1½ SM visibility.

B– 1,605 feet MSL and 1 SM visibility.

C– 1,780 feet MSL and 1 SM visibility.

7-36. Answer C. GFDIC 7A, Approach Chart Legend
The landing minimums sections specifies minimums for flying the LDA RWY 6 approach with and without glide slope. If you can identify SKIRT OM for the LDA approach without the glide slope, you may use the lower minimums of 1,780 feet MSL and 1 SM visibility.

7-37   **PLT083**
(Refer to figure 244.)

How should the pilot identify the missed approach point for the S-LDA/GS 6 approach to Roanoke Regional?

A– Arrival at 1,605 feet on the glide slope.

B– Arrival at JOKNI.

C– Time expired for distance from RAMKE to JOKNI.

7-37. Answer A. GFDIC 7A, Approach Chart Legend
The S-LDA GS 6 approach requires use of the glide slope. The missed approach point is the decision altitude (DA), which is shown in the landing minimums section as 1,605 feet MSL for S-LDA/GS 6

7-38   **PLT083**
(Refer to figure 170.)

What are the landing minimums for a category A airplane flying the ILS RWY 33 approach with the Dallas-Love Field altimeter setting?

A– 933 feet MSL and 1 SM visibility.

B– 894 feet MSL and 1 SM visibility.

C– 1,240 feet MSL and 1 SM visibility.

7-38 Answer A. GFDIC 7A, Approach Chart Legend
The notes and limitations box of the pilot briefing information section states that if you cannot receive the local altimeter setting on UNICOM, you must use the Dallas-Love Field altimeter setting and increase all DAs by 39 feet. The DA shown in the landing minimums section for the S-ILS 33 approach is 894 feet MSL (894 + 39 = 933).

7-39   **PLT083**
(Refer to figure 131.)

The control tower at BOS reports "tall vessels" in the approach area. What are the VOR/DME RNAV RWY 4R straight-in approach minimums for Category A aircraft.

A– 890/24.

B– 840/40.

C– 890/40.

7-39. Answer B. GFDIC 7A, Approach Chart Legend
In the heading section on the figure it states when the control tower reports tall vessels in approach area; increase S-4R Cat A visibility to RVR 4000. The Category A straight in minimums for the VOR/DME RNAV RWY 4R are 840/24, with the tall vessels in the area you should have an RVR of 4000.

7-40   **PLT083**
(Refer to figure 131.)

What is the landing distance available for the VOR/DME RNAV RWY 4R approach at BOS?

A– 7,000 feet.

B– 10,005 feet.

C– 8,850 feet.

7-40. Answer C. GFDIC 7A, Approach Chart Legend
Runway length depicted on the chart is the physical length of the runway (end-to-end, including displaced thresholds) but excluding areas designated as stopways. Where a displaced threshold is shown and/or part of the runway is otherwise not available for landing an annotation placed above the runway diagram is added to indicated the landing length of the runway.

7-41   **PLT083**
(Refer to figure 131.)

During a missed approach from the VOR/DME RNAV RWY 4R approach at BOS, what course should be flown to the missed approach holding waypoint?

A– 033°.

B– 036°.

C– Runway heading.

7-41. Answer A. GFDIC 7A, Approach Chart Legend
The profile view of the chart shown in the figure shows missed approach instructions and a heading of 033° and 3,000 feet to the WAXEN holding fix.

7-42   **PLT083**
(Refer to figure 131.)

Other than VOR/DME RNAV, what additional navigation equipment is required to conduct the VOR/DME RNAV RWY 4R approach at BOS?

A– None.

B– VNAV.

C– Transponder with altitude encoding and Marker Beacon.

7-42. Answer A. GFDIC 7A, IFH, Approach Chart Legend
The minimum equipment required to fly the approach is indicated by the procedure title and/or notes on the approach chart.

7-43   **PLT382**
Which procedure should be followed by a pilot who is circling to land in a Category B airplane, but is maintaining a speed 5 knots faster than the maximum specified for that category?

A– Use the approach minimums appropriate for Category C.

B– Use Category B minimums.

C– Use Category D minimums since they apply to all circling approaches.

7-43. Answer A. GFDIC 7A, IFH
Obstacle clearance for circling approaches is based on turning radius, which is directly related to speed. Therefore, you should use the approach minimums for the category speeds you are using.

7-44   PLT292
How can an IAF be identified on a Standard Instrument Approach Procedure (SIAP) Chart?

A– All fixes that are labeled IAF.

B– Any fix illustrated within the 10 mile ring other than the FAF or stepdown fix.

C– The procedure turn and the fixes on the feeder facility ring.

7-44. Answer A. GFDIC 7A, Approach Chart Legend
Initial approach fixes (IAFs) are labeled with the letters "IAF."

7-45   PLT083
(Refer to figure 131.)

What determines the MAP for the straight-in VOR/DME RNAV RWY 4R approach at BOS?

A– RULSY waypoint.

B– .5 NM to RULSY waypoint.

C– 2.5 NM to RULSY at 840 feet MSL.

7-45. Answer B. GFDIC 7A, Approach Chart Legend
The profile view of the VOR/DME RNAV RWY 4R approach chart shows the missed approach profile beginning at 0.5 NM from RULSY waypoint, There is also a note in the plan view, which indicates the MAP is 0.5 NM from RULSY WP.

7-46   PLT382
RVR minimums for landing are prescribed in an IAP, but RVR is inoperative and cannot be reported for the intended runway at the time. Which of the following would be an operational consideration?

A– RVR minimums which are specified in the procedures should be converted and applied as ground visibility.

B– RVR minimums may be disregarded, providing the runway has an operative HIRL system.

C– RVR minimums may be disregarded, providing all other components of the ILS system are operative.

7-46. Answer A. GFDIC 7A, IFH, FAR 91.175
When the runway visual range (RVR) equipment is inoperative or not reported, you may covert RVR minimums to ground visibility in statute miles. The conversions are listed in a table in the Terminal Procedures Publication.

7-47   **PLT382**

Aircraft approach categories are based on

A– certificated approach speed at maximum gross weight.

B– 1.3 times the stall speed in landing configuration at maximum gross landing weight.

C– 1.3 times the stall speed at maximum gross weight.

7-47. Answer B. GFDIC 7A, IFH

Approach categories are based on computed approach speeds, which are 1.3 V_{S0}. This is 1.3 times the aircraft's power-off stall speed in the landing configuration at the maximum certificated landing weight.

7-48   **PLT292**

Which fixes on the IAP Charts are initial approach fixes?

A– Any fix on the en route facilities ring, the feeder facilities ring, and those at the start of arc approaches.

B– Only the fixes at the start of arc approaches and those on either the feeder facilities ring or en route facilities ring that have a transition course shown to the approach procedure.

C– Any fix that is identified by the letters IAF.

7-48. Answer C. GFDIC 7A, AIM

Initial approach fixes are specifically indicated on approach procedure charts with the letters "IAF."

7-49   **PLT382**

If the RVR is not reported, what meteorological value should you substitute for 2,400 RVR?

A– A ground visibility of 1/2 NM.

B– A slant range visibility of 2,400 feet for the final approach segment of the published approach procedure.

C– A ground visibility of 1/2 SM.

7-49. Answer C. GFDIC 7A, Approach Chart Legend, FAR 91.175

The Terminal Procedures Publication contains a table in the front of each volume to convert RVR to miles. Using this table, you will find that 2400 RVR is equivalent to 1/2 SM ground visibility.

7-50 PLT382
The RVR minimums for takeoff or landing are published in an IAP, but RVR is inoperative and cannot be reported for the runway at the time. Which of the following would apply?

A– RVR minimums which are specified in the procedure should be converted and applied as ground visibility.

B– RVR minimums may be disregarded, providing the runway has an operative HIRL system.

C– RVR minimums may be disregarded, providing all other components of the ILS system are operative.

7-50. Answer A. GFDIC 7A, Approach Chart Legend, FAR 91.175
Use the table in the Terminal Procedures Publication to convert RVR to prevailing visibility.

7-51 PLT382
If the RVR equipment is inoperative for an IAP that requires a visibility of 2,400 RVR, how should the pilot expect the visibility requirement to be reported in lieu of the published RVR?

A– As a slant range visibility of 2,400 feet.

B– As an RVR of 2,400 feet.

C– As a ground visibility of 1/2 SM.

7-51. Answer C. GFDIC 7A, FAR 91.175
Use a table in the Terminal Procedures Publication to convert RVR to miles. Using this table, you will find that 2400 RVR is equivalent to 1/2 SM ground visibility.

7-52 PLT455
An airport may not be qualified for alternate use if

A– the airport has AWOS-3 weather reporting.

B– the airport is located next to a restricted or prohibited area.

C– the navaids used for the final approach are unmonitored.

7-52. Answer C. GFDIC 7A, IPH
Not all airports can be used as alternate airports. An airport may not qualify as an alternate if the airport navaid is unmonitored or is GPS based, or if weather reporting capabilities are not available. To use an airport as an alternate, the forecast weather at the airport must meet certain qualifications at the estimated time of arrival. Standard alternate minimums for a precision approach are a 600-foot ceiling and 2 SM visibility. For a non-precision approach, the minimums are an 800-foot ceiling and 2 SM visibility. Standard alternate minimums apply unless higher alternate minimums are listed for an airport.

7-53 PLT077
(Refer to figure 156.)

Where would you find the charted location of each hot spot at Centennial Airport (APA) in Denver Colorado?

A– On the airport diagram chart for APA.

B– In the *Airport/Facility Directory*.

C– On the ILS RWY 35 instrument approach chart for APA.

7-53. Answer A. GFDIC 7A, Airport Diagram Legend
In addition to the airport sketch on approach charts, a full page airport diagram is provided for selected airports where complex runway and taxiway configurations exist. The airport diagram shows locations of runway incursion hot spots on runways and taxiways. The Hot Spots section of the Terminal Procedures Publication provides detailed information for each hot spot on the airport diagram.

7-54 PLT077
(Refer to figure 178.)

What does the Y indicate in the procedure title of the ILS or LOC Y RWY 13L approach?

A– The procedure does not meet the criteria for a straight-in landing.

B– Two or more approaches use the same primary navigation source for Runway 13L.

C– Simultaneous approaches are authorized with Runway 13R.

7-54. Answer B. GFDIC 7A, Approach Chart Legend
If two or more approaches use the same primary navigation source for a particular runway, a letter (starting with Z and working back through the alphabet) appears in the procedure title.

7-55 PLT077
(Refer to figure 179.)

During the ILS RWY 31 procedure at RBD, the minimum altitude for glide slope interception is

A– 2,182 feet MSL.

B– 1,100 feet MSL.

C– 2,200 feet MSL.

7-55. Answer C. GFDIC 7A, Approach Chart Legend
The glide slope intercept altitude of 2,200 feet MSL is designated by the lightning bolt symbol on the profile view. Because it is underlined, it is a minimum altitude.

7-56   **PLT077**
(Refer to figure 180.)

During the LOC/DME RWY 34 approach, what is the procedure for the final descent?

A— At MYKES descend from 2,000 feet MSL to 1,060 feet MSL. After reaching 2.4 DME, descend to land if the required visual references are in sight.

B— At MYKES, descend to 797 feet MSL and land if the required visual references are in sight.

C— At MYKES descend from 2,000 feet MSL to 1,060 feet MSL. After passing 2.4 DME, descend to 797 feet MSL to 1.1 DME. Then, descend to land if the required visual references are in sight.

7-56. Answer A. GFDIC 7A, Approach Chart Legend
The symbol at 2.4 DME indicates a visual descent point (VDP). A VDP is the point from which you can make a normal descent to landing if you have the required visual references in sight and you are starting from the MDA. Remain at the MDA of 1,060 feet MSL until you reach 2.4 DME to ensure you clear terrain or obstacles before descending to land.

7-57   **PLT077**
(Refer to figures 180 and 181.)

What frequency should be used to obtain an IFR clearance if departing Arlington Municipal Airport at 0600 local standard time?

A— 135.975

B— 121.875

C— 118.85

7-57. Answer C. GFDIC 7A, Approach Chart Legend
The asterisk next to the control tower frequency on the approach chart indicates that the Arlington tower operates part time. The A/FD indicates that the tower operates from 1300 to 0300Z. Subtract 6 hours (as shown in the first line of the A/FD excerpt) to obtain the local operating time of 0700 to 2100. If you leave at 0600, the tower will be closed and you must obtain your clearance from Regional Approach Control on 118.85 as indicated in the Communications sections of the approach chart and A/FD.

7-58   **PLT077**
(Refer to figures 185 and 186.)

What is the appropriate tower frequency to use when flying the ILS RWY 10R approach?

A— 118.7

B— 123.775

C— 124.35

7-58. Answer B. GFDIC 7A, Approach Chart Legend
The airport frequencies are listed in the communications sections of the both the airport diagram and the approach chart. The tower frequency specified for Runway 10R-28L is 123.775.

7-59   PLT077

(Refer to figure 219.)

What does the A indicate in the procedure title of the RNAV (GPS)-A approach?

A– The procedure does not meet the criteria for a straight-in landing.

B– Two or more approaches use the same primary navigation source for approaches at the airport.

C– The approach procedure is not authorized at night.

7-59. Answer A. GFDIC 7A, Approach Chart Legend
When a procedure title has an alphabetical suffix, such as VOR-A, it means the procedure does not meet the criteria for a straight-in landing. A circling approach is required to complete the landing and only circling landing minimums are published.

7-60   PLT077

(Refer to figure 222.)

In which situation is flying the holding pattern course reversal necessary?

A– On a course of 136° from FIM VORTAC.

B– On a course of 054° from VTU VOR/DME.

C– On a course of 311° from SMO VOR/DME to SILEX.

7-60. Answer C. GFDIC 7A, Approach Chart Legend
You must enter the holding pattern to reverse your course at SILEX IAF when flying on a course of 311° from SMO VOR/DME. The courses from FIM and VTU indicate "NoPT" which means that no course reversal is required from these IAFs.

7-61   PLT354

(Refer to figure 233.)

What is a restriction for performing the RNAV (GPS) RWY 17 approach?

A– The approach to LPV minimums is not authorized if the temperature is below −17°C (2°F) or above 24°C (114°F).

B– Performing a procedure turn is not authorized.

C– The approach procedure is not authorized when arriving from ADM VORTAC.

7-61. Answer B. GFDIC 7A, Approach Chart Legend
A procedure turn is not authorized for this approach as indicated by the notation in the profile view (Procedure Turn NA). This applies to the entry from any location.

7-62   PLT038
(Refer to figure 245.)

What does the B indicate in the procedure title of the RNAV (GPS)-B approach?

A– Two or more approaches use the same primary navigation source for approaches at the airport.

B– Simultaneous approach procedure may be in operation with this approach procedure.

C– The procedure may only be flown to circling minimums.

7-62. Answer C. GFDICM 7A, Approach Chart Legend
When a procedure title has an alphabetical suffix, such as RNAV (GPS)-B, it means the procedure does not meet the criteria for a straight-in landing. A circling approach is required to complete the landing and only circling minimums are published.

7-63   PLT038
(Refer to figure 250.)

What is a consideration for flying the GPS RWY 3 approach at night?

A– Pilot-controlled lighting for Runway 3 must be activated on 122.8

B–.All MDAs are increased by 40 feet for approaches at night.

C– The procedure is not authorized at night.

7-63. Answer C. GFDICM 7A, Approach Chart Legend
The notes and limitations box of the pilot briefing information states that the GPS RWY 3 approach procedure is not authorized at night. Runway 3 does not have pilot-controlled approach lighting as indicated in the airport sketch.

7-64   PLT077
(Refer to figure 251.)

At what location at Oshkosh/Wittman Regional Airport does an increased risk of collision or runway incursion exist?

A– No increased risk exists at this airport.

B– At the intersection of Taxiways B and B1.

C– At the intersection of Runway 22 and Taxiway E.

7-64. Answer B. GFDICM 7A, Approach Chart Legend
Two runway incursion hot spots are circled on the airport diagram and are referenced by the callouts HS 1 and HS 2. HS 1 indicates that an increased risk of collision exists at the intersection of Taxiways B and B1.

7-65   **PLT038**
(Refer to figure 252.)

During the ILS RWY 36 procedure at OSH, the minimum altitude for glide slope interception is

A– 2,700 feet MSL.

B– 2,610 feet MSL.

C– 1,008 feet MSL.

7-65. Answer A. GFDICM 7A, Approach Chart Legend
The glide slope intercept altitude of 2,700 feet MSL is designated by the lightning bolt symbol on the profile view. Because it is underlined, it is a minimum altitude.

7-66   **PLT281**
(Refer to figures 224 and 226.)

What is true about the runway lighting for Runway 16 at Lake County Airport in Leadville, CO?

A– The PAPI on the right side of the runway and the MIRL and can be activated on 122.8.

B– The PAPI on the left side of the runway and the MIRL can be activated on 122.8.

C– The PAPI on the left side of the runway and the MIRL can be activated on 119.85.

7-66. Answer B. GFDICM 7A, Approach Chart Legend, A/FD Legend
Runway 16 has pilot-controlled lighting which is indicated by the "L" symbol on the approach chart and on the airport sketch. The airport sketch also indicates that the PAPI is located on the left side of the Runway 16. The Communications section of the approach chart and the A/FD Airport Remarks indicate that the lighting can be activated on the CTAF of 122.8.

SECTION B — APPROACH PROCEDURES

PREPARING FOR AN APPROACH

- After you have been advised as to which approach to expect, you should conduct a thorough approach chart review to familiarize yourself with the specific approach procedure.
- If ATC does not specify a particular approach but states, "cleared for approach," you may execute any one of the authorized IAPs for that airport.
- Feeder routes provide a transition from the enroute structure to the IAF or to a facility from which a course reversal is initiated.

STRAIGHT-IN APPROACH AND LANDING

- The terms straight-in approach and straight-in landing have specific definitions when used in ATC clearances or in reference to landing minimums.
- A straight-in approach may be initiated from a fix closely aligned with the final approach course, may commence from the completion of a DME arc, or you may receive vectors to the final approach course.
- A straight-in approach does not require nor authorize a procedure turn or course reversal.
- A NoPT arrival sector allows flights inbound on Victor airways within the sector to proceed straight in on the final approach course.

RADAR PROCEDURES

- ATC radar approved for approach control service is used for course guidance to the final approach course, ASR and PAR approaches, and the monitoring of nonradar approaches.
- Radar vectors to the final approach course provide a method of intercepting and proceeding inbound on the published instrument approach procedure. During an instrument approach procedure, a published course reversal is not required when radar vectors are provided.
- If it becomes apparent the heading assigned by ATC will cause you to pass through the final approach course, you should maintain that heading and question the controller.

COURSE REVERSALS

- A course reversal may be depicted on a chart as a procedure turn, a racetrack pattern (holding pattern), or a teardrop procedure. If a teardrop or holding pattern is shown on an approach chart, you must execute the course reversal as depicted. The maximum speed in a course reversal is 200 knots IAS.
- Course reversals must be completed within the distance specified on the chart which is typically 10 nautical miles from the primary navaid or fix indicated on the approach chart.
- When more than one circuit of a holding pattern is needed to lose altitude or become better established on course, the additional circuits can be made only if you advise ATC and ATC approves.

TIMED APPROACHES

- Timed approaches from a holding fix are generally conducted at airports where the radar system for traffic sequencing is out of service or is not available and numerous aircraft are waiting for approach clearance. This can only be conducted at airports which have operating control towers.
- If more than one missed approach procedure is available, a timed approach from a holding fix may be conducted if none require a course reversal. If only one missed approach procedure is available, a timed approach from a holding fix may be conducted if the reported ceiling and visibility minimums are equal to or greater than the highest prescribed circling minimums for the IAP.

- When timed approaches are in progress, you will be given advance notice of the time you should leave the holding fix. When making a timed approach from a holding pattern at the outer marker, adjust the holding pattern so you will leave the outer marker inbound at the assigned time.

DESCENDING ON THE APPROACH

- When you are cleared for an approach while being radar vectored, you must maintain your last assigned altitude until established on a segment of the published approach. If you are above the altitude designated for the course reversal, you may begin descent as soon as you cross the IAF.
- Normally, you should descend at a rate that allows you to reach the MDA prior to the MAP so that you are in a position to establish a normal rate of descent from the MDA to the runway, using normal maneuvers.
- To descend below the DH or MDA, you must be able to identify specific visual references, as well as comply with visibility and operating requirements which are listed in FAR 91.175.
- VASI lights can help you maintain the proper descent angle to the runway once you have established visual contact with the runway environment. If a glide slope malfunction occurs during an ILS approach and you have the VASI in sight, you may continue the approach using the VASI glide slope in place of the electronic glideslope.
- Visual illusions are the product of various runway conditions, terrain features, and atmospheric phenomena which can create the sensation of incorrect height above the runway or incorrect distance from the runway threshold. When landing on a narrower-than-usual runway, the aircraft will appear to be higher than actual, leading to a lower-than-normal approach. An upsloping runway creates the same illusion.

CIRCLING AND SIDESTEP MANEUVERS

- A circling approach is necessary if the instrument approach course is not aligned within 30° of the runway. In addition, you may find that an unfavorable wind or a runway closure makes a circling approach necessary.
- Each circling approach is confined to a protected area which varies with aircraft approach category.
- When executing a circling approach, if you operate at a higher speed than is designated for your aircraft approach category, you should use the minimums of the next higher category.
- Some approaches have only circling minimums published even when aligned with the runway. You may still execute a straight-in landing if you have the runway in sight in sufficient time to make a normal approach for landing and you have been cleared to land.
- When cleared to execute a sidestep maneuver, you are expected to fly the approach to the primary runway and begin the approach to a landing on the parallel runway as soon as possible after you have it in sight.

MISSED APPROACHES

- The most common reason for a missed approach is low visibility conditions that do not permit you to establish required visual cues.
- If an early missed approach is initiated before reaching the MAP, you should proceed to the missed approach point at or above the MDA or DH before executing a turning maneuver.
- If you lose visual reference while circling to land from an instrument approach and ATC radar service is not available, you should initiate a missed approach by making a climbing turn toward the landing runway and continue the turn until established on the missed approach course.

VISUAL AND CONTACT APPROACHES

- If the ceiling is at least 1,000 feet AGL and visibility is at least 3 statute miles, ATC may clear you for a visual approach in lieu of the published approach procedure.
- ATC can issue a clearance for a contact approach upon your request when the reported ground visibility at the airport is 1 statute mile or greater. ATC cannot initiate a contact approach.
- Charted Visual Flight Procedures (CVFPs) may be established at some controlled airports for environmental or noise considerations, as well as when necessary for the safety and efficiency of air traffic operations.

7-67   **PLT420**

How is your flight plan closed when your destination airport has IFR conditions and there is no control tower or flight service station (FSS) on the field?

A– The ARTCC controller will close your flight plan when you report the runway in sight.

B– You may close your flight plan any time after starting the approach by contacting any FSS or ATC facility.

C– Upon landing, you must close your flight plan by radio or by telephone to any FSS or ATC facility.

7-67. Answer C. GFDIC 7B, AIM

When landing at an airport without a control tower, you are responsible for closing your IFR flight plan. If the weather conditions are below VFR at the destination airport, you can close your flight plan by radio or telephone to any flight service station or ATC facility.

7-68   **PLT420**

If only one missed approach procedure is available, which of the following conditions is required when conducting "timed approaches from a holding fix"?

A– The pilot must contact the airport control tower prior to departing the holding fix inbound.

B– The reported ceiling and visibility minimums must be equal to or greater than the highest prescribed circling minimums for the IAP.

C– The reported ceiling and visibility minimums must be equal to or greater than the highest prescribed straight-in MDA minimums for the IAP.

7-68. Answer B. GFDIC 7B, AIM

When only one missed approach procedure is available, the weather must be at or above circling minimums for the approach.

7-69   **PLT420**

Prior to conducting "timed approaches from a holding fix," which one of the following is required:

A– The time required to fly from the primary facility to the field boundary must be determined by a reliable means.

B– The airport where the approach is to be conducted must have a control tower in operation.

C– The pilot must have established two-way communications with the tower before departing the holding fix.

7-69. Answer B. GFDIC 7B, AIM

A control tower must be in operation at an airport where timed approaches from a holding fix are being conducted.

7-70   PLT170
When making a "timed approach" from a holding fix at the outer marker, the pilot should adjust the

A– holding pattern to start the procedure turn at the assigned time.

B– airspeed at the final approach fix in order to arrive at the missed approach point at the assigned time.

C– holding pattern to leave the final approach fix inbound at the assigned time.

7-70. Answer C. GFDIC 7B, AIM
The pilot is expected to adjust the holding pattern in order to leave the final approach fix inbound at the assigned time.

7-71   PLT170
If the pilot loses visual reference while circling to land from an instrument approach and ATC radar service is not available, the missed approach action should be to

A– execute a climbing turn to parallel the published final approach course and climb to the initial approach altitude.

B– climb to the published circling minimums then proceed direct to the final approach fix.

C– make a climbing turn toward the landing runway and continue the turn until established on the missed approach course.

7-71. Answer C. GFDIC 7B, AIM
An initial climbing turn toward the landing runway should enable the aircraft to remain within the circling and missed approach obstacle clearance areas. The pilot should then intercept and fly the missed approach course.

7-72   PLT170
When the approach procedure involves a procedure turn, the maximum speed should not be greater than

A– 180 knots IAS.

B– 200 knots IAS.

C– 250 knots IAS.

7-72. Answer B. GFDIC 7B, AIM
During a procedure turn, the maximum speed of 200 knots indicated should be observed.

7-73   **PLT420**

While being radar vectored, an approach clearance is received. The last assigned altitude should be maintained until

A– reaching the FAF.

B– advised to begin descent.

C– established on a segment of a published route or IAP.

7-73. Answer C. GFDIC 7B, AIM
To ensure obstacle clearance, the pilot should maintain the last assigned altitude until established on a segment of a published route or approach procedure.

7-74   **PLT083**
(Refer to figure 232.)

What options are available concerning the course reversal for LOC RWY 35 approach to Duncan/Halliburton Field?

A– The type of turn is optional as long as it is made within 10 NM of GYROE on the same side as the procedure turn symbol.

B– The turn must be performed using the headings depicted within 10 NM of GYROE.

C– The type of turn is optional as long as it is made within 10 NM of the airport.

7-74. Answer A. GFDIC 7B, AIM
When the procedure turn symbol is shown, you may reverse course any way that you want to as long as you turn on the same side of the course as the procedure turn symbol and remain within the distance from the designated fix shown on the profile view.

7-75   **PLT083**
(Refer to figure 232.)

When flying the LOC RWY 35 approach at Duncan/Halliburton Airport, the point on the procedure turn where the turn inbound is initiated is determined by

A– DME and timing to remain within the 10-NM limit.

B– Timing for a 2 minute maximum.

C– Estimating groundspeed and radius of turn.

7-75. Answer A. GFDIC 7B, AIM
When the procedure turn symbol is shown, you may reverse course any way that you want to as long as you turn on the same side of the course as the procedure turn symbol and remain within the distance from the designated fix shown on the profile view. Use DME or timing to remain within the 10-NM limit.

7-76   PLT420
(Refer to figure 234.)

If your aircraft was cleared for the ILS RWY 18 at Lincoln Municipal and crossed the Lincoln VOR at 5,000 feet MSL, at what point in the teardrop could a descent to 3,200 feet commence?

A– As soon as intercepting LOC inbound.

B– Immediately.

C– Only at the point authorized by ATC.

7-76. Answer B. GFDIC 7B, AIM
As soon as you cross the IAF to commence the procedure turn, you may start your descent to the course reversal altitude (3,200 feet). You must maintain this altitude until intercepting the localizer inbound..

7-77   PLT420
(Refer to figure 234.)

If cleared for the ILS 18 approach at Lincoln Municipal from over HUSKR, it means the flight should

A– land straight in on runway 18.

B– comply with straight-in landing minimums.

C– begin final approach without making a procedure turn.

7-77. Answer C. GFDIC 7B, AIM
The route from HUSKR is marked "NoPT," which means that a procedure turn is not authorized. You would intercept the localizer and fly the final approach inbound. Straight-in landing minimums apply if you are not circling to land on another runway. In contrast to a straight-in landing, a straight-in approach means that you should not perform any published procedure to reverse your course, which is the case in this example.

7-78   PLT420
(Refer to figure 236.)

If cleared for a straight-in LOC approach from over OALDY, it means the flight should

A– land straight in on Runway 31.

B– comply with straight-in landing minimums.

C– begin final approach without making a procedure turn.

7-78. Answer C. GFDIC 7B, AIM
You would intercept the localizer and fly the final approach inbound without making a procedure turn. Straight-in landing minimums apply if you are not circling to land on another runway. In contrast to a straight-in landing, a straight-in approach means that you should not perform any published procedure to reverse your course, which is the case in this example.

7-79   PLT420

If an early missed approach is initiated before reaching the MAP, the following procedure should be used unless otherwise cleared by ATC.

A– Proceed to the missed approach point at or above the MDA or DH before executing a turning maneuver.

B– Begin a climbing turn immediately and follow missed approach procedures.

C– Maintain altitude and continue past MAP for 1 minute or 1 mile whichever occurs first.

7-79. Answer A. GFDIC 7B, AIM
Since obstacle clearance is not guaranteed for a turn prior to the MAP, you should fly the approach to the MAP before turning. Altitude should be at or above the published minimums.

7-80   PLT420

When more than one circuit of the holding pattern is needed to lose altitude or become better established on course, the additional circuits can be made

A– at pilot's discretion.

B– only in an emergency.

C– only if pilot advises ATC and ATC approves.

7-80. Answer C. GFDIC 7B, AIM
When cleared for an approach by ATC, you are expected to commence the approach inbound without additional turns in holding. If extra circuits in the holding pattern are needed, you must receive approval from ATC.

7-81   PLT420

When simultaneous approaches are in progress, how does each pilot receive radar advisories?

A– On tower frequency.

B– On approach control frequency.

C– One pilot on tower frequency and the other on approach control frequency.

7-81. Answer A. GFDIC 8B, AIM
At some point on the final approach, pilots are instructed to monitor the tower frequency. The radar controller has the capability to override the tower controller on the tower frequency to issue advisories, if required.

7-82   **PLT420**

During an instrument approach, under what conditions, if any, is the holding pattern course reversal not required?

A– When radar vectors are provided.

B– When cleared for the approach.

C– None, since it is always mandatory.

7-82. Answer A. GFDIC 7B, AIM
When a holding pattern is used in lieu of a procedure turn, it must be followed, except when "NoPT" is shown or when you are given radar vectors.

7-83   **PLT430**

During an instrument precision approach, terrain and obstacle clearance depends on adherence to

A– minimum altitude shown on the IAP.

B– terrain contour information.

C– natural and man-made reference point information.

7-83. Answer A. GFDIC 7B, AIM
The instrument approach procedures are designed to provide terrain and obstacle clearance if you observe the depicted altitudes, flight paths, and minimums.

7-84   **PLT420**
(Refer to figure 247.)

How should a pilot reverse course to get established on the inbound course of the ILS RWY 9, if radar vectoring or the three IAF's are not utilized?

A– Execute a standard 45° procedure turn toward Seal Beach VORTAC or Pomona VORTAC.

B– Make an appropriate entry to the depicted holding pattern at EXPAM INT.

C– Use any type of procedure turn, but remain within 10 NM of Riverside VOR.

7-84. Answer B. GFDIC 7B, AIM
When not utilizing one of the three IAFs or radar vectors for navigation to the final approach, you are expected to proceed to the holding fix and enter the depicted holding pattern at the EXPAM intersection (INT). A solid heavy line indicates that this is a holding pattern used in lieu of a procedure turn

7-85   PLT406

A pilot is making an ILS approach and is past the OM to a runway which has a VASI. What action should the pilot take if an electronic glide slope malfunction occurs and the pilot has the VASI in sight?

A– The pilot should inform ATC of the malfunction and then descend immediately to the localizer DH and make a localizer approach.

B– The pilot may continue the approach and use the VASI glide slope in place of the electronic glide slope.

C– The pilot must request an LOC approach, and may descend below the VASI at the pilot's discretion.

7-85. Answer B. GFDIC 7B, FAR 91.175, 91.129

When the ILS glide slope fails, you may continue the approach to localizer-only minimums, and, if you have sufficient visual references for the intended runway, may continue the approach visually. In this case, the VASI may be used, and you should follow the VASI glide path.

7-86   PLT420

You arrive at your destination airport on an IFR flight plan. Which is a prerequisite condition for the performance of a contact approach?

A– A ground visibility of at least 2 SM.

B– A flight visibility of at least 1/2 NM.

C– Clear of clouds and at least 1 SM flight visibility.

7-86. Answer C. GFDIC 3C, AIM

A contact approach cannot be initiated by ATC. This procedure may be used instead of the published procedure to expedite your arrival, as long as the airport has a standard or special instrument approach procedure, and you can remain clear of clouds with a reported visibility of at least 1 statute mile.

7-87   PLT420

You are being vectored to the ILS approach course, but have not been cleared for the approach. It becomes evident that you will pass through the localizer course. What action should be taken?

A– Turn outbound and make a procedure turn.

B– Continue on the assigned heading and query ATC.

C– Start a turn to the inbound heading and inquire if you are cleared for the approach.

7-87. Answer B. GFDIC 7B, AIM

Sometimes, ATC controllers will vector you through the final approach course to achieve traffic spacing. You should be informed of such an action; if not, maintain your heading and question the controller.

7-88   PLT221

When cleared to execute a published sidestep maneuver for a specific approach and landing on the parallel runway, at what point is the pilot expected to commence this maneuver?

A– At the published minimum altitude for a circling approach.

B– As soon as possible after the runway or runway environment is in sight.

C– At the localizer MDA minimum and when the runway is in sight.

7-88. Answer B. GFDIC 7B, AIM

To enhance traffic separation and obstacle clearance, you should maneuver to the parallel runway as soon as you have it or the runway environment in sight.

7-89   PLT420

When may a pilot make a straight-in landing, if using an IAP having only circling minimums?

A– A straight-in landing may not be made, but the pilot may continue to the runway at MDA and then circle to land on the runway.

B– The pilot may land straight-in if the runway is the active runway and he has been cleared to land.

C– A straight-in landing may be made if the pilot has the runway in sight in sufficient time to make a normal approach for landing, and has been cleared to land.

7-89. Answer C. GFDIC 7B, AIM

Circling minimums only are required when runway and final approach course alignment is exceeded by 30° or more. In this case, straight-in minimums are not published. However, if you have the runway in sight and no excessive maneuvering is required, you may continue straight in for landing. At a tower-controlled airport, you must also be cleared to land. At nontowered airports, it is a good practice to overfly the airport to observe traffic and wind indicators before landing.

7-90   PLT420

While being vectored, if crossing the ILS final approach course becomes imminent and an approach clearance has not been issued, what action should be taken by the pilot?

A– Turn outbound on the final approach course, execute a procedure turn, and inform ATC.

B– Turn inbound and execute the missed approach procedure at the outer marker if approach clearance has not been received.

C– Maintain the last assigned heading and query ATC.

7-90. Answer C. GFDIC 7B, AIM

Air traffic controllers will occasionally need to increase traffic separation by giving aircraft a vector through the ILS final approach course. You should be notified when this happens, but if not, maintain the last assigned heading and ask the controller for clarification.

7-91   PLT420

Which of the following conditions is required before "timed approaches from a holding fix" may be conducted?

A— If more than one missed approach procedure is available, only one may require a course reversal.

B— If more than one missed approach procedure is available, none may require a course reversal.

C— Direct communication between the pilot and the tower must be established prior to beginning the approach.

7-91. Answer B. GFDIC 7B, AIM

If more than one missed approach procedure is available, none of them can require a course reversal. Presumably, this will prevent conflicts with inbound traffic.

7-92   PLT420

Assume this clearance is received:

"CLEARED FOR ILS RUNWAY 07 LEFT APPROACH, SIDE-STEP TO RUNWAY 07 RIGHT."

When would the pilot be expected to commence the side-step maneuver?

A— As soon as possible after the runway environment is in sight.

B— Any time after becoming aligned with the final approach course of Runway 07 left, and after passing the final approach fix.

C— After reaching the circling minimums for Runway 07 right.

7-92. Answer A. GFDIC 7B, AIM

One benefit of a side-step is that it expedites arrivals of aircraft flying an ILS approach. For this reason, you should begin the side-step maneuver as soon as you can after establishing visual contact with the runway environment.

7-93   PLT280

Due to visual illusion, when landing on a

narrower-than-usual runway, the aircraft will appear to be

A— higher than actual, leading to a lower-than-normal approach.

B— lower than actual, leading to a higher-than-normal approach.

C— higher than actual, leading to a higher-than-normal approach.

7-93. Answer A. GFDIC 7B, IFH

A narrower-than-usual runway can create the illusion that you are higher than you actually are, leading to a lower approach.

7-94   **PLT280**

What visual illusion creates the same effect as a narrower-than-usual runway?

A– An unsloping runway.

B– A wider-than-usual runway.

C– A downsloping runway.

7-94. Answer A. GFDIC 7B, IFH
An upsloping runway can create the illusion that your aircraft is higher than it actually is, leading to a lower approach.

7-95   **PLT083**

(Refer to figure 49.)

When conducting the LOC/DME RWY 21 approach at PDX, what is the Minimum Safe Altitude (MSA) while maneuvering between the BTG VORTAC and CREAK intersection?

A– 3,400 feet MSL.

B– 5,700 feet MSL.

C– 6,200 feet MSL.

7-95. Answer C. GFDIC 7A, Approach Chart Legend
Between 300° and 120°, in the northeast sector, the MSA on the figure is 6,200 feet MSL. 3,500 feet MSL represents the southwest sector. 6,200 feet MSL represents the minimum altitude to be flown until reaching CREAK intersection inbound.

7-96   **PLT083**

(Refer to figure 49.)

You have been cleared to the CREAK intersection via the BTG 054° radial at 7,000 feet. Approaching CREAK, you are cleared for the LOC/DME RWY 21 approach to PDX. Descent to procedure turn altitude should not begin prior to

A– completion of the procedure turn, and established on the localizer.

B– CREAK outbound.

C– intercepting the glide slope.

7-96. Answer B. GFDIC 8B
Once cleared for the approach, if you are above the altitude designated for course reversal, you may begin descent as soon as you cross the IAF, which in this case, is CREAK Intersection.

7-97   **PLT083**

(Refer to figure 49.)

What is the usable runway length for landing on runway 21 at PDX?

A– 6,000 feet.

B– 7,000 feet.

C– 7,900 feet.

7-97. Answer A. GFDIC 8C

Runway length depicted on the chart is the physical length of the runway (end-to-end, including displaced thresholds) but excluding areas designated as stopways. Where a displaced threshold is shown and/or part of the runway is otherwise not available for landing an annotation placed above the runway diagram is added to indicated the landing length of the runway.

7-98   **PLT170**

(Refer to figure 250.) For a stabilized approach, the aircraft would be in a configuration for approach or landing and descending at about

A– 480 feet per minute to MDA.

B– 480 feet per nautical mile below 1,580 feet MSL.

C– a descent rate of less than 1,000 FPM below 1,080 feet MSL and bank angles of less than 15° below 500 feet AGL.

7-98. Answer C. GFDIC 7B, IPG, IPH

You should stabilize your approach by 1,000 feet above the airport elevation in IFR weather conditions and by 500 feet above the airport elevation in VFR weather conditions. Use a descent rate of less than 1,000 feet per minute and avoid excessive bank angles. To determine a specific rate of descent to fly a stabilized approach to the MDA, you must know the airplane's approach speed.

INSTRUMENT APPROACHES

SECTION A — VOR AND NDB APPROACHES

- VOR and NDB approaches primarily fall into two categories — those that use an on-airport facility and those with an off-airport facility. On approaches with on-airport navaids, the FAP often serves as the FAF.

- Preparation to fly an approach should begin well before flying the procedure. Determine which approaches are in use or likely to be in use at the destination airport, and review the approach procedures as early as possible. Obtain weather information, if possible, for the destination airport and analyze whether a successful approach is likely.

- ATC may clear you to fly the approach of your choice, but they will more likely clear you for a specific approach.

- A published procedure turn or similar course reversal is mandatory unless you are vectored to the final approach course by ATC, or unless your particular approach transition indicates NoPT. Typically, you accomplish a course reversal by flying outbound for two minutes, turning to a charted heading 45° left or right of your outbound course and flying for one minute, then making a 180° opposite direction turn back to re-intercept the inbound course.

- When cleared for an approach, you generally should descend promptly to the minimum altitude published for your current route segment or approach transition, or other altitude assigned by ATC.

- Complete your before landing checklist prior to the FAF, or if there is no FAF, before intercepting the final approach course. If you have retractable landing gear, it is generally best to extend it when starting your descent inbound to the FAF.

- Make sure you know what rate of descent is required to reach stepdown altitudes or the MDA by the appropriate time. If you do not have the runway environment in sight when reaching the MDA, or if you lose sight of it at any time while circling, it is imperative that you immediately execute the missed approach procedure.

- If you do not have the runway environment in sight when reaching the MDA, or if you lose sight of it at any time while circling, it is imperative that you immediately execute the missed approach procedure.

- If you have the runway environment in sight with the required visibility, you may land. Do not descend below the MDA until you are in a position from which you can safely descend for landing.

- When executing a missed approach, notify ATC, and, depending on your circumstances, request a clearance to fly the approach again, or request a clearance to your alternate.

- DME is required on certain approaches that indicate DME in the procedure title. Even on those approaches that do not require DME, using DME to identify stepdown fixes may allow lower minimums.

- NDB approach procedures are similar to VOR approaches. However, the precision with which you complete the approach is dependent on your skill in ADF tracking and on the accuracy of your heading indicator.

8-1   PLT083

(Refer to figure 127.)

If cleared for NDB RWY 28 approach (Lancaster/Fairfield) over ZZV VOR, the flight would be expected to

Category A aircraft

Last assigned altitude 3,000 feet

A— proceed straight in from CRISY, descending to MDA after CASER.

B— proceed to CRISY, then execute the teardrop procedure as depicted on the approach chart.

C— proceed direct to CASER, then straight in to S-28 minimums of 1620-1.

8-1. Answer A. GFDIC 8A, AIM

Near the ZZV VOR is the note "NoPT." This indicates that a procedure turn is not authorized for an approach beginning at the ZZV IAF. You are expected to fly the published routing straight in from CRISY, and descend at the FAF to the S-28 (straight-in) minimums of 1,620 feet, using the published visibility of 1 SM

8-2   PLT420

(Refer to figure 240.)

At which points may you initiate a descent to the next lower minimum altitude when cleared for the VOR/DME RWY 36 approach, from the COPUK IAF?

A— Start descent from 8,900 when established on the PUC R-189, from 7,500 when at HUNIK (8.3 DME), from 7,500 at 1.4 DME, and from 6,240 when landing requirements are met.

B— Start descent from 8,900 when established on the PUC R-189, from 8,000 when at HUNIK (8.3 DME), from 7,500 at WELEN (5.1 DME), and from 6,240 when past 1.4 DME and when landing requirements are met.

C— Start descent from 8,900 at the R-164, from 8,000 when established on the final approach course, from 7,500 at WELEN (5.1 DME), and from 6,600 when landing requirements are met.

8-2. Answer B. GFDIC 8A, Approach Chart Legend

You remain at 8,900 feet while on the arc until established on the 189° radial inbound. Then, you may descend to 8,000 feet MSL. At HUNIK, you may descend to 7,500 feet MSL. And at WELEN, you may descend to the MDA of 6,240 fee MSL. Remain at the MDA until you are past the VDP of 1.4 DME. Then you may descend to land if landing requirements are met. The mimimum altitudes that you must maintain are shown on the plan view and the profile view. The MDA is shown in the landing minimums section.

8-3   PLT083

(Refer to figure 246.)

If you do not have the required visual references in sight, when should you initiate the missed approach procedure when on the final approach segment for the NDB-A approach?

A— After the time from WHIPS to 4.1 NM has elapsed based on your groundspeed.

B— Upon reaching the NAUSET NDB.

C— Upon reaching the DA of 600 feet MSL.

8-3. Answer A. GFDIC 8A, Approach Chart Legend, IFH

The missed approach point (MAP) is shown on the profile view as 4.1 NM from WHIPS. You must use the conversion table to determine the appropriate time to reach the MAP for your groundspeed.

SECTION B — ILS APPROACHES

OVERVIEW

- The instrument landing system (ILS) is a precision approach navigational aid which provides highly accurate course, glide slope, and distance guidance to a given runway. ILS approaches are classified as Category I, Category II, or Category III.

- The ILS localizer transmitter emits a navigational signal from the far end of the runway to provide you with information regarding your alignment with the runway centerline.

ILS COMPONENTS

- The basic components of an ILS approch are the localizer, glide slope, and the outer marker, compass locator, or fix identified in the approach procedure used to provide range information. An inner marker (IM) is installed at locations where Category II and III ILS operations have been certified.

- The approach procedure may use a compass locator, precision radar, surveillance radar, or published DME, VOR, or NDB fixes instead of an outer marker.

- The glide slope signal provides vertical navigation information for descent to the lowest authorized decision altitude for the associated approach procedure. The glide slope may not be reliable below decision altitude.

- If the glide slope is inoperative or fails during your approach, the localizer (GS out) minimums apply. In this case, you may continue the approach to the applicable MDA.

- Prior to intercepting the ILS glide slope, you should concentrate on stabilizing airspeed and altitude while establishing a magnetic heading which will maintain the aircraft on the localizer centerline. Once your descent rate stabilizes, use power as needed to maintain a constant approach speed.

- When a compass locator is installed in conjunction with the outer marker, it is called an outer compass locator (LOM). The LOM identifier is the first two letters of the localizer identifier.

- When the aircraft passes through the signal array of a marker beacon, a colored light flashes on the marker beacon receiver and a Morse code identification sounds. The outer marker is indicated by a blue light and a series of dashes.

- Certain approach and runway lighting configurations can qualify precision approaches for lower minimums. If an ILS visual aid is inoperative, the visibility requirements are raised on approaches where 1,800 RVR is authorized.

- Higher landing minimums may be required if some components of an ILS are inoperative. If more than one component is not available for use, you should adjust the minimums by applying only the greatest increase in altitude and/or visibility required by the failure of a single component.

INTERPRETING THE INSTRUMENTS

- When using a basic VOR indicator, normal sensing occurs inbound on the front course and outbound on the back course. Reverse sensing occurs inbound on the back course and outbound on the front course.

- You can avoid reverse sensing when using an HSI by setting the published inbound course under the course index. This applies regardless of your direction of travel, whether inbound or outbound on either the front or back course

- Full-scale deviation of the glide slope needle is 0.7° above or below the center of the glide slope beam.

FLYING THE APPROACH

- The rate of descent you must maintain to stay on glide slope must decrease if your groundspeed decreases, and vice versa. If the glide slope and localizer are centered but your airspeed is too fast, your initial adjustment should be to reduce power.

- Since localizer and glide slope indications become more sensitive as you get closer to the runway, you should strive to fly an ILS approach so that you do not need heading corrections greater than 2° after you have passed the outer marker.

- On an ILS approach, you must execute a missed approach if you have not established the required visual references at the DA.

- When advised to change to advisory frequency, you should broadcast your position and intentions on the CTAF.

PARALLEL AND SIMULTANEOUS APPROACHES

- Parallel (dependent) ILS approach operations may be conducted on parallel runways with centerlines at least 2,500 feet apart. Simultaneous (independent) parallel ILS approaches may be conducted to airports with parallel runway centerlines separated by 4,300 to 9,000 feet. When certain requirements are met, including the installation of a precision runway monitor, simultaneous close parallel ILS approach procedures may be established at airports with parallel runway centerlines less than 4,300 feet apart.

- You will be informed by ATC or through the ATIS broadcast if parallel approaches are in progress. A dependent parallel ILS approach provides aircraft with a minimum of 1.5 miles diagonal separation between successive aircraft on the adjacent localizer course if the runway is at least 2,500 feet but no more than 4,300 feet apart. From 4,300 feet to 9,000 feet apart the minimum diagonal separation is 2 miles.

- When simultaneous approaches are in progress, each pilot may receive radar advisories on the tower frequency.

OTHER APPROACH FACILITIES

- A localizer-type directional aid (LDA) is an approach system which uses a localizer course that is not aligned with the runway centerline. If the final approach course is aligned to within 30° of the runway centerline, straight-in landing minimums may be available. The LDA course width is between 3° and 6°.

- A simplified directional facility (SDF) course is fixed at either 6° or 12° wide. Since most SDF courses are aligned within 3° of the runway bearing, SDF approaches are typically published with straight-in minimums.

8-4   **PLT277**
What marker beacon indicator lights and code identifies an outer marker?

A– Blue – alternate dots and dashes.

B– White – dots.

C– Blue – dashes.

8-4. Answer C. GFDIC 8B, AIM
The outer marker is identified by continuous dashes at the rate of two per second, and a flashing blue light. The inner marker is identified by dots and a white beacon light.

8-5   **PLT090**
(Refer to figures 85 and 86.)

Which combination of indications confirm that you are approaching WAGGE intersection slightly to the right of the LOC centerline on departure?

A– 1 and 3.

B– 1 and 4.

C– 2 and 3.

Figure 86. CDI and OBS Indicators.

8-5. Answer C. GFDIC 8B, IFH
When outbound on the localizer back course, you will have correct sensing, so a fly left (CDI 2) is appropriate. When approaching WAGGE, you will have a fly right because you are north of, and approaching, the 062° radial of the SWR VORTAC. CDI 3 indicates you are approaching WAGGE.

8-6   **PLT090**
(Refer to figures 96 and 97.)

To which aircraft position(s) does HSI presentation "A" correspond?

A– 9 and 6.

B– 9 only.

C– 6 only.

8-6. Answer A. GFDIC 8B, IFH
Both aircraft number 9 and 6 are on a heading of north, directly over the extended centerline. This is indicated by the localizer, which from either position, shows a centered CDI.

8-7   **PLT090**
(Refer to figures 96 and 97.)

To which aircraft position(s) does HSI presentation "B" correspond?

A– 11.

B– 5 and 13.

C– 7 and 11.

8-7. Answer B. GFDIC 8B, IFH
Both aircraft number 5 and 13 are on a heading of east, south of the course. Because the back course of 090° is selected, the CDI is reverse sensing.

8-8   **PLT090**
(Refer to figures 96 and 97.)

To which aircraft position does HSI presentation "C" correspond?

A– 9.

B– 4.

C– 12.

8-8. Answer C. GFDIC 8B, IFH
The aircraft in position 12 is heading 090° inbound on the back course with the back course set and the CDI is centered.

8-9   **PLT090**
(Refer to figures 96 and 97.)

To which aircraft position does HSI presentation "D" correspond?

A– 1.

B– 10.

C– 2.

8-9. Answer C. GFDIC 8B, IFH
The aircraft in position 2 is the only one on a north-west heading. With the back course of 090° dialed in, reverse sensing would put the CDI behind the aircraft.

8-10   **PLT090**
(Refer to figures 96 and 97.)

To which aircraft position(s) does HSI presentation "E" correspond?

A– 8 only.

B– 3 only.

C– 8 and 3.

8-10. Answer C. GFDIC 8B, IFH
Both aircraft in positions 8 and 3 would experience reverse sensing with the course selector set on the back course.

8-11   **PLT090**
(Refer to figures 96 and 97.)

To which aircraft position does HSI presentation "F" correspond?

A– 4.

B– 11.

C– 5.

8-11. Answer A. GFDIC 8B, IFH
The aircraft in position 4 is the only one aligned with the localizer front course and the CDI is centered.

8-12   **PLT090**
(Refer to figures 96 and 97.)

To which aircraft position(s) does HSI presentation "G" correspond?

A– 7 only.

B– 7 and 11.

C– 5 and 13.

8-12. Answer B. GFDIC 8B, IFH
Both aircraft in positions 7 and 11 are on the localizer front course heading, but north of course.

8-13   **PLT090**
(Refer to figures 96 and 97.)

To which aircraft position does HSI presentation "H" correspond?

A– 8.

B– 1.

C– 2.

8-13. Answer B. GFDIC 8B, IFH
The aircraft in position 1 is the only one on a southwest heading of 215°. The CDI indicates that the aircraft is established on a 45° intercept to the inbound localizer course of 270°.

8-14 **PLT090**
(Refer to figures 96 and 97.)

To which aircraft position does HSI presentation "I" correspond?

A– 4.

B– 12.

C– 11.

8-14. Answer C. GFDIC 8B, IFH
The aircraft in position 11 is on a heading of west with the course selector set on the back course of 090°. This results in reverse sensing and a CDI deflection to the right.

8-15 **PLT292**
(Refer to figure 118.)

During the ILS RWY 12L procedure at DSM, what altitude minimum applies if the glide slope becomes inoperative?

A– 1,420 feet.

B– 1,360 feet.

C– 1,121 feet.

8-15. Answer B. GFDIC 8B, Approach Chart Legend
When the glide slope is inoperative, the nonprecision localizer approach minimums apply. Assuming a straight-in approach, the localizer MDA for this approach is 1,360 feet for all aircraft categories.

8-16 **PLT170**
When installed with the ILS and specified in the approach procedures, DME may be used

A– in lieu of the OM.

B– in lieu of visibility requirements.

C– to determine distance from TDZ.

8-16. Answer A. GFDIC 8B, FAR 91.175
When authorized in the approach procedure, DME, VOR, or an NDB may be substituted for the outer marker (OM).

8-17 **PLT292**
How does a pilot determine if DME is available on an ILS/LOC?

A– IAP indicate DME/TACAN channel in LOC frequency box.

B– LOC/DME are indicated on en route low altitude frequency box.

C– LOC/DME frequencies available in the Airman's Information Manual.

8-17. Answer A. GFDIC 8B, Approach Chart Legend
FAA approach charts include the DME/TACAN channel in the LOC frequency box. An example would be the notation "Chan 79" underneath the frequency and identifier.

8-18   PLT420

Which of the following statements is true regarding Parallel ILS approaches?

A– Parallel ILS approach runway centerlines are separated by at least 4,300 feet and standard IFR separation is provided on the adjacent runway.

B– Parallel ILS approaches provide aircraft a minimum of 1 1/2 miles radar separation between successive aircraft on the adjacent localizer course.

C– Landing minimums to the adjacent runway will be higher than the minimums to the primary runway, but will normally be lower than the published circling minimums.

8-18. Answer B. GFDIC 8B, AIM

Aircraft are afforded a minimum of 1.5 miles radar separation diagonally between successive aircraft on the adjacent localizer/azimuth course when runway centerlines are at least 2,500 feet but no more than 4,300 feet apart.

8-19   PLT420
(Refer to figure 247.)

When preparing to fly the ILS RWY 9 approach in a category A airplane at Riverside Municipal Airport, what action should the pilot take if the local altimeter setting cannot be obtained?

A– Fly the localizer approach because the ILS is not authorized.

B– Increase the DA by 46 feet and the visibility by 1/8 SM.

C– Use the Chino altimeter setting and increase the DA by 46 feet.

8-19. Answer C. GFDIC 8B, IFH, FAR 91.175

The notes and limitations box of the pilot briefing section describes the actions to take if the local altimeter setting is not available. You must use the Chino altimeter setting and raise the DA by 46 feet. The visibility remains the same unless you are flying a the localizer approach in a category C or D airplane.

8-20   PLT170
(Refer to figure 133.)

Why are two VOR/LOC receivers recommended to obtain an MDA of 1160 when making an S-LOC 9 approach to Riverside Municipal?

A– To obtain R-327 of PDZ when on the localizer course.

B– In order to identify Riverside VOR.

C– To utilize the published stepdown fix.

8-20. Answer C. GFDIC 8B, Approach Chart Legend

On final approach, after the FAF, one VOR/LOC receiver must be continuously tuned to the final approach course frequency. A second receiver is required to identify any VOR radial stepdown fixes. On this approach, the stepdown fix, AGNES, is identified off the PDZ VOR, so a second receiver is necessary. After AGNES, you may descend from 1,260 feet to the straight-in localizer MDA of 1,160 feet.

8-21   **PLT083**

(Refer to figure 247.)

What is the minimum altitude descent procedure if cleared for the S-ILS 9 approach from Seal Beach VORTAC if the airplane is able to meet the missed approach climb requirement of 270 feet per NM to 2,500 feet MSL?

A– Descend and maintain 3,000 to JASER INT, descend to and maintain 2,500 until crossing EXPAM, descend and maintain 1,280 (DA).

B– Descend and maintain 3,000 to JASER INT, descend to 2,500 when established on the LOC course, intercept and maintain the GS to 1,096 (DA).

C– Descend and maintain 3,000 to JASER INT, descend to 2,500 while established on the LOC course inbound, intercept and maintain the GS to 960 (DA).

8-21. Answer C. GFDIC 8B, Approach Chart Legend

From Seal Beach VORTAC (SLI), the published minimum altitude to JASER INT is 3,000 feet. Since this is a NoPT routing at JASER, you would proceed inbound on the final approach course without executing a procedure turn and, when established on the localizer course, descend to the glide slope intercept altitude of 2,500 feet. Then, intercept the glide slope and descend to the ILS decision altitude (DA) of 960 feet. The asterisk indicates that this minimum applies if you can meet the missed approach climb requirement of 270 feet per NM as indicated in the notes and limitations box of the pilot briefing information section.

8-22   **PLT361**

What is a difference between an SDF and an LDA facility?

A– The SDF course width is either 6° or 12° while the LDA course width is approximately 5°.

B– The SDF course has no glide slope guidance while the LDA does.

C– The SDF has no marker beacons while the LDA has at least an OM.

8-22. Answer A. GFDIC 8B, AIM

A localizer-type directional aid (LDA) is comparable in use and accuracy to a localizer, but it is not a part of a complete ILS nor is it aligned with the runway centerline. An LDA has a course width between 3° and 6°. A simplified directional facility (SDF) has a fixed course width of either 6° or 12°.

8-23   **PLT357**

What is the difference between a localizer type directional aid (LDA) and the ILS localizer?

A– The LDA is not aligned with the runway.

B– The LDA uses a course width of 6° or 12°, while an ILS uses only 5°.

C– The LDA signal is generated from a VOR-type facility and has no glide slope.

8-23. Answer A. GFDIC 8B, AIM

The primary difference between an LDA and an ILS is that an LDA is not aligned with the runway centerline.

8-24   PLT361
How wide is an SDF course?

A– Either 3° or 6°.

B– Either 6° or 12°.

C– Varies from 5° to 10°.

8-24. Answer B. GFDIC 8B, AIM
A simplified directional facility (SDF) course is fixed at either 6° or 12° wide.

8-25   PLT361
What are the main differences between the SDF and the localizer of an ILS?

A– The useable off-course indications are limited to 35° for the localizer and up to 90° for the SDF.

B– The SDF course may not be aligned with the runway and the course may be wider.

C– The course width for the localizer will always be 5° while the SDF course will be between 6° and 12°.

8-25. Answer B. GFDIC 8B, AIM
Unlike an ILS, an SDF may be offset from the runway centerline, normally not more than 3°, and no glide slope information is provided. In addition, an SDF course width is either 6° or 12°, while an ILS course is typically 5° wide.

8-26   PLT277
Which range facility associated with the ILS is identified by the first two letters of the localizer identification group?

A– Inner marker.

B– Outer marker.

C– Locator outer marker (LOM).

8-26. Answer C. GFDIC 8B, AIM
A compass locator at the outer marker transmits the first two letters of the localizer identifier. Marker beacons not combined with a compass locator do not transmit two-letter identifiers.

8-27   PLT277
Which range facility associated with the ILS can be identified by a two-letter coded signal?

A– Inner marker.

B– Outer marker.

C– Compass locator.

8-27. Answer C. GFDIC 8B, AIM
A compass locator at the outer marker transmits the first two letters of the localizer identifier. Marker beacons not combined with a compass locator do not transmit two-letter identifiers.

8-28   PLT420

Which pilot action is appropriate if more than one component of an ILS is unusable?

A– Use the highest minimum required by any single component that is unusable.

B– Request another approach appropriate to the equipment that is useable.

C– Raise the minimums a total of that required by each component that is unusable.

8-28. Answer A. GFDIC 8B, IFH

When components of an ILS are inoperative, higher minimums may be required, but the effect is not cumulative. You would use the highest minimums required by the inoperative status of any single component.

8-29   PLT170

Which substitution is permitted when an ILS component is inoperative?

A– A compass locator or precision radar may be substituted for the ILS outer marker.

B– ADF or VOR bearings which cross the outer marker site may be substituted for this marker.

C– DME, when located at the localizer antenna site, should be substituted for the outer marker.

8-29. Answer A. GFDIC 8B, IFH, FAR 91.175

A compass locator or precision radar may be used in place of the outer marker.

8-30   PLT420

When being radar vectored for an ILS approach, at what point may you start a descent from your last assigned altitude to a lower minimum altitude if cleared for the approach?

A– When established on a segment of a published route or IAP.

B– You may descend immediately to published glide slope interception altitude.

C– Only after you are established on the final approach unless informed otherwise by ATC.

8-30. Answer A. GFDIC 8B, AIM

To ensure obstacle clearance, you must maintain your last assigned altitude until established on a segment of the published routing or approach procedure.

8-31   PLT420

If all ILS components are operating and the required visual references are not established, the missed approach should be initiated upon

A— arrival at the DA on the glide slope.

B— arrival at the runway threshold.

C— expiration of the time listed on the approach chart for missed approach.

8-31. Answer A. GFDIC 8B, IFH, FAR 91.175

The decision altitude (DA) is the missed approach point for a precision approach. If you do not have the required visual references at the DA, you must immediately initiate the missed approach.

8-32   PLT125

The rate of descent required to stay on the ILS glide slope

A— must be increased if the groundspeed is decreased.

B— will remain constant if the indicated airspeed remains constant.

C— must be decreased if the groundspeed is decreased.

8-32. Answer C. GFDIC 8B, AC 00-54

To maintain a constant glide angle, your vertical speed depends on your speed over the ground. If your groundspeed decreases, you will have to reduce your rate of descent to stay on the glide slope. The rate of descent must be increased when the groundspeed is increased, not decreased.

8-33   PLT277

Which indications will a pilot receive where an IM is installed on a front course ILS approach?

A— One dot per second and a steady amber light.

B— Six dots per second and a flashing white light.

C— Alternate dashes and a blue light.

8-33. Answer B. GFDIC 8B, AIM

An inner marker (IM) is identified by a continuous series of dots at the rate of six per second and a flashing white light.

8-34   PLT125

To remain on the ILS glide path, the rate of descent must be

A— decreased if the airspeed is increased.

B— decreased if the groundspeed is increased.

C— increased if the groundspeed is increased.

8-34. Answer C. GFDIC 8B, AC 00-54

When groundspeed increases, you must increase your rate of descent to remain on the glide slope.

8-35   PLT125
The rate of descent on the glide slope is dependent upon

A– true airspeed.

B– calibrated airspeed.

C– groundspeed.

8-35. Answer C. GFDIC 8B, Rate of Descent Table
The rate of descent needed to maintain the glide slope varies with groundspeed.

8-36   PLT170
The glide slope and localizer are centered, but the airspeed is too fast. Which should be adjusted initially?

A– Pitch and power.

B– Power only.

C– Pitch only.

8-36. Answer B. GFDIC 8B, IFH
The power should be reduced first to begin slowing the airplane. As airspeed decreases, the pitch will tend to decrease, and you should make the necessary corrections to pitch the nose upward in order to maintain the glide slope.

8-37   PLT420
If during an ILS approach in IFR conditions, the approach lights are not visible upon arrival at the DA, the pilot is

A– required to immediately execute the missed approach procedure.

B– permitted to continue the approach and descend to the localizer MDA.

C– permitted to continue the approach to the approach threshold of the ILS runway.

8-37. Answer A. GFDIC 8B, FAR 91.175
This question assumes that no other runway visual references are visible. In this case, you may not continue the approach below the DA and must immediately execute the missed approach.

8-38   PLT420
Immediately after passing the final approach fix inbound during an ILS approach in IFR conditions, the glide slope warning flag appears. The pilot is

A– permitted to continue the approach and descend to the DA.

B– permitted to continue the approach and descend to the localizer MDA.

C– required to immediately begin the prescribed missed approach procedure.

8-38. Answer B. GFDIC 8B, AIM
If the glide slope fails, you are permitted to continue the approach, using localizer-only minimums. You would descend to the MDA and continue to the MAP. If the runway environment is not in sight at the MAP, you must execute a missed approach.

8-39   PLT292
(Refer to figure 217.)

During the approach to DSM before you can begin the ILS RWY 13 procedure, the glide slope fails and you are cleared for the LOC RWY 13 at DSM, what altitude minimum applies?

A– 1,420 feet.

B– 1,380 feet.

C– 1,121 feet.

8-39. Answer B. GFDIC 8B, IFH
If the glide slope fails, you are permitted to continue the approach, using localizer-only minimums of 1,380 feet MSL, shown in the landing minimums section for S-LOC 13.

8-40   PLT420
Which substitution is appropriate during an ILS approach?

A– A VOR radial crossing the outer marker site may be substituted for the outer marker.

B– LOC minimums should be substituted for ILS minimums whenever the glide slope becomes inoperative.

C– DME, when located at the localizer antenna site, should be substituted for the outer marker.

8-40. Answer B. GFDIC 8B, AIM, FAR 91.175
When the glide slope becomes inoperative, you may use LOC minimums and fly a nonprecision approach to the LOC MDA.

8-41   PLT004
During a precision radar or ILS approach, the rate of descent required to remain on the glide slope will

A– remain the same regardless of groundspeed.

B– increase as the groundspeed increases.

C– decrease as the groundspeed increases.

8-41. Answer B. GFDIC 8B, AC 00-54
When making a precision radar or ILS approach, the aircraft's rate of descent will vary with changes in groundspeed. If your groundspeed increases, the rate of descent required to stay on the glide slope must also increase. If your groundspeed decreases, the rate of descent must also decrease.

8-42   PLT170

When tracking inbound on the localizer, which of the following is the proper procedure regarding drift corrections?

A– Drift corrections should be accurately established before reaching the outer marker and completion of the approach should be accomplished with heading corrections no greater than 2°.

B– Drift corrections should be made in 5° increments after passing the outer marker.

C– Drift corrections should be made in 10° increments after passing the outer marker.

8-42. Answer A. GFDIC 8B, IFH

On the narrow localizer course, establish your drift correction prior to the outer marker. Since overcontrolling can be a problem, heading corrections should be no greater than 2° after passing the outer marker.

8-43   PLT360

What international Morse Code identifier is used to identify a specific interim standard microwave landing system?

A– A two letter Morse Code identifier preceded by the Morse Code for the letters "IM".

B– A three letter Morse Code identifier preceded by the Morse Code for the letter "M".

C– A three letter Morse Code identifier preceded by the Morse Code for the letters "ML".

8-43. Answer B. AIM

MLS identification is a four-letter designation starting with the letter M. It is transmitted in International Morse Code at least six times per minute by the approach azimuth (and back azimuth) ground equipment.

8-44   PLT049

(Refer to figures 139 and 140.)

Which displacement from the localizer and glide slope at the 1.9 NM point is indicated?

A– 710 feet to the left of the localizer centerline and 140 feet below the glide slope.

B– 710 feet to the right of the localizer centerline and 140 feet above the glide slope.

C– 430 feet to the right of the localizer centerline and 28 feet above the glide slope.

8-44. Answer B. GFDIC 8B, IFH

Figure 140 indicates that the aircraft is 2 dots above the glide slope and 2 dots to the right of the localizer. At 1.9 NM this corresponds to 710 feet to the right of the localizer centerline and 140 feet above the glide slope.

8-45   PLT049
(Refer to figures 139 and 141.)

Which displacement from the localizer centerline and glide slope at the 1,300-foot point from the runway is indicated?

A– 21 feet below the glide slope and approximately 320 feet to the right of the runway centerline.

B– 28 feet above the glide slope and approximately 250 feet to the left of the runway centerline.

C– 21 feet above the glide slope and approximately 320 feet to the left of the runway centerline.

8-45. Answer C. GFDIC 8B, IFH
Figure 8-9 indicates that the aircraft is approximately 1-1/2 dots above the glide slope and between 1-1/2 and 2 dots to the left of the localizer. At 1,300 feet, this best corresponds to 21 feet above the glide slope and approximately 320 feet to the left of the runway centerline.

8-46   PLT049
(Refer to figures 139 and 142.)

Which displacement from the localizer and glide slope at the outer marker is indicated?

A– 1,550 feet to the left of the localizer centerline and 210 feet below the glide slope.

B– 1,550 feet to the right of the localizer centerline and 210 feet above the glide slope.

C– 775 feet to the left of the localizer centerline and 420 feet below the glide slope.

8-46. Answer A. GFDIC 8B, IFH
Figure 142 indicates that the aircraft is approximately 1 dot below the glide slope and 2 dots to the left of the localizer. At the outer marker, this corresponds to 210 feet below glide slope and approximately 1,550 feet to the left of the centerline.

8-47   PLT083
(Refer to figure 49.)

What determines the MAP on the LOC/DME RWY 21 approach at Portland International Airport?

A– I-GPO 1.2 DME.

B– 5.8 NM from ROBOT FAF.

C– 160° radial of BTG VORTAC.

8-47. Answer A. GFDIC 8C, Approach Chart Legend
The missed approach point shown on the referenced figure is located at I-GPO 1.2 DME.

8-48 PLT083

(Refer to figures 44 and 49.)

What is the MDA and visibility criteria for a straight-in LOC/DME RWY 21 approach at Portland International?

A– 1,100 feet MSL; visibility 1 SM.

B– 680 feet MSL; visibility 1 SM.

C– 680 feet MSL; visibility 1 NM

8-48. Answer B. GFDIC 7A, Approach Chart legend

The provided flight plan and aircraft information lists the VSO at 77 knots. To determine the proper approach category, multiply 1.3 x VSO (1.3 x 77 = 100.1). This falls into the Category B approach minimums (91 to 120 knots). The approach minimums for Category A and B are 680 feet MSL and 1 statute mile visibility.

8-49 PLT004

(Refer to figure 49.)

With a groundspeed of 120 knots, approximately what minimum rate of descent will be required between I-GPO 7 DME fix (ROBOT) and the I-GPO 4 DME fix?

A– 1,200 fpm.

B– 500 fpm.

C– 800 fpm.

8-49. Answer C. GFDIC 8C, Approach Chart Legend

Traveling at 120 knots between I-GPO 7 DME fix (ROBOT) at 2300 feet MSL to I-GPO 4 DME fix should take you 1-1/2 minutes. To descend a total of 1,200 feet in a minute and a half you should be descending at 800 ft/min.

8-50 PLT292

Precision Runway Monitoring (PRM) is:

A– an airborne RADAR system for monitoring approaches to two runways.

B– a RADAR system for monitoring approaches to closely spaced parallel runways.

C– a high update rate RADAR system for monitoring multiple aircraft ILS approaches to a single runway.

8-50. Answer B. GFDIC 8B, IFH

Historically, parallel runways had to be at least 4,300 feet apart for ATC to authorize simultaneous approaches; however, this is no longer the case with the advent of a system called the precision runway monitor (PRM). The PRM uses a radar offering one second (or faster) updates on targets, a high-resolution color ATC display, audio and visual alert systems for controllers, and software for projecting aircraft track vectors. This system, which can display turns as they occur, does not require any extra equipment on the aircraft or sensors on the airport other than the PRM electronically guided antenna.

8-51   PLT170
How can the pilot determine, for an ILS runway equipped with MALSR, that there may be a penetration of the obstacle identification surfaces (OIS), and care should be taken in the visual segment to avoid any obstacles?

A– The runway has a visual approach slope indicator (VASI.)

B– The published visibility for the ILS is no lower than 3/4 SM.

C– The approach chart has a visual descent point (VDP) published.

8-51. Answer B. GFDIC 8B, IPH
The visibility published on an approach chart is dependent on many variables, including the height above touchdown for straight-in approaches, or height above airport elevation for circling approaches. Other factors include the approach light system coverage, and type of approach procedure, such as precision, nonprecision, circling or straight-in. Another factor determining the minimum visibility is the penetration of the 34:1 and 20:1 surfaces. These surfaces are inclined planes that begin 200 feet out from the runway and extend outward to 10,000 feet. If there is a penetration of the 34:1 surface, the published visibility can be no lower than 3/4 SM. If there is penetration of the 20:1 surface, the published visibility can be no lower than 1 SM with a note prohibiting straight-in approaches to the affected runway at night (both straight-in and circling). Circling may be permitted at night if penetrating obstacles are marked and lighted. If the penetrating obstacles are not marked and lighted, a note is published that night circling is "Not Authorized." Pilots should be aware of these penetrating obstacles when entering the visual and/or circling segments of an approach and take adequate precautions to avoid them.

8-52   PLT292
A Precision Runway Monitoring (PRM) approach may require

A– monitoring of two communication frequencies simultaneously.

B– special training and monitoring of two ILS receivers simultaneously.

C– tracking performance parameters within the "decision region" of: 1/3 dot localizer and 1/2 dot glide slope displacement.

8-52. Answer A. GFDIC 8B, IPG, IPH
A precision runway monitoring (PRM) approach uses high-update radar, high resolution ATC displays, and PRM-certified controllers to permit a decreased separation distance between parallel runways. To fly a PRM approach, you must meet specific training requirements and dual VHF equipment is required in your aircraft. You must monitor two communication frequencies simultaneously – one for the PRM monitor controller and the other for the tower controller.

SECTION C — RNAV APPROACHES

APPROACH DESIGN

- The terminal arrival area (TAA) approach design has icons on the plan view to indicate minimum altitudes that you must maintain as you arrive from the enroute structure to a specific initial approach fix, therefore, no MSA is published.
- The Basic T approach segment configuration consists of three areas: the straight-in area, the left base area, and the right base area. Modifications to this configuration might be necessary to accommodate operational requirements.
- For fly-by waypoints (depicted with the waypoint symbol), the GPS receiver anticipates the turn and displays navigation indications that prevent you from overshooting the next flight segment.
- For fly-over waypoints (depicted by the waypoint symbol enclosed in a circle), navigation indications will not provide guidance for a turn until you pass over the waypoint, followed either by an intercept maneuver to the next flight segment or by direct flight to the next waypoint.

GPS APPROACH EQUIPMENT

- To fly RNAV (GPS) approach procedures with lateral navigation, your GPS equipment must be certified according to TSO-C129 or TSO-C196.
- To fly GPS approaches that incorporate vertical navigation using WAAS, your GPS equipment must be certified according to TSO-C145 or TSO-C146.
- You can determine the allowable uses for the specific GPS installation by referring to the airplane flight manual (AFM) or AFM supplement.
- Baro-VNAV systems calculate a glide path based on an altimeter setting and are subject to high and low temperature limitations.
- A WAAS-certified GPS unit determines a glide path by its vertical and horizontal GPS position independent of the altimeter setting, and its operation is not limited by temperature.
- If your airplane is equipped with a GPS receiver certified for instrument approaches, you are not required to monitor or have ground-based navigation equipment to perform an RNAV (GPS) approach at the destination.
- If your GPS equipment is not WAAS-certified, you may use GPS to perform an approach at an alternate airport only if the alternate airport has an approved instrument approach procedure other than GPS.
- If your GPS equipment is WAAS-certified, you can use an airport that only has a GPS approach available as an alternate.

LANDING MINIMUMS

- Lateral navigation (LNAV) course guidance has larger integrity limits than those of a localizer, and the approach is flown to a minimum descent altitude (MDA).
- Lateral navigation/vertical navigation (LNAV/VNAV) minimums apply to approaches that provide lateral and vertical guidance using baro-VNAV or WAAScertified equipment.
- Although the integrity limits for LNAV/VNAV approaches are larger than those for a precision approach, the landing minimum is a decision altitude (DA).
- LPV (localizer performance with vertical guidance) minimums apply to approaches that provide lateral and vertical guidance to a decision altitude with integrity limits that are close to an ILS precision approach.
- Your GPS equipment must be WAAS-certified before you can fly approaches to LPV minimums; baro-VNAV equipment does not provide the required precision.
- Approaches to localizer performance (LP) minimums are published in locations where vertical guidance is not feasible due to terrain, obstacles, or other operational limitations. These approaches have integrity limits close to a localizer and have an MDA for a landing minimum.

RAIM

- If RAIM is not available when you set up a GPS approach, you should use another type of navigation and approach system.

- If the GPS receiver does not sequence into the approach mode or indicates RAIM failure prior to the final approach fix, do not descend to the DA or MDA. Proceed to the missed approach point, perform the missed approach procedure, and contact ATC as soon as possible.

- If a RAIM failure occurs after the final approach fix, the GPS receiver continues to operate without a failure indication for up to five minutes so you can complete the approach.

8-53   PLT083
(Refer to figure 171.)

Under which condition should the missed approach procedure for the RNAV (GPS) RWY 33 approach be initiated?

A— When time has expired for 4.1 NM past the FAF.

B— Upon reaching the MDA of 1,240 feet MSL.

C— Upon reaching the missed approach waypoint of RW33.

8-53. Answer C. GFDIC 8C, AIM
When performing an RNAV (GPS) approach, you begin the missed approach at the missed approach waypoint. The waypoint is shown as RW33 on the plan and profile view.

8-54   PLT354
How can a pilot determine if a Global Positioning System (GPS) installed in an aircraft is approved for IFR enroute and IFR approaches?

A— Flight manual supplement.

B— GPS operator's manual.

C— Aircraft owner's handbook.

8-54. Answer A. GFDIC 8C, AC 90-94
All GPS IFR operations should be conducted in accordance with the FAA Approved Flight Manual (AFM) or Flight Manual Supplement. The type and degree of authorized operations for a GPS receiver are specified in these documents.

8-55   PLT083
(Refer to figure 242.)

How should the missed approach point be identified when executing the RNAV (GPS) RWY 36 approach at Bill and Hillary Clinton National/Adams Field?

A— When the GPS display indicates that the airplane reaching the RW36 waypoint.

B— Upon arrival at 760 feet on the glide path.

C— When time has expired for 5.3 NM past the FAF.

8-55. Answer A. GFDIC 8C, IFH
When performing an RNAV (GPS) approach, you begin the missed approach at the missed approach waypoint. The waypoint is shown as RW36 on the plan and profile view.

8-56   PLT083

(Refer to figure 242.)

What procedure should be used to intercept the approach course for the RNAV (GPS) RWY 36 approach if arriving from the northeast at 4,000 feet MSL and cleared to DOVQA?

A– At DOVQA, fly a course of 270° and descend to 2,000 feet MSL. Turn right to intercept the approach course of 360° at FEHXE and descend to 760 feet MSL to KAGBE.

B– At DOVQA, fly a course of 270° and descend to 3,300 feet MSL. AT FEHXE, turn left to fly a parallel entry to the holding pattern course reversal. Intercept the approach course of 360°after turning inbound back to FEHXE.

C– At DOVQA, fly a course of 270° and descend to 3,300 feet MSL. Turn right to intercept the approach course of 360° at FEHXE.

8-56. Answer C. GFDIC 8C, IFH

The course line from DOVQA indicates a course of 270° to FEHXE at 3,300 feet MSL. "NoPT" indicates that you are not allowed to perform a procedure turn and must turn to intercept the approach course of 360° at FEHXE.

8-57   PLT083

(Refer to figure 242.)

What airborne equipment is required to be operative for the RNAV (GPS) RWY 36 approach at your destination, Bill and Hillary Clinton National/Adams Field?

A– A GPS unit certified under TSO-C145() or TSO-C146() for IFR approaches with both lateral and vertical guidance.

B– A GPS unit certified under TSO-C129() or TSO-C196() for IFR approaches with lateral guidance.

C– A GPS unit certified under TSO-C129() or TSO-C196() for IFR approaches with lateral guidance and ground-based navigation equipment for an approach procedure other than GPS.

8-57. Answer B. GFDIC 8C, AIM

You must have a GPS unit that is certified under TSO-C129() or TSO-C196() for IFR approaches. This approach procedure has lateral guidance only as indicated by the LNAV landing minimum so you are not required to have GPS with WAAS capability certified under TSO-C145 or TSO-C146. You are also not required to monitor or have ground-based navigation equipment to perform an RNAV (GPS) approach at your destination.

8-58   PLT354

If Receiver Autonomous Integrity Monitoring (RAIM) is not available when setting up a GPS approach, the pilot should

A— continue the approach, expecting to recapture the satellites before reaching the FAF.

B— use a navigation system other than GPS for the approach.

C— continue to the MAP and hold until the satellites are recaptured.

8-58. Answer B. GFDIC 8C, AIM

Receiver Autonomous Integrity Monitoring (RAIM) is essential for conducting GPS approaches. Loss of RAIM is like an OFF flag or no identifier on a VOR. This question asks what you should do if loss of RAIM occurs or is predicted to occur, before beginning the approach.

8-59   PLT354

Your onboard GPS-based FMS/RNAV unit is IFR certified under TSO-C129() or TSO-C196(). Your destination is below minimums for the GPS RNAV approach and you proceed to your filed alternate. You know that

A— GPS units certified under TSO-C129() or TSO-C196() are not authorized for alternate approach requirements; subsequently, you must use an approach procedure based on ground based navaids.

B— once diverted to the alternate airport, you may fly a GPS-based approach as long as there is an operational ground-based navaid and appropriate airborne receiver for use as a backup.

C— if your aircraft is equipped with a second TSO-C129() certified GPS as a backup in place of a ground-based navaid receiver, you may complete the approach even if the IAP is based on ground-based navaids.

8-59. Answer B. GFDIC 8C, AIM

If your onboard GPS-based FMS/RNAV unit is certified under TSO-C129 or TSO-C196, you are not required to monitor or have ground-based navigation equipment to perform an RNAV (GPS) approach at the destination. However, although you may perform an approach at an alternate airport using GPS equipment, any required alternate airport must have an approved instrument approach procedure other than GPS that is anticipated to be operational and available at the estimated time of arrival, and that the airplane is equipped to fly.

8-60   PLT455

When your aircraft is equipped with a TSO-C129() or TSO-C196() GPS, an airport may not be qualified for alternate use if

A— the only standard approach procedure is GPS at the destination and alternate.

B— the airport has only AWOS-3 weather reporting and no LAAS equipment operational.

C— the airport is next to a restricted or prohibited area.

8-60. Answer A. GFDIC 8C, AIM

If your aircraft is equipped with a TSO-C129 or TSO-C196 GPS, you are not required to monitor or have ground-based navigation equipment to perform an RNAV (GPS) approach at the destination. However, although you may perform an approach at an alternate airport using GPS equipment, any required alternate airport must have an approved instrument approach procedure other than GPS that is anticipated to be operational and available at the estimated time of arrival, and that the airplane is equipped to fly.

8-61   PLT354
Hand-held GPS systems, and GPS systems certified for VFR operation, may be used during IFR operations as

A– the principal reference to determine enroute way-points.

B– an aid to situational awareness.

C– the primary source of navigation.

8-61. Answer B. GFDIC 8C, AIM
Hand-held GPS systems are not authorized for IFR navigation, instrument approaches, or as a principal flight reference. During IFR operations they may be considered only as an aid to situational awareness.

8-62   PLT354
A hand-held GPS system

A– may be used for IFR operations in VFR weather conditions.

B– is not authorized for IFR navigation.

C– may be used in IFR weather conditions only for en route navigation.

8-62. Answer B. GFDIC 2C, 8C, AIM
Hand-held GPS systems are not authorized for IFR navigation, instrument approaches, or as a principal flight reference. During IFR operations they may be considered only as an aid to situational awareness.

8-63   PLT354
During IFR en route and terminal operations using an approved GPS system for navigation, ground based navigational facilities

A– are only required during the approach portion of the flight.

B– must be operational along the entire route.

C– must be operational only if RAIM predicts an outage.

8-63. Answer B. GFDIC 8C, AIM
GPS domestic enroute and terminal IFR operations can be conducted as long as the avionics can receive all of the ground-based facilities appropriate for the route of flight and any required alternates. Ground-based facilities necessary for these routes must also be operation

8-64   PLT083

(Refer to figure 249.)

Why is there a note stating a temperature limitation for executing this approach with baro-VNAV equipment?

A– The descent gradient exceeds the maximum standard of 400-foot per nautical mile at low temperatures.

B– The decision altitude and final approach segment height above obstacles or terrain is unsafe when temperatures are below or above the limitations.

C– The missed approach climb gradient exceeds the airplane maximum standard of 40 to 1 at low temperatures.

8-64. Answer B. GFDIC 8A, AIM

Under standard atmospheric conditions of pressure and temperature, an accurate barometric altimeter will read true altitude when set to 29.92. However, as conditions vary from standard, indicated altitude deviates from true altitude. When temperatures fall significantly below standard, the true altitude of an aircraft will be lower than indicated altitude. In these conditions, descent to the MDA or DA would compromise required obstruction and/or terrain clearance. More information on true altitude is provided in Chapter 2 of the GFDIC.

8-65   PLT083

(Refer to figure 249.)

What waypoints are designated as fly-over waypoints?

A– FAF and AGHAN.

B– Missed approach and AGHAN.

C– Missed approach and the IAFs.

8-65. Answer B. GFDIC 8C, Approach Chart Legend

Missed approach points and missed approach holding points are normally fly-over waypoints. The approach chart legend in Appendix 1 shows that a fly-over waypoint has a circle around the waypoint symbol. Both AGHAN and the missed approach point, RW30, have circled waypoint symbols.

8-66   PLT083

(Refer to figure 249.)

At what point is the pilot authorized to descend below 5,300 feet when cleared to the AJCIZ waypoint from the west?

A– 30 NM from AJCIZ.

B– 15 NM from AJCIZ.

C– After completing the holding pattern course reversal.

8-66. Answer B. GFDIC 8C, Approach Chart Legend

The TAA icon quadrant for aircraft approaching AJCIZ from the west shows that you can descend to 5,300 feet MSL within the 30 NM arc, but not below it. Within the 15 NM arc, you can descend below 5,300 feet MSL to 4,700 feet MSL.

8-67   **PLT083**

(Refer to figure 187.)

ATIS is reporting that the MALSR is inoperative. What restrictions apply to the RNAV (GPS) X RWY 28L approach?

A— The visibility for the approach to LPV minimums is increased to RVR 4500.

B— An approach to LNAV minimums is not authorized.

C— The DA for the approach to LNAV/VNAV minimums is increased to 720 feet MSL.

8-67. Answer A. GFDIC 8C, Approach Chart Legend
The notes and limitations box of the pilot briefing information indicates that "for inoperative MALSR, increase LPV all Cats visibility to RVR 4500" Approaches to LNAV/VNAV and LNAV minimums also require an increase in visibility minimums.

8-68   **PLT083**

(Refer to figure 191.)

What aircraft equipment is required to fly the RNAV (GPS) RWY 19 approach to LPV minimums?

A— A GPS unit certified under TSO-C129() or TSO-C196() for IFR approaches with lateral guidance.

B— A GPS unit certified under TSO-C129() or TSO-C196() with baro-VNAV capability.

C— A GPS unit with WAAS capability certified under TSO-C145() or TSO-C146() for IFR approaches with both lateral and vertical guidance.

8-68. Answer C. GFDIC 8C, AIM
To fly an RNAV (GPS) approach to LPV minimums your GPS equipment must have WAAS capability and be certified under TSO-C145() or TSO-C146(). Baro-VNAV equipment does not provide the required precision.

8-69   PLT083
(Refer to figure 194.)

What is the correct procedure for flying the final approach segment to LPV minimums?

A– Begin a descent at IREZO to the MDA of 2,280 feet. Perform a missed approach at the RW15 waypoint if the required visual references are not in sight.

B– Intercept the glide path at 3,500 feet at IREZO. Descend on the glide path to the DA of 1,947 feet. If the required visual references are not in sight at the DA, perform a missed approach.

C– Intercept the glide path at 3,500 feet at IREZO. Descend on the glide path to the DA of 1,947 feet. If the required visual references are not in sight at 1.7 NM to RW08, perform a missed approach.

8-69. Answer B. GFDIC 8C, Approach Chart Legend
The glide slope intercept altitude is 3,500 feet MSL as indicated by the lightning bolt symbol. You should intercept the glide slope at this altitude at IREZO. For an approach with a decision altitude (DA), you must perform a missed approach if you reach the DA and do not have the required visual references in sight. The visual descent point (VDP) at 1.7 NM to RW08 is for the LNAV approach only.

8-70   PLT083
(Refer to figure 197.)

What limitations apply to flying the RNAV (GPS) RWY 35L approach at Houston/David Wayne Hooks Memorial Airport if the aircraft does not have GPS equipment with WAAS capability?

A– The approach may be flown to LPV minimums if the GPS equipment has baro-VNAV capability.

B– The approach procedure is not authorized for aircraft without WAAS-certified GPS equipment.

C– The approach may be flown using lateral navigation to LNAV minimums if the GPS equipment is certified for IFR approach procedures.

8-70. Answer B. GFDIC 8C, AIM
If your GPS equipment is authorized for IFR approaches, you may perform an approach using lateral navigation to LNAV minimums. If your GPS equipment does not have WAAS capability, you are not authorized to fly RNAV (GPS) approaches with lateral and vertical guidance to LPV minimums. You may use baro-VNAV equipment to fly to LNAV/VNAV minimums but baro-VNAV does not have the required precision to fly to the lower LPV minimums.

8-71 PLT083
(Refer to figure 212.)

What procedure should you follow to fly the initial and intermediate approach segments from NIBBE?

A– Fly a course of 199° to SUTLE at 6,000 feet MSL. Enter the holding pattern to reverse course. Then, intercept the approach course of 278° and descend to 5,200 feet MSL.

B– Fly a course of 199° to SUTLE at 6,000 feet MSL. Turn right to intercept the approach course of 278° and descend to 5,200 feet MSL.

C– Fly a course of 199° to SUTLE at 6,000 feet MSL. Turn right to intercept the approach course of 278° and descend to 3,820 feet MSL.

8-71. Answer B. GFDIC 8C, Approach Chart Legend
On the plan view of the RNAV (GPS) RWY 28 approach, the course from NIBBE has the notation of "NoPT" so no course reversal is approach when flying from this IAF. When reaching NIBBE, you intercept the approach course of 278° and descend to 5,200 feet MSL, the glide path intercept altitude, as shown on the profile view.

8-72 PLT083
(Refer to figure 212.)

What aircraft equipment is required to fly the GPS RWY 19 approach?

A– A GPS unit certified under TSO-C129() or TSO-C196() for IFR approaches with lateral guidance.

B– A GPS unit certified under TSO-C129() or TSO-C196() with baro-VNAV capability.

C– A GPS unit with WAAS capability certified under TSO-C145() or TSO-C146() for IFR approaches with both lateral and vertical guidance.

8-72. Answer A. GFDIC 8C, AIM
The GPS RWY 19 approach provides lateral guidance only. You must have a GPS unit certified under TSO-C129() or TSO-C196() for IFR approaches with lateral guidance.

8-73   **PLT083**
(Refer to figure 218.)

What restrictions apply to the RNAV (GPS) RWY 5 approach when flying the approach to LPV minimums if the local altimeter setting is not available?

A– Use the altimeter setting for Ankeny Regional Airport and increase the DA to 1,228 feet MSL.

B– Use the altimeter setting for Ankeny Regional Airport and increase the required visibility to 5000 RVR.

C– No restrictions apply. Fly the approach to the DA shown in the landing minimums section.

8-73. Answer A. GFDIC 8C, Approach Chart Legend
The notes and limitations box of the pilot briefing information section specifies that if the local altimeter setting is not received, use Ankeny Regional altimeter setting and increase all DAs/MDAs by 40 feet. The DA for the LPV approach is 1188 + 40 = 1228.

8-74   **PLT083**
(Refer to figure 229.)

What is the procedure for flying the final approach segment when flying the RNAV (GPS) RWY 13 approach to LNAV minimums?

A– From CAVOV, descend to 1,280 feet MSL and continue the descent to landing if the required visual references are in sight.

B– From CAVOV, descend to 1,500 feet MSL. At ZEDUS, descend to 1,280 feet MSL. After passing the VDP of 1.4 NM to RW13, descend to 997 feet MSL. At RW13 waypoint, descend to land if the required visual references are in sight.

C– From CAVOV, descend to 1,500 feet MSL. At ZEDUS, descend to 1,280 feet MSL. After passing the VDP of 1.4 NM to RW13, descend to land if the required visual references are in sight.

8-74. Answer C. GFDIC 8C, Approach Chart Legend
The profile view shows a descent to 1500 from CAVOV when flying to LNAV minimums. You must maintain 1,500 feet MSL until reaching ZEDUS. At this point, you may descend to the MDA of 1,280 feet MSL as shown in the landing minimums section. For obstacle clearance, remain at the MDA until you are past the VDP or 1.4 NM to RW13.

8-75   **PLT083**

(Refer to figure 235.)

What procedure applies to arriving on a course of 350° to OWSEW?

A– From 30 NM to 8 NM, maintain a minimum altitude of 3,500 feet MSL. From 8 NM to OWSEW, maintain a minimum altitude of 3,100 feet MSL. At OWSEW, perform the holding pattern course reversal.

B– From 30 NM to 13 NM, maintain a minimum altitude of 4,100 feet MSL. From 13 NM to OWSEW, maintain a minimum altitude of 3,500 feet MSL. At OWSEW, perform the holding pattern course reversal.

C– From 30 NM to 8 NM, maintain a minimum altitude of 3,500 feet MSL. From 8 NM to OWSEW, maintain a minimum altitude of 3,100 feet MSL. At OWSEW, intercept the 319° approach course without performing the course reversal.

8-75. Answer C. GFDIC 8C, Approach Chart Legend
If you are proceeding to OWSEW on a course of 350° from the southeast, your course falls with the boundaries of 229° clockwise to 049° shown on the TAA icon. The minimum altitudes are 3,500 feet from 30 NM to 8 NM and 3,100 feet from 8 NM to OWSEW. The TAA icon also indicates "NoPT" from this direction so you may not perform the holding pattern course reversal.

8-76   **PLT083**

(Refer to figure 237.)

What landing minimums apply to a category B aircraft flying the RNAV (GPS) RWY 10 approach to LPV minimums with the Rickenbacker International Airport altimeter setting?

A– DA 1,170 feet MSL and visibility 1 SM.

B– DA 1,218 feet MSL and visibility 1¼ SM.

C– DA 1,230 feet MSL and visibility 1¼ SM.

8-76. Answer B. GFDIC 8C, Approach Chart Legend
The notes and limitations box of the pilot briefing information section specifies that if the local altimeter setting is not received and you are using Rickenbacker International Airport altimeter setting, you must increase all DAs by 48 feet. (1,170 + 48 = 1,218) In addition, the LPV and LNAV/VNAV visibility minimum for all aircraft categories increases by ¼ mile to 1¼ SM.

8-77   PLT083
(Refer to figure 241.)

What is indicated by the LP minimums shown for the RNAV (GPS) RWY 36 approach?

A– The aircraft's GPS equipment must have WAAS capability to use the LP MDA of 6,300 feet MSL.

B– The approach procedure provides both vertical and lateral guidance.

C– The aircraft's GPS equipment must have baro-VNAV to use the LP MDA of 6,300 feet MSL.

8-77. Answer A. GFDIC 8C, AIM
Approaches with localizer performance (LP) minimums have integrity limits close to a localizer and your GPS equipment must have WAAS capability to fly to these minimums. Baro-VNAV equipment does not have the required precision. Approaches to LP minimums provide lateral guidance only to an MDA.

8-78   PLT083
(Refer to figure 243.)

To fly the RNAV (GPS) RWY 6 to an MDA of 1,780 feet MSL, your aircraft must have GPS equipment approved for IFR approaches with

A– Baro-VNAV capability.

B– lateral navigation capability only.

C– WAAS capability.

8-78. Answer C. GFDIC 8C, AIM
Although, approaches to localizer performance (LP) minimums provide lateral guidance only, you must have WAAS capability to fly to LP minimums. Approaches to LP minimums have integrity limits close to a localizer. Baro-VNAV equipment does not have the required precision.

8-79   PLT083
(Refer to figure 248.)

When flying the RNAV (GPS) RWY 27 approach, what minimums apply to a category B aircraft without WAAS or baro-VNAV GPS equipment?

A– MDA 2,100 feet MSL and visibility 1¼ SM.

B– MDA 2,100 feet MSL and visibility 1½ SM.

C– DA 1,368 feet MSL and visibility 2 SM.

8-79. Answer B. GFDIC 8C, Approach Chart Legend,
If your aircraft does not have WAAS or baro-VNAV GPS equipment, you may only use lateral guidance and fly to LNAV minimums. The LNAV MDA and visibility for a category B aircraft shown in the landing minimums section are 2100-1½.

8-80   **PLT083**

(Refer to figure 253.)

What is the procedure for flying the initial and interme-diate approach segments when cleared to the FABVU IAF from the north?

A— Maintain 3,000 feet MSL to FABVU. At FABVU, descend to 2,500 feet in the holding pattern course reversal. Intercept the approach course and descend on the glide path to DAGTE.

B— Within 30 NM of FAVBU, maintain 3,100 feet MSL. Within 10 NM of FAVBU, maintain 3,000 feet MSL. At FABVU, intercept the approach course and descend on the glide path to 1,040 feet MSL.

C— Within 30 NM of FAVBU, maintain 3,100 feet MSL. Within 10 NM of FAVBU, maintain 3,000 feet MSL. At FABVU, intercept the approach course and descend to 2,500 feet MSL to DAGTE.

8-80. Answer C. GFDIC, 8C, Approach Chart Legend

If you are proceeding to FABVU IAF from the north, your course falls within the boundaries of 094° clock-wise to 274° shown on the TAA icon. The minimum alti-tudes are 3,100 feet MSL from 30 NM to 10 NM and 3,000 feet MSL from 10 NM to FABVU. The TAA icon also indicates "NoPT" from this direction so you may not perform the holding pattern course reversal. The profile view indicates a descent to 2,500 feet MSL from FAVBU to DAGTE.

CHAPTER 9

METEOROLOGY

SECTION A — WEATHER FACTORS

THE ATMOSPHERE

- The atmosphere commonly is divided into a number of layers according to its thermal characteristics. The lowest layer, the troposphere, is where most weather occurs.
- In the troposphere, temperatures decrease with altitude up to the tropopause, where an abrupt change in the temperature lapse rate occurs. The average height of the troposphere in the middle latitudes is 36,000 to 37,000 feet. The temperature in the lower part of the stratosphere (up to approximately 66,000 feet) experiences relatively small changes in temperature with an increase in altitude.

ATMOSPHERIC CIRCULATION

- Uneven heating of the earth's surface is the driving force behind all weather. The special characteristics of water also affect the release of heat into the atmosphere, and dramatically affect the weather.
- Atmospheric circulation patterns are caused by differences in pressure. Wind flows outward from high pressure areas to low pressure areas.
- Above the friction layer, the wind does not flow directly from a high to a low because of Coriolis force, which deflects air to the right in the northern hemisphere. The result is a wind that flows in a clockwise direction leaving a high and in a counterclockwise, or cyclonic, direction when entering a low.
- Near the surface, friction reduces the effects of Coriolis force and causes the wind to flow more directly from a high to low pressure area. This causes the wind to cross the isobars at an angle, rather than flowing parallel to them.
- A low pressure area, or trough, is an area of rising air, which results in generally unfavorable weather conditions. A high pressure area, or ridge, is characterized by descending air, which encourages dissipation of clouds and results in generally favorable weather conditions. Because of the wind circulation patterns, you will most likely experience a crosswind from the left when flying from a high to a low in the northern hemisphere, with stronger winds as you approach the low.
- Convective circulation patterns associated with sea breezes are caused by land absorbing and radiating heat faster than water. Cool air must sink to force warm air upward.
- Moisture is added to a parcel of air by evaporation and sublimation. The amount of water vapor that air can hold increases with temperature. When the temperature cools to the dewpoint, the air is saturated.
- At 100% humidity, water vapor condenses, forming clouds, fog or dew. Frost forms when the temperature of the collecting surface is below the dewpoint and the dewpoint is below freezing.
- Precipitation occurs when water vapor condenses out of the air and becomes heavy enough to fall to earth. The type of precipitation is influenced by the temperature and other conditions under which condensation occurs. Upward currents enhance the growth rate of precipitation.
- The presence of ice pellets normally indicates freezing rain at higher altitudes. The presence of wet snow indicates the temperature is above freezing at your flight altitude.
- Virga is best described as streamers of rain trailing beneath clouds which evaporate before reaching the ground.

STABILITY

- When unsaturated air is forced to ascend a mountain slope, it cools at the rate of approximately 3°C per 1,000 feet. When saturated air is lifted, it cools at a lower rate, which could cause it to be warmer than the surrounding air. The standard temperature of the surrounding air at sea level is 15°C, and it decreases at an average rate of 2°C per 1,000 feet.

- Stability is the atmosphere's resistance to vertical motion. Air is stable when a lifted parcel of air is cooler than the ambient air. Dry air tends to cool more when lifted and tends to be more stable. The ambient lapse rate allows you to determine atmospheric stability.

- Ambient air with a low or inverted lapse rate tends to be stable. A common type of ground- or surface-based temperature inversion is that which is produced by ground radiation on clear, cool nights with calm or light wind. When humidity is high you can expect poor visibility due to fog, haze, or low clouds.

CLOUDS

- Clouds occur when water vapor condenses. They are divided into four basic families: low, middle, high, and clouds with vertical development.

- Cumulus clouds are formed when unstable air is lifted. Stratiform clouds are formed when stable air is lifted. The lifting of moist, unstable air results in good visibility outside the cloud, showery precipitation, and turbulence. However, the lifting of moist, stable air results in continuous precipitation, little or no turbulence, and poor visibility.

- Towering cumulus clouds indicate convective turbulence. Fair weather cumulus clouds indicate turbulence at and below the cloud level. To estimate the bases of cumulus clouds, in thousands of feet, divide the temperature/dewpoint spread at the surface by 2.5°C (4.4°F). If using the quick estimate method, divide the temperature/dewpoint spread by 4°F (2.2°C).

- The suffix nimbus, used in naming clouds, means a rain cloud.

- High clouds are composed mostly of ice crystals.

AIRMASSES AND FRONTS

- An airmass is a large body of air that covers an extensive area and has fairly uniform temperature and moisture content. A front is a discontinuity between two airmasses. A cold front occurs when cold air displaces warmer air. A warm front occurs when warm air overruns colder air.

- Cooling from below increases the stability of an airmass and warming from below decreases it. Steady precipitation, in contrast to showers, preceding a front is an indication of stratiform clouds with little or no turbulence.

- When a cold airmass moves over, or is heated by, a warm surface, the result is cumuliform clouds, turbulence, and good visibility. When the air is moist and unstable, the updrafts are particularly strong, resulting in cumulonimbus clouds.

- An occlusion occurs when a cold front overtakes another front. In a cold front occlusion, the air ahead of the warm front is warmer than the air behind the overtaking cold front.

- A frontal cyclone starts as a slow-moving cold front or stationary front and can end as a cold front occlusion with potentially severe weather.

HIGH ALTITUDE WEATHER

- A jetstream is defined as wind of 50 knots or greater. They are found in bands of strong westerly winds that occur at breaks in the tropopause in the northern hemisphere. While they can provide beneficial winds when flying west to east, they also can be associated with strong turbulence.

- The strength and location of the jetstream is normally weaker and farther north in the summer. During the winter months in the middle latitudes, the jet stream shifts toward the south and speed increases.

9-1   PLT301
A common type of ground or surface based temperature inversion is that which is produced by

A– warm air being lifted rapidly aloft in the vicinity of mountainous terrain.

B– the movement of colder air over warm air, or the movement of warm air under cold air.

C– ground radiation on clear, cool nights when the wind is light.

9-1. Answer C. GFDIC 9A, AW
An inversion means the temperature increases (instead of decreases) with an increase in altitude. When an inversion exists, visibility is often restricted by fog, haze, smoke, and low clouds. One of the most familiar types of ground- or surface-based inversions forms from radiation cooling just above the ground on clear, cool nights when the wind is light.

9-2   PLT510
The primary cause of all changes in the Earth's weather is

A– variation of solar energy received by the Earth's regions.

B– changes in air pressure over the Earth's surface.

C– movement of the air masses.

9-2. Answer A. GFDIC 9A, AW
The primary cause of weather is uneven heating of the earth's surface by the sun; solar radiation is the driving force that sets the atmosphere in motion.

9-3   PLT203
A characteristic of the stratosphere is

A– an overall decrease of temperature with an increase in altitude.

B– a relatively even base altitude of approximately 35,000 feet.

C– relatively small changes in temperature with an increase in altitude.

9-3. Answer C. GFDIC 9A, AW
The stratosphere is above the tropopause. The base of the stratosphere varies with latitude and season from about 20,000 feet at the poles to 60,000 feet at the equator. This layer is characterized by relatively small changes in temperature with increasing altitude.

9-4   PLT344
Steady precipitation, in contrast to showers, preceding a front is an indication of

A– stratiform clouds with moderate turbulence.

B– cummuliform clouds with little or no turbulence.

C– stratiform clouds with little or no turbulence.

9-4. Answer C. GFDIC 9A, AW
Steady precipitation usually indicates the presence of moist, stable air that supports the development of stratiform clouds with little or no turbulence. Showery precipitation indicates the presence of moist, unstable air which is characterized by cumulus clouds with moderate or greater turbulence.

9-5   PLT344

The presence of ice pellets at the surface is evidence that

A– there are thunderstorms in the area.

B– a cold front has passed.

C– there is freezing rain at a higher altitude.

9-5. Answer C. GFDIC 9A, AW

Rain that remains a liquid even though its temperature is below freezing is referred to as freezing rain. Ice pellets result if the rain freezes as it falls. This always indicates freezing rain at some higher altitude and the existence of a layer of warmer air aloft.

9-6   PLT493

Which conditions result in the formation of frost?

A– The temperature of the collecting surface is at or below freezing and small droplets of moisture are falling.

B– When dew forms and the temperature is below freezing.

C– Temperature of the collecting surface is below the dewpoint of surrounding air and the dewpoint is colder than freezing.

9-6. Answer C. GFDIC 9A, AW

On cool nights, the surface of an aircraft may cool below the dewpoint of the surrounding air. When this happens, moisture condenses out of the air in the form of dew. If the temperature of the aircraft is at or below the dewpoint and the dewpoint is below freezing, moisture will deposit directly as ice crystals or frost rather than condensing as dew.

9-7   PLT512

To which meteorological condition does the term "dewpoint" refer?

A– The temperature to which air must be cooled to become saturated.

B– The temperature at which condensation and evaporation are equal.

C– The temperature at which dew will always form.

9-7. Answer A. GFDIC 9A, AW

When the dewpoint is reached, the air contains all the moisture it can hold at that temperature, and it is said to be saturated.

9-8   PLT344

What temperature condition is indicated if wet snow is encountered at your flight altitude?

A– The temperature is above freezing at your altitude.

B– The temperature is below freezing at your altitude.

C– You are flying from a warm air mass into a cold air mass.

9-8. Answer A. GFDIC 9A, AW

Precipitation that forms by sublimation falls as snow if the temperature of the air remains below freezing. Melting snow indicates that the temperature is above freezing at your altitude.

9-9   PLT512

The amount of water vapor which air can hold largely depends on

A– relative humidity.

B– air temperature.

C– stability of air.

9-10   PLT192

Clouds, fog, or dew will always form when

A– water vapor condenses.

B– water vapor is present.

C– the temperature and dewpoint are equal.

9-11   PLT516

What causes surface winds to flow across the isobars at an angle rather than parallel to the isobars?

A– Coriolis force.

B– Surface friction.

C– The greater density of the air at the surface.

9-12   PLT516

Winds at 5,000 feet AGL on a particular flight are southwesterly while most of the surface winds are southerly. This difference in direction is primarily due to

A– a stronger pressure gradient at higher altitudes.

B– friction between the wind and the surface.

C– stronger Coriolis force at the surface.

9-13   PLT516

What relationship exists between the winds at 2,000 feet above the surface and the surface winds?

A– The winds at 2,000 feet and the surface winds flow in the same direction, but the surface winds are weaker due to friction.

B– The winds at 2,000 feet tend to parallel the isobars while the surface winds cross the isobars at an angle toward lower pressure and are weaker.

C– The surface winds tend to veer to the right of the winds at 2,000 feet and are usually weaker.

9-9. Answer B. GFDIC 9A, AW

The amount of water vapor which air can hold largely depends on air temperature. Since warm air is not as dense as cold air, it can hold more water vapor than cold air. When the air temperature is the same as the dewpoint, the air is 100 percent saturated. As the air temperature increases above the dewpoint, the saturation percentage decreases below 100 percent.

9-10. Answer A. GFDIC 9A, AW

Condensation identifies a change in state of water vapor. When this happens in the atmosphere, clouds, fog, or dew will always form.

9-11. Answer B. GFDIC 9A, AW

When the pressure gradient force and Coriolis force are balanced, airflow circulation aloft is parallel to the isobars. Within about 2,000 feet of the ground, surface friction slows the wind, and Coriolis force is weakened. Pressure gradient force then predominates, causing the wind to flow at an angle to the isobars.

9-12. Answer B. GFDIC 9A, AW

When the pressure gradient force and Coriolis force are balanced, airflow circulation aloft is parallel to the isobars. Within about 2,000 feet of the ground, surface friction slows the wind, and Coriolis force is weakened. Pressure gradient force then predominates, causing the wind to flow at an angle to the isobars.

9-13. Answer B. GFDIC 9A, AW

When the pressure gradient force and Coriolis force are balanced, airflow circulation aloft is parallel to the isobars. Within about 2,000 feet of the ground, surface friction slows the wind, and Coriolis force is weakened. Pressure gradient force then predominates, causing the wind to flow at an angle to the isobars. At an altitude of about 2,000 feet AGL, the effect of surface friction on the wind decreases. Because of this, Coriolis force strengthens and tends to make the wind blow parallel to the isobars.

9-14   PLT510
Which force, in the Northern Hemisphere, acts at a right angle to the wind and deflects it to the right until parallel to the isobars?

A– Centrifugal.

B– Pressure gradient.

C– Coriolis.

9-14. Answer C. GFDIC 9A, AW
Coriolis force acts at a right angle to the wind and deflects the air to the right in the Northern Hemisphere

9-15   PLT301
The most frequent type of ground or surface based temperature inversion is that produced by

A– radiation on a clear, relatively still night.

B– warm air being lifted rapidly aloft in the vicinity of mountainous terrain.

C– the movement of colder air under warm air, or the movement of warm air over cold air.

9-15. Answer A. GFDIC 9A, AW
Temperature inversions are usually confined to fairly shallow layers and may occur near the surface or at higher altitudes. They usually develop in stable air with little or no wind and turbulence. One of the most familiar types of a ground- or surface-based inversion is from radiation cooling just above the ground on clear, cool nights when the wind is light.

9-16   PLT301
What feature is associated with a temperature inversion?

A– A stable layer of air.

B– An unstable layer of air.

C– Air mass thunderstorms.

9-16. Answer A. GFDIC 9A, AW
Temperature inversions are usually confined to fairly shallow layers and may occur near the surface or at higher altitudes. They usually develop in stable air with little or no wind and turbulence. One of the most familiar types of a ground- or surface-based inversion is from radiation cooling just above the ground on clear, cool nights when the wind is light. Typical conditions associated with temperature inversions include stable air with little, or no, wind and turbulence.

9-17   PLT511
What type of clouds will be formed if very stable moist air is forced upslope?

A– First stratified clouds and then vertical clouds.

B– Vertical clouds with increasing height.

C– Stratified clouds with little vertical development.

9-17. Answer C. GFDIC 9A, AW
When air is forced aloft from orographic lifting, the stability of the air before it is lifted determines the type of clouds that will form. For example, if stable, moist air is forced up a slope, stratus-type clouds with little vertical development typically form. The stable air resists further upward movement. On the other hand, if unstable, moist air is lifted aloft, clouds with vertical development usually form.

9-18 PLT511
The general characteristics of unstable air are

A– good visibility, showery precipitation, and cumuliform type clouds.

B– good visibility, steady precipitation, and stratiform type clouds.

C– poor visibility, intermittent precipitation, and cumuliform type clouds.

9-18. Answer A. GFDIC 9A, AW
Unstable air is usually turbulent, with good surface visibility outside of scattered rain showers and cumuliform-type clouds, including clouds with extensive vertical development. In contrast, stable air is generally smooth, with restricted visibilities in widespread areas of stratiform clouds and steady rain or drizzle.

9-19 PLT173
Which is a characteristic of stable air?

A– Fair weather cumulus clouds.

B– Stratiform clouds.

C– Unlimited visibility.

9-19. Answer B. GFDIC 9A, AW
Unstable air is usually turbulent, with good surface visibility outside of scattered rain showers and cumuliform-type clouds, including clouds withextensive vertical development. In contrast, stable air is generally smooth, with restricted visibilities in widespread areas of stratiform clouds and steady rain or drizzle.

9-20 PLT511
What type clouds can be expected when an unstable air mass is forced to ascend a mountain slope?

A– Layered clouds with little vertical development.

B– Stratified clouds with considerable associated turbulence.

C– Clouds with extensive vertical development.

9-20. Answer C. GFDIC 9A, AW
When air is forced aloft from orographic lifting, the stability of the air before it is lifted determines the type of clouds that will form. For example, if stable, moist air is forced up a slope, stratus-type clouds with little vertical development typically form. The stable air resists further upward movement. On the other hand, if unstable, moist air is lifted aloft, clouds with vertical development usually form.

9-21 PLT511
What are the characteristics of stable air?

A– Good visibility, steady precipitation, and stratus type clouds.

B– Poor visibility, intermittent precipitation, and cumulus type clouds.

C– Poor visibility, steady precipitation, and stratus type clouds.

9-21. Answer C. GFDIC 9A, AW
Unstable air is usually turbulent, with good surface visibility outside of scattered rain showers and cumuliform-type clouds, including clouds with extensive vertical development. In contrast, stable air is generally smooth, with restricted visibilities in widespread areas of stratiform clouds and steady rain or drizzle.

9-22 PLT173
What are some characteristics of unstable air?

A– Nimbostratus clouds and good surface visibility.

B– Turbulence and poor surface visibility.

C– Turbulence and good surface visibility.

9-22. Answer C. GFDIC 9A, AW
Unstable air is usually turbulent, with good surface visibility outside of scattered rain showers and cumuliform-type clouds, including clouds with extensive vertical development. In contrast, stable air is generally smooth, with restricted visibilities in widespread areas of stratiform clouds and steady rain or drizzle.

9-23   PLT173

Stability can be determined from which measurement of the atmosphere?

A– Low level winds.

B– Ambient lapse rate.

C– Atmospheric pressure.

9-23. Answer B. GFDIC 9A, AW

The ambient lapse rate is the rate at which the air cools with an increase in altitude. If the lapse rate is large, warm air is encouraged to rise creating unstable conditions. If the lapse rate is small, lifting is suppressed resulting in stable conditions.

9-24   PLT511

What determines the structure or type of clouds which form as a result of air being forced to ascend?

A– The method by which the air is lifted.

B– The stability of the air before lifting occurs.

C– The amount of condensation nuclei present after lifting occurs.

9-24. Answer B. GFDIC 9A, AW

Assuming moisture is present, the stability of the air before lifting occurs plays a major role in determining the structure or type of clouds that form when air is lifted. For example, when stable air is forced aloft, stratus-type clouds with little vertical development commonly form. If unstable air is lifted aloft, clouds with vertical development will usually form.

9-25   PLT192

Which of the following combinations of weather producing variables would likely result in cumuliform type clouds, good visibility, rain showers, and possible clear type icing in clouds?

A– Unstable, moist air, and no lifting mechanism.

B– Stable, dry air, and orographic lifting.

C– Unstable, moist air, and orographic lifting.

9-25. Answer C. GFDIC 9A, AW

Unstable, moist air that is lifted orographically usually results in turbulent conditions, with good surface visibility outside of scattered rain showers and cumuliform-type clouds. With temperatures near or below freezing, an accumulation of clear ice is possible.

9-26   PLT024

Unsaturated air flowing upslope will cool at the rate of approximately (dry adiabatic lapse rate)

A– 3°C per 1,000 feet.

B– 2°C per 1,000 feet.

C– 2.5°C per 1,000 feet.

9-26. Answer A. GFDIC 9A, AW

The adiabatic lapse rate is the rate at which air cools as it is lifted. The rate depends on the amount of moisture present in the air. The dry adiabatic lapse rate is 3°C per 1,000 feet. The moist adiabatic lapse rate varies from 1.1°C to 2.8°C per 1,000 feet.

9-27   PLT301

A temperature inversion will normally form only

A– in stable air.

B– in unstable air.

C– when a stratiform layer merges with a cumuliform mass.

9-27. Answer A. GFDIC 9A, AW

Temperature inversions normally occur in stable air with little, or no, wind and turbulence.

9-28   PLT511

Frontal waves normally form on

A– slow moving cold fronts or stationary fronts.

B– slow moving warm fronts and strong occluded fronts.

C– rapidly moving cold fronts or warm fronts.

9-28. Answer A. GFDIC 9A, AW

A frontal wave is a phenomenon which results primarily from the interaction of two contrasting airmasses. The wave usually begins as a disturbance along a slow moving cold front or stationary front.

9-29   PLT511

Which are characteristics of an unstable cold air mass moving over a warm surface?

A– Cumuliform clouds, turbulence, and poor visibility.

B– Cumuliform clouds, turbulence, and good visibility.

C– Stratiform clouds, smooth air, and poor visibility.

9-29. Answer B. GFDIC 9A, AW

The characteristics of an unstable cold airmass are similar to that of any unstable airmass that is forced aloft. The unstable air promotes the development of cumuliform clouds, turbulence, and good visibility outside of clouds or precipitation.

9-30   PLT192

The suffix "nimbus", used in naming clouds, means a

A– cloud with extensive vertical development.

B– raincloud.

C– dark massive, towering cloud.

9-30. Answer B. GFDIC 9A, AW

The term prefix "nimbo" and the suffix "nimbus" are used to describe a raincloud. "Cumulo" is used to describe clouds with extensive vertical development. "Cumulonimbus" describes massive towering clouds, such as those in a thunderstorm.

9-31   PLT192

What are the four families of clouds?

A– Stratus, cumulus, nimbus, and cirrus.

B– Clouds formed by updrafts, fronts, cooling layers of air, and precipitation into warm air.

C– High, middle, low, and those with extensive vertical development.

9-31. Answer C. GFDIC 9A, AW

The four families of clouds are: high, middle, low, and those with extensive vertical development.

9-32   PLT511

Which weather phenomenon is always associated with the passage of a frontal system?

A– A wind change.

B– An abrupt decrease in pressure.

C– Clouds, either ahead or behind the front.

9-32. Answer A. GFDIC 9A, AW

The most reliable indications that you are crossing a front are a change in wind direction, wind speed, or both. Although the exact new direction of the wind is difficult to predict, the wind always shifts to the right in the northern hemisphere.

9-33   PLT495

What is indicated by the term "embedded thunderstorms"?

A— Severe thunderstorms are embedded within a squall line.

B— Thunderstorms are predicted to develop in a stable air mass.

C— Thunderstorms are obscured by massive cloud layers and cannot be seen.

9-33. Answer C. GFDIC 9A, AW

When a thunderstorm is obscured by other cloud formations, it is said to be embedded. When IFR conditions exist, this can be particularly hazardous, since you cannot see the thunderstorms. Maximum use of ground and/or airborne radar is recommended when embedded thunderstorms are reported, or even suspected.

9-34   PLT192

Fair weather cumulus clouds often indicate

A— turbulence at and below the cloud level.

B— poor visibility.

C— smooth flying conditions.

9-34. Answer A. GFDIC 9A, AW

Cumulus clouds form in convective currents resulting from the uneven heating of the earth's surface. Widely spaced cumulus clouds that form in fairly clear skies are called fair weather cumulus and indicate a shallow layer of instability. You can expect turbulence at and below the cloud level, but little icing or precipitation.

9-35   PLT203

The average height of the troposphere in the middle latitudes is

A— 20,000 feet.

B— 25,000 feet.

C— 37,000 feet.

9-35. Answer C. GFDIC 9A, AW

For a given latitude, it is higher in the summer than it is in the winter. In the mid-latitudes, it averages about 37,000 feet.

9-36   PLT192

A high cloud is composed mostly of

A— ozone.

B— condensation nuclei.

C— ice crystals.

9-36. Answer C. GFDIC 9A, AW

Because of the extremely cold temperatures, high clouds are composed mainly of ice crystals.

9-37   PLT511

An air mass is a body of air that

A— has similar cloud formations associated with it.

B— creates a wind shift as it moves across the Earth's surface.

C— covers an extensive area and has fairly uniform properties of temperature and moisture.

9-37. Answer C. GFDIC 9A, AW

An airmass is a large body of air with fairly uniform temperature and moisture content. It usually forms where air remains stationary or nearly stationary for several days.

9-38   PLT344

What enhances the growth rate of precipitation?

A– Advective action.

B– Upward currents.

C– Cyclonic movement.

9-38. Answer B. GFDIC 9A, AW

Once a water droplet forms, it grows as it collides and merges with other droplets. This process produces large precipitation particles. If these particles encounter any upward currents, the process will continue and the growth rate will be increased. Precipitation formed by merging drops with mild upward currents can produce light to moderate rain. Strong upward currents support the largest drops and can produce heavy rain and hail.

9-39   PLT344

Which precipitation type normally indicates freezing rain at higher altitudes?

A– Snow.

B– Hail.

C– Ice pellets.

9-39. Answer C. GFDIC 9A, AW

Ice pellets result if rain freezes as it falls. This usually indicates freezing rain at some higher altitude and the existence of a layer of warmer air aloft.

9-40   PLT302

The strength and location of the jetstream is normally

A– stronger and farther north in the winter.

B– weaker and farther north in the summer.

C– stronger and farther north in the summer.

9-40. Answer B. GFDIC 9A, AW

In the mid-latitudes, the jetstream is usually weaker in the summer than in the winter. This is because its mean position shifts north in the summer. As the jet stream moves north, its core descends to a lower altitude, and its average speed usually decreases.

9-41   PLT301

Which weather conditions should be expected beneath a low level temperature inversion layer when the relative humidity is high?

A– Smooth air and poor visibility due to fog, haze, or low clouds.

B– Light wind shear and poor visibility due to haze and light rain.

C– Turbulent air and poor visibility due to fog, low stratus type clouds, and showery precipitation.

9-41. Answer A. GFDIC 9A, AW

In order for a low-level temperature inversion to exist, the air must be stable. This, combined with a high relative humidity, usually results in smooth air with poor visibility in fog, haze, or low clouds.

9-42   PLT203

Which feature is associated with the tropopause?

A– Absence of wind and turbulent conditions.

B– Absolute upper limit of cloud formation.

C– Abrupt change in temperature lapse rate.

9-42. Answer C. GFDIC 9A, AW

The top of the troposphere is called the tropopause and serves as the boundary between the troposphere and the stratosphere. The location of the tropopause is usually characterized by a pronounced change in the temperature lapse rate. In the northern hemisphere there are two breaks in the tropopause; one is between the polar and subtropical airmasses and the other is between the subtropical and tropical airmasses.

SECTION B — WEATHER HAZARDS

THUNDERSTORMS

- When sufficient moisture is present, cumulus cloud build-ups indicate the presence of convective turbulence.
- Thunderstorm formation requires an unstable lapse rate, a lifting force, and a relatively high moisture level.
- The life cycle of a thunderstorm consists of three distinct stages. The cumulus stage is characterized by continuous updrafts. Thunderstorms reach the greatest intensity during the mature stage, which is signaled by the beginning of precipitation at the surface. As the storm dies during the dissipating stage, updrafts weaken and downdrafts become predominant.
- Airmass thunderstorms are relatively short-lived storms and are usually isolated or scattered over a large area. They form in convective currents, which are most active on warm summer afternoons when the winds are light. Severe thunderstorms contain wind gusts of 50 knots or more, hail 3/4 inch in diameter or larger, and/or tornadoes.
- Cumulonimbus clouds by themselves indicate severe turbulence. Other indications of turbulence are very frequent lightning and roll clouds.
- Some weather hazards associated with thunderstorms, such as lightning, hail, and turbulence are not confined to the cloud itself. Wind shear areas can be found on all sides of a thunderstorm, as well as directly under it.
- Embedded thunderstorms are particularly dangerous to IFR pilots. Because they are obscured by massive cloud layers, they are more difficult to avoid.
- Airborne weather radar can help you avoid thunderstorms. However, it provides no assurance of avoiding IFR weather conditions. If using radar, avoid intense radar echoes by at least 20 miles and do not fly between them if they are less than 40 miles apart.
- A squall line is a narrow band of active thunderstorms that often forms 50 to 200 miles ahead of a fast moving cold front and contains some of the most severe types of weather-related hazards.
- If you encounter turbulence during flight, establish maneuvering or penetration speed, maintain a level flight attitude, and accept variations in airspeed and altitude. If encountering turbulence during the approach to a landing, it is recommended that you increase the airspeed slightly above normal approach speed to attain more positive control.

WAKE TURBULENCE

- Wake turbulence is created when an aircraft generates lift. The greatest vortex strength occurs when the generating aircraft is heavy, slow, in a clean configuration, and at a high angle of attack.
- Wingtip vortices can exceed the roll rate of an aircraft, especially when flying in the same direction as the generating aircraft.
- Wingtip vortices tend to sink below the flight path of the aircraft which generated them. They are most hazardous during light, quartering tailwind conditions. You should avoid the area below and behind an aircraft generating wake turbulence, especially at low altitude where even a momentary wake encounter could be hazardous.
- A helicopter can produce vortices similar to wingtip vortices of a large fixed-wing airplane.

OTHER TURBULENCE

- Turbulence that momentarily causes slight, erratic changes in altitude and/or attitude should be reported as light. Moderate turbulence causes noticeable changes in altitude and/or attitude, but aircraft control remains positive.
- Mechanical turbulence is often experienced in the traffic pattern when wind forms eddies as it blows over hangars, stands of trees, or other obstructions.
- Any front traveling at a speed of 30 knots or more produces at least a moderate amount of turbulence.
- Turbulence that is encountered above 15,000 feet AGL that is not associated with cumuliform cloudiness, including thunderstorms, is reported as clear air turbulence. Clear air turbulence often develops in or near the jet stream, which is a narrow band of high altitude winds near the tropopause.
- A common location of clear air turbulence is in an upper trough on the polar side of a jet stream. The jet stream and associated clear air turbulence can sometimes be visually identified in flight by long streaks of cirrus clouds.

- Strong mountain wave turbulence can be anticipated when the winds across a ridge are 40 knots or more, and the air is stable. The crests of mountain waves may be marked by lens-shaped, or lenticular, clouds. The presence of rotor clouds on the lee side of the mountain also indicates the possibility of strong turbulence.
- The greatest turbulence normally occurs as you approach the lee side of mountain ranges, ridges, or hilly terrain in strong headwinds.

WIND SHEAR

- Wind shear is a sudden, drastic change in wind speed and/or direction. It can exist at any altitude and may occur in a vertical or horizontal direction.
- Wind shear is often associated with a strong low-level temperature inversion with strong winds above the inversion, a jet stream, a thunderstorm, or a frontal zone.
- Wind shear can also occur prior to the passage of a warm front and following the passage of a cold front.
- During an approach, monitoring the power and vertical velocity required to remain on the proper glideslope is the most important and most easily recognized means of being alerted to possible wind shear. When the wind changes to more of a headwind, the aircraft initially tends to balloon above the glidepath, and then drop below the glidepath because of lower groundspeed. To correct, reduce power momentarily, and then increase it once established in the headwind conditions. The reverse actions are needed if flying into conditions of less headwind or more tailwind.
- Microbursts are one of the most dangerous sources of wind shear. A microburst is an intense, localized downdraft seldom lasting longer than 15 minutes from the time the burst first strikes the ground until dissipation. The maximum downdrafts encountered in a microburst may be as strong as 6,000 feet per minute.
- In a microburst, strong wind flows outward in every direction at the surface. An aircraft entering a microburst initially experiences a headwind, with increasing performance, and then a tailwind, with decreasing performance combined with a strong downdraft. If encountering a headwind of 45 knots within a microburst, you would expect a total shear across the microburst of 90 knots.

RESTRICTIONS TO VISIBILITY

- Restrictions to visibility can include fog, haze, smoke, smog, and dust.
- Formation of fog is encouraged by the presence of small particles in the air on which condensation can occur. Industrial areas typically produce more fog since the burning of fossil fuels produces more of these condensation nuclei.
- Radiation fog forms over fairly flat land on clear, calm nights when the air is moist and there is a small temperature/dewpoint spread.
- Advection fog is most likely to form in coastal areas when moist air moves over colder ground or water. It can appear suddenly during the day or night and is more persistent than radiation fog.
- Advection fog and upslope fog are both dependent upon wind for their formation. However, surface winds stronger than 15 knots tend to dissipate or lift advection fog into low stratus clouds.
- Volcanic ash clouds are highly abrasive to aircraft and engines, and they also restrict visibility.
- Precipitation-induced fog is most commonly associated with warm fronts and is a result of saturation due to evaporation of precipitation.
- Steam fog forms when very cold air moves over a warmer water surface.
- Restrictions to visibility, such as haze, create the illusion of being at a greater distance above the runway, which can cause a pilot to fly a lower-than-normal approach.

ICING

- The three types of structural ice are rime, clear, and mixed.
- The accumulation of ice on an aircraft increases drag and weight and decreases lift and thrust.
- Ice pellets usually indicate the presence of freezing rain at a higher altitude. Freezing rain is hazardous because it is most likely to have the highest rate of accumulation of structural icing. The presence of freezing rain at your altitude indicates the temperature is above freezing at some higher altitude.

- Since high clouds typically do not consist of liquid water, they are least likely to contribute to aircraft structural icing.
- The freezing level is where the temperature is 0°C. You can estimate the freezing level by dividing the temperature in °C above zero, by the lapse rate of 2°C per 1,000 feet.
- If frost is not removed from the wings before flight, it may cause an early airflow separation which decreases lift and increases drag. This causes the airplane to stall at a lower-than-normal angle of attack.

HYDROPLANING

- Hydroplaning occurs when the tires float on top of a thin layer of water on the runway. It results in poor or nil braking action at high speeds, and may result in an aircraft skidding off the side or end of the runway.
- High aircraft speed, standing water, slush, and a smooth runway texture are factors conducive to hydroplaning.

COLD WEATHER OPERATIONS

- During preflight in cold weather, crankcase breather lines should receive special attention because they are susceptible to being clogged by ice from crankcase vapors that have condensed and subsequently frozen.
- It is recommended that during cold weather operations, you should preheat the cabin, as well as the engine.

9-43   PLT105
Which is true regarding the use of airborne weather-avoidance radar for the recognition of certain weather conditions?

A– The radarscope provides no assurance of avoiding instrument weather conditions.

B– The avoidance of hail is assured when flying between and just clear of the most intense echoes.

C– The clear area between intense echoes indicates that visual sighting of storms can be maintained when flying between the echoes.

9-43. Answer A. GFDIC 9B, AC 00-24B
Airborne weather radar is designed as an aid for avoiding severe weather, not for penetrating it. Weather radar detects precipitation based on echo returns of significant raindrops; it does not detect minute droplets or other phenomenon such as hail, turbulence, and updrafts/downdrafts. Therefore, it should not be relied on to avoid instrument weather associated with clouds and fog or certain other severe weather conditions.

9-44   PLT492
If the air temperature is +8°C at an elevation of 1,350 feet and a standard (average) temperature lapse rate exists, what will be the approximate freezing level?

A– 3,350 feet MSL.

B– 5,350 feet MSL.

C– 9,350 feet MSL.

9-44. Answer B. GFDIC 9B, AW
The standard, or average, temperature lapse rate is approximately 2°C per 1,000 feet. If the temperature at 1,350 feet is 8°C, divide 8°C by 2°C to determine how much higher the freezing level is (8 ÷ 2 = 4). This means the freezing level is 4,000 feet above 1,350 feet, or 5,350 feet MSL.

9-45   PLT495
Which weather phenomenon signals the beginning of the mature stage of a thunderstorm?

A– The start of rain at the surface.

B– Growth rate of cloud is maximum.

C– Strong turbulence in the cloud.

9-45. Answer A. GFDIC 9B, AW
There are three stages for a typical thunderstorm — cumulus, mature, and dissipating. In the cumulus stage, a lifting action initiates the vertical movement of air. As the air rises and cools to the dewpoint, water vapor condenses forming cumuliform clouds. This first stage is dominated by rapid cloud growth and the presence of updrafts that can reach speeds of 3,000 f.p.m. Updrafts continue to increase up to speeds of 6,000 f.p.m. early in the mature stage. Thunderstorms reach the greatest intensity during the mature stage, which is signaled by the beginning of precipitation at the surface. A corresponding downdraft is typical and may reach a velocity of 2,500 f.p.m. When the cell becomes an area of predominant downdrafts, it is considered to be in the dissipating stage.

9-46   PLT192
Which clouds have the greatest turbulence?

A– Towering cumulus.

B– Cumulonimbus.

C– Altocumulus castellanus.

9-46. Answer B. GFDIC 9B, AW
Cumulonimbus clouds usually have the greatest turbulence because of the existence of both up- and downdrafts. Cumulonimbus is synonymous with thunderstorms.

9-47   PLT263
Standing lenticular clouds, in mountainous areas, indicate

A– an inversion.

B– unstable air.

C– turbulence.

9-47. Answer C. GFDIC 9B, AW
Standing lenticular altocumulus clouds are formed on the crests of waves created by barriers in the wind flow. The clouds show little movement and are characterized by their smooth, polished edges. The presence of these clouds is a good indication of very strong turbulence, and they should be avoided.

9-48   PLT263
The presence of standing lenticular altocumulus clouds is a good indication of

A– a jetstream.

B– very strong turbulence.

C– heavy icing conditions.

9-48. Answer B. GFDIC 9B, AW
Standing lenticular altocumulus clouds are formed on the crests of waves created by barriers in the wind flow. The clouds show little movement and are characterized by their smooth, polished edges. The presence of these clouds is a good indication of very strong turbulence, and they should be avoided.

9-49   PLT192
Which family of clouds is least likely to contribute to structural icing on an aircraft?

A– Low clouds.

B– High clouds.

C– Clouds with extensive vertical development.

9-49. Answer B. GFDIC 9B, AW
High clouds are the least likely to contribute to structural icing since they are composed mainly of ice crystals.

9-50   PLT294

If you encounter in-flight icing and ATC asks you to report your conditions, what are the official reportable icing values that you are expected to use?

A– Light, moderate, severe, extreme.

B– Trace, light, moderate, severe.

C– Few, light, moderate, severe.

9-50. Answer B. GFDIC 9B, IFH

In weather forecasts or pilot reports, aircraft structural icing is normally classified as trace, light, moderate, or severe depending on the accumulation rate.

9-51   PLT495

Where can wind shear associated with a thunderstorm be found? Choose the most complete answer.

A– In front of the thunderstorm cell (anvil side) and on the right side of the cell.

B– In front of the thunderstorm cell and directly under the cell.

C– On all sides of the thunderstorm cell and directly under the cell.

9-51. Answer C. GFDIC 9B, AW

Near the surface, under a thunderstorm, there is typically an area of low-level turbulence which develop as downdrafts emerge and spread out at the surface. These create a shear zone that spreads outward in all directions from the center of the storm.

9-52   PLT475

Where do squall lines most often develop?

A– In an occluded front.

B– In a cold air mass.

C– Ahead of a cold front.

9-52. Answer C. GFDIC 9B, AW

Squall lines are a narrow band of active thunderstorms which normally contain very severe weather. They often form 50 to 200 miles ahead of a fast moving cold front, although the existence of a front is not necessary for a squall line to from.

9-53   PLT518

Where does wind shear occur?

A– Exclusively in thunderstorms.

B– Wherever there is an abrupt decrease in pressure and/or temperature.

C– With either a wind shift or a windspeed gradient at any level in the atmosphere.

9-53. Answer C. GFDIC 9B, AW

A wind shear is a sudden, drastic shift in wind speed and/or direction that may occur at any altitude in a vertical or horizontal plane.

9-54   PLT518
What is an important characteristic of wind shear?

A– It is primarily associated with the lateral vortices generated by thunderstorms.

B– It usually exists only in the vicinity of thunderstorms, but may be found near a strong temperature inversion.

C– It may be associated with either a wind shift or a windspeed gradient at any level in the atmosphere.

9-54. Answer C. GFDIC 9B, AIM, AW
A wind shear is a sudden, drastic shift in wind speed and/or direction that may occur at any altitude in a vertical or horizontal plane.

9-55   PLT518
Which is a characteristic of low level wind shear as it relates to frontal activity?

A– With a warm front, the most critical period is before the front passes the airport.

B– With a cold front, the most critical period is just before the front passes the airport.

C– Turbulence will always exist in wind shear conditions.

9-55. Answer A. GFDIC 9B, AW
With fronts, the most common places for wind shear is either just before or just after the front passes. With a warm front, wind shear occurs just before the front passes. In a cold front, wind shear occurs just after the front passes. Studies indicate the amount of wind shear in a warm front is generally greater than in a cold front.

9-56   PLT495
During the life cycle of a thunderstorm, which stage is characterized predominantly by downdrafts?

A– Cumulus.

B– Dissipating.

C– Mature.

9-56. Answer B. GFDIC 9B, AW
The cumulus stage is primarily updrafts. The mature stage is a mixture of up and downdrafts. The dissipating stage is mostly downdrafts.

9-57   PLT495
Which weather phenomenon is always associated with a thunderstorm?

A– Lightning.

B– Heavy rain showers.

C– Supercooled raindrops.

9-57. Answer A. GFDIC 9B, AW
Remember, lightning causes thunder. By definition, lightning is one of the hazards always associated with thunderstorms and it may occur throughout the cloud. While it rarely causes personal injury or substantial damage to the aircraft in flight, it can cause temporary loss of vision, puncture the aircraft skin, or damage electronic navigation and communications equipment.

9-58   PLT495
Which thunderstorms generally produce the most severe conditions, such as heavy hail and destructive winds?

A– Warm front.

B– Squall line.

C– Air mass.

9-58. Answer B. GFDIC 9B, AW
A squall line is a nonfrontal band of thunderstorms that contains the most severe types of weather-related hazards including heavy hail and destructive winds.

9-59   PLT495
What is an indication that downdrafts have developed and the thunderstorm cell has entered the mature stage?

A– The anvil top has completed its development.

B– Precipitation begins to fall from the cloud base.

C– A gust front forms.

9-59. Answer B. GFDIC 9B, AW
Thunderstorms reach the greatest intensity during the mature stage, which is signaled by the beginning of precipitation at the surface. Resulting downdrafts during this stage may reach velocities of 2,500 f.p.m. When the cell becomes an area of predominant downdrafts, it is considered to be in the dissipating stage.

9-60   PLT495
What are the requirements for the formation of a thunderstorm?

A– A cumulus cloud with sufficient moisture.

B– A cumulus cloud with sufficient moisture and an inverted lapse rate.

C– Sufficient moisture, an unstable lapse rate, and a lifting action.

9-60. Answer C. GFDIC 9B, AW
There are three conditions necessary to create a thunderstorm. They are an unstable lapse rate, some type of lifting action, and a relatively high moisture content. If these conditions exist, cumulus clouds typically begin to form.

9-61   PLT518
What is an important characteristic of wind shear?

A– It is an atmospheric condition that is associated exclusively with zones of convergence.

B– The Coriolis phenomenon in both high and low level air masses is the principal generating force.

C– It is an atmospheric condition that may be associated with a low level temperature inversion, a jet stream, or a frontal zone.

9-61. Answer C. GFDIC 9B, AW
Typically, wind shear is associated with temperature inversions, the jet stream, thunderstorms, and frontal zones. It's also important to remember that wind shear can occur in any direction and at any altitude.

9-62   PLT493
Why is frost considered hazardous to flight operation?

A– Frost changes the basic aerodynamic shape of the airfoil.

B– Frost decreases control effectiveness.

C– Frost causes early airflow separation resulting in a loss of lift.

9-62. Answer C. GFDIC 9B, AW
Frost is an element which poses a serious hazard. It interferes with smooth airflow over the wings and can cause early airflow separation, resulting in a loss of lift. Frost also increases drag and, when combined with the loss of lift, may prevent the aircraft from becoming airborne.

9-63   PLT274

In which meteorological environment is aircraft structural icing most likely to have the highest rate of accumulation?

A– Cumulonimbus clouds.

B– High humidity and freezing temperature.

C– Freezing rain.

9-63. Answer C. GFDIC 9B, AW

The condition most likely to result in rapid formation of hazardous icing is freezing rain. This occurs as an aircraft flies through the colder air below a frontal surface where the temperature is between 0°C and -15°C. When rain falling from warmer air above strikes the aircraft, it spreads rapidly and freezes, creating a layer of clear ice. Clear ice is the most serious of the various forms of ice because it has the fastest rate of accumulation, adheres tenaciously to the aircraft, and is more difficult to remove than rime ice.

9-64   PLT128

A generally recommended practice for autopilot usage during cruise flight in icing conditions is

A– having the autopilot continuously engaged while monitoring the system for abnormal trim, trim rate, or attitude.

B– disengaging the autopilot and hand flying the airplane.

C– periodically disengaging and immediately reengaging the altitude hold function.

9-64. Answer B. GFDIC 9B, IPH

It is generally recommended that you disengage the autopilot and hand fly the airplane in icing conditions. Using the autopilot can mask the aerodynamic effects of icing and could cause control problems or a stall. In addition, if the autopilot servo control power is exceeded in icing conditions causing the autopilot to automatically disconnect, you will not be prepared for an immediate control deflection.

9-65   PLT344

What is an operational consideration if you fly into rain which freezes on impact?

A– You have flown into an area of thunderstorms.

B– Temperatures are above freezing at some higher altitude.

C– You have flown through a cold front.

9-65. Answer B. GFDIC 9B, AW

Freezing rain (rain that freezes on impact with the aircraft's surface) is an indication of warmer air at higher altitudes.

9-66   PLT226

Under which condition does advection fog usually form?

A– Moist air moving over colder ground or water.

B– Warm, moist air settling over a cool surface under no wind conditions.

C– A land breeze blowing a cold air mass over a warm water current.

9-66. Answer A. GFDIC 9B, AW

Advection fog is caused when a low layer of warm, moist air moves over a cooler surface, which may be either land or water. It is most common under cloudy skies along coastlines where sea breezes transport air from the warm water to cooler land.

9-67   PLT120
If you fly into severe turbulence, which flight condition should you attempt to maintain?

A– Constant airspeed (V_A).

B– Level flight attitude.

C– Constant altitude and constant airspeed.

9-67. Answer B. GFDIC 9B, AW
If you enter turbulence unexpectedly, enter a thunderstorm, or expect that you may encounter turbulence, reduce power to slow the airplane to maneuvering speed VAor less and attempt to maintain a level flight attitude.

9-68   PLT226
Which weather condition can be expected when moist air flows from a relatively warm surface to a colder surface?

A– Increased visibility.

B– Convective turbulence due to surface heating.

C– Fog.

9-68. Answer C. GFDIC 9B, AW
When a low layer of warm, moist air moves from a warm surface to a cooler surface, advection fog can be expected.

9-69   PLT226
Fog is usually prevalent in industrial areas because of

A– atmospheric stabilization around cities.

B– an abundance of condensation nuclei from combustion products.

C– increased temperatures due to industrial heating.

9-69. Answer B. GFDIC 9B, AW
Fog requires both sufficient moisture and condensation nuclei on which water vapor can condense. Because there is an abundance of condensation nuclei in industrial areas, fog is common.

9-70   PLT226
In which situation is advection fog most likely to form?

A– An air mass moving inland from the coast in winter.

B– A light breeze blowing colder air out to sea.

C– Warm, moist air settling over a warmer surface under no wind conditions.

9-70. Answer A. GFDIC 9B, AW
Advection fog is caused when a low layer of warm, moist air moves over a cooler surface, which may be either land or water. It is most common under cloudy skies along coastlines where sea breezes transport air from the warm water to cooler land.

9-71   PLT226
In what localities is advection fog most likely to occur?

A– Coastal areas.

B– Mountain slopes.

C– Level inland areas.

9-71. Answer A. GFDIC 9B, AW
Advection fog is caused when a low layer of warm, moist air moves over a cooler surface, which may be either land or water. It is most common under cloudy skies along coastlines where sea breezes transport air from the warm water to cooler land.

9-72   PLT226
What types of fog depend upon a wind in order to exist?

A– Steam fog and downslope fog.

B– Precipitation-induced fog and ground fog.

C– Advection fog and upslope fog.

9-72. Answer C. GFDIC 9B, AW
Advection fog is caused when a low layer of warm, moist air moves over a cooler surface, which may be either land or water. It is most common under cloudy skies along coastlines where sea breezes transport air from the warm water to cooler land. Upslope fog forms when moist, stable air is forced up a sloping land mass. Like advection fog, upslope fog can form in moderate to strong winds and under cloudy skies.

9-73   PLT226
What situation is most conducive to the formation of radiation fog?

A– Warm, moist air over low, flatland areas on clear, calm nights.

B– Moist, tropical air moving over cold, offshore water.

C– The movement of cold air over much warmer water.

9-73. Answer A. GFDIC 9B, AW
Radiation fog, often called ground fog, forms with warm, moist air over fairly low, level land areas on clear, calm nights.

9-74   PLT226
Which conditions are favorable for the formation of radiation fog?

A– Moist air moving over colder ground or water.

B– Cloudy sky and a light wind moving saturated warm air over a cool surface.

C– Clear sky, little or no wind, small temperature/ dewpoint spread, and over a land surface.

9-74. Answer C. GFDIC 9B, AW
Radiation fog, often called ground fog, forms with warm, moist air over fairly low, level land areas on clear, calm nights.

9-75   PLT128
Test data indicate that ice, snow, or frost having a thickness and roughness similar to medium or coarse sandpaper on the leading edge and upper surface of an airfoil can

A– reduce lift by as much as 30 percent and increase drag by 40 percent.

B– reduce lift by as much as 50 percent and increase drag by as much as 50 percent.

C– increase drag and reduce lift by as much as 25 percent.

9-75. Answer A. GFDIC 9B, AC 20-117
According to AC 20-117, wind tunnel and flight tests indicate that ice, frost, or snow formations on the leading edge and upper surface of a wing, having a thickness similar to medium or coarse sandpaper, can reduce wing lift by as much as 30% and increase drag by 40%. These changes in lift and drag will significantly increase stall speed, reduce controllability and alter aircraft flight characteristics.

9-76   PLT501

A pilot reporting turbulence that momentarily causes slight, erratic changes in altitude and/or attitude should report it as

A– light turbulence.

B– moderate turbulence.

C– light chop.

9-76. Answer A. GFDIC 9B, AIM

Light turbulence can be described as turbulence that momentarily causes slight, erratic changes in altitude or attitude. In addition, you should feel slight strains against your seat belt.

9-77   PLT518

Hazardous wind shear is commonly encountered near the ground

A– during periods when the wind velocity is stronger than 35 knots.

B– during periods when the wind velocity is stronger than 35 knots and near mountain valleys.

C– during periods of strong temperature inversion and near thunderstorms.

9-77. Answer C. GFDIC 9B, AW

Wind shear is a sudden and drastic shift in wind speed and/or direction that may occur at any altitude and in any direction. Wind shear is commonly associated with strong temperature inversions, the jet stream, thunderstorms, and along fronts.

9-78   PLT317

What is the expected duration of an individual microburst?

A– Two minutes with maximum winds lasting approximately 1 minute.

B– One microburst may continue for as long as 2 to 4 hours.

C– Seldom longer than 15 minutes from the time the burst strikes the ground until dissipation.

9-78. Answer C. GFDIC 9B, AIM

A microburst is an intense, localized downdraft of brief duration which spreads out in all directions when it reaches the surface. This creates severe horizontal and vertical wind shears which pose serious hazards to aircraft, particularly those near the surface, An individual microburst usually lasts no longer than 15 minutes from the time the burst first strikes the ground until dissipation.

9-79   PLT317

Maximum downdrafts in a microburst encounter may be as strong as

A– 8,000 feet per minute.

B– 7,000 feet per minute.

C– 6,000 feet per minute.

9-79. Answer C. GFDIC 9B, AIM

An individual microburst typically covers an area of less than two and a half miles in diameter at the surface. Peak winds last two to four minutes and attendant downdrafts can be as strong as 6,000 feet per minute.

9-80   **PLT317**

An aircraft that encounters a headwind of 45 knots, within a microburst, may expect a total shear across the microburst of

A– 40 knots.

B– 80 knots.

C– 90 knots.

9-80. Answer C. GFDIC 9B, AIM

A headwind of 45 knots may result in a 90-knot wind shear (headwind to tailwind change for a traversing aircraft) across the microburst.

9-81   **PLT317**

(Refer to figure 13.)

If involved in a microburst encounter, in which aircraft positions will the most severe downdraft occur?

A– 4 and 5.

B– 2 and 3.

C– 3 and 4.

9-81. Answer C. GFDIC 9B, AIM

Positions 3 and 4 represent the center of the microburst where the strongest downdrafts will be experienced. At these points, the strength of downdrafts can reach 6,000 feet per minute.

9-82   **PLT317**

(Refer to figure 13.)

When penetrating a microburst, which aircraft will experience an increase in performance without a change in pitch or power?

A– 3.

B– 2.

C– 1.

9-82. Answer C. GFDIC 9B, AIM

An aircraft will experience an increase in performance without a change in pitch or power whenever a headwind is experienced. When encountering a microburst, an aircraft will experience a headwind on initial entry into the phenomenon.

9-83   **PLT317**

(Refer to figure 13.)

The aircraft in position 3 will experience which effect in a microburst encounter?

A– Decreasing headwind.

B– Increasing tailwind.

C– Strong downdraft.

9-83. Answer C. GFDIC 9B, AIM

The center of the microburst represents the area of strongest downdrafts.

9-84   PLT317
(Refer to figure 13.)

What effect will a microburst encounter have upon the aircraft in position 4?

A– Strong tailwind.

B– Strong updraft.

C– Significant performance increase.

9-84. Answer A. GFDIC 9B, AIM
Position 4 represents the point where downdrafts begin transitioning to strong tailwinds causing aircraft performance to decrease.

9-85   PLT317
(Refer to figure 13.)

How will the aircraft in position 4 be affected by a microburst encounter?

A– Performance increasing with a tailwind and updraft.

B– Performance decreasing with a tailwind and downdraft.

C– Performance decreasing with a headwind and downdraft.

9-85. Answer B. GFDIC 9B, AIM
Position 4 represents the point where downdrafts begin transitioning to strong tailwinds causing aircraft performance to decrease.

9-86   PLT509
What wind condition prolongs the hazards of wake turbulence on a landing runway for the longest period of time?

A– Direct headwind.

B– Direct tailwind.

C– Light quartering tailwind.

9-86. Answer C. GFDIC 9B, AIM
A light, quartering tailwind can move the upwind vortex of a preceding aircraft onto the runway in the touchdown zone.

9-87   PLT509
Wake turbulence is near maximum behind a jet transport just after takeoff because

A– the engines are at maximum thrust output at slow airspeed.

B– the gear and flap configuration increases the turbulence to maximum.

C– of the high angle of attack and high gross weight.

9-87. Answer C. GFDIC 9B, AIM
Wake turbulence is greatest behind large, heavy aircraft at slow speeds and high angles of attack. Engine thrust provides a type of wake turbulence. It is usually called jet engine blast, but it may be referred to as thrust stream turbulence.

9-88   PLT509

What effect would a light crosswind of approximately 7 knots have on vortex behavior?

A– The light crosswind would rapidly dissipate vortex strength.

B– The upwind vortex would tend to remain over the runway.

C– The downwind vortex would tend to remain over the runway.

9-88. Answer B. GFDIC 9B, AIM

Since vortices tend to drift at 2 to 3 knots laterally, a light crosswind tends to hold the upwind vortex over the runway.

9-89   PLT509

When landing behind a large jet aircraft, at which point on the runway should you plan to land?

A– If any crosswind, land on the windward side of the runway and prior to the jet's touchdown point.

B– At least 1,000 feet beyond the jet's touchdown point.

C– Beyond the jet's touchdown point.

9-89. Answer C. GFDIC 9B, AIM

Because wake turbulence tends to sink, you should stay above the preceding airplane's glide path and land beyond its touchdown point.

9-90   PLT518

When passing through an abrupt wind shear which involves a shift from a tailwind to a headwind, what power management would normally be required to maintain a constant indicated airspeed and ILS glide slope?

A– Higher than normal power initially, followed by a further increase as the wind shear is encountered, then a decrease.

B– Lower than normal power initially, followed by a further decrease as the wind shear is encountered, then an increase.

C– Higher than normal power initially, followed by a decrease as the shear is encountered, then an increase.

9-90. Answer B. GFDIC 9B, AC 00-54

As the wind shears to less tailwind, or to a headwind, it will be necessary to lower power to avoid ballooning above the glide slope. Later, increased power will be needed because of slower groundspeed.

9-91   PLT518

What effect will a change in wind direction have upon maintaining a 3° glide slope at a constant true airspeed?

A– When groundspeed decreases, rate of descent must increase.

B– When groundspeed increases, rate of descent must increase.

C– Rate of descent must be constant to remain on the glide slope.

9-91. Answer B. GFDIC 9B, AC 00-54

This question essentially addresses a wind shear situation. As groundspeed increases, you must descend at a greater rate to remain on glide slope.

9-92   **PLT518**

While flying a 3° glide slope, a constant tailwind shears to a calm wind. Which conditions should the pilot expect?

A– Airspeed and pitch attitude decrease and there is a tendency to go below glide slope.

B– Airspeed and pitch attitude increase and there is a tendency to go below glide slope.

C– Airspeed and pitch attitude increase and there is a tendency to go above glide slope.

9-92. Answer C. GFDIC 9B, AC 00-54

When a tailwind shears to a calm wind or headwind, indicated airspeed will increase, causing the aircraft to pitch up, and go above the glide slope. The pitch attitude change is caused by the airplane's tendency to seek the trimmed airspeed.

9-93   **PLT144**

Under which conditions is hydroplaning most likely to occur?

A– When rudder is used for directional control instead of allowing the nosewheel to contact the surface early in the landing roll on a wet runway.

B– During conditions of standing water, slush, high speed, and smooth runway texture.

C– During a landing on any wet runway when brake application is delayed until a wedge of water begins to build ahead of the tires.

9-93. Answer B. GFDIC 9B, AFH

Standing water, slush, high aircraft speed, and a smooth runway texture all contribute to hydroplaning.

9-94   **PLT518**

Thrust is managed to maintain IAS, and glide slope is being flown. What characteristics should be observed when a headwind shears to be a constant tailwind?

A– PITCH ATTITUDE: Increases; REQUIRED THRUST: Increased, then reduced; VERTICAL SPEED: Increases; IAS: Increases, then decreases to approach speed.

B– PITCH ATTITUDE: Decreases; REQUIRED THRUST: Increased, then reduced; VERTICAL SPEED: Increases; IAS: Decreases, then increases to approach speed.

C– PITCH ATTITUDE: Increases; REQUIRED THRUST: Reduced, then increased; VERTICAL SPEED: Decreases; IAS: Decreases, then increases to approach speed.

9-94. Answer B. GFDIC 9B, AC 00-54

This situation would cause a loss in indicated airspeed (IAS) with a resulting decrease in pitch attitude. You would need to increase power (thrust) to regain the lost airspeed, then reduce it again due to the higher groundspeed from the tailwind. The higher groundspeed also requires a higher rate of descent to maintain the glide slope.

9-95   PLT518

While flying a 3° glide slope, a headwind shears to a tailwind. Which conditions should the pilot expect on the glide slope?

A– Airspeed and pitch attitude decrease and there is a tendency to go below glide slope.

B– Airspeed and pitch attitude increase and there is a tendency to go above glide slope.

C– Airspeed and pitch attitude decrease and there is a tendency to remain on the glide slope.

9-95. Answer A. GFDIC 9B, AC 00-54

When a headwind changes to a tailwind, the indicated airspeed will decrease and cause the pitch attitude to decrease. As the nose pitches down, the aircraft will tend to go below glide slope if no corrections are made.

9-96   PLT280

What effect does haze have on the ability to see traffic or terrain features during flight?

A– Haze causes the eyes to focus at infinity, making terrain features harder to see.

B– The eyes tend to overwork in haze and do not detect relative movement easily.

C– Haze creates the illusion of being a greater distance than actual from the runway, and causes pilots to fly a lower approach.

9-96. Answer C. GFDIC 9B, AIM

Visual obscuration caused by such elements as rain, haze, or even a dark runway environment can cause you to fly a lower approach.

9-97   PLT518

When a climb or descent through an inversion or wind shear zone is being performed, the pilot should be alert for which of the following change in airplane performance?

A– A fast rate of climb and a slow rate of descent.

B– A sudden change in airspeed.

C– A sudden surge of thrust.

9-97. Answer B. GFDIC 9B, AW

Wind shear is a sudden shift in wind speed and/or direction that may occur at any altitude and at any time. Wind shear is associated with temperature inversions, the jet stream, thunderstorms, and frontal inversions. When flying through wind shear, be alert for a sudden change in airspeed and carry an extra margin of speed if you suspect an inversion or wind shear

SECTION C — PRINTED REPORTS AND FORECASTS

METARS

- An aviation routine weather report (METAR) is an observation of surface weather written in a standard format which typically contains 10 or more separate elements.
- A non-routine aviation weather report (SPECI) is issued when a significant change in one or more of the elements of a METAR has occurred.
- A non-routine aviation weather report (SPECI) is issued when a significant change in one or more of the elements of a METAR has occurred.
- Prevailing visibility is the greatest distance an observer can see and identify objects through at least half of the horizon.
- Runway visual range (RVR) is based on what a pilot in a moving aircraft should see when looking down the runway. If included in a METAR, RVR is reported following prevailing visibility.
- A ceiling is the height above ground level of the lowest layer of clouds aloft which is reported as broken (BKN) or overcast (OVC), or the vertical visibility (VV) into an obscuration. For example, VV008 indicates that the sky is obscured with a vertical visibility of 800 feet.
- If the top of a layer is known, you can easily determine its thickness by adding the airport's elevation (MSL) to the height of the cloud base (AGL) found in a METAR observation, then subtract the height of the cloud tops.
- The beginning of the remarks section is indicated by the code RMK. The remarks section reports weather considered significant to aircraft operations, which are not covered in the previous sections of the METAR.

RADAR WEATHER REPORTS

- Radar weather reports (SDs) define general areas of precipitation, particularly thunderstorms.
- The abbreviation MT is used to denote maximum tops of the precipitation in the clouds. Heights are reported in hundreds of feet MSL followed by the radial and distance in nautical miles from the reporting location.

PILOT WEATHER REPORTS

- The bases and tops of cloud layers, in-flight visibility, icing conditions, wind shear, and turbulence may be included in a pilot weather report (PIREP).
- PIREPs are the best source for current weather between reporting stations.

TERMINAL AERODROME FORECASTS

- Terminal aerodrome forecasts (TAFs) are issued 4 times per day, and predict the weather at a specific airport for a 24-hour period of time. A TAF should be your primary source of weather information for your destination.
- In a TAF, the contraction VRB indicates that the wind direction is variable. A calm wind (3 knots or less) is indicated by 00000KT.
- P6SM in terminal aerodrome forecast implies that the prevailing visibility is expected to be greater than 6 statute miles.
- The letters SKC are used in a terminal aerodrome forecast to indicate "sky clear."
- The letters WS indicate that low-level wind shear which is not associated with convective activity may be present during the valid time of the forecast. For example, WS005/27050KT indicates that the wind at 500 feet AGL is 270° at 50 knots.
- The term PROB40 2102 +TSRA in a terminal aerodrome forecast indicates that there is approximately a 40% probability of thunderstorms with heavy rain between 2100Z and 0200Z.

AVIATION AREA FORECASTS

- Aviation area forecasts are issued three times each day and generally include a total forecast period of 18 hours. They cover a geographical group of states or well known areas.
- An aviation area forecast (FA) is a good source of information for weather at airports which do not have terminal aerodrome forecasts, as well as for enroute weather.
- The VFR clouds and weather section of an aviation area forecast summarizes sky conditions, cloud heights, visibility, obstructions to vision, precipitation, and sustained surface winds of 20 knots or greater.
- When the wind is forecast to be 20 knots or greater the categorical outlook in the aviation area forecast includes the contraction WND.

WINDS AND TEMPERATURES ALOFT FORECASTS

- An estimate of wind direction in relation to true north, wind speed in knots, and the temperature in degrees Celsius for selected altitudes can be found in the winds and temperatures aloft forecast (FD).
- A winds and temperatures aloft forecast (FD) does not include winds within 1,500 feet of the station elevation. Likewise temperatures for the 3,000-foot level or for a level within 2,500 feet of the station elevation are omitted.
- Wind direction and speed information on an FD are shown by a four-digit code. The first two digits are the wind direction in tens of degrees. Wind speed is shown by the second two digits. The last two digits indicate the temperature in degrees Celsius. All temperatures above 24,000 feet are negative and the minus sign is omitted.
- To decode a forecast of winds between 100 and 199 knots, subtract 50 from the two-digit direction code and multiply by 10. Then, add 100 to the two-digit wind speed code. The code 9900 indicates the winds are light and variable.

SEVERE WEATHER

- A convective outlook (AC) forecasts general thunderstorm activity for the next 24-hour period.
- Severe weather watch bulletins (WW) are issued only when required. They outline areas of possible severe thunderstorms or tornadoes.

9-97   PLT288

The body of a Terminal Aerodrome Forecast (TAF) covers a geographical proximity within a

A– 5 statute mile radius from the center of an airport runway complex.

B– 5 nautical mile radius of the center of an airport.

C– 5 to 10 statute mile radius from the center of an airport runway complex.

9-97. Answer A. GFDIC 9C, AWS

Terminal aerodrome forecasts are issued four times a day and are normally valid for a 24-hour period. The TAF is a concise statement of the expected meteorological conditions within a 5-statute-mile radius from the center of an airport's runway complex.

9-98   PLT076

What wind direction and speed is represented by the entry 9900+00 for 9,000 feet, on a Winds and Temperatures Aloft Forecast (FD)?

A– Light and variable; less than 5 knots.

B– Vortex winds exceeding 200 knots.

C– Light and variable; less than 10 knots.

9-98. Answer A. GFDIC 9C, AWS

A code of 9900 indicates light and variable winds (less than five knots).

9-99   PLT051
What does a Convective Outlook (AC) describe for a following 24 hour period?

A– General thunderstorm activity.

B– A severe weather watch bulletin.

C– When forecast conditions are expected to continue beyond the valid period.

9-99. Answer A. GFDIC 9C, AWS
According to Advisory Circular 00-45D, a convective outlook (AC) includes areas of high, moderate, or slight risk of severe thunderstorms.

9-100   PLT288
Which primary source should be used to obtain forecast weather information at your destination for the planned ETA?

A– Area Forecast.

B– Radar Summary and Weather Depiction Charts.

C– Terminal Aerodrome Forecast (TAF).

9-100. Answer C. GFDIC 9C, AWS
The terminal aerodrome forecast (TAF) is the only printed weather report that gives you forecast information for a 24-hour period at your destination. The terminal aerodrome forecast allows you to select the most favorable approach, based on the forecast winds, visibility, and ceiling. You also need this forecast to determine if an alternate airport is required. If one is required, you need the TAF for the alternate to see if it qualifies.

9-101   PLT072
A "VRB" wind entry in a Terminal Aerodome Forecast (TAF) will be indicated when the wind is

A– 3 knots or less.

B– 6 knots or less.

C– 9 knots or less.

9-101. Answer A. GFDIC 9C, AWS
A variable wind is encoded as VRB when wind direction fluctuates due to convective activity or low wind speeds (3 knots or less).

9-102   PLT072
When the visibility is greater than 6 SM on a TAF it is expressed as

A– 6PSM.

B– P6SM.

C– 6SMP.

9-102. Answer B. GFDIC 9C, AWS
The presence of the "P", which indicates plus, preceding the visibility entry of a terminal aerodrome forecast specifically implies that the visibility is greater than 6 statute miles.

9-103   PLT291
"WND" in the categorical outlook in the Aviation Area Forecast means that the wind during that period is forecast to be

A– sustained surface wind speed of 6 knots or stronger.

B– sustained surface wind speed of 15 knots or stronger.

C– sustained surface wind speed of 20 knots or stronger.

9-103. Answer C. GFDIC 9C, AWS
In an Area Forecast, this abbreviation by itself means winds, sustained or gusty, are expected to be 20 knots or greater. The contraction "WND" is included in the outlook if winds, sustained or gusty, are expected to be 20 knots or greater.

9-104   PLT072
What is the forecast wind at 1800Z in the following TAF?

KMEM 091740Z 091818 00000KT 1/2SM RAFG OVC005=

A– Calm.

B– Unknown.

C– Not recorded.

9-104. Answer A. GFDIC 9C, AIM, AWS
A calm wind entry, "00000KT," in a terminal aerodrome forecast specifically implies that the wind is expected to be 3 knots or less.

9-105   PLT059
What significant sky condition is reported in this METAR observation?

METAR KBNA 091250Z 33018KT 290V360 1/2SM R31/2700FT +SN BLSNFG VV008 00/M03 A2991 RMK RAE42SNB42

A– Runway 31 ceiling is 2700 feet.

B– Sky is obscured with vertical visibility of 800 feet.

C– Measured ceiling is 300 feet overcast.

9-105. Answer B. GFDIC 9C, AIM, AWS
Total obscuration of the sky is reported in hundreds of feet preceded by "VV." In this case, the vertical visibility is 800 feet.

9-106   PLT316
When are severe weather watch bulletins (WW) issued?

A– Every 12 hours as required.

B– Every 24 hours as required.

C– Unscheduled and issued as required.

9-106. Answer C. GFDIC 9C, AWS
Severe weather watch bulletins are issued only when required to define an area of possible severe thunderstorms or tornadoes.

9-107   PLT284
When is the temperature at one of the forecast altitudes omitted at a specific location or station in the Winds and Temperatures Aloft Forecast (FD)?

A– When the temperature is standard for that altitude.

B– For the 3,000 foot altitude (level) or when the level is within 2,500 feet of station elevation.

C– Only when the winds are omitted for that altitude (level).

9-107. Answer B. GFDIC 9C, AWS
A winds and temperatures aloft forecast (FD) does not forecast winds within 1,500 feet of the station elevation, or temperatures for the 3,000-foot level or for any level within 2,500 feet of the station elevation.

9-108   PLT284

When is the wind group at one of the forecast altitudes omitted at a specific location or station in the Winds and Temperatures Aloft Forecast (FD)? When the wind

A– is less than 5 knots.

B– is less than 10 knots.

C– at the altitude is within 1,500 feet of the station elevation.

9-108. Answer C. GFDIC 9C, AWS

A winds and temperatures aloft forecast (FD) does not forecast winds within 1,500 feet of the station elevation, or temperatures for the 3,000-foot level or for any level within 2,500 feet of the station elevation.

9-109   PLT076

Decode the excerpt from the Winds and Temperature Aloft Forecast (FD) for OKC at 39,000 feet.

FT	3000	9000	12000	24000	39000
OKC	9900	2018+00	2130-06	2361-30	830558

A– Wind 130° at 50 knots, temperature -58°C.

B– Wind 330° at 105 knots, temperature -58°C.

C– Wind 330° at 205 knots, temperature -58°C.

9-109. Answer B. GFDIC 9C, AWS

If the wind speed for a specific station is between 100 and 199 knots, 50 should be subtracted from the wind direction code and 100 added to the speed. In this example, "830558" indicates the wind at OKC is from 330° (83 – 50 = 33 or 330°) at 105 knots (05 + 100 = 105 knots).You can recognize this when you see a coded direction that exceeds "36" or 360°. The last two digits of the sequence always represents the temperature. Above 24,000 feet, the "–" is omitted because temperatures are always negative.

9-110   PLT284

Which values are used for winds aloft forecasts?

A– Magnetic direction and knots.

B– Magnetic direction and MPH.

C– True direction and knots.

9-110. Answer C. GFDIC 9C, AWS

The winds and temperatures aloft forecast (FD) provides an estimate of wind direction in relation to true north, wind speed in knots, and temperature in degrees Celsius for selected stations and altitudes.

9-111   PLT076

(Refer to figure 2.)

What approximate wind direction, speed, and temperature (relative to ISA) should a pilot expect when planning for a flight over PSB at FL 270?

A– 260° magnetic at 93 knots; ISA +7°C.

B– 280° true at 113 knots; ISA +3°C.

C– 255° true at 93 knots; ISA +6°C.

9-111. Answer C. GFDIC 9C, AWS

If your desired cruising altitude falls between forecast levels, you must interpolate to find the forecast winds. In this example, you must interpolate between the PSB winds aloft forecast at 24,000 feet, "2368-26" and those at 30,000 feet, "781939." The first step is to decode the wind information at 30,000 feet. Since 27,000 feet is directly between 24,000 and 30,000, add one-half the difference between the wind direction, speed, and temperature at these altitudes to the 24,000 foot information to determine the winds and temperature at 27,000 feet.

Altitude	Wind Dir	Wind Spd	Temp
30,000	280°	119	−39°C
24,000	230°	68	−26°C
	50°	51	13°
27,000	255°	93	−33°C

The International Standard Atmosphere (ISA) temperature at 27,000 feet (FL 270) is approximately −39°C. This is based on a 2°C per 1,000-foot lapse rate. Therefore, −33°C is ISA plus 6°C.

9-112   PLT076

(Refer to figure 2.)

What approximate wind direction, speed, and temperature (relative to ISA) should a pilot expect when planning for a flight over ALB at FL 270?

A– 270° magnetic at 97 knots; ISA -4°C.

B– 260° true at 110 knots; ISA +5°C.

C– 275° true at 97 knots; ISA +4°C.

9-112. Answer C. GFDIC 9C, AWS

For this question, you must interpolate between the ALB winds and temperatures at 24,000 feet and 30,000 feet. The answer is 275° true at 97 knots and +4°C above standard.

Altitude	Wind Dir	Wind Spd	Temp
30,000	280°	119	−39°C
24,000	230°	68	−26°C
	50°	51	13°
27,000	255°	93	−33°C

The International Standard Atmosphere (ISA) temperature at 27,000 feet (FL 270) is −39°C; this is based on a 2°C per 1,000-foot lapse rate. Therefore −35° is ISA + 4°C.

9-113   PLT076

(Refer to figure 2.)

What approximate wind direction, speed, and temperature (relative to ISA) should a pilot expect when planning for a flight over EMI at FL 270?

A– 265° true; 100 knots; ISA +3 °C.

B– 270° true; 110 knots; ISA +5 °C.

C– 260° magnetic; 100 knots; ISA -5 °C.

9-113. Answer A. GFDIC 9C, AWS

To solve, you must interpolate between the EMI winds and temperatures at 24,000 feet and 30,000 feet. The answer is 265° true at 100 knots and +3°C above standard.

Altitude	Wind Dir	Wind Spd	Temp
30,000	280°	118	–42°C
24,000	270°	77	–28°C
	10°	41	14°
27,000	275°	97	–35°C

The International Standard Atmosphere (ISA) temperature at 27,000 feet (FL 270) is –39°C; this is based on a 2°C per 1,000-foot lapse rate. Therefore –36° is ISA plus 3°C.

9-114   PLT059

The station originating the following weather report has a field elevation of 1,300 feet MSL. From the bottom of the overcast cloud layer, what is its thickness? (tops of OVC are reported at 3800 feet).

SPECI KOKC 092228Z 28024G36KT 3/4SM BKN008 OVC020 28/23 A3000

A– 500 feet.

B– 1,700 feet.

C– 2,500 feet.

9-114. Answer A. GFDIC 9C, AIM, AWS

The note indicates the top of the overcast is at 3,800 feet MSL. In the SPECI, the overcast begins at 2,000 feet AGL. By adding the field elevation, 1,300 feet MSL, to the height of the cloud base, 2,000 feet AGL, you can determine that the cloud base is 3,300 feet MSL. Then subtract the height of the cloud base from the reported cloud top. The overcast is calculated to be 500 feet thick (3,800 – 3,300=500).

9-115   PLT061

Which response most closely interprets the following PIREP?

UA/OV OKC 063064/TM 1522/FL080/TP C172/ TA-04/WV 245040/TB LGT/RM IN CLR.

A– 64 nautical miles on the 63 degree radial from Oklahoma City VOR at 1522 UTC, flight level 8,000 ft. Type of aircraft is a Cessna 172.

B– Reported by a Cessna 172, turbulence and light rime icing in climb to 8,000 ft.

C– 63 nautical miles on the 64 degree radial from Oklahoma City, thunderstorm and light rain at 1522 UTC.

9-115. Answer A. GFDIC 9C, AWS

In this PIREP, which is identified by the letters "UA," the aircraft's position is designated by the letters "OV" followed by the distance, direction, and reference facility. The aircraft is 64 nautical miles from Oklahoma City VOR on the 063° radial. The time is 1522 (TM 1522) and the aircraft is at 8,000 feet MSL (FL080). The type of aircraft is a Cessna 172 (TP C172). The outside air temperature is minus four degrees Celsius (TA–04), the wind is 245° at 40 knots (WV 245040), and the pilot is experiencing light turbulence (TB LGT). The remarks section, which begins with the letters "RM," indicates the aircraft is in clear skies.

9-116   PLT284
A station is forecasting wind and temperature aloft at FL 390 to be 300° at 200 knots; temperature -54°C. How would this data be encoded in the FD?

A– 300054.

B– 809954.

C– 309954.

9-116. Answer B. GFDIC 9C, AWS
When the wind speed is forecast at 200 knots or greater, 50 is added to the wind direction and the wind speed is coded as 99. The answer is 809954. The wind direction is encoded as 80 (30 + 50 = 80), the speed as 99 (200 knots or greater), and the temperature as 54 indicating –54°C. All temperatures above 24,000 feet are negative; therefore, the minus sign is omitted for temperatures above 24,000 feet.

9-117   PLT291
Area forecasts generally include a forecast period of 18 hours and cover a geographical

A– terminal area.

B– area less than 3,000 square miles.

C– area the size of several states.

9-117. Answer C. GFDIC 9C, AWS
An Aviation Area Forecast (FA) is a forecast of general weather conditions over an area the size of several states.

9-118   PLT291
"WND" in the categorical outlook in the Aviation Area Forecast means that the wind during that period is forecast to be

A– sustained surface wind speed of 6 knots or greater.

B– sustained surface wind speed of 15 knots or greater.

C– sustained surface wind speed of 20 knots or greater.

9-118. Answer C. GFDIC 9C, AWS
The contraction "WND" appended to any category indicates that the sustained surface wind is expected to be 20 knots of more, or surface wind gusts are expected to be 25 knots or more during the majority of the six-hour outlook period.

9-119   PLT026
A ceiling is defined as the height of the

A– highest layer of clouds or obscuring phenomena aloft that covers over 6/10 of the sky.

B– lowest layer of clouds that contributed to the overall overcast.

C– lowest layer of clouds or obscuring phenomena aloft that is reported as broken or overcast.

9-119. Answer C. GFDIC 9C, AWS
TA ceiling is the AGL height of the lowest broken (BKN) or overcast (OVC) layer, or vertical visibility into an obscuration.

9-120   PLT059

The reporting station originating this Aviation Routine Weather Report has a field elevation of 620 feet. If the reported sky cover is one continuous layer, what is its thickness? (tops of OVC are reported at 6,500 feet)

METAR KMDW 121856Z AUTO 32005KT 1 1/2SM

+RABR OVC007 17/16 A2980

A– 5,180 feet.

B– 5,800 feet.

C– 5,880 feet.

9-120. Answer A. GFDIC 9C, AIM, AWS

The note indicates the top of the overcast is at 6,500 feet MSL. In the METAR, the overcast begins at 700 feet AGL. By adding the field elevation, 620 feet MSL, to the height of the cloud base, 700 feet AGL, you can determine that the cloud base is 1,320 feet MSL. Then subtract the height of the cloud base from the reported cloud top. The overcast is calculated to be 5,180 feet thick (6,500 − 1,320 = 5180).

9-121   PLT072

What is the wind shear forecast in the following TAF?

TAF KCVG 231051Z 231212 12012KT 4SM -RA BR OVC008 WS005/27050KT TEMPO 1719 1/2SM -RA FG FM1930 09012KT 1SM -DZ BR VV003 BECMG 2021 5SM HZ=

A– 5 feet AGL from 270° at 50 KT.

B– 50 feet AGL from 270° at 50KT.

C– 500 feet AGL from 270° at 50 KT.

9-121. Answer C. GFDIC 9C, AIM, AWS

When wind shear is reported in a TAF, it always comes after the sky conditions group. Following the wind shear indicator (WS), is the altitude of the forecast wind shear reported in hundreds of feet AGL, then the wind direction and speed. In this example, the wind shear is forecast at 500 feet AGL from 270° at 50 knots.

9-122   PLT059

What is meant by the entry in the remarks section of METAR surface report for KBNA?

METAR KBNA 211250Z 33018KT 290V260 1/2SM R31/2700FT +SN BLSNFG VV008 00/M03 A2991 RMK RAE42SNB42

A– The wind is variable from 290° to 360.

B– Heavy blowing snow and fog on runway 31.

C– Rain ended 42 past the hour, snow began 42 past the hour.

9-122. Answer C. GFDIC 9C, AIM, AWS

The "RAE42SNB42" in this report indicates rain ended at 42 minutes after the hour and snow began at 42 minutes after the hour.

9-123   PLT051

What information is provided by a Convective Outlook (AC)?

A– It describes areas of probable severe icing and severe or extreme turbulence during the next 24 hours.

B– It provides prospects of both general and severe thunderstorm activity during the following 24 hours.

C– It indicates areas of probable convective turbulence and the extent of instability in the upper atmosphere (above 500 MB).

9-123. Answer B. GFDIC 9C, AWS

The convective outlook (AC) forecasts general thunderstorm activity for the next 24-hour period. Areas with a high, moderate, or slight risk of severe thunderstorms are included, as well as areas where thunderstorms may approach severe limits.

9-124 PLT061
Interpret this PIREP.

MRB UA/OV MRB/TM1430/FL060/TPC182/SK BKN BL/WX RA/TB MDT.

A– Ceiling 6,000 feet intermittently below moderate thundershowers; turbulence increasing westward.

B– FL 60,000, intermittently below clouds; moderate rain, turbulence increasing with the wind.

C– At 6,000 feet; between layers; moderate turbulence; moderate rain.

9-124. Answer C. GFDIC 9C, AWS
You can identify this as a pilot report by the notation "UA." The coding "OV MRB/TM 1430/FL060" indicates the aircraft is over Martinsburg at 1430Z and 6,000 feet. "SK BKN BL/WX RA/TB MDT" indicates sky broken, between layers, moderate rain and turbulence.

9-125 PLT051
Which weather forecast describes prospects for an area coverage of both severe and general thunderstorms during the following 24 hours?

A– Terminal Aerodrome Forecast.

B– Convective outlook.

C– Radar Summary Chart.

9-125. Answer B. GFDIC 9C, AWS
The convective outlook (AC) forecasts thunderstorm activity for a 24-hour period. The forecast includes areas where thunderstorms may approach severe conditions, as well as the areas containing a high, moderate, or slight risk of severe thunderstorms.

9-126 PLT288
From which primary source should you obtain information regarding the weather expected to exist at your destination at your estimated time of arrival?

A– Weather Depiction Chart.

B– Radar Summary and Weather Depiction Chart.

C– Terminal Aerodrome Forecast.

9-126. Answer C. GFDIC 9C, AIM, AWS
The terminal aerodrome forecast (TAF) is the only printed weather report that gives you forecast information for a 24-hour period at your destination. The terminal aerodrome forecast allows you to select the most favorable approach, based on the forecast winds, visibility, and ceiling. You also need this forecast to determine if an alternate airport is required. If one is required, you need the TAF for the alternate to see if it qualifies.

9-127 PLT290
AIRMET's are issued on a scheduled basis every

A– six hours.

B– 15 minutes after the hour only.

C– 15 minutes until the AIRMET is canceled.

9-127. Answer A. GFDIC 9C, AIM
AIRMETs are issued on a scheduled basis every six hours and corrected or updated as necessary.

9-128   PLT290

Which meteorological condition is issued in the form of a SIGMET (WS)?

A– Widespread sand or dust storms affecting at leat 3,000 square miles or an area deemed to have a significant effect on the safety of aircraft operations.

B– Moderate icing.

C– Sustained winds of 30 knots or greater at the surface.

9-128. Answer A. GFDIC 9E, AIM

SIGMETs (WSs) are issued for hazardous weather that might be significant to all aircraft. SIGMET criteria include severe or extreme turbulence and severe icing (when not associated with thunderstorms), as well as widespread dust storms, sandstorms, and volcanic ash. SIGMETs are issued for weather that affects an area of at least 3,000 square miles at any one time. AIRMETs apply to weather that might be hazardous to light aircraft only, such as moderate turbulence or icing, or sustained surface winds greater than 30 knots.

9-129   PLT290

SIGMETS are unscheduled weather products that are valid for

A– a period not to exceed 4 hours, but may be reissued for additional 4 hour periods.

B– 2 to 12 hours, depending on the severity of the weather.

C– 6 hours, unless associated with hurricanes or tropical cyclones.

9-129. Answer A. GFDIC 9B, AWS

SIGMETS are unscheduled forecasts that are valid for four hours, but if the SIGMET relates to hurricanes, it is valid for six hours.

SECTION D — GRAPHIC WEATHER PRODUCTS

SURFACE ANALYSIS CHART

- The solid lines that depict sea level pressure patterns are called isobars. When they are close together, the pressure gradient is stronger and the wind velocities are stronger.
- A surface analysis chart is a good source for general weather information over a wide area, depicting the actual positions of fronts, pressure patterns, temperatures, dewpoint, wind, weather, and obstructions to vision at the valid time of the chart.
- A dashed line on a surface analysis chart indicates a weak pressure gradient.

WEATHER DEPICTION CHART

- The weather depiction chart provides a graphic display of VFR and IFR weather, as well as the type of precipitation.
- A ( ]) plotted to the right of a station circle on the weather depiction chart means the station is an automated observation location.
- When total sky cover is FEW or scattered, the height shown on the weather depiction chart is the base of the lowest layer.

RADAR SUMMARY CHART

- Radar summary charts are the only weather charts which show lines and cells of thunderstorms as well as other heavy precipitation. You can also determine the tops and bases of the echoes, the intensity of the precipitation, and the echo movement.
- A radar summary chart is most effective when used in combination with other charts, reports, and forecasts.

CONSTANT PRESSURE ANALYSIS CHART

- A constant pressure analysis chart provides observed winds aloft, temperature and dewpoint information. You can also use this chart to determine temperatures.
- Hatching on a constant pressure analysis chart indicates wind speeds between 70 and 110 knots.

WINDS AND TEMPERATURES ALOFT FORECASTS

An estimate of wind direction in relation to true north, wind speed in knots, and the temperature in degrees Celsius for selected altitudes can be found in the winds and temperatures aloft forecast (FD).

LOW AND HIGH LEVEL SIGNIFICANT WEATHER PROGNOSTIC CHARTS

- A low-level significant weather prognostic chart depicts weather conditions forecast to exist at 12, and 24 hours in the future. This chart is valid up to 24,000 feet MSL.
- In a high-level significant weather prognostic chart the areas enclosed in scalloped lines indicate that you should expect cumulonimbus clouds (CBs), icing, and moderate or greater turbulence.
- A high-level significant weather prognostic chart forecasts clear air turbulence, tropopause height, sky coverage, embedded thunderstorms, and jet stream velocities between 24,000 feet MSL and 63,000 feet MSL.

COMPOSITE MOISTURE STABILITY CHART

- A freezing level panel of the composite moisture stability chart is an analysis of observed freezing level data from upper air observations.
- The difference found by subtracting the temperature of a parcel of air theoretically lifted from the surface to 500 millibars and the existing temperature at 500 millibars is called the lifted index.

9-130   PLT353
What important information is provided by the Radar Summary Chart that is not shown on other weather charts?

A– Lines and cells of hazardous thunderstorms.

B– Types of precipitation.

C– Areas of cloud cover and icing levels within the clouds.

9-130. Answer A. GFDIC 9D, AWS
The radar summary chart is unique because it shows areas of precipitation, thunderstorm cells, and lines of cells. In addition, the chart provides echo heights of the tops and bases of associated precipitation areas, size, shape, and intensity of returns, as well as the intensity trend and direction of movement.

9-131   PLT283
What flight planning information can a pilot derive from constant pressure charts?

A– Clear air turbulence and icing conditions.

B– Levels of widespread cloud coverage.

C– Winds and temperatures aloft.

9-131. Answer C. GFDIC 9D, AWS
The constant pressure analysis chart is an upper air weather map on which all information is referenced to a specified pressure level. The observed data for each reporting location are plotted on the chart. The information includes the observed temperature and temperature/dewpoint spread, the wind direction, the wind speed, the height of the pressure surface, and any changes in height over the previous 12 hours.

9-132   PLT289
(Refer to figure 4.)

What is the meaning of a bracket (]) plotted to the right of the station circle on a weather depiction chart?

A– The station represents the en route conditions within a 50 mile radius.

B– The station is an automated observation location.

C– The station gives local overview of flying conditions for a six hour period.

9-132. Answer B. GFDIC 9D, AWS
The sky cover symbols used in the station model are only the same as those used for the surface analysis chart. The only exception is that automated stations are depicted with a bracket (]) to the right of the station circle.

9-133   PLT289
(Refer to figure 4.)

The Weather Depiction Chart indicates the heaviest precipitation is occurring in

A– north central Florida.

B– north central Minnesota.

C– central South Dakota.

9-133. Answer B. GFDIC 9D, AWS
In north central Minnesota, the presence of a group of four dots within the shaded area indicates continuous rain, heavy at the time of observation, throughout the area.

9-134   PLT289
(Refer to figure 4.)

The Weather Depiction Chart in the area of northwestern Wyoming, indicates

A– overcast with scattered rain showers.

B– 1,000-foot ceilings and visibility 3 miles or more.

C– 500-foot ceilings and continuous rain, less than 3 miles visibility.

9-134. Answer C. GFDIC 9D, AWS
The shaded area within the contour indicates the area is IFR with ceilings less than 1,000 feet and visibility less than 3 miles. The solid black station symbol indicates the sky is overcast. Continuous rain is indicated by the two dots. The 5 below the station model indicates a ceiling of 500 feet.

9-135   PLT071
The Surface Analysis Chart depicts

A– actual pressure systems, frontal locations, cloud tops, and precipitation at the time shown on the chart.

B– frontal locations and expected movement, pressure centers, cloud coverage, and obstructions to vision at the time of chart transmission.

C– actual frontal positions, pressure patterns, temperature, dewpoint, wind, weather, and obstructions to vision at the valid time of the chart.

9-135. Answer C. GFDIC 9D, AWS
The surface analysis chart shows weather conditions as they existed at the observation time shown on the chart. Included are actual frontal positions, sea level pressure patterns, highs and lows, temperature and dewpoint, wind direction and speed, local weather, and obstructions to vision.

9-136   PLT068
The Low-Level Significant Weather Prognostic Chart depicts weather conditions

A– that are forecast to exist at a valid time shown on the chart.

B– as they existed at the time the chart was prepared.

C– that existed at the time shown on the chart which is about 3 hours before the chart is received.

9-136. Answer A. GFDIC 9D, AWS
The low-level significant weather prognostic chart is valid from the surface to the 400-millibar pressure level (24,000 feet). The chart depicts weather conditions that are forecast to exist during the valid time of the chart. The chart is divided into four different panels: the upper panels are 12- and 24-hour forecasts of weather between the surface and 24,000 feet, while the two lower panels are 12- and 24-hour forecasts of surface weather conditions.

9-137   PLT068
Which meteorological conditions are depicted by a prognostic chart?

A– Conditions existing at the time of the observation.

B– Interpretation of weather conditions for geographical areas between reporting stations.

C– Conditions forecast to exist at a specific time shown on the chart.

9-137. Answer C. GFDIC 9D, AWS
The low-level significant weather prognostic chart is valid from the surface to the 400-millibar pressure level (24,000 feet). The chart depicts weather conditions that are forecast to exist during the valid time of the chart. The chart is divided into four different panels: the upper panels are 12- and 24-hour forecasts of weather between the surface and 24,000 feet, while the two lower panels are 12- and 24-hour forecasts of surface weather conditions.

9-138   PLT068

(Refer to figure 5.)

What is the meaning of the symbol depicted as used on the U.S. Low-Level Significant Weather Prog Chart?

A– Showery precipitation (e.g. rain showers) embedded in an area of continuous rain covering half or more of the area.

B– Continuous precipitation (e.g. rain) covering half or more of the area.

C– Showery precipitation (e.g. thunderstorms/rain showers) covering half or more of the area.

9-139   PLT068

A prognostic chart depicts the conditions

A– existing at the surface during the past 6 hours.

B– which presently exist from the 1,000 millibar through the 700 millibar level.

C– forecast to exist at a specific time in the future.

9-140   PLT068

(Refer to figure 18.)

(SFC PROG) A planned low altitude flight from northern Florida to southern Florida at 00Z is likely to encounter

A– intermittent rain or rain showers, moderate turbulence, and freezing temperatures above 8,000 feet.

B– showery precipitation, thunderstorms/rain showers covering half or more of the area.

C– showery precipitation covering less than half the area, no turbulence below 18,000 feet, and freezing temperatures above 12,000 feet.

9-138. Answer A. GFDIC 9D, AWS

An area which is expected to have continuous or intermittent precipitation is enclosed by a solid line. If only showers are expected, the area is enclosed with a dot-dash line. When precipitation covers one-half or more of the area, it is shaded. The symbols within the circle indicate continuous rain with rain showers. Therefore, the figure represents an area of showery precipitation embedded in an area of continuous rain.

9-139. Answer C. GFDIC 9D, AWS

The low-level significant weather prognostic chart is valid from the surface to the 400-millibar pressure level (24,000 feet). The chart depicts weather conditions that are forecast to exist during the valid time of the chart. The chart is divided into four different panels: the upper panels are 12- and 24-hour forecasts of weather between the surface and 24,000 feet, while the two lower panels are 12- and 24-hour forecasts of surface weather conditions.

9-140. Answer B. GFDIC 9D, AWS

The only panels valid for the proposed departure time are the two panels on the left. The top panel indicates moderate to severe turbulence from the surface to 24,000 feet. The lower panel indicates showery precipitation, thunderstorms and rain showers covering more than half of the state.

9-141   PLT068
(Refer to figure 18.)

The 24 Hour Low Level Significant Weather Prog at 12Z indicates that southwestern West Virginia will likely experience

A– ceilings less than 1,000 feet, visibility less than 3 miles.

B– clear sky and visibility greater than 6 miles.

C– ceilings 1,000 to 3,000 feet and visibility 3 to 5 miles.

9-141. Answer A. GFDIC 9D, AWS
The 24-hour panels are located on the right. The top panel indicates IFR conditions over southwestern West Virginia. Ceilings less then 1,000 feet and/or visibility less than 3 miles are depicted by the smooth contour line.

9-142   PLT068
(Refer to figure 18, SFC-400MB.)

The U.S. Low Level Significant Weather Surface Prog Chart at 00Z indicates that northwestern Colorado and eastern Utah can expect

A– moderate or greater turbulence from the surface to FL 240.

B– moderate or greater turbulence above FL 240.

C– no turbulence is indicated.

9-142. Answer A. GFDIC 9D, AWS
The 12-hour significant weather prognostic shows northwestern Colorado and eastern Utah enclosed in a dashed line. This indicates an area of moderate or greater nonconvective turbulence is predicted as indicated by the legend between the top two panels. The expected range is shown in hundreds of feet. The number "240/" indicates the turbulence is expected from the surface to 24,000 feet.

9-143   PLT068
(Refer to figure 18.)

The chart symbols shown in the Gulf of Mexico at 12Z and extending into AL, GA, SC and northern FL indicate a

A– tropical storm.

B– hurricane.

C– tornado originating in the Gulf of Mexico.

9-143. Answer A. GFDIC 9D, AWS
The symbol in the lower right panel indicates a tropical storm off the southern coast of the Florida panhandle, Alabama, and Georgia. The textual note indicates tropical storm Jerry is located 29.8 degrees north latitude by 84.8 degrees west longitude.

9-144   PLT068
(Refer to figure 7.)

What weather conditions are depicted within the area indicated by arrow E?

A– Frequent embedded thunderstorms, less than 1/8 coverage, and tops at FL370.

B– Frequent lightning in thunderstorms at FL370.

C– Occasional cumulonimbus, 1/8 to 4/8 coverage, bases below 24,000 feet MSL, and tops at 40,000 feet MSL.

9-144. Answer C. GFDIC 9D, AWS
The altitude of the "CB" is "400/XXX." The "XXX" means the bases start below the lower limit of the chart, which is FL240. "Occasional" means 1/8 to 4/8 coverage.

9-145   **PLT068**
(Refer to figure 7.)

What weather conditions are depicted within the area indicated by arrow D?

A– Existing isolated cumulonimbus clouds, tops above 43,000 feet with less than 1/8 coverage.

B– Forecast isolated embedded cumulonimbus clouds with tops at 43,000 feet MSL, and less than 1/8 coverage.

C– Forecast isolated thunderstorms, tops at FL 440, more than 1/8 coverage.

9-145. Answer B. GFDIC 9D, AWS
The prognostic chart is a FORECAST, not a report of existing conditions. Use a WEATHER DEPICTION CHART to look at existing conditions. "Isolated" means less than one-eighth coverage. The forecast conditions by arrow D show isolated embedded cumulonimbus clouds with tops at 43,000 feet MSL.

9-146   **PLT068**
(Refer to figure 7.)

What weather conditions are predicted within the area indicated by arrow C?

A– Light turbulence at FL 370 within the area outlined by dashes.

B– Moderate turbulence at 32,000 feet MSL.

C– Moderate to severe CAT has been reported at FL 320.

9-146. Answer B. GFDIC 9D, AWS
The dashed line around Area C indicates moderate turbulence from below FL240 up to FL350.

9-147   **PLT068**
(Refer to figure 7.)

What weather conditions are depicted within the area indicated by arrow B?

A– Light to moderate turbulence at and above 37,000 feet MSL.

B– Moderate turbulence from below 24,000 feet MSL to 37,000 feet MSL.

C– Moderate to severe CAT is forecast to exist at FL 370.

9-147. Answer B. GFDIC 9D, AWS
The prognostic chart is a FORECAST. Use a WEATHER DEPICTION CHART to look at existing conditions. Heavy dashed lines indicate an area of turbulence. The symbol for moderate turbulence is shown. The altitude of the turbulence is "370/XXX." The "XXX" means the bases start below the lower limit of the chart, which is 24,000 feet MSL.

9-148   **PLT068**
(Refer to figure 7.)

What information is indicated by arrow A?

A– The height of the tropopause in meters above sea level.

B– The height of the existing layer of CAT.

C– The height of the tropopause in hundreds of feet above MSL.

9-148. Answer C. GFDIC 9D, AWS
The high-level significant prog chart covers the altitude range of 400 millibars (24,000 feet) to 70 millibars (63,000 feet). However, three-digit numbers contained in boxes represent the forecast height of the tropopause in hundreds of feet MSL, or flight levels. Arrow A indicates that the height of the tropopause is 53,000 feet MSL.

9-149   PLT068

(Refer to figure 7.)

What weather conditions are depicted within the area indicated by arrow F?

A– 1/8 to 4/8 coverage, occasional embedded thunderstorms, maximum tops at 51,000 feet MSL.

B– Occasionally embedded cumulonimbus, bases below 24,000 feet with tops to 48,000 feet.

C– 2/8 to 6/8 coverage, occasional embedded thunderstorms, tops at FL 540.

9-149. Answer B. GFDIC 9D, AWS

Scalloped lines enclose areas of expected embedded cumulonimbus (CB) clouds. The altitude of the embedded CB is depicted by 480/XXX which means the tops are 48,000 feet and the bases are below 24,000 which is the lower limit of the chart. "Occasional" means 1/8 to 4/8 coverage.

9-150   PLT353

(Refer to figure 8.)

What weather conditions are depicted in the area indicated by arrow A on the Radar Summary Chart?

A– Moderate to strong echoes; echo tops 30,000 feet MSL; line movement toward the northwest.

B– Weak to moderate echoes; average echo bases 30,000 feet MSL; cell movement toward the southeast; rain showers with thunder.

C– Strong to very strong echoes; echo tops 30,000 feet MSL; thunderstorms and rain showers.

9-150. Answer C. GFDIC 9D, AWS

The radar summary chart provides a graphic depiction of certain types of weather phenomena, primarily precipitation. It shows size, shape, and intensity of echo returns with various contour levels. The first contour level indicates weak to moderate echoes, the second contour level indicates strong and very strong echoes, and the third contour level indicates intense and extreme echoes. Tops of echoes are indicated if a number is displayed above a solid line. A base is indicated if a number is displayed below a solid line. Arrow A is pointing out a second contour level of strong to very strong echoes with tops at 30,000 feet MSL. In addition, the notation "TRW" indicates thunderstorms and rain showers.

9-151   PLT353

(Refer to figure 8.)

What weather conditions are depicted in the area indicated by arrow D on the Radar Summary Chart?

A– Echo tops 4,100 feet MSL, strong to very strong echoes within the smallest contour, and area movement toward the northeast at 50 knots.

B– Intense to extreme echoes within the smallest contour, echo tops 29,000 feet MSL, and cell movement toward the northeast at 50 knots.

C– Strong to very strong echoes within the smallest contour, echo bases 29,000 feet MSL, and cell in northeast Nebraska moving northeast at 50 knots.

9-151. Answer B. GFDIC 9D, AWS

The radar summary chart provides a graphic depiction of certain types of weather phenomena, primarily precipitation. It shows size, shape, and intensity of echo returns with various contour levels. The first contour level indicates weak to moderate echoes, the second contour level indicates strong and very strong echoes, and the third contour level indicates intense and extreme echoes. Tops of echoes are indicated if a number is displayed above a solid line. A base is indicated if a number is displayed below a solid line. Arrow D is pointing out an area of intense to extreme echoes with echo tops at 29,000 feet MSL. In addition, the arrow pointing to "50" shows the cell is moving toward the northeast at 50 knots.

9-152   PLT068

(Refer to figure 7.)

The area indicated by arrow H indicates

A– light turbulence below 34,000 feet.

B– isolated embedded cumulonimbus clouds with bases below FL180 and tops at FL340.

C– moderate turbulence at and below 34,000 feet.

9-152. Answer C. GFDIC 9D, AWS

Heavy dashed lines indicate an area of turbulence. The symbol for moderate turbulence is shown. The altitude of the turbulence is 340/XXX, The "XXX" means the bases start below 24,000 feet MSL, the lower limit of the chart.

9-153   PLT353

(Refer to figure 8.)

What weather conditions are depicted in the area indicated by arrow C on the Radar Summary Chart?

A– Average echo bases 2,800 feet MSL, thundershowers, and intense to extreme echo intensity.

B– Cell movement toward the northwest at 20 knots, intense echoes, and echo bases 28,000 feet MSL.

C– Area movement toward the northest, strong to very strong echoes, and echo tops 28,000 feet MSL.

9-153. Answer C. GFDIC 9D, AWS

The radar summary chart provides a graphic depiction of certain types of weather phenomena, primarily precipitation. It shows size, shape, and intensity of echo returns with various contour levels. The first contour level indicates weak to moderate echoes, the second contour level indicates strong and very strong echoes, and the third contour level indicates intense and extreme echoes. Tops of echoes are indicated if a number is displayed above a solid line. A base is indicated if a number is displayed below a solid line. Arrow C is pointing to an area of strong to very strong echoes with tops at 28,000 feet MSL.

9-154   PLT353

(Refer to figure 8.)

What weather conditions are depicted in the area indicated by arrow B on the Radar Summary Chart?

A– Weak echoes, heavy rain showers, area movement toward the southeast.

B– Weak to moderate echoes, rain showers increasing in intensity.

C– Strong echoes, moderate rain showers, no cell movement.

9-154. Answer B. GFDIC 9D, AWS

The radar summary chart provides a graphic depiction of certain types of weather phenomena, primarily precipitation. It shows size, shape, and intensity of echo returns with various contour levels. The first contour level indicates weak to moderate echoes, the second contour level indicates strong and very strong echoes, and the third contour level indicates intense and extreme echoes. Tops of echoes are indicated if a number is displayed above a solid line. A base is indicated if a number is displayed below a solid line. Arrow B is pointing out an area of weak to moderate echoes. Rain showers, increasing in intensity, are indicated by the "RW+" near the cell.

9-155 PLT353

(Refer to figure 8.)

What weather conditions are depicted in the area indicated by arrow E on the Radar Summary Chart?

A– Highest echo tops 30,000 feet MSL, weak to moderate echoes, thunderstorms and rain showers, and cell movement toward northwest at 15 knots.

B– Echo bases 29,000 to 30,000 feet MSL, strong echoes, rain showers increasing in intensity, and area movement toward northwest at 15 knots.

C– Thundershowers decreasing in intensity; area movement toward northwest at 15 knots; echo bases 30,000 feet MSL.

9-155. Answer A. GFDIC 9D, AWS

The radar summary chart provides a graphic depiction of certain types of weather phenomena, primarily precipitation. It shows size, shape, and intensity of echo returns with various contour levels. The first contour level indicates weak to moderate echoes, the second contour level indicates strong and very strong echoes, and the third contour level indicates intense and extreme echoes. Tops of echoes are indicated if a number is displayed above a solid line. A base is indicated if a number is displayed below a solid line. Arrow E is pointing out an area of weak to moderate echoes in thunderstorms and rain showers (TRW) with tops at 30,000 feet MSL. In addition, the arrow pointing to "15" means the cell is moving to the northwest at 15 knots.

9-156 PLT353

For most effective use of the Radar Summary Chart during preflight planning, a pilot should

A– consult the chart to determine more accurate measurements of freezing levels, cloud cover, and wind conditions between reporting stations.

B– know the chart displays precipitation only; it does not display clouds, fog, fronts, or other boundaries.

C– utilize the chart as the only source of information regarding storms and hazardous conditions existing between reporting stations.

9-156. Answer B. GFDIC 9D, AWS

Because the radar summary chart primarily displays precipitation, you should use it with other charts, reports and forecasts to get a comprehensive picture of the existing and forecast weather.

9-157 PLT353

(Refer to figure 8.)

What weather conditions are depicted in the area indicated by arrow G on the Radar Summary Chart?

A– Echo bases 10,000 feet MSL; cell movement toward northeast at 15 knots; weak to moderate echoes; rain.

B– Area movement toward northeast at 15 knots; rain decreasing in intensity; echo bases 1,000 feet MSL; strong echoes.

C– Strong to very strong echoes; area movement toward northeast at 15 knots; echo tops 10,000 feet MSL; light rain.

9-157. Answer A. GFDIC 9D, AWS

The radar summary chart provides a graphic depiction of certain types of weather phenomena, primarily precipitation. It shows size, shape, and intensity of echo returns with various contour levels. The first contour level indicates weak to moderate echoes, the second contour level indicates strong and very strong echoes, and the third contour level indicates intense and extreme echoes. Tops of echoes are indicated if a number is displayed above a solid line. A base is indicated if a number is displayed below a solid line. Arrow G is pointing out an area with weak to moderate intensity with bases at 10,000 feet MSL. In addition, the arrow pointing to "15" means the cell is moving to the northeast at 15 knots.

9-158   PLT353

(Refer to figure 8.)

What weather conditions are depicted in the area indicated by arrow F on the Radar Summary Chart?

A— Line of echoes; thunderstorms; highest echo tops 45,000 feet MSL; no line movement indicated.

B— Echo bases vary from 15,000 feet to 46,000 feet MSL; thunderstorms increasing in intensity; line of echoes moving rapidly toward the north.

C— Line of severe thunderstorms moving from south to north; echo bases vary from 4,400 feet to 4,600 feet MSL; extreme echoes.

9-158. Answer A. GFDIC 9D, AWS

The radar summary chart provides a graphic depiction of certain types of weather phenomena, primarily precipitation. It shows size, shape, and intensity of echo returns with various contour levels. The first contour level indicates weak to moderate echoes, the second contour level indicates strong and very strong echoes, and the third contour level indicates intense and extreme echoes. Tops of echoes are indicated if a number is displayed above a solid line. A base is indicated if a number is displayed below a solid line. Arrow F is pointing out a line of echoes and thunderstorms with tops at 45,000 feet MSL and no movement.

9-159   PLT066

(Refer to figure 9.)

The Severe Weather Outlook Chart, which is used primarily for advance planning, provides what information?

A— An 18-hour categorical outlook with a 48-hour valid time for severe weather watch, thunderstorm lines, and of expected tornado activity.

B— A preliminary 12-hour outlook for severe thunderstorm activity and probable convective turbulence.

C— A 24-hour severe weather outlook for possible thunderstorm activity.

9-159. Answer C. GFDIC 9D, AWS

The severe weather outlook chart provides a 48-hour outlook for thunderstorm activity as well as severe thunderstorms. This chart is prepared five times a day for the next 24 hours (Day 1 convective outlook) and twice a day for the following 24 hours (Day 2 convective outlook).

9-160   PLT066

(Refer to figure 9.)

Using the DAY 2 CONVECTIVE OUTLOOK, what type of thunderstorms, if any, may be encountered on a flight from Montana to central California?

A— Moderate risk area, surrounded by a slight risk area, of possible severe turbulence.

B— General.

C— None.

9-160. Answer B. GFDIC 9D, AWS

The severe weather outlook chart provides a 48-hour outlook for thunderstorm activity. A line with an arrowhead depicts forecast general thunderstorm activity. When facing in the direction of the arrow, thunderstorm activity is expected to the right of the line. General thunderstorms (non-severe) are outlined, but with no label on the graphic map.

9-161   PLT068

(Refer to figure 20.)

What is the maximum wind velocity forecast in the jet stream shown on the high level Significant Weather Prognostic Chart over Canada?

A– 80 knots.

B– 103 knots.

C– 130 knots.

9-161. Answer C. GFDIC 9D, AWS

The maximum forecast jet stream core speed, when more than 80 knots, is depicted by shafts, pennants, and feathers. In this case the maximum wind velocity forecast in the jet stream is depicted by two pennants and three feathers. The speed value of the pennants is fifty knots each and the feathers have a value of ten knots each.

9-162   PLT068

(Refer to figure 20.)

What is the height of the tropopause over Kentucky?

A– FL300 sloping to FL 400.

B– FL340.

C– FL390.

9-162. Answer B. GFDIC 9D, AWS

All heights on high-level significant weather prognostic charts are depicted in flight levels. The five sided polygon located over Kentucky indicates the lowest height of the tropopause. In this example, the tropopause height is at flight level 340.

9-163   PLT084

(Refer to figure 12.)

What is the approximate wind direction and velocity at 34,000 feet (see arrow C)?

A– 290°/50 knots.

B– 330°/50 knots.

C– 090°/48 knots.

9-163. Answer A. GFDIC 9D, AWS

To determine the wind direction, first consider the general orientation of the wind direction indicator. This station indicates a wind from the northwest. The "9" at the end of the direction indicator is the second digit of the wind direction rounded to the nearest 10°. In this example, the wind is from 290°. You determine the wind speed by adding the barbs on the wind direction indicator. A flag represents 50 knots, a barb 10 knots, and a half a barb 5 knots. The wind speed in this example is 50 knots.

9-164   PLT084

(Refer to figure 12.)

The wind direction and velocity on the Observed Winds Aloft Chart (see arrow A) is indicated from the

A– northeast at 35 knots.

B– northwest at 47 knots.

C– southwest at 35 knots.

9-164. Answer C. GFDIC 9D, AWS

To determine the wind direction, first consider the general orientation of the wind direction indicator. You determine the wind speed by adding the barbs on the wind direction indicator. A flag represents 50 knots, a barb 10 knots, and a half a barb 5 knots. The wind is southwest, or 230°, at 35 knots.

9-165   PLT066
(Refer to figure 9.)

What type of thunderstorm activity is expected over Montana on April 4th at 0800Z?

A– None.

B– A slight risk of severe thunderstorms.

C– General.

9-165. Answer A. GFDIC 9D, AWS
For the correct chart you need to refer to the day 1 convective outlook. The severe weather outlook chart provides a 48-hour outlook for thunderstorm activity. A line with an arrowhead depicts forecast general thunderstorm activity. When facing in the direction of the arrow, thunderstorm activity is expected to the right of the line. Since Montana is to the left of the line there is no thunderstorm activity expected on April 4th at 0800Z.

9-166   PLT084
(Refer to figure 12.)

What is the approximate wind direction and velocity at CVG at 34,000 feet (see arrow A)?

A– 040°/35 knots.

B– 097°/40 knots.

C– 230°/35 knots.

9-166. Answer C. GFDIC 9D, AWS
To determine the wind direction, first consider the general orientation of the wind direction indicator. You determine the wind speed by adding the barbs on the wind direction indicator. A flag represents 50 knots, a barb 10 knots, and a half a barb 5 knots. Arrow A is pointing at CVG. The wind direction is 230° at 35 knots.

9-167   PLT084
(Refer to figure 12.)

What is the approximate wind direction and velocity at BOI (see arrow B)?

A– 270°/55 knots.

B– 250°/95 knots.

C– 080°/95 knots.

9-167. Answer B. GFDIC 9D, AWS
To determine the wind direction, first consider the general orientation of the wind direction indicator. You determine the wind speed by adding the barbs on the wind direction indicator. A flag represents 50 knots, a barb 10 knots, and a half a barb 5 knots. The wind direction is 250° at 95 knots.

9-168   PLT068
(Refer to figure 7.)

The symbol on the U.S. HIGH-LEVEL SIGNIFICANT WEATHER PROG, indicated by arrow G, represents the

A– wind direction at the tropopause (300°).

B– height of the tropopause.

C– height of maximum wind shear (30,000 feet).

9-168. Answer B. GFDIC 9D, AWS
The three-digit numbers contained in boxes represent the forecast height of the tropopause measured from Mean Sea Level. Arrow G indicates that the height of the tropopause is 30,000 feet MSL. Wind direction is shown using shafts, pennants and barbs. Areas of moderate or greater turbulence are enclosed by bold dashed lines.

SECTION E — SOURCES OF WEATHER INFORMATION

- Enroute flight advisory service (EFAS) provides enroute aircraft with timely and meaningful weather advisories pertinent to the type of flight intended, route, and altitude.

- EFAS is obtained by contacting flight watch, using the name of the ARTCC facility identification in your area, your aircraft identification, and name of the nearest VOR, on 122.0 MHz below FL180.

- In-flight aviation weather advisories consisting of AIRMETs, SIGMETs, and convective SIGMETs are forecasts that advise enroute aircraft of the development of potentially hazardous weather, and information on volcanic eruptions that are occurring or expected to occur. All in-flight advisories in the contiguous U.S. are issued by the National Aviation Weather Advisory Unit in Kansas City, MO. All in-flight advisories use the same location identifiers (either VORs, airports, or well-known geographic areas) to describe the hazardous weather areas.

- Convective SIGMETs contain either an observation and a forecast, or just a forecast, for tornadoes, significant thunderstorm activity, or hail 3/4 inch or greater in diameter.

- A center weather advisory (CWA) is an unscheduled advisory issued by an ARTCC to alert pilots of existing or anticipated adverse weather conditions within the next two hours. A CWA may be issued prior to an AIRMET or SIGMET when PIREPs suggest AIRMET or SIGMET conditions exist. Even if adverse weather is not sufficiently intense or widespread for a SIGMET or AIRMET, a CWA may be issued if conditions are expected to affect the safe flow of air traffic within the ARTCC area of responsibility.

- AIRMETs and center weather advisories (CWA) provide an enroute pilot with information about moderate icing, moderate turbulence, winds of 30 knots or more at the surface, and extensive mountain obscurement.

- Weather advisory broadcasts, including severe weather forecast alerts (AWW), convective SIGMETs, and SIGMETs, are provided by ARTCCs on all frequencies, except emergency, when any part of the area described is within 150 miles of the airspace under their jurisdiction.

- The hazardous in-flight weather advisory service (HIWAS) is a continuous broadcast of in-flight weather advisories over selected VORs of SIGMETs, convective SIGMETs, AIRMETs, severe weather forecast alerts (AWW), and center weather advisories (CWA).

- A transcribed weather broadcast (TWEB) provides specific information concerning expected sky cover, cloud tops, visibility, weather, and obstructions to vision in a route format. To obtain continuous transcribed information, including winds aloft and route forecasts for a cross-country flight, you could monitor a TWEB on a low-frequency radio receiver. TWEB mostly has been replaced by HIWAS.

9-169   PLT290

SIGMET's are issued as a warning of weather conditions potentially hazardous

A— particularly to light aircraft.

B— to all aircraft.

C— only to light aircraft operations.

9-169. Answer B. GFDIC 9E, AWS

SIGMETs (WSs) are issued for hazardous weather which may be significant to all aircraft. According to the AIM, whether the condition described is potentially hazardous to a particular flight is for the pilot and/or aircraft dispatcher (in Part 121 operations) to evaluate on the basis of experience and operational limits of the aircraft. SIGMET criteria include the following: severe or extreme turbulence, severe icing, and widespread duststorms, sandstorms, and volcanic eruptions or volcanic ash lowering surface and/or inflight visibilities to less than three miles. An AIRMET is issued for weather that may be hazardous to light aircraft.

9-170   PLT290

Which meteorological condition is issued in the form of a SIGMET (WS)?

A– Widespread sand or duststorms affecting at least 3,000 square miles or an area deemed to have a significant effect on the safety of aircraft operations.

B– Moderate icing.

C– Sustained winds of 30 knots or greater at the surface.

9-170. Answer A. GFDIC 9E, AWS

SIGMETs (WSs) are issued for hazardous weather which may be significant to all aircraft. According to the AIM, whether the condition described is potentially hazardous to a particular flight is for the pilot and/or aircraft dispatcher (in Part 121 operations) to evaluate on the basis of experience and operational limits of the aircraft. SIGMET criteria include the following: severe or extreme turbulence, severe icing, and widespread duststorms, sandstorms, and volcanic eruptions or volcanic ash lowering surface and/or inflight visibilities to less than three miles. An AIRMET is issued for weather that may be hazardous to light aircraft.

9-171   PLT513

Which forecast provides specific information concerning expected sky cover, cloud tops, visibility, weather, and obstructions to vision in a route format?

A– DFW FA 131240.

B– MEM TAF 132222.

C– 249 TWEB 252317.

9-171. Answer C. GFDIC 9E, AWS

Transcribed weather broadcasts (TWEBs) are similar to area forecasts (FAs) except the information is in a route format. Information pertaining to forecast sky cover, cloud tops, visibilities, weather, and obstructions to vision are described for a corridor 25 miles to either side of the route.

9-172   PLT290

What is the maximum forecast period for AIRMET's?

A– Two hours.

B– Four hours.

C– Six hours.

9-172. Answer C. GFDIC 9E, AWS

AIRMETs are issued for the same six areas as the Area Forecasts, and they have a maximum forecast period of six hours.

9-173   PLT515

The Hazardous Inflight Weather Advisory Service (HIWAS) is a continuous broadcast over selected VORs of

A– SIGMETs, CONVECTIVE SIGMETs, AIRMETs, Severe Weather Forecasts Alerts (AWW), and Center Weather Advisiories.

B– SIGMETs, CONVECTIVE SIGMETs, AIRMETs, Wind Shear Advisiories, and Severe Weather Forecast Alerts (AWW).

C– Wind Shear Advisories, Radar Weather Reports, SIGMETs, CONVECTIVE SIGMETs, AIRMETs, and Center Weather Advisories (CWA).

9-173. Answer A. GFDIC 9E, AWS

HIWAS broadcasts include summarized AIRMETs, SIGMETs, convective SIGMETs, AWWs, CWAs and, on occasion, urgent PIREPs. In areas where HIWAS is implemented, you should be aware that ARTCC, terminal ATC, and FSS facilities have discontinued their normal broadcasts of in-flight advisories.

9-174   **PLT292**

What does the Runway Visual Range (RVR) value, depicted on certain straight-in IAP Charts, represent?

A– The slant range distance the pilot can see down the runway while crossing the threshold on glide slope.

B– The horizontal distance a pilot should see when looking down the runway from a moving aircraft.

C– The slant visual range a pilot should see down the final approach and during landing.

9-174. Answer B. GFDIC 9E, AIM

RVR is horizontal visual range, not slant range. It is based on the measurement of a transmissometer located near the touchdown point of the instrument runway and represents the horizontal distance a pilot will see down the runway from the approach end.

9-175   **PLT515**

On what frequency should you obtain En Route Flight Advisory Service below FL 180?

A– 122.1T/112.8R.

B– 123.6.

C– 122.0.

9-175. Answer C. GFDIC 9E, AIM

Unless otherwise indicated, the standard EFAS frequency below 18,

IFR FLIGHT CONSIDERATIONS

SECTION A — IFR EMERGENCIES

DISTRESS AND URGENCY CONDITIONS

- The *Aeronautical Information Manual* defines an emergency as a condition of distress or urgency. Pilots in distress are threatened by serious and/or imminent danger and require immediate assistance. An urgency situation, such as low fuel quantity, requires timely but not immediate assistance.
- In an emergency, you may deviate from any rule in FAR Part 91 to the extent necessary to meet the emergency. ATC may request a detailed report of an emergency when priority assistance has been given, even though no rules have been violated.

COMMUNICATION PROCEDURES

- During a flight in IFR conditions, do not hesitate to declare an emergency and obtain an amended clearance when a distress condition is encountered.
- The frequency of 121.5 MHz may be used to declare an emergency in the event you are unable to contact ATC on other frequencies.
- In a distress situation, begin your initial call with the word *"MAYDAY,"* preferably repeated three times. Use *"PAN-PAN"* in the same manner in an urgency situation.
- Your transponder may be used to declare an emergency by squawking code 7700.
- A special emergency is a condition of air piracy and should be indicated by squawking code 7500 on your transponder.
- FAR Part 91 requires that you report the malfunction of any navigational, approach, or communications equipment while operating in controlled airspace under IFR. In the malfunction report you should include the aircraft ID, equipment affected, the degree to which the flight will be impaired by the failure, and any assistance you require from ATC.

MINIMUM FUEL

- If your remaining fuel quantity is such that you can accept little or no delay, you should alert ATC with a minimum fuel advisory. Declaring minimum fuel to ATC indicates an emergency situation is possible should any undue delay occur.
- If the remaining usable fuel supply suggests the need for traffic priority to ensure a safe landing, you should declare an emergency due to low fuel and report fuel remaining in minutes.

INSTRUMENT FAILURE

- Gyroscopic instruments include the attitude indicator, heading indicator, and turn coordinator. These instruments are subject to vacuum and electrical system failures.
- During an instrument failure your first priority is to fly the airplane, navigate accurately, and then communicate with ATC.
- Radar approach procedures may be available to assist you during an emergency situation requiring an instrument approach.
- A radar instrument approach that provides only azimuth navigational guidance is referred to as an airport surveillance radar (ASR) approach. A surveillance approach may be used at airports for which civil radar instrument approach minimums have been published.

- In addition to headings, the information a radar controller provides without request during an ASR approach includes; when to commence descent to the MDA, the aircraft's position each mile on final from the runway, and arrival at the MAP.

- During a precision approach (PAR), the controller provides you with highly accurate navigational guidance in azimuth and elevation as well as trend information to help you make the proper corrections while on the approach path.

- A no-gyro approach may be requested when you have experienced a gyroscopic instrument failure. Controllers provide course guidance by stating *"turn right, stop turn"*, and *"turn left"* to align you with the approach path. Turns should be made at standard rate until you have been handed off to the final approach controller, at which point they should be made at one-half standard rate.

COMMUNICATION FAILURE

- You can use your transponder to alert ATC to a radio communication failure by squawking code 7600.

- During a communication failure while operating under IFR, you are expected to follow the lost communication procedures specified in the regulations.

- During a communication failure in VFR conditions, remain in VFR conditions, land as soon as practicable, and call ATC.

- If you lose communication with ATC during your flight, you must fly the highest of the assigned altitude, MEA, or the altitude ATC has advised may be expected in a further clearance.

- If an approach is available at your clearance limit, begin the approach at the expect further clearance (EFC) time. If an approach is not available at your clearance limit, proceed from the clearance limit at your EFC to the point at which an approach begins.

10-1   PLT391

While flying on an IFR flight plan, you experience two-way communications radio failure while in VFR conditions. In this situation, you should continue your flight under

A– VFR and land as soon as practicable.

B– IFR and maintain the last assigned route and altitude to your flight plan destination.

C– VFR and proceed to your flight plan destination.

10-1. Answer A. GFDIC 10A, FAR 91.185

If you experience a communications failure in VFR conditions or if you encounter VFR conditions subsequent to the failure, you should continue the flight under VFR conditions and land as soon as practicable.

10-2   PLT318

What does declaring "minimum fuel" to ATC imply?

A– Traffic priority is needed to the destination airport.

B– Emergency handling is required to the nearest useable airport.

C– Merely an advisory that indicates an emergency situation is possible should any undue delay occur.

10-2. Answer C. GFDIC 10A, AIM

Declaring "minimum fuel" is simply an advisory which tells ATC that you can accept little or no delay upon reaching your destination. It does not indicate an emergency, but undue delay may result in an emergency situation.

10-3   **PLT208**

During an IFR flight in IMC, a distress condition is encountered, (fire, mechanical, or structural failure). The pilot should

A– not hesitate to declare an emergency and obtain an amended clearance.

B– wait until the situation is immediately perilous before declaring an emergency.

C– contact ATC and advise that an urgency condition exists and request priority consideration.

10-3. Answer A. GFDIC 10A, AIM

The AIM defines distress as a condition of being threatened by serious and/or imminent danger and of requiring immediate assistance. In this situation, do not hesitate to declare an emergency immediately and request an amended clearance.

10-4   **PLT444**

When may ATC request a detailed report of an emergency even though a rule has not been violated?

A– When priority has been given.

B– Any time an emergency occurs.

C– When the emergency occurs in controlled airspace.

10-4. Answer A. GFDIC 10A, FAR 91.123

Each pilot in command who is given priority in an emergency by ATC, shall submit a detailed report of that emergency within 48 hours to the manager of that ATC facility, if requested. The key criteria in this regulation is if priority has been given in an emergency, no matter where it happened or when.

10-5   **PLT391**

What action should you take if your No. 1 VOR receiver malfunctions while operating in controlled airspace under IFR? Your aircraft is equipped

with two VOR receivers. The No. 1 receiver has VOR/Localizer/Glide Slope capability, and the No. 2 receiver has only VOR/Localizer capability.

A– Continue the approach and request a VOR or NDB approach.

B– Report the malfunction immediately to ATC.

C– Continue the flight as cleared; no report is required.

10-5. Answer B. GFDIC 10A, FAR 91.187

If operating in controlled airspace under IFR, you must report any inflight malfunctions of navigational, approach, or communication equipment to ATC as soon as practical. In the report, you should include the degree to which your ability to operate under IFR in the ATC system is impaired and the type of ATC assistance you may need.

10-6   **PLT391**

During an IFR flight in IMC, you enter a holding pattern (at a fix that is not the same as the approach fix) with an EFC time of 1530. At 1520, you experience complete two way communications failure. Which procedure should you follow to execute the approach to a landing?

A– Depart the holding fix to arrive at the approach fix as close as possible to the EFC time and complete the approach.

B– Depart the holding fix at the EFC time, and complete the approach.

C– Depart the holding fix at the earliest of the flight planned ETA or the EFC time, and complete the approach.

10-6. Answer B. GFDIC 10A, FAR 91.185
If the clearance limit is not a fix from which an approach begins, leave the clearance limit at the expect-further clearance time if one has been received.

10-7   **PLT391**

Which procedure should you follow if you experience two-way communications failure while holding at a holding fix with an EFC time? (The holding fix is not the same as the approach fix.)

A– Depart the holding fix to arrive at the approach fix as close as possible to the EFC time.

B– Depart the holding fix at the EFC time.

C– Proceed immediately to the approach fix and hold until EFC.

10-7. Answer B. GFDIC 10A, FAR 91.185
FAR Part 91.185(c)(3)(ii) states, "If the clearance limit is not a fix from which an approach begins, leave the clearance limit at the expect-further-clearance time if one has been received, or if none has been received, upon arrival over the clearance limit, and proceed to a fix from which an approach begins and commence descent or descent and approach as close as possible to the estimated time of arrival as calculated from the filed or amended (with ATC) estimated time enroute."

10-8   **PLT391**

You are in IMC and have two-way radio communications failure. If you do not exercise emergency authority, what procedure are you expected to follow?

A– Set transponder to code 7600, continue flight on assigned route and fly at the last assigned altitude or the MEA, whichever is higher.

B– Set transponder to code 7700 for 1 minute, then to 7600, and fly to an area with VFR weather conditions.

C– Set transponder to 7700 and fly to an area where you can let down in VFR conditions.

10-8. Answer A. GFDIC 10A, FAR 91.185, AIM
If an aircraft experiences a loss of two-way radio capability, the pilot should adjust the transponder to reply on MODE A/3, Code 7600 and continue on the assigned route at the last assigned altitude or the MEA, which ever is higher.

10-9 PLT391

Which procedure should you follow if, during an IFR flight in VFR conditions, you have two-way radio communications failure?

A– Continue the flight under VFR and land as soon as practicable.

B– Continue the flight at assigned altitude and route, start approach at your ETA, or, if late, start approach upon arrival.

C– Land at the nearest airport that has VFR conditions.

10-9. Answer A. GFDIC 10A, FAR 91.185

FAR Part 91.185(b) states, "If the failure occurs in VFR conditions, or if VFR conditions are encountered after the failure, each pilot shall continue the flight under VFR and land as soon as practicable."

10-10 PLT391

What altitude and route should be used if you are flying in IMC and have two way radio communications failure?

A– Continue on the route specified in your clearance, fly at an altitude that is the highest of last assigned altitude, altitude ATC has informed you to expect, or the MEA.

B– Fly direct to an area that has been forecast to have VFR conditions, fly at an altitude that is at least 1,000 feet above the highest obstacles along the route.

C– Descend to MEA and, if clear of clouds, proceed to the nearest appropriate airport. If not clear of clouds, maintain the highest of the MEA's along the clearance route.

10-10. Answer A. GFDIC 10A, FAR 91.185

FAR Part 91.185(c)(2) states, "At the highest of the following altitudes or flight levels for the route segment being flown: the altitude or flight level assigned in the last ATC clearance received; the minimum altitude (converted, if appropriate, to minimum flight level as prescribed in FAR Part 91.121(c) for IFR operations; or the altitude or flight level ATC has advised may be expected in a further clearance."

10-11 PLT391

(Refer to figure 87.)

While holding at the 10 DME fix east of LCH for an ILS approach to Rwy 15 at Lake Charles Muni Airport, ATC advises you to expect clearance for the approach at 1015. At 1000 you experience two-way radio communications failure. Which procedure should be followed?

A– Squawk 7600 and listen on the LOM frequency for instructions from ATC. If no instructions are received, start your approach at 1015.

B– Squawk 7700 for 1 minute, then 7600. After 1 minute, descend to the minimum final approach fix altitude. Start your approach at 1015.

C– Squawk 7600; plan to begin your approach at 1015.

10-11. Answer C. GFDIC 10A, FAR 91.185

From the information given, it is not clear where you are holding or where the IAF for the approach is located. FAR Part 91.185(3) states that, "When the clearance limit is a fix from which an approach begins, commence descent or descent and approach as close as possible to the expect-further-clearance time if one has been received . . ."You should begin your approach at 1015 and squawk 7600 as soon as the radio failure is detected.

10-12   PLT391

In the event of two way radio communications failure while operating on an IFR clearance in VFR conditions the pilot should continue

A– by the route assigned in the last ATC clearance received.

B– the flight under VFR and land as soon as practical.

C– the flight by the most direct route to the fix specified in the last clearance.

10-12. Answer B. GFDIC 10A, FAR 91.185, AIM

If your radio fails in VFR, or if you encounter VFR conditions after the failure, continue the flight under VFR and land as soon as practicable.

10-13   PLT170

Where may you use a surveillance approach?

A– At any airport that has an approach control.

B– At any airport which has radar service.

C– At airports for which civil radar instrument approach minimums have been published.

10-13. Answer C. GFDIC 10A, AIM

This type of approach requires airport surveillance radar (ASR) and published civil radar instrument approach minimums.

10-14   PLT170

Which information, in addition to headings, does the radar controller provide without request during an ASR approach?

A– The recommended altitude for each mile from the runway.

B– When reaching the MDA.

C– When to commence descent to MDA, the aircraft's position each mile on final from the runway, and arrival at the MAP.

10-14. Answer C. GFDIC 10A, AIM

The radar controller will inform you when to begin descent to the MDA, advise you of your position each mile on final from the runway, and notify you when at the MAP.

10-15   PLT170

During a "no-gyro" approach and prior to being handed off to the final approach controller, the pilot should make all turns

A– one-half standard rate unless otherwise advised.

B– any rate not exceeding a 30° bank.

C– standard rate unless otherwise advised.

10-15. Answer C. GFDIC 10A, AIM

When executing a "no-gyro" approach, all turns before the final approach should be at standard rate. After the aircraft has been turned onto the final approach course, all turns should be half standard rate. In addition, all turns should be executed immediately upon receipt of instructions from ATC.

10-16   PLT170

After being handed off to the final approach controller during a "no-gyro" surveillance or precision approach, the pilot should make all turns

A– one-half standard rate.

B– based upon the groundspeed of the aircraft.

C– standard rate.

10-16. Answer A. GFDIC 10A, AIM

When executing a "no-gyro" approach, all turns before the final approach should be at standard rate. After the aircraft has been turned onto the final approach course, all turns should be half standard rate. In addition, all turns should be executed immediately upon receipt of instructions from ATC.

SECTION B — IFR DECISION MAKING

- Accidents involving IFR conditions are roughly 65 percent fatal. Obtaining your instrument rating and maintaining IFR currency greatly reduces your risk for these types of accidents.
- Accidents are rarely attributed to a single cause, but are the result of a series of poor choices.

SAFE HABIT PATTERNS

- You should consider filing an IFR flight plan for every flight, and close that flight plan only when a safe landing is assured.
- Though you work closely with ATC under IFR, you remain the final authority as to the safety of the flight. You may also need to coordinate responsibility with other pilots that fly with you.
- Flying with a safety pilot to practice instrument maneuvers will help you maintain currency and proficiency.

PERSONAL MINIMUMS CHECKLIST

- Developing a personal minimums checklist will assist you in determining the feasibility of a particular flight. You should take into account your currency and experience when deciding which conditions you feel comfortable flying in.
- Five hazardous attitudes affect your decisions, and you should examine your choices to ensure that you make the proper response when one of these attitudes affects your flight.

COMMUNICATION

- To avoid confusion, be sure to read back all important parts of a clearance, and ask for clarification when there is an instruction you do not understand.
- Barriers to communication include preconceived notions of upcoming clearances, abbreviated clearances, and words that have more than one meaning.

RESOURCE USE

- Effective use of resources occurs when you understand and utilize all the people and equipment available to you during a flight.
- Plan for each IFR flight thoroughly before you leave the ground, including fuel requirements, alternates available, and missed approach instructions. It is also helpful to program any navigation information before engine start. The more you can rehearse ahead of time, the more prepared you will be in the event of a problem.
- During a high workload situation, identify the most important tasks and make those a priority. Do not allow yourself to fixate on an extraneous issue.
- FAA studies show that pilots flying airplanes with new advanced avionics tend to make poor decisions at a higher rate than general aviation pilots as a whole, which increases risk. These pilots overrely on the avionics and are tempted to operate outside their personal or the environmental limits because they believe the equipment will compensate for their shortcomings

SITUATIONAL AWARENESS

- Visualization techniques can be used to create a mental picture of the flight overall.
- You can avoid CFIT by maintaining positional awareness: staying abreast of your altitude, the proper procedures in use, and the terrain surrounding the airport.
- Loss of situational awareness can occur when you are confused by clearances, misunderstand onboard equipment, or do not communicate properly with others in the cockpit.
- Advanced avionics, including digital flight instrumentation, is intended to reduce pilot workload. However, If you are not continually monitoring avionics information, you can become complacent and lose situational awareness.

10-17   PLT104
When a pilot believes advanced avionics enable operations closer to personal or environmental limits,

A– greater utilization of the aircraft is achieved.

B– risk is increased.

C– risk is decreased.

10-17. Answer B. GFDIC 10B, RMH
FAA studies show that pilots flying airplanes with new advanced avionics tend to make poor decisions at a higher rate than general aviation pilots as a whole, which increases risk. These pilots overrely on the avionics and are tempted to operate outside their personal or the environmental limits because they believe the equipment will compensate for their shortcomings.

10-18   PLT104
Automation in aircraft has proven

A– to present new hazards in its limitations.

B– that automation is basically flawless.

C– effective in preventing accidents.

10-18. Answer A. GFDIC 10B, RMH
You must be thoroughly familiar with the operation and limitations of the automation systems in your airplane in order to manage these systems effectively. If you are not continually monitoring the information from avionics and automation systems, their use can present new hazards by reducing situational awareness and increasing complacency.

10-19   PLT104
The lighter workloads associated with glass (digital) flight instrumentation

A– are instrumental in decreasing flight crew fatigue.

B– have proven to increase safety in operations.

C– may lead to complacency by the flight crew.

10-19. Answer C. GFDIC 10B, RMH
Advanced avionics, including digital flight instrumentation, is intended to reduce pilot workload. However, If you are not continually monitoring the avionics information, you can become complacent and lose situational awareness.

SECTION C — IFR FLIGHT PLANNING

FLIGHT PLANNING

- When you begin the IFR flight planning process, take a preliminary look at factors like weather, airplane performance and equipment, potential routes, and your instrument proficiency that may prevent you from making the flight.

- Availability of preferred IFR routes, aircraft performance considerations, and fuel economy will influence route selection.

- Preferred IFR routes beginning with a fix indicate that departing aircraft will normally be routed to the fix via a departure procedure (DP), or radar vectors. Check for published departure or arrival procedures relevant to your intended flight.

- NOTAMs should be reviewed for items like navaid and lighting outages or runway closures that can significantly affect your flight.

- Review the A/FD for specific information about departure and arrival airports as well as possible alternate airports that are pertinent to your flight.

- Begin gathering weather data several days before your flight in order to obtain a general overview of weather patterns.

- Although weather information may be obtained from numerous sources including newspapers, television, and the internet, these sources should not be considered suitable alternatives to a flight service station or DUATS standard briefing.

- In case the weather at your intended destination is forecast to have a ceiling less than 2,000 feet or visibility less than 3 miles, you need to file an alternate.

- A good alternate airport should be far enough away to be unaffected by weather at your destination, be equipped with appropriate communications and weather reporting capabilities, and have more than one approach.

- The most current enroute and destination weather information for an instrument flight should be obtained from the FSS. Once your weather briefing is complete, you can make your go/no-go decision and begin planning the flight if conditions are favorable.

NAVIGATION

- For IFR flight, you are required to have working navigation equipment appropriate to the ground facilities to be used.

- It is your responsibility as pilot in command to make sure that the VOR check has been accomplished within the past 30 days, and the transponder has been checked within the past 24 calendar months. Transponder checks must be entered in aircraft logbooks. There also must be a written record of the VOR test, which includes the date, place, bearing error, and the signature of the person performing the test.

- The navigation log is a convenient way for you to complete your preflight planning, organize your flight, and provide you with a concise textual description of your flight.

- You may determine that a Loran C equipped aircraft is approved for IFR operations by checking the Airplane Flight Manual Supplement.

FILING AND FLYING YOUR FLIGHT PLAN

- Before filing your flight plan, ensure you have all of the blocks in the flight plan form filled in correctly with information needed by flight service to process the flight plan. The information needed includes the correct aircraft equipment code, route, destination, and fuel available information. The point of first intended landing at your destination should be used to compute the estimated time enroute on an IFR flight plan.

- If you are flying to an airport that does not have an operating control tower, you are responsible for closing your own IFR flight plan by phone through FSS, or by direct communications with ATC.

- Unless you have better-than-VFR conditions forecast from one hour before to one hour after your ETA at your destination, you must include an alternate airport in your flight plan. To list an airport with a precision approach as an alternate, the forecast at the ETA at the alternate must be at least a 600-foot ceiling and 2 miles visibility.

- If you actually proceed to the selected alternate, then the landing minimums used at that airport should be the minimums specified for the approach procedure selected.

10-20 **PLT224**

Preferred IFR routes beginning with a fix indicate that departing aircraft will normally be routed to the fix by

A— the established airway(s) between the departure airport and the fix.

B— an instrument departure procedure (DP), or radar vectors.

C— direct route only.

10-20. Answer B. GFDIC 10C, AIM

Preferred IFR routes beginning or ending with a fix usually indicates that aircraft will be routed to or from these fixes via a DP, radar vector, or STAR. If one is not listed, consult the enroute chart to find the most practical route for the flight. In all cases, remember to check applicable minimum enroute altitudes that may be beyond your aircraft's climb capabilities.

10-21 **PLT224**

(Refer to figure 1.)

The time entered in block 12 for an IFR flight should be based on which fuel quantity?

A— Total fuel required for the flight.

B— Total useable fuel on board.

C— The amount of fuel required to fly to the destination airport, then to the alternate, plus a 45 minute reserve.

10-21. Answer B. GFDIC 10C, AIM

When indicating the fuel on board, block 12, you should include the total time at normal cruising speed for the usable fuel on board, expressed in hours and minutes.

10-22 **PLT224**

(Refer to figure 1.)

What information should be entered in block 7 of an IFR flight plan if the flight has three legs, each at a different altitude?

A— Altitude for first leg.

B— Altitude for first leg and highest altitude.

C— Highest altitude.

10-22. Answer A. GFDIC 10C, AIM

The altitude listed in block 7 for an IFR flight plan should be the requested initial cruising altitude. If you want to change altitude, direct your request to the controller during flight.

10-23 **PLT224**

(Refer to figure 1.)

Which equipment determines the code to be entered in block 3 as a suffix to aircraft type on the flight plan form?

A— DME, ADF, and airborne radar.

B— DME, transponder, and ADF.

C— DME, transponder, and RNAV.

10-23. Answer C. GFDIC 10C, AIM

When determining the equipment capability suffix to be entered in block 3 of a flight plan, remember that the suffix is based on whether the aircraft is equipped with DME, transponder, TACAN-only equipment, and/or RNAV.

10-24   PLT012
(Refer to figures 21, 21A, 22, 22A, 23, 24, 25 and 26.)

After departing GJT and arriving at Durango Co., La Plata Co. Airport, you are unable to land because of weather. How long can you hold over DRO before departing for return flight to the alternate, Grand Junction Co., Walker Field Airport?

Total useable fuel on board......................... 68 gallons.

Average fuel consumption......................... 15 GPH.

Wind and velocity at 16,000...................... 2308-16°.

A– 1 hour 33 minutes.

B– 1 hour 37 minutes.

C– 1 hour 42 minutes.

10-24. Answer A. GFDIC 10C, PHB
In order to determine how long you can hold over DRO, you must subtract the fuel required to get to DRO, the fuel required to get back to Grand Junction, and the fuel reserve (45 minutes). Your total fuel on board is 4 hours and 30 minutes. Begin by determining your time enroute to DRO and your time enroute back to GJT.

True airspeed ....175 kts
Cruising altitude ....15,000 feet
Variation ....14°E
Wind..230/08

Check Points	Mag Crs	Mag Wnd	GS	Dist	Time
GJT					
JNC					
HERM	151				:24:00
MANCA	151	216/08	171	75	:26:19
APP/ LND	092				:18:30
TOTAL					1:08:49

True airspeed ....174 knots
Cruising altitude ....16,000 feet
Variation ....14°E
Wind..230/08

Check Points	Mag Crs	Mag Wnd	GS	Dist	Time
DRO					
MANCA	272				:14:30
HERM	333	216/8	177	75	:25:25
JNC	331	216/8	171	35	:11:52
APP/ LND					:12:00
TOTAL					1:03:47

The flight to DRO requires 17.2 gallons of fuel (1:08:49 × 15gph = 17.2) and the return flight requires 15.9 gallons (1:03:47 × 15 gph = 15.9). When you subtract the enroute (17.2), return (15.9), and reserve (11.3) fuel required, you will have 23.6 gallons left for holding over DRO (68 – 17.2 – 15.9 – 11.3 = 23.6). This equates to approximately 1 hour 34 minutes of fuel (23.6 ÷ 15 = 1:34).

10-25   PLT012

(Refer to figures 21, 22 and 24.)

(Refer to FD excerpt below, and use the wind entry closest to the flight planned altitude.) Determine the time to be entered in block 10 of the flight from GJT to DRO.

Route of Flight...Figure 21

Flight log & MAG VAR.............................Figure 22

Enroute chart..Figure 24

FT	12,000	18,000
FNM	2408-05	2208-21

A– 1 hour 08 minutes.

B– 1 hour 03 minutes.

C– 58 minutes.

10-25. Answer A. GFDIC 10C, PHB

This question requires you to find the estimated time enroute (ETE) for block 10 on the flight plan. Use the flight log to record the necessary information.

You'll also need information from the other figures referenced in the question. A first step is to compute ground-speed from each leg of the route using the winds aloft data. Since winds aloft are reported in true direction, you can simplify the problem by converting them to magnetic. Remember, airways are oriented to magnetic north. Then, determine distances and times using all available information to find the total ETE.

True airspeed ....175 kts

Cruising altitude ....15,000 feet

Variation ....14°E

Wind..220/08

Check Points	Mag Crs	Mag Wnd	GS	Dist	Time
GJT					
JNC					
HERM	151				:24:00
MANCA	151	206/08	170	75	:26:28
APP/ LND	092				:18:30
TOTAL					1:08:58

10-26   PLT012

(Refer to figures 21, 22 and 24.)

What fuel would be consumed on the flight between Grand Junction Co. and Durango, Co. if the average fuel consumption is 17.5 GPH?

A– 17 gallons.

B– 20 gallons.

C– 25 gallons.

10-26. Answer B. GFDIC 10C, PHB

Refer to the estimated time enroute (ETE) from Grand Junction to Durango that you determined for question 10-25. With an ETE of 1:08:58 and a fuel burn of 17.5 gallons per hour, you are burning approximately 20 gallons of fuel during this flight. (1.15 hours x 17.5 GPH = 20.125 gallons)

10-27   PLT012

(Refer to figures 27, 28, 31, 161, 162, 163, 164, and 165.)

(Refer to the FD excerpt below, and use the wind entry closest to the flight planned altitude.) Determine the time to be entered in block 10 of the flight plan.

Route of Flight...Figures 27, 28, 31, 161, 163, and 164

Flight log & MAG VAR...............................Figure 28

GNATS SIX DEPARTURE..............Figures 163, 164

FT	3000	6000	9000
OTH	0507	2006+03	2215-05

A— 1 hour 10 minutes.

B— 1 hour 15 minutes.

C— 1 hour 20 minutes.

10-27. Answer C. GFDIC 10C, PHB

This question requires you to find the estimated time enroute (ETE) for block 10 on the flight plan. Use the flight log to record the necessary information.

You'll also need information from the other figures referenced in the question. A first step is to compute groundspeed for each leg of the route using the winds aloft data. Since winds aloft are reported in true direction, you can simplify the problem by converting them to magnetic. Remember, airways are oriented to magnetic north. Then, determine distances and times using all available information to find the total ETE.

To compute the time from MERLI to MOURN Intersection, you must determine the length of the 15 DME arc off the OED VORTAC. To do this, take the number of degrees traveled on the arc (333 − 251 = 82), times the number of miles (15), and divide the product by 60. The length of the arc is 20.5 NM (82 × 15 ÷ 60 = 20.5). The total distance to MOURN Intersection is 36.5 (20.5 + 16 = 36.5).

True airspeed	155 kts
Cruising altitude	8,000 feet
Variation	20°E
Wind	220/15

Check Points	Mag Crs	Mag Wnd	GS	Dist	Time
MFR					
MERLI					:11:00
MOURN	333	36.5			:16:13
RBG	287	200/15	153	19	:07:27
OTH	272	200/15	150	38	:15:12
EUG	024	200/15	170	59	1:08:49
APP/LND		200/15			:10:00
TOTAL					1:20:41

Your total time to Mahlon Sweet Field is 1 hour, 20 minutes, and 41 seconds.

10-28   PLT053

(Refer to figure 32.)

What aircraft equipment code should be entered in block 3 of the flight plan?

A— A.

B— C.

C— I.

10-28. Answer C. GFDIC 10C, AIM

Area Navigation (RNAV) and a Mode C transponder requires an "/I" equipment code suffix.

10-29   PLT012

(Refer to figures 32, 33, 34, 35, 35A, 169, and 171.)

(Refer to the FD excerpt below, and use the wind entry closest to the flight planned altitude.) Determine the time to be entered in block 10 of the flight plan.

Route of Flight.... Figures 32, 33, 34, 35A, 169, and 171

Flight log & MAG VAR................................ Figure 32

RNAV (GPS) RWY 33................................Figure 171

FT	3000	6000	9000	12000
DAL	2027	2239+13	2240+08	2248+05

A– 1 hour 35 minutes.

B– 1 hour 41 minutes.

C– 1 hour 46 minutes.

10-29. Answer A. GFDIC 10C, PHB

This question requires you to find the estimated time enroute (ETE) for block 10 on the flight plan. Use the flight log to record the necessary information. You'll also need information from the other figures referenced in the question. A first step is to compute groundspeed for each leg of the route using the winds aloft data. Since winds aloft are reported in true direction, you can simplify the problem by converting them to magnetic. Remember, airways are oriented to magnetic north. Then, determine distances and times using all available information to find the total ETE.

True airspeed ....180 kts
Cruising altitude ....8,000 feet
Variation ....4°E
Wind..220/40

Check Points	Mag Crs	Mag Wnd	GS	Dist	Time
HOT					
MARKI	221				:12:00
TXK	210	216/40	140	55	:23:34
TXK/ BUJ3	272	216/40	155	61	:23:37
BUJ3	239	216/40	142	59	:24:56
APP/ LND					:10:00
TOTAL					1:34:07

Your total time to Dallas Addison is 1 hour, 34 minutes, and 7 seconds.

10-30   PLT053

(Refer to figure 38.)

What aircraft equipment code should be entered in block 3 of the flight plan?

A– C.

B– I.

C– A.

10-30. Answer B. GFDIC 10C, AIM

RNAV and a transponder with altitude encoding equipment requires an "/I" equipment code.

10-31   PLT012

(Refer to figures 38, 39, 40 and 41.) (Refer to the FD excerpt below, and use the wind entry closest to the flight planned altitude.)

Determine the time to be entered in block 10 of the flight plan.

Route of Flight.............................Figures 38, 39, and 40

Flight log & MAG VAR.................................Figure 39

ACTON TWO ARRIVAL..............................Figure 41

FT	6000	9000	12000
ABI	2033+13	2141+13	2142+05

A– 1 hour 24 minutes.

B– 1 hour 26 minutes.

C– 1 hour 31 minutes.

10-31. Answer C. GFDIC 10C, PHB

This question requires you to find the estimated time enroute (ETE) for block 10 on the flight plan. Use the flight log to record the necessary information.

You'll also need information from the other figures referenced in the question. A first step is to compute groundspeed for each leg of the route using the winds aloft data. Since winds aloft are reported in true direction, you can simplify the problem by converting them to magnetic. Remember, airways are oriented to magnetic north. Then, determine distances and times using all available information to find the total ETE.

True airspeed ....156 kts
Cruising altitude ....11,000 feet
Variation ....11°E
Wind..210/42

Check Points	Mag Crs	Mag Wnd	GS	Dist	Time
21XS					
BGS					:06:00
LORAN	075	199/42	176	42	:14:19
ABI	076	199/42	175	40	:13:43
COTTN	087	199/42	167	63	:22:38
AQN	075	199/42	176	50	:17:03
CREEK	040	199/42	194	32	:09:54
APP/LND					:08:00
TOTAL					1:31:37

10-32   PLT053

(Refer to figure 44.)

What aircraft equipment code should be entered in block 3 of the flight plan?

A– A.

B– C.

C– I.

10-32. Answer C. GFDIC 10C, AIM

Having RNAV and a transponder with altitude encoding equipment requires an "/I" equipment code.

10-33   PLT012

(Refer to figures 44, 45, 182, 183, and 184.)

Determine the time to be entered in block 10 of the flight plan. (Refer to the FD excerpt below, and use the wind entry closest to the flight planned altitude.)

Route of flight...................Figures 44, 45, 182, and 183

Flight log & MAG VAR................................Figure 45

GROMO THREE DEPARTURE.........Figures 182, 183

FT	3000	6000	9000	12000
YKM	1615	1926+12	2032+08	2035+05

A– 54 minutes.

B– 1 hour 02 minutes.

C– 1 hour 07 minutes.

10-33. Answer B. GFDIC 10C, PHB

This question requires you to find the estimated time enroute (ETE) for the block 10 entry on the flight plan form. Use the flight log to record the necessary information. You'll also need information from other figures referenced in this question. The first step is to compute groundspeed for each leg of the route using the winds aloft data. Since winds aloft are reported in true direction, you can simplify the problem by converting them to magnetic. Remember, airways are oriented to magnetic north. Then, determine distance and times using all available information to find the total ETE.

True airspeed ....180 kts
Cruise altitude..12,000 ft
Variation ....20°E
Wind...200°/35 kts

Check Points	Mag Crs	Mag Wnd	GS	Dist	Time
YKM		180/35			
HITCH		180/35		16	:10:00
VOR/COP	206	180/35	148	37	:15:00
BTG	234	180/35	157	53	:20:15
PDX	160	180/35	147	10	:04:05
ARPT		180/35			:13:00
TOTAL					1:02:20

The distances between YKM and HITCH (16), and BTG and PDX (10) are conservative estimates based on the enroute map.

10-34   PLT053

(Refer to figure 50.)

What aircraft equipment code should be entered in block 3 of the flight plan?

A– I.

B– T.

C– U.

10-34. Answer A. GFDIC 10C, AIM

The aircraft indicated in the flight plan, N2468 is equipped with a Mode C transponder, RNAV and DME. This would correspond with the "I" designation.

10-35   **PLT012**

(Refer to figures 50, 51, 53, 189, and 190.)

Determine the time to be entered in block 10 of the flight plan. (Refer to the FD excerpt below, and use the wind entry closest to the flight planned altitude.)

Route of flight......................Figures 50, 51, 53, and 189

Flight log and MAG VAR...............................Figure 51

HABUT FOUR DEPARTURE ....Figure 189

FT	3000	6000	9000
SBA	0610	2115+05	2525+00

A– 43 minutes.

B– 46 minutes.

C– 51 minutes.

10-35. Answer C. GFDIC 10C, PHB

This question requires you to find the estimated time enroute (ETE) for the block 10 entry on the flight plan form. Use the flight log to record the necessary information. You'll also need information from other figures referenced in this question. The first step is to compute groundspeed for each leg of the route using the winds aloft data. Since winds aloft are reported in true direction, you can simplify the problem by converting them to magnetic. Remember, airways are oriented to magnetic north. Then, determine distance and times using all available information to find the total ETE.

True airspeed ....158 kts
Cruise altitude...8,000 ft
Variation ....16°E
Wind...250°/25 kts

Check Points	Mag Crs	Mag Wnd	GS	Dist	Time
HABUT	253	234/25			:08:00
GVO	343	234/25	164	6.4	:02:20
MQO	307	234/25	149	54.0	:21:45
PRB	358	234/25	171	26.0	:09:07
APP/LDG					:10:00
TOTAL					:51:12

10-36   **PLT053**

(Refer to figure 69.)

What aircraft equipment code should be entered in block 3 of the flight plan?

A– A.

B– B.

C– U.

10-36. Answer A. GFDIC 10C, AIM

The figure lists the available equipment, and the equipment code entry in block 3 consists of a slash (/) and a letter designation. An aircraft with DME and a transponder with Mode C encoding altimeter meets the equipment requirements for a "/A" designation.

10-37   **PLT012**

(Refer to figures 69, 70, 71 and 72.)

Determine the time to be entered in block 10 of the flight plan. (Refer to the FD excerpt below, and use the wind entry closest to the flight planned altitude.)

Route of flight.............................Figures 69, 70, and 71

Flight log and MAG VAR.............................Figure 70

JUDDS TWO ARRIVAL
        and Excerpt from AFD..........................Figure 72

FT	3000	6000	9000
BDL	3320	3425+05	3430+00

A– 1 hour 14 minutes.

B– 58 minutes.

C– 50 minutes.

10-37. Answer B. GFDIC 10C, PHB

If your calculations are accurate, they will not agree with any of the answers provided. (B) is closest, and is apparently the result when you do not convert true winds to magnetic before performing the calculations. This question requires you to find the estimated time enroute (ETE) for the block 10 entry on the flight

plan form. Use the flight log to record the necessary information. You'll also need information from other figures referenced in this question. The first step is to compute groundspeed for each leg of the route using the winds aloft data. Since winds aloft are reported

in true direction, you can simplify the problem by converting them to magnetic. Remember, airways are oriented to magnetic north. Then, determine distance and times using all available information to find the total ETE.

True airspeed ....128 kts
Cruise altitude..5,000 ft
Variation ....14°W
Wind ....340°/25

Check Points	Mag Crs	Mag Wnd	GS	Dist	Time
4N1					
SHAFF		354/25			:08:00
HELON	029	354/25	107	24	:13:30
IGN	102	354/25	133	21	:09:30
COP	112	354/25	138	15	:06:30
JUDDS	100	354/25	133	17	:07:30
BRISS	057	354/25	115	6	:03:00
APP/LDG					:12:00
TOTAL					1:00:00

10-38   **PLT053**

(Refer to figure 74.)

What aircraft equipment code should be entered in block 3 of the flight plan?

A– T.

B– U.

C– A.

10-38. Answer C. GFDIC 10C, AIM

See Aircraft Equipment Suffixes in Appendix B. It indicates that for aircraft equipped with DME and a transponder with altitude encoding capability, you should enter "/A" in block 3 of the flight plan.

10-39   PLT012

(Refer to figures 74, 75, 78, 172/172A, and 211.)

Determine the time to be entered in block 10 of the flight plan. (Refer to the FD excerpt below, and use the wind entry closest to the flight planned altitude.)

Route of flight......................Figures 74, 75, 78, and 211

Flight log & MAG VAR................................Figure 75

STAKK THREE DEPARTURE....................Figure 211

FT	6000	9000	12000	18000
BIL	2414	2422+11	2324+05	2126+11

A— 1 hour 15 minutes.

B— 1 hour 20 minutes.

C— 1 hour 25 minutes.

10-39. Answer A. GFDIC 10C, PHB

This question requires you to find the estimated time enroute (ETE) for the block 10 entry on the flight plan. Use the flight log to record the necessary information. You'll also need information from other figures referenced in the question. A first step is to compute ground-speed for each leg of the route using the winds aloft data. Since winds aloft are reported in true direction, you can simplify the problem by converting them to magnetic. Remember, airways are oriented to magnetic north. Then, determine distances and times using all available information to find the total ETE.

True airspeed ....160 kts
Cruising altitude ....11,000 feet
Variation ....18°E
Wind..230/24

Check Points	Mag Crs	Mag Wnd	GS	Dist	Time
HLN					
SWEDD	103				:15:00
BZN	140	212/24	151	44	:17:29
COP	110	212/24	163	13	:04:47
LVM	063	212/24	180	20	:06:40:
REEPO	067	212/24	179	39	:13:04
BIL	069	212/24	179	38	:12:44
APP/LND					:15:00
TOTAL					1:24:44

10-40   PLT455

The most current enroute and destination flight information for planning an instrument flight should be obtained from

A— the ATIS broadcast.

B— the FSS.

C— Notices to Airmen (Class II).

10-40. Answer B. GFDIC 10C, AIM

Planning for an instrument flight should include a pre-flight weather briefing. This briefing should consist of the latest or most current weather, airport, and enroute NAVAID information. This briefing service may be obtained from an FSS, either by telephone, by radio when airborne, or in person.

10-41   PLT012
(Refer to figure 91.)

What should be the approximate elapsed time from BZN VOR to DBS VORTAC, if the wind is 24 knots from 260° and your intended TAS is 185 knots? (VAR 17°E.)

A– 33 minutes.

B– 37 minutes.

C– 39 minutes.

10-41. Answer C. GFDIC 10C, PHB
This question requires you to calculate the groundspeed and then complete a time speed-distance problem.

1. Determine the distance between BZN VOR and DBS VORTAC (111 NM as indicated in the box near V343).

2. Convert the wind to magnetic (260° − 17° = 243°).

3. Determine the groundspeed using your flight computer.

   a. Enter the wind direction and speed (243° true at 24 knots).

   b. Enter the true airspeed (185 knots)

   c. Enter magnetic course 186°.

   d. GS = 171 knots

4. Determine the time enroute using your flight computer (111 NM at 171 kts = 38 57). This is rounded to 39 min.

10-42   PLT012
(Refer to figure 91.)

Southbound on V257, at what time should you arrive at DBS VORTAC if you crossed over CPN VORTAC at 0850 and over DIVID intersection at 0854?

A– 0939.

B– 0943.

C– 0947.

10-42. Answer B. GFDIC 10C, PHB
To solve the problem you must first solve for groundspeed (GS). Use the speed and remaining distance to determine your ETE to DBS VORTAC, then add this to the ATA over DIVID Int. to determine your ETA over DBS VORTAC.

1. Determine GS

   a. (0854 − 0850 = 4 min.)

   b. The distance between CPN and DIVID Int. is 9 NM

   c. Groundspeed = 135 kts (9 ÷ :04:00 = 135)

2. Determine distance between DIVID Int. and DBS VORTAC. (110 NM)

3. The time to DBS VORTAC is :48:53 (110 ÷ 135 = :48:53).

4. The ETE from DIVID to DBS VORTAC plus the ATA over DIVID is :52:53 (:48:53 + 04:00 = :52:53). This is your total ETE to DBS.

5. The ETA over DBS is 09:42:53 (8:50:00 + :52:53 = 9:42:53).

10-43   PLT380
If a pilot elects to proceed to the selected alternate, the landing minimums used at that airport should be the

A— minimums specified for the approach procedure selected.

B— alternate minimums shown on the approach chart.

C— minimums shown for that airport in a separate listing of "IFR Alternate Minimums."

10-43. Answer A. GFDIC 10C, IFH
Once a pilot proceeds to the alternate, it now becomes the destination, and published landing minimums for that approach apply.

10-44   PLT359
By which means may a pilot determine if a Loran C equipped aircraft is approved for IFR operations?

A— Not necessary; Loran C is not approved for IFR.

B— Check aircraft logbook.

C— Check the Airplane Flight Manual Supplement.

10-44. Answer C. GFDIC 10C, AIM
Approval of LORAN-C receivers for IFR operations will be documented in the Airplane Flight Manual Supplement, on FAA Form 337 or in aircraft maintenance records, or by a placard in the airplane.

10-45   PLT380
When a pilot elects to proceed to the selected alternate airport, which minimums apply for landing at the alternate?

A— 600-1 if the airport has an ILS.

B— Ceiling 200 feet above the published minimum; visibility 2 miles.

C— The landing minimums for the approach to be used.

10-45. Answer C. GFDIC 10C, IFH
When you proceed to your alternate, it now becomes your destination, and you may use the published landing minimums for the approach you will use. Remember, alternate minimums are used only for flight planning purposes.

10-46   PLT379
What are the alternate minimums that must be forecast at the ETA for an airport that has a precision approach procedure?

A— 400-foot ceiling and 2 miles visibility.

B— 600-foot ceiling and 2 miles visibility.

C— 800-foot ceiling and 2 miles visibility.

10-46. Answer B. GFDIC 10C, FAR 91.169
To use an airport with a precision approach as an alternate, it must be forecast to have a ceiling of at least 600 feet and a visibility of 2 miles at the estimated time of arrival (ETA).

10-47   PLT455

What point at the destination should be used to compute estimated time enroute on an IFR flight plan?

A– The final approach fix on the expected instrument approach.

B– The initial approach fix on the expected instrument approach.

C– The point of first intended landing.

10-47. Answer C. GFDIC 10C, FAR 91.153, FAR 91.169
Both IFR and VFR flight plans include the estimated time enroute to the point of first intended landing.

FEDERAL AVIATION REGULATIONS

SECTION A — 14 CFR PART 61 — CERTIFICATION: PILOTS AND FLIGHT INSTRUCTORS

WHEN AN INSTRUMENT RATING IS REQUIRED

- The pilot in command of a civil aircraft must have an instrument rating when operating under IFR, in weather conditions less than the minimum for VFR flight, or in Class A airspace. An instrument rating is required for any flight on an IFR flight plan even if the flight is in VFR conditions.
- An instrument rating is required for most commercial operations. A newly certificated commercial airplane pilot must hold an instrument pilot rating to carry passengers for hire on cross-country flights of more than 50 NM and to carry passengers for hire at night.

INSTRUMENT CURRENCY

- To maintain IFR currency, you must, within the preceding six months, perform at least six instrument approaches, holding procedures, and intercepting and tracking courses through the use of navigation systems. These procedures must be performed and logged under actual or simulated instrument conditions, either in flight in the appropriate category of aircraft for the instrument privileges sought or in a flight simulator or flight training device that is representative of the aircraft category for the instrument privileges sought.
- After your recent IFR experience lapses, you may not act as pilot in command under IFR. However, you have an additional six months in which to gain the necessary instrument experience, with the help of a safety pilot or CFII, or using a simulator. After that time, you must pass an instrument proficiency check before you can again act as PIC under IFR.
- An instrument proficiency check must be in the category of aircraft involved, and given by an approved FAA examiner, instrument instructor, or FAA inspector. After successfully completing an instrument proficiency check, you remain current for 6 months even if no further IFR flights are made.

LOGGING INSTRUMENT TIME

- If a pilot enters the condition of flight in the pilot logbook as simulated instrument conditions, the place and type of each instrument approach completed and name of safety pilot must also be entered.
- A certificated instrument flight instructor may log as instrument flight time all time during which the instructor acts as instrument instructor in actual instrument weather conditions.
- When on an instrument flight plan, you may log as instrument time only the time you controlled the aircraft solely by reference to flight instruments.

11-1   PLT442

No pilot may act as pilot-in-command of an aircraft under IFR or in weather conditions less than the minimums prescribed for VFR unless that pilot has, within the preceding 6 calendar months, completed at least

A— three instrument approaches and logged 3 hours.

B— six instrument flights under actual IFR conditions.

C— six instrument approaches, holding procedures, intercepting and tracking courses using navigational systems, or passed an instrument proficiency check.

11-2   PLT448

What limitation is imposed on a newly certificated commercial airplane pilot if that person does not hold an instrument pilot rating?

A— The carrying of passengers or property for hire on cross-country flights at night is limited to a radius of 50 nautical miles (NM).

B— The carrying of passengers for hire on cross-country flights is limited to 50 NM for night flights, but not limited for day flights.

C— The carrying of passengers for hire on cross-country flights is limited to 50 NM and the carrying of passengers for hire at night is prohibited.

11-3   PLT442

What portion of dual instruction time may a certificated instrument flight instructor log as instrument flight time?

A— All time during which the instructor acts as instrument instructor, regardless of weather conditions.

B— All time during which the instructor acts as instrument instructor in actual instrument weather conditions.

C— Only the time during which the instructor flies the aircraft by reference to instruments.

11-1. Answer C. FAR 61.57

Six approaches, holding procedures, and intercepting and tracking courses through the use of navigation systems are required. An instrument proficiency check also meets the requirement.

11-2. Answer C. FAR 61.133

If a commercial pilot is certified without an instrument rating, his/her pilot certificate will be endorsed with a limitation prohibiting the carriage of passengers for hire in airplanes on cross-country flights beyond 50 nautical miles, or at night.

11-3. Answer B. FAR 61.51

A certificated instrument flight instructor may log instrument time during that portion of the flight he/she acts as an instrument flight instructor in actual instrument weather conditions.

11-4   PLT409

Which flight time may be logged as instrument time when on an instrument flight plan?

A— All of the time the aircraft was not controlled by ground references.

B— Only the time you controlled the aircraft solely by reference to flight instruments.

C— Only the time you were flying in IFR weather conditions.

11-4. Answer B. FAR 61.51

You may log instrument flight time only for that flight time that you operate an aircraft solely by reference to instruments. This can done in actual or simulated instrument flight conditions.

11-5   PLT442

To meet the minimum instrument experience requirements, within the last 6 calendar months you need

A— six hours in the same category aircraft.

B— six hours in the same category aircraft, and at least 3 of the 6 hours in actual IFR conditions.

C— six instrument approaches, holding procedures, and intercepting and tracking courses in the appropriate category of aircraft.

11-5. Answer C. FAR 61.57

Six approaches, holding procedures, and intercepting and tracking courses through the use of navigation systems are required. An instrument proficiency check also meets the requirement.

11-6   PLT442

After your recent IFR experience lapses, how much time do you have before you must pass an instrument competency check to act as pilot-in-command under IFR?

A— 6 months.

B— 90 days.

C— 12 months.

11-6. Answer A. FAR 61.57

If you do not meet the recent instrument experience requirements during the prescribed 6 months, you have 6 additional calendar months to meet the experience requirements.

11-7   PLT442

An instrument rated pilot, who has not logged any instrument time in 1 year or more, cannot serve as pilot-in-command under IFR, unless the pilot

A– passes an instrument proficiency check in the category of aircraft involved, followed by 6 hours and six instrument approaches, 3 of those hours in the category of aircraft involved.

B– passes an instrument proficiency check in the category of aircraft involved, given by an approved FAA examiner, instrument instructor, or FAA inspector.

C– completes the required 6 hours and six approaches, followed by an instrument proficiency check given by an FAA-designated examiner.

11-7. Answer B. FAR 61.57

If you do not meet the recent instrument experience requirements during the prescribed 6 months or 6 calendar months thereafter, you may not act as pilot in command under IFR or in weather conditions less than VFR until you pass an instrument proficiency check.

11-8   PLT442

A pilot's recent IFR experience expires on July 1 of this year. What is the latest date the pilot can meet the IFR experience requirement without having to take an instrument proficiency check?

A– December 31, this year.

B– June 30, next year.

C– July 31, this year.

11-8. Answer A. FAR 61.57

If you do not meet the recent instrument experience requirements during the prescribed 6 months, you have 6 additional calendar months to meet the experience requirements.

11-9   PLT442

What minimum conditions are necessary for the instrument approaches required for IFR currency?

A– The approaches may be made in an aircraft, flight simulator, or flight training device.

B– At least three approaches must be made in the same category of aircraft to be flown.

C– At least three approaches must be made in the same category and class of aircraft to be flown.

11-9. Answer A. FAR 61.57

To maintain instrument currency, you must complete 6 instrument approaches. The approaches must be made in the appropriate category of aircraft or in a flight simulator or flight training device that is representative of the appropriate aircraft category.

11-10   PLT442

A pilot may satisfy the recent flight experience require-ment necessary to act as pilot in command in IMC in powered aircraft by logging within the six calendar months preceding the month of the flight

A– six instrument approaches, holding procedures, and intercepting and tracking courses using navigational systems.

B– six instrument approaches and three hours under actual or six hours in simulated IFR conditions; three of the approaches must be in the category of aircraft involved.

C– six hours of instrument time under actual or simulated IFR conditions, including at least six instrument approaches. Three of the six hours must be in flight in any category aircraft.

11-10. Answer A. FAR 61.57

Six approaches, holding procedures, and intercepting and tracking courses through the use of navigation systems are required. An instrument proficiency check also meets the requirement.

11-11   PLT442

How long does a pilot meet the recency of experience requirements for IFR flight after successfully complet-ing an instrument competency check if no further IFR flights are made?

A– 6 calendar months.

B– 90 days.

C– 12 calendar months.

11-11. Answer A. FAR 61.57

An instrument competency check satisfies the recent IFR experience requirements for 6 months.

11-12   PLT442

What recent instrument flight experience requirements must be met before you may act as pilot in command of an airplane under IFR?

A– A minimum of six instrument approaches in an aircraft, at least three of which must be in the same category within the preceding 6 calendar months.

B– A minimum of six instrument approaches in an airplane, or an approved simulator (airplane) or ground trainer, within the preceding 6 calendar months.

C– A minimum of six instrument approaches, at least three of which must be in an aircraft within the preceding 6 calendar months.

11-12. Answer B. FAR 61.57

Before a pilot can act as pilot in command of an airplane under IFR, the pilot must have logged six instrument approaches under actual or simulated instrument conditions, either in flight in the appropriate category of aircraft, or in a flight simulator or flight training device that is representative of the aircraft category. In addition, the pilot must have performed holding procedures, as well as intercepting and tracking courses through the use of navigation systems.

11-13   PLT442

What additional instrument experience is required for you to meet the recent flight experience requirements to act as pilot in command of an airplane under IFR? Your present instrument experience within the preceding 6 calendar months is:

1) 3 hours with holding, intercepting, and tracking courses in an approved airplane flight simulator.

2) two instrument approaches in an airplane.

A— Three hours of simulated or actual instrument flight time in a helicopter, and two instrument approaches in an airplane or helicopter.

B— Four instrument approaches in an airplane, or an approved airplane flight simulator or training device.

C— Three instrument approaches in an airplane.

11-13. Answer B. FAR 61.57

Before acting as pilot in command of an airplane under IFR or in weather conditions less than VFR, you must have logged, within the preceding 6 calendar months, at least six instrument approaches, holding procedures, and intercepting and tracking courses through the use of navigation systems.

11-14   PLT442

To meet the minimum required instrument flight experience to act as pilot in command of an aircraft under IFR, you must have logged within the six calendar months preceding the month of the flight, in the same category of aircraft:

A— holding procedures, intercepting and tracking courses through the use of navigation systems, and six instrument approaches.

B— six hours of instrument time in any aircraft, and six instrument approaches.

C— six instrument approaches, three of which must be in the same category and class of aircraft to be flown, and six hours of instrument time in any aircraft.

11-14. Answer A. FAR 61.57

Six approaches, holding procedures, and intercepting and tracking courses through the use of navigation systems are required.

11-15   PLT448

A certificated commercial pilot who carries passengers for hire at night or in excess of 50 NM is required to have at least

A— a First-Class Medical Certificate.

B— an associated type rating if the airplane is of the multiengine class.

C— an instrument rating in the same category and class of aircraft.

11-15. Answer C. FAR 61.133

In order to carry passengers for hire at night or in excess of 50 nautical miles, you must hold a commercial pilot certificate with an instrument rating in the same category and class of aircraft listed on the commercial pilot certificate.

11-16   PLT448

You intend to carry passengers for hire on a night VFR flight in a single engine airplane within a 25 mile radius of the departure airport. You are required to possess at least which rating(s)?

A– A Commercial Pilot Certificate with a single engine land rating.

B– A Commercial Pilot Certificate with a single engine and instrument (airplane) rating.

C– A Private Pilot Certificate with a single engine land and instrument airplane rating.

11-16. Answer B. FAR 61.133

In order to carry passengers for hire at night or in excess of 50 nautical miles, you must hold a commercial pilot certificate with an instrument rating in the same category and class of aircraft listed on the commercial pilot certificate.

11-17   PLT448

Do regulations permit you to act as pilot in command of a helicopter in IMC if you hold a Private Pilot Certificate with ASEL, airplane instrument rating, rotorcraft category, and helicopter class rating?

A– Yes, if you comply with the recent IFR experience requirements for a helicopter.

B– No, however, you may do so if you hold an Airline Transport Pilot-Helicopter Certificate, limited to VFR.

C– No, you must hold either an unrestricted Airline Transport Pilot-Helicopter Certificate or a helicopter instrument rating.

11-17. Answer C. FAR 61.167

Since an instrument rating is category specific, you may not operate an airplane in IMC without an instrument airplane rating. However, if you hold an unrestricted Airline Transport Rating you are entitled to the same privileges as a pilot who holds a commercial pilot certificate with an instrument rating.

11-18   PLT448

Under which condition must the pilot-in-command of a civil aircraft have at least an instrument rating?

A– When operating in the Continental Control Area.

B– For a flight in VFR conditions while on an IFR flight plan.

C– For any flight above an altitude of 1,200 feet AGL, when the visibility is less than 3 miles.

11-18. Answer B. FAR 61.3

To operate an aircraft under instrument flight rules or in weather conditions less than those prescribed for VFR, you must hold an instrument rating and meet the IFR recent experience requirements.

11-19   PLT448

Which limitation is imposed on the holder of a Commercial Pilot Certificate if that person does not hold an instrument rating?

A— That person is limited to private pilot privileges at night.

B— The carrying of passengers or property for hire on cross country flights at night is limited to a radius of 50 NM.

C— The carrying of passengers for hire on cross country flights is limited to 50 NM and the carrying of passengers for hire at night is prohibited.

11-19. Answer C. FAR 61.133

In order to carry passengers for hire, you must hold a commercial pilot certificate. In addition, to carry passengers for hire at night or on cross-country flights beyond 50 NM, you must hold an instrument rating.

11-20   PLT448

To carry passengers for hire in an airplane on cross-country flights of more than 50 NM from the departure airport, the pilot-in-command is required to hold at least

A— a Category II pilot authorization.

B— a First Class Medical certificate.

C— a Commercial Pilot Certificate with an instrument rating.

11-20. Answer C. FAR 61.133

In order to carry passengers for hire, you must hold a commercial pilot certificate. In addition, to carry passengers for hire at night or on cross-country flights beyond 50 NM, you must hold an instrument rating.

11-21   PLT448

You are flying with another pilot and the enroute weather conditions are IMC. However, during the descent to your destination for an ILS approach, you encounter VMC weather conditions prior to reaching the initial approach fix. You know that to log the ILS approach toward instrument currency requirements,

A— the flight must remain on an IFR flight plan throughout the approach and landing

B— the ILS approach can be credited only if you use a view-limiting device.

C— the ILS approach can be credited regardless of actual weather if you are issued an IFR clearance.

11-21. Answer B. FAR 61.51

You may log instrument flight time only for that flight time that you operate an aircraft solely by reference to instruments. This can done in actual or simulated instrument flight conditions.

SECTION B — 14 CFR PART 91 — GENERAL OPERATING AND FLIGHT RULES

PREFLIGHT PLANNING

- FAR 91.103 requires that a pilot in command, before beginning a flight, become familiar with all available information concerning that flight. For a flight under IFR or a flight not in the vicinity of an airport, this information must specifically include weather reports and forecasts, fuel requirements, alternatives available if the planned flight cannot be completed, and any known traffic delays of which the pilot in command has beenadvised by ATC. For any flight, the PIC must determine the runway lengths at airports of intended use, and takeoff and landing distance information for the aircraft.

- An alternate airport must be listed in an IFR flight plan when the forecast ceiling and visibility is less than 2,000 feet and 3 statute miles (SM), from 1 hour before to 1 hour after the ETA.

- To list as an alternate an airport that has that has only a VOR approach or other nonprecision approach with standard alternate minimums, the forecast at the ETA must be at least an 800 foot ceiling and 2 SM visibility. If the airport has an available precision approach and you are equipped to fly it, then the required minimums area 600-foot ceiling and 2 SM visibility.

- If an airport has no approved IAP, and you wish to list it as an alternate, the ceiling and visibility at ETA must allow descent from the MEA, approach, and landing, under basic VFR.

- If weather conditions are such that it is required to designate an alternate airport on your IFR flight plan, you should plan to carry enough fuel to arrive at the first airport of intended landing, fly from that airport to the alternate airport, and fly thereafter for 45 minutes at normal cruising speed.

- Except when necessary for takeoff or landing or unless otherwise authorized by the Administrator, the minimum altitude for IFR flight is 2,000 feet above the highest obstacle over designated mountainous terrain; 1,000 feet above the highest obstacle over terrain elsewhere.

IFR CLEARANCE REQUIRED

- You may not enter controlled airspace under IFR unless you file a flight plan and receive a clearance prior to entering controlled airspace.

- You must have an instrument rating and an IFR clearance for flight in Class A airspace, even in visual meteorological conditions (VMC).

- A pilot on an IFR flight plan is responsible for avoiding other aircraft whenever weather conditions permit.

TRANSPONDER REQUIRED

- In the 48 contiguous states, excluding the airspace at or below 2,500 feet AGL, an operable coded transponder equipped with Mode C capability is required in all controlled airspace at and above 10,000 feet MSL.

- In addition to a VOR receiver and two-way communications capability, an operable coded transponder having Mode C capability is required for IFR operation in Class B airspace?

- ATC may authorize a deviation from the FAR 91 requirement for a transponder in class B airspace, if a request for the proposed flight is made to ATC at least 1 hour before the flight. If an aircraft's transponder fails during flight within Class B airspace, ATC may authorize deviation from the transponder requirement to allow aircraft to continue to the airport of ultimate destination.

- A transponder is required within and above Class C airspace, and at any altitude within 4 NM of the primary airport in Class C airspace.

- Generally, a transponder is not required for flight within Class D airspace. However, if this Class D airspace is within 30 NM of the primary airport within Class B airspace, a transponder is required because it is within the 30 NM mode C veil.

OXYGEN REQUIREMENTS

If an unpressurized aircraft is operated above 12,500 feet MSL, but not more than 14,000 feet MSL, the minimum flightcrew is required to use supplemental oxygen for the time beyond 30 minutes. Above 14,000 feet MSL, the minimum flightcrew is required to use supplemental oxygen continuously. Above 15,000 feet MSL, oxygen must be available for passengers.

OTHER REGULATIONS

- The use of certain portable electronic devices is prohibited on aircraft that are being operated under IFR or in certain commercial passenger-carrying operations.
- A person who occupies the other control seat as safety pilot during simulated instrument flight must be appropriately rated in the aircraft.

11-22   PLT445

Before beginning any flight under IFR, the

pilot-in-command must become familiar with all available information concerning that flight including:

A– all instrument approaches at the destination airport.

B– an alternate airport and adequate takeoff and landing performance at the destination airport.

C– the runway lengths at airports of intended use, and the aircraft's takeoff and landing data.

11-22. Answer C. FAR.91.103

For any flight conducted under IFR or any flight not in the vicinity of an airport, this information must include runway lengths at airports of intended use, takeoff and landing distances, weather reports and forecasts, fuel requirements, alternatives available if the flight cannot be completed, and any known traffic delays.

11-23   PLT415

The use of certain portable electronic devices is prohibited on aircraft that are being operated under

A– IFR.

B– VFR.

C– DVFR.

11-23. Answer A. FAR 91.21

For any flight, no person nor may any operator or pilot in command allow the operation of any portable electronic device on any U.S. registered civil aircraft operated by a holder of an air carrier operating certificate or while under IFR.

11-24   **PLT413**

During your preflight planning for an IFR flight, you determine that the first airport of intended landing has no instrument approach prescribed in 14 CFR part 97. The weather forecast for one hour before through one hour after your estimated time of arrival is 3000' scattered with 5 miles visibility. To meet the fuel requirements for this flight, you must be able to fly to the first airport of intended landing,

A— then to the alternate airport, and then for 30 minutes at normal cruising speed.

B— and then fly for 45 minutes at normal cruising speed.

C— then to the alternate airport, and then for 45 minutes at normal cruising speed.

11-24. Answer C. FAR 91.167

Since the airport of intended landing has no instrument approach prescribed, the pilot has to plan for enough fuel to get to the original destination, an alternate destination, and be able to fly for an additional 45 minutes.

11-25   **PLT430**

Except when necessary for takeoff or landing or unless otherwise authorized by the Administrator, the minimum altitude for IFR flight is

A— 3,000 feet over all terrain.

B— 3,000 feet over designated mountainous terrain; 2,000 feet over terrain elsewhere.

C— 2,000 feet above the highest obstacle over designated mountainous terrain; 1,000 feet above the highest obstacle over terrain elsewhere.

11-25. Answer C. FAR 91.177

The minimum altitude for IFR flight in mountainous areas is 2,000 feet above the highest obstacle within a horizontal distance of 4 nautical miles from the course to be flown. In all other areas, it's 1,000 feet above the highest obstacle within 4 nautical miles from the course to be flown.

11-26   **PLT430**

Unless otherwise prescribed, what is the rule regarding altitude and course to be maintained during an IFR off airways flight over mountainous terrain?

A— 2,000 feet above the highest obstacle within 4 NM of course.

B— 1,000 feet above the highest obstacle within a horizontal distance of 4 NM of course.

C— 2,000 feet above the highest obstacle within a horizontal distance of 5 NM of course.

11-26. Answer . GFDIC 5A, FAR 91.177

When flying in an area with no published MEA, MOCA, or other procedural altitude prescribed in 14 CFR Part 95 or Part 97, you may fly an off-airways IFR flight over mountainous terrain no lower than 2,000 feet above the highest obstacle within a horizontal distance of four nautical miles from the course line.

11-27   PLT405
If the aircraft's transponder fails during flight within Class B airspace,

A– the pilot should immediately request clearance to depart the Class B airspace.

B– ATC may authorize deviation from the transponder requirement to allow aircraft to continue to the airport of ultimate destination.

C– aircraft must immediately descend to 1,200 feet AGL and proceed to destination.

11-27. Answer B. FAR 91.215
If your transponder fails while in Class B airspace, ATC may authorize you to continue to your destination, including any intermediate stops, and/or proceed to a place where repairs can be made.

11-28   PLT442
To meet instrument experience requirements of 14 CFR part 61, section 61.57(c), a pilot enters the condition of flight in the pilot logbook as simulated instrument conditions. What qualifying information must be entered?

A– Location and type of each instrument approach completed and name of safety pilot.

B– Number and type of instrument approaches completed and route of flight.

C– Name and pilot certificate number of safety pilot and type of approaches completed.

11-28. Answer A. FAR 61.51
The logbook entries must include the location and type of each instrument approach completed, and the name of the safety pilot for each simulated instrument flight.

11-29   PLT442
What minimum conditions are necessary for the instrument approaches required for IFR currency?

A– The approaches may be made in an aircraft, flight simulator, or flight training device.

B– At least three approaches must be made in the same category of aircraft to be flown.

C– At least three approaches must be made in the same category and class of aircraft to be flown.

11-29. Answer A. FAR 61.57
To maintain instrument currency, you must complete six instrument approaches. The approaches must be made in the appropriate category of aircraft or in a flight simulator or flight training device that is representative of the appropriate aircraft category.

11-30 PLT443

What are the minimum qualifications for a person who occupies the other control seat as safety pilot during simulated instrument flight?

A– Private pilot certificate with appropriate category and class ratings for the aircraft.

B– Private pilot with appropriate category, class, and instrument ratings.

C– Private pilot with instrument rating.

11-30. Answer A. FAR 91.109

No person may operate an aircraft in simulated instrument flight unless the other control seat is occupied by an appropriately rated safety pilot. Appropriately rated means the safety pilot must hold at least a private pilot certificate with the category and class ratings appropriate to the aircraft to be flown. The safety pilot does not need to hold an instrument rating.

11-31 PLT161

When are you required to have an instrument rating for flight in VMC?

A– Flight through an MOA.

B– Flight into class A airspace.

C– Flight into an ADIZ.

11-31. Answer B. FAR 91.135

All flights in Class A airspace must be conducted on an instrument flight plan by an instrument rated pilot.

11-32 PLT443

The pilot in command of a civil aircraft must have an instrument rating only when operating

A– in weather conditions less than the minimum prescribed for VFR flight.

B– under IFR, in weather conditions less than the minimum for VFR flight or in class A airspace.

C– under IFR in positive control airspace.

11-32. Answer B. FAR 61.3, FAR 91.135

To operate an aircraft under instrument flight rules, in weather conditions less than VFR, or in Class A airspace, you must hold an instrument rating and meet the IFR recent experience requirements.

11-33   PLT413

What are the minimum fuel requirements in IFR conditions, if the first airport of intended landing is forecast to have a 1,500 foot ceiling and 3 miles visibility at flight-planned ETA? Fuel to fly to the first airport of intended landing,

A– and fly thereafter for 45 minutes at normal cruising speed.

B– fly to the alternate, and fly thereafter for 30 minutes at normal cruising speed.

C– fly to the alternate, and fly thereafter for 45 minutes at normal cruising speed.

11-33. Answer C. FAR 91.167, FAR 91.169

An alternate airport must be filed if the weather reports and/or forecasts for your intended destination indicate that from 1 hour before to 1 hour after your estimated time of arrival (ETA) the ceiling is to be less than 2,000 feet above the airport elevation or the visibility less than 3 statute miles. In addition, when filing an alternate, the aircraft must carry enough fuel to fly to that alternate plus an additional 45 minutes at normal cruising speed.

11-34   PLT445

Before beginning any flight under IFR, the

pilot-in-command must become familiar with all available information concerning that flight. In addition, the pilot must

A– list an alternate airport on the flight plan and become familiar with the instrument approaches to that airport.

B– list an alternate airport on the flight plan and confirm adequate takeoff and landing performance at the destination airport.

C– be familiar with the runway lengths at airports of intended use, and the alternatives available if the flight cannot be completed.

11-34. Answer C. FAR 91.103

You are required to become familiar with all available information concerning any flight. For all flights not in the vicinity of an airport or under IFR, the information must include runway lengths at airports of intended use, takeoff and landing distance information, weather reports and forecasts, fuel requirements, alternatives available if the planned flight cannot be completed, and any known traffic delays.

11-35   PLT161

In the 48 contiguous states, excluding the airspace at or below 2,500 feet AGL, an operable coded transponder equipped with Mode C capability is required in all controlled airspace at and above

A– 12,500 feet MSL.

B– 10,000 feet MSL.

C– Flight level (FL) 180.

11-35. Answer B. FAR 91.215

An operable Mode C transponder is required when at or above 10,000 feet MSL, excluding the airspace at or below 2,500 feet AGL.

11-36   PLT161
A coded transponder equipped with altitude reporting capability is required in all controlled airspace

A– at and above 10,000 feet MSL, excluding at and below 2,500 feet AGL.

B– at and above 2,500 feet above the surface.

C– below 10,000 feet MSL, excluding at and below 2,500 feet AGL.

11-36. Answer A. FAR 91.215
An operable Mode C transponder is required when at or above 10,000 feet MSL, excluding the airspace at or below 2,500 feet AGL.

11-37   PLT438
If an unpressurized aircraft is operated above 12,500 feet MSL, but not more than 14,000 feet MSL, for a period of 2 hours 20 minutes, how long during that time is the minimum flightcrew required to use supplemental oxygen?

A– 2 hours 20 minutes.

B– 1 hour 20 minutes.

C– 1 hour 50 minutes.

11-37. Answer C. FAR 91.211
When operating an unpressurized aircraft above 12,500 feet MSL, up to and including 14,000 feet MSL, for more than 30 minutes, the flightcrew must use supplemental oxygen. When 30 minutes is subtracted from the 2 hours and 20 minutes, the result is 1 hour and 50 minutes, which represents the time the flightcrew must use supplemental oxygen.

11-38   PLT405
Aircraft being operated under IFR are required to have, in addition to the equipment required for VFR and night, at least

A– a slip skid indicator.

B– dual VOR receivers.

C– distance measuring equipment.

11-38. Answer A. FAR 91.205
In addition to the normal equipment required for flight under VFR and night the aircraft must have appropriate two-way radio capability, a gyroscopic rate-of-turn indicator, a slip-skid indicator, a sensitive altimeter, a clock, an adequate electrical supply, a gyroscopic pitch and bank indicator, and a directional gyro.

11-39   PLT438
What is the maximum cabin pressure altitude at which a pilot can fly for longer than 30 minutes without using supplemental oxygen?

A– 10,500 feet.

B– 12,000 feet.

C– 12,500 feet.

11-39. Answer C. FAR 91.211
The maximum pressure altitude at which you can fly without the use of supplemental oxygen for longer than 30 minutes is 12,500 feet.

11-40   PLT438

What is the maximum IFR altitude you may fly in an unpressurized aircraft without providing passengers with supplemental oxygen?

A– 12,500 feet.

B– 14,000 feet.

C– 15,000 feet.

11-40. Answer C. FAR 91.211

When flying above a pressure altitude of 15,000 feet MSL, each occupant must have supplemental oxygen available to them.

11-41   PLT438

What is the oxygen requirement for an unpressurized aircraft at 15,000 feet?

A– All occupants must use oxygen for the entire time at this altitude.

B– Crew must start using oxygen at 12,000 feet and passengers at 15,000 feet.

C– Crew must use oxygen for the entire time above 14,000 feet and passengers must be provided supplemental oxygen only above 15,000 feet.

11-41. Answer C. FAR 91.211

When flying between a pressure altitude of 14,001 feet MSL and 15,000 feet MSL, the minimum flight crew must be provided with, and use, supplemental oxygen the entire time.

11-42   PLT405

To meet the requirements for flight under IFR, an aircraft must be equipped with certain operable instruments and equipment. One of those required is

A– a radar altimeter.

B– a transponder with altitude reporting capability.

C– a clock with sweep second pointer or digital presentation.

11-42. Answer C. FAR 91.205

In addition to the normal equipment required for flight under VFR and night the aircraft must have appropriate two-way radio capability, gyroscopic rate-of-turn indicator, slip-skid indicator, sensitive altimeter, a clock, adequate electrical supply, gyroscopic pitch and bank, and a directional gyro. The clock should display hours, minutes, and seconds with a sweep second pointer or a digital presentation.

11-43   PLT379

What minimum weather conditions must be forecast for your ETA at an alternate airport, that has only a VOR approach with standard alternate minimums, for the airport to be listed as an alternate on the IFR flight plan?

A— 800 foot ceiling and 2 statute miles visibility.

B— 800 foot ceiling and 1 statute mile visibility.

C— 1,000 foot ceiling and visibility to allow descent from minimum en route altitude (MEA), approach, and landing under basic VFR.

11-43. Answer A. FAR 91.169

To be listed as an alternate airport in an IFR flight plan, current weather forecasts must indicate at the estimated time of arrival at the alternate that the ceiling and visibility will be at least 800 feet and 2 statute miles for a nonprecision approach, such as a VOR. If a precision approach is available the criteria are ceiling 600 feet and 2 statute miles visibility.

11-44   PLT379

For aircraft other than helicopters, is an alternate airport required for an IFR flight to ATL (Atlanta Hartsfield) if the proposed ETA is 1930Z?

TAF KATL 121720Z 121818 20012KT 5SM HZ BKN030 FM2000 3SM TSRA OVC025CB FM2200 33015G20KT P6SM BKN 015 OVC040 BECMG 0608 02008KT BKN 040 BECMG 1012 00000KT P6SM CLR=

A— No, because the ceiling and visibility are forecast to be at or above 2,000 feet and 3 miles within 1 hour before to 1 hour after the ETA.

B— No, because the ceiling and visibility are forecast to remain at or above 1,000 feet and 3 miles, respectively.

C— Yes, because the ceiling could fall below 2,000 feet within 2 hours before to 2 hours after the ETA.

11-44. Answer A. FAR 91.169

An alternate airport must be filed if the weather reports and/or forecasts for your intended destination indicate, that from 1 hour before to 1 hour after your estimated time of arrival (ETA), the ceiling is to be less than 2,000 feet AGL and the visibility less than 3 statute miles. In this example, the forecast indicates that from 1800Z to 2000Z, there will be visibility of 5 miles, and broken ceilings at 3,000 feet. From 2000Z to 2200Z, the destination is still forecast to be not less than 2,000 feet and 3 miles.

11-45   PLT379

For aircraft other than helicopters, what minimum conditions must exist at the destination airport to avoid listing an alternate airport on an IFR flight plan when a standard IAP is available?

A— From 1 hour before to 1 hour after ETA, forecast ceiling 2,000, and visibility 3 miles.

B— From 2 hours before to 2 hours after ETA, forecast ceiling 2,000, and visibility 2 and 1/2 miles.

C— From 2 hours before to 2 hours after ETA, forecast ceiling 3,000, and visibility 3 miles.

11-45. Answer A. FAR 91.169

An alternate airport must be filed if the weather reports and/or forecasts for your intended destination indicate, that from 1 hour before to 1 hour after your estimated time of arrival (ETA), the ceiling is to be less than 2,000 feet AGL and the visibility less than 3 statute miles. In this example, the forecast indicates that from 1800Z to 2000Z, there will be visibility of 5 miles, and broken ceilings at 3,000 feet. From 2000Z to 2200Z, the destination is still forecast to be not less than 2,000 feet and 3 miles.

11-46   PLT379
For aircraft other than helicopters, under what conditions are you not required to list an alternate airport on an IFR flight plan if 14 CFR part 97 prescribes a standard IAP for the destination airport?

A– When the ceiling is forecast to be at least 1,000 feet above the lowest of the MEA, MOCA, or initial approach altitude and the visibility is 2 miles more than the minimum landing visibility within 2 hours of your ETA at the destination airport.

B– When the weather reports or forecasts indicate the ceiling and visibility will be at least 2,000 feet and 3 miles for 1 hour before to 1 hour after your ETA at the destination airport.

C– When the ceiling is forecast to be at least 1,000 feet above the lowest of the MEA, MOCA, or initial approach altitude within 2 hours of your ETA at the destination airport.

11-46. Answer B. FAR 91.169
An alternate airport is not required for aircraft other than helicopters, when the ceilings will be 2,000 feet above the airport elevation, and visibility will be at least 3 statute miles or higher for a period 1 hour before to 1 hour after the ETA.

11-47   PLT379
For aircraft other than helicopters, what forecast weather minimums are required to list an airport as an alternate on an IFR flight plan if the airport has VOR approach only?

A– Ceiling and visibility at ETA, 800 feet and 2 miles, respectively.

B– Ceiling and visibility from 2 hours before until 2 hours after ETA, 800 feet and 2 miles, respectively.

C– Ceiling and visibility at ETA, 600 feet and 2 miles, respectively.

11-47. Answer A. FAR 91.169
To include an alternate airport in an IFR flight plan, the current weather forecasts must indicate that, at the estimated time of arrival, the ceiling and visibility are at least 600 feet and 2 statute miles respectively for airports with a precision approach and a ceiling and visibility of at least 800 feet and 2 statute miles for airports with a nonprecision approach, such as a VOR.

11-48   PLT379

What are the minimum weather conditions that must be forecast to list an airport as an alternate when the airport has no approved IAP?

A– The ceiling and visibility at ETA, 2,000 feet and 3 miles, respectively.

B– The ceiling and visibility from 2 hours before until 2 hours after ETA, 2,000 feet and 3 miles, respectively.

C– The ceiling and visibility at ETA must allow descent from MEA, approach, and landing, under basic VFR.

11-48. Answer C. FAR 91.169

If no instrument approach procedure exists at your selected alternate, the weather conditions at your ETA must allow you to descend from the MEA and conduct an approach and landing under basic VFR conditions.

11-49   PLT379

For aircraft other than helicopters, what minimum weather conditions must be forecast for your ETA at an alternate airport that has a precision approach procedure, with standard alternate minimums, in order to list it as an alternate for the IFR flight?

A– 600 foot ceiling and 2 SM visibility from 2 hours before to 2 hours after your ETA.

B– 600 foot ceiling and 2 SM visibility at your ETA.

C– 800 foot ceiling and 2 SM visibility at your ETA.

11-49. Answer B. FAR 91.169

To include an alternate airport in an IFR flight plan, the current weather forecasts must indicate that, at the estimated time of arrival, the ceiling and visibility are at least 600 feet and 2 statute miles respectively for airports with a precision approach and a ceiling and visibility of at least 800 feet and 2 statute miles for airports with a nonprecision approach, such as a VOR.

11-50   PLT366

Which publication covers the procedures required for aircraft accident and incident reporting responsibilities for pilots?

A– FAR Part 61.

B– FAR Part 91.

C– NTSB Part 830.

11-50. Answer C. NTSB 830.1

NTSB 830 contains rules pertaining to the notification and reporting of aircraft accidents and incidents. In addition, NTSB 830 also explains the requirements for the preservation of aircraft wreckage, mail, cargo, and records involving all civil aircraft in the United Sates.

11-51   PLT415
When is a pilot on an IFR flight plan responsible for avoiding other aircraft?

A– At all times when not in radar contact with ATC.

B– When weather conditions permit, regardless of whether operating under IFR or VFR.

C– Only when advised by ATC.

11-51. Answer B. FAR 91.113
When weather conditions permit, regardless of whether an operation is conducted under IFR or VFR, you should be vigilant to see and avoid other aircraft.

11-52   PLT161
The aircraft's transponder fails during flight within Class D airspace.

A– The pilot should immediately request clearance to depart the Class D airspace.

B– No deviation is required because a transponder is not required in Class D airspace.

C– Pilot must immediately request priority handling to proceed to destination.

11-52. Answer B. FAR 91.215
Anytime you have an inoperative transponder, you may request an authorization from ATC which will allow you to deviate from the transponder requirement. However a transponder is not required to operate in Class D airspace.

11-53   PLT161
In addition to a VOR receiver and two-way communications capability, which additional equipment is required for IFR operation in Class B airspace?

A– DME and an operable coded transponder having Mode C capability.

B– Standby communications receiver, DME, and coded transponder.

C– An operable coded transponder having Mode C capability.

11-53. Answer C. FAR 91.215, FAR 91.131
The applicable FARs state that you must have an operable transponder and it must have Mode C capability. This requirement is in addition to the requirement for an operable VOR or TACAN receiver and a two-way radio. Only these three types of avionic equipment are required for IFR operations in Class B airspace.

11-54   PLT405

When an aircraft is not equipped with a transponder, what requirement must be met before ATC will authorize a flight within Class B airspace?

A– A request for the proposed flight must be made to ATC at least 1 hour before the flight.

B– The proposed flight must be conducted when operating under instrument flight rules.

C– The proposed flight must be conducted in visual meteorological conditions (VMC).

11-54. Answer A. FAR 91.215, AIM
FAR Part 91.215(d)(3) states, "For operation of an aircraft that is not equipped with a transponder, the request must be made at least one hour before the proposed operation." This request must be made to the ATC facility having jurisdiction over the affected airspace.

11-55   PLT405

Prior to operating an aircraft not equipped with a transponder in Class B airspace, a request for a deviation must be submitted to the

A– FAA Administrator at least 24 hours before the proposed operation.

B– nearest FAA General Aviation District Office 24 hours before the proposed operation.

C– controlling ATC facility at least 1 hour before the proposed flight

11-55. Answer C. FAR 91.215, AIM
FAR Part 91.215(d)(3) states, "For operation of an aircraft that is not equipped with a transponder, the request must be made at least one hour before the proposed operation." This request must be made to the ATC facility having jurisdiction over the affected airspace.

11-56   PLT438
(Refer to figure 91)

What are the oxygen requirements for an IFR flight eastbound on V520 from DBS VORTAC in an unpressurized aircraft at the MEA?

A– The required minimum crew must be provided and use supplemental oxygen for that part of the flight of more than 30 minutes.

B– The required minimum crew must be provided and use supplemental oxygen for that part of the flight of more than 30 minutes, and the passengers must be provided supplemental oxygen.

C– The required minimum crew must be provided and use supplemental oxygen.

11-56. Answer C. FAR 91.211
The MEA eastbound on V520 from DBS VORTAC is 15,000 feet MSL. At cabin pressure altitudes above 14,000 feet MSL, the required minimum flight crew must be provided with and use supplemental oxygen during the entire flight at those altitudes.

11-57   PLT379

An airport without an authorized IAP may be included on an IFR flight plan as an alternate, if the current weather forecast indicates that the ceiling and visibility at the ETA will

A— allow for descent from the IAF to landing under basic VFR conditions.

B— be at least 1,000 feet and 1 mile.

C— allow for a descent from the MEA approach, and a landing under basic VFR conditions.

11-57. Answer C. FAR 91.169

If an airport does not have an instrument approach procedure, the minimum IFR altitude in the area is the MEA. From the MEA, you must be able to proceed VFR to the airport for approach and landing.

FAA LEGENDS

ABBREVIATIONS

The following abbreviations are those commonly used within this Directory. Other abbreviations may be found in the Legend and are not duplicated below. The abbreviations presented are intended to represent grammatical variations of the basic form. (Example—"req" may mean "request," "requesting," "requested," or "requests").

abv	above	MSAW	minimum safe altitude warning
acft	aircraft		
AER	approach end rwy	NFCT	non-federal control tower
AFSS	Automated Flight Service Station	ngt	night
AGL	above ground level	npi	non precision instrument
apch	approach		
arpt	airport	NSTD	nonstandard
avbl	available	ntc	notice
bcn	beacon	opr	operate, operator, operational
blo	below		
byd	beyond	ops	operations
clsd	closed	OTS	out of service
ctc	contact	ovrn	overrun
dalgt	daylight	PAEW	personnel and equipment working
dsplcd	displaced		
durn	duration	p-line	power line
eff	effective	PPR	prior permission required
emerg	emergency		
extd	extend, extended	req	request
FBO	fixed-based operator	rgt tfc	right traffic
FCT	FAA Contract Tower	rqr	request
fld	field	rwy	runway
FSS	Flight Service Station	SPB	Seaplane Base
hr	hour	SR	sunrise
indef	indefinite	SS	sunset
ints	intensity	svc	service
invof	in the vicinity of	tfc	traffic
LAA	Local Airport Advisory	thld	threshold
ldg	landing	tkf	take-off
lgtd	lighted	tmpry	temporary
lgts	lights	twr	tower
med	medium	twy	taxiway
MSL	mean sea level		

LEGEND 1.—Abbreviations.

DIRECTORY LEGEND
SAMPLE

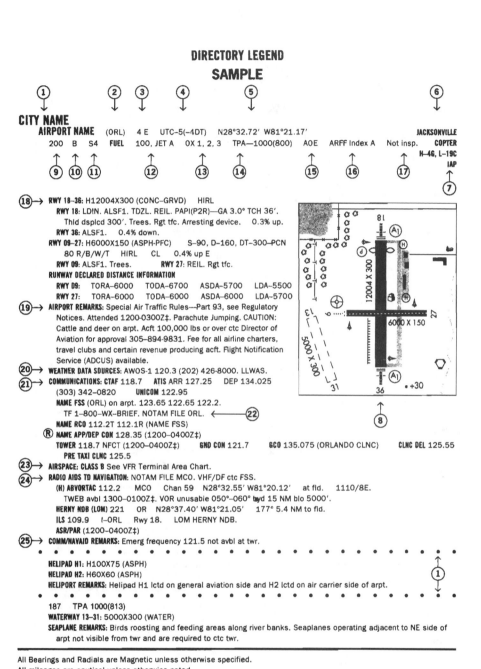

CITY NAME
AIRPORT NAME (ORL) 4 E UTC–5(–4DT) N28°32.72' W81°21.17'   **JACKSONVILLE**
  200 B S4 **FUEL** 100, JET A OX 1, 2, 3 TPA—1000(800) AOE ARFF Index A Not insp. **COPTER**
      H–4G, L–19C
      IAP

RWY 18–36: H12004X300 (CONC–GRVD) HIRL
  RWY 18: LDIN. ALSF1. TDZL. REIL. PAPI(P2R)—GA 3.0° TCH 36'.
    Thld dsplcd 300'. Trees. Rgt tfc. Arresting device. 0.3% up.
  RWY 36: ALSF1. 0.4% down.
RWY 09–27: H6000X150 (ASPH-PFC) S–90, D–160, DT–300–PCN
  80 R/B/W/T HIRL CL 0.4% up E
  RWY 09: ALSF1. Trees. **RWY 27:** REIL. Rgt tfc.
RUNWAY DECLARED DISTANCE INFORMATION
  RWY 09: TORA–6000 TODA–6700 ASDA–5700 LDA–5500
  RWY 27: TORA–6000 TODA–6000 ASDA–6000 LDA–5700
AIRPORT REMARKS: Special Air Traffic Rules—Part 93, see Regulatory
  Notices. Attended 1200-0300Z‡. Parachute Jumping. CAUTION:
  Cattle and deer on arpt. Acft 100,000 lbs or over ctc Director of
  Aviation for approval 305–894-9831. Fee for all airline charters,
  travel clubs and certain revenue producing acft. Flight Notification
  Service (ADCUS) available.
WEATHER DATA SOURCES: AWOS-1 120.3 (202) 426-8000. LLWAS.
COMMUNICATIONS: CTAF 118.7 ATIS ARR 127.25 DEP 134.025
  (303) 342–0820 **UNICOM** 122.95
  NAME FSS (ORL) on arpt. 123.65 122.65 122.2.
    TF 1–800–WX–BRIEF. NOTAM FILE ORL.
  NAME RCO 112.2T 112.1R (NAME FSS)
  ℞ **NAME APP/DEP CON** 128.35 (1200–0400Z‡)
    TOWER 118.7 NFCT (1200–0400Z‡)   **GND CON** 121.7   **GCO** 135.075 (ORLANDO CLNC)   **CLNC DEL** 125.55
    PRE TAXI CLNC 125.5
AIRSPACE: CLASS B See VFR Terminal Area Chart.
RADIO AIDS TO NAVIGATION: NOTAM FILE MCO. VHF/DF ctc FSS.
  (H) ABVORTAC 112.2 MCO Chan 59 N28°32.55' W81°20.12' at fld. 1110/8E.
    TWEB avbl 1300–0100Z‡. VOR unusable 050°–060° byd 15 NM blo 5000'.
  HERNY NDB (LOM) 221 OR N28°37.40' W81°21.05' 177° 5.4 NM to fld.
  ILS 109.9 I–ORL Rwy 18. LOM HERNY NDB.
  ASR/PAR (1200–0400Z‡)
COMM/NAVAID REMARKS: Emerg frequency 121.5 not avbl at twr.
• •

  HELIPAD H1: H100X75 (ASPH)
  HELIPAD H2: H60X60 (ASPH)
  HELIPORT REMARKS: Helipad H1 lctd on general aviation side and H2 lctd on air carrier side of arpt.
• •

  187 TPA 1000(813)
  WATERWAY 13–31: 5000X300 (WATER)
  SEAPLANE REMARKS: Birds roosting and feeding areas along river banks. Seaplanes operating adjacent to NE side of
    arpt not visible from twr and are required to ctc twr.

All Bearings and Radials are Magnetic unless otherwise specified.
All mileages are nautical unless otherwise noted.
All times are UTC except as noted.
The horizontal reference datum of this publication is North American Datum of 1983 (NAD83), which for charting purposes
is considered equivalent to World Geodetic System 1984 (WGS 84).

LEGEND 2.—Airport/Facility Directory.

DIRECTORY LEGEND

⑧   SKETCH LEGEND

RUNWAYS/LANDING AREAS

Hard Surfaced . . . .

Metal Surface . . . .

Sod, Gravel, etc. . . . .

Light Plane, ...
Ski Landing Area or Water

Under Construction . . . . .

Closed . . . .

Helicopter Landings Area . . . . (H)

Displaced Threshold . . . .

Taxiway, Apron and Stopways . .

MISCELLANEOUS BASE AND CULTURAL FEATURES

Buildings . . . .

Power Lines . . . .

Fence . . . .

Towers . . . .

Tanks . . . .

Oil Well . . . .

Smoke Stack . . . .

Obstruction 5812

Controlling Obstruction . . . . +5812

Trees . . . .

Populated Places . . . .

Cuts and Fills . . . . . . Cut Fill

Cliffs and Depressions . .

Ditch . . . .

Hill . . . .

RADIO AIDS TO NAVIGATION

VORTAC . . . ⬠   VOR . . . . ⬡

VOR/DME . . ◇   NDB . . . . ⊙

TACAN . . . . ⬠   NDB/DME . . . . ⊡

MISCELLANEOUS AERONAUTICAL FEATURES

Airport Beacon . . . .   ☆

Wind Cone . . . .

Landing Tee . . . .

Tetrahedron . . . .

Control Tower . . . .

APPROACH LIGHTING SYSTEMS

A dot "•" portrayed with approach lighting letter identifier indicates sequenced flashing lights (F) installed with the approach lighting system e.g. Ⓐ Negative symbology, e.g., Ⓐ Ⓥ indicates Pilot Controlled Lighting (PCL).

Runway Centerline Lighting . . . . .

Ⓐ Approach Lighting System ALSF-2 . .

Ⓐ₁ Approach Lighting System ALSF-1 . .

Ⓐ₂ Short Approach Lighting System SALS/SALSF . . . .

Ⓐ₃ Simplified Short Approach Lighting System (SSALR) with RAIL . . . . .

Ⓐ₄ Medium Intensity Approach Lighting System (MALS and MALSF)/(SSALS
Ⓐ₄ and SSALF) . . . .

Ⓐ₅ Medium Intensity Approach Lighting System (MALSR) and RAIL . . . . . .

Ⓐ₆ Omnidirectional Approach Lighting System (ODALS) . . . .

Ⓓ Navy Parallel Row and Cross Bar . . .

Ⓘ Air Force Overrun . . . .

Ⓥ Visual Approach Slope Indicator with Standard Threshold Clearance provided

Ⓥ₂ Pulsating Visual Approach Slope Indicator (PVASI)

Ⓥ₃ Visual Approach Slope Indicator with a threshold crossing height to accomodate long bodied or jumbo aircraft

Ⓥ₄ Tri-color Visual Approach Slope Indicator (TRCV)

Ⓥ₅ Approach Path Alignment Panel (APAP)

Ⓟ Precision Approach Path Indicator (PAPI)

LEGEND 3.—Airport/Facility Directory.

DIRECTORY LEGEND
LEGEND

This Directory is an alphabetical listing of data on record with the FAA on all airports that are open to the public, associated terminal control facilities, air route traffic control centers and radio aids to navigation within the conterminous United States, Puerto Rico and the Virgin Islands. Airports are listed alphabetically by associated city name and cross referenced by airport name. Facilities associated with an airport, but with a different name, are listed individually under their own name, as well as under the airport with which they are associated.

The listing of an airport in this directory merely indicates the airport operator's willingness to accommodate transient aircraft, and does not represent that the facility conforms with any Federal or local standards, or that it has been approved for use on the part of the general public.

The information on obstructions is taken from reports submitted to the FAA. It has not been verified in all cases. Pilots are cautioned that objects not indicated in this tabulation (or on charts) may exist which can create a hazard to flight operation.

Detailed specifics concerning services and facilities tabulated within this directory are contained in Aeronautical Information Manual, Basic Flight Information and ATC Procedures.

The legend items that follow explain in detail the contents of this Directory and are keyed to the circled numbers on the sample on the preceding pages.

① CITY/AIRPORT NAME

Airports and facilities in this directory are listed alphabetically by associated city and state. Where the city name is different from the airport name the city name will appear on the line above the airport name. Airports with the same associated city name will be listed alphabetically by airport name and will be separated by a dashed rule line. All others will be separated by a solid rule line. (Designated Helipads and Seaplane Landing Areas (Water) associated with a land airport will be separated by a dotted line.)

② LOCATION IDENTIFIER

A three or four character code assigned to airports. These identifiers are used by ATC in lieu of the airport name in flight plans, flight strips and other written records and computer operations.

③ AIRPORT LOCATION

Airport location is expressed as distance and direction from the center of the associated city in nautical miles and cardinal points, i.e., 4 NE.

④ TIME CONVERSION

Hours of operation of all facilities are expressed in Coordinated Universal Time (UTC) and shown as "Z" time. The directory indicates the number of hours to be subtracted from UTC to obtain local standard time and local daylight saving time UTC−5(−4DT). The symbol ‡ indicates that during periods of Daylight Saving Time effective hours will be one hour earlier than shown. In those areas where daylight saving time is not observed that (−4DT) and ‡ will not be shown. All states observe daylight savings time except Arizona, Hawaii and that portion of Indiana in the Eastern Time Zone and Puerto Rico and the Virgin Islands.

⑤ GEOGRAPHIC POSITION OF AIRPORT

Positions are shown in degrees, minutes and hundredths of a minute and represent the approximate center of mass of all usable runways.

⑥ CHARTS

The Sectional Chart and Low and High Altitude Enroute Chart and panel on which the airport or facility is located. Helicopter Chart locations will be indicated as, i.e., COPTER.

⑦ INSTRUMENT APPROACH PROCEDURES

IAP indicates an airport for which a prescribed (Public Use) FAA Instrument Approach Procedure has been published.

⑧ AIRPORT SKETCH

·The airport sketch, when provided, depicts the airport and related topographical information as seen from the air and should be used in conjunction with the text. It is intended as a guide for pilots in VFR conditions. Symbology that is not self-explanatory will be reflected in the sketch legend. The airport sketch will be oriented with True North at the top. Airport sketches will be added incrementally.

⑨ ELEVATION

The highest point of an airport's usable runways measured in feet from mean sea level. When elevation is sea level it will be indicated as (OO). When elevation is below sea level a minus (−) sign will precede the figure.

⑩ ROTATING LIGHT BEACON

B indicates rotating beacon is available. Rotating beacons operate dusk to dawn unless otherwise indicated in AIRPORT REMARKS.

⑪ SERVICING

S1: Minor airframe repairs.
S2: Minor airframe and minor powerplant repairs.

S3: Major airframe and minor powerplant repairs.
S4: Major airframe and major powerplant repairs.

LEGEND 4.—Airport/Facility Directory.

DIRECTORY LEGEND

⑫ FUEL

CODE	FUEL	CODE	FUEL
80	Grade 80 gasoline (Red)	B+	Jet B—Wide-cut turbine fuel with icing inhibitor, freeze point–50° C.
100	Grade 100 gasoline (Green)		
100LL	100LL gasoline (low lead) (Blue)	J8	(JP–8 Military specification) Jet A–1, kerosene with icing inhibitor, freeze point–47°C.
115	Grade 115 gasoline		
A	Jet A—Kerosene freeze point–40° C.	J8+100	(JP–8 Mil-spec) Jet A–1, Kerosene with FS–II*, FP** minus 47°C, with fuel additive package that improves thermo stability characteristics of JP–8.
A1	Jet A-1—Kerosene freeze point–47°C.		
A1+	Jet A-1—Kerosene with icing inhibitor, freeze point–47° C.		
B	Jet B—Wide-cut turbine fuel, freeze point–50° C.	MOGAS	Automobile gasoline which is to be used as aircraft fuel.

NOTE: Automobile Gasoline. Certain automobile gasoline may be used in specific aircraft engines if a FAA supplemental type cetificate has been obtained. Automobile gasoline which is to be used in aircraft engines will be identified as ''MOGAS'', however, the grade/type and other octane rating will not be published.

Data shown on fuel availability represents the most recent information the publisher has been able to acquire. Because of a variety of factors, the fuel listed may not always be obtainable by transient civil pilots. Confirmation of availability of fuel should be made directly with fuel dispensers at locations where refueling is planned.

⑬ OXYGEN

OX 1   High Pressure   OX 3   High Pressure—Replacement Bottles
OX 2   Low Pressure   OX 4   Low Pressure—Replacement Bottles

⑭ TRAFFIC PATTERN ALTITUDE

Traffic Pattern Altitude (TPA)—The first figure shown is TPA above mean sea level. The second figure in parentheses is TPA above airport elevation.

⑮ AIRPORT OF ENTRY, LANDING RIGHTS, ANO CUSTOMS USER FEE AIRPORTS

U.S. CUSTOMS USER FEE AIRPORT—Private Aircraft operators are frequently required to pay the costs associated with customs processing.
AOE—Airport of Entry—A customs Airport of Entry where permission from U.S. Customs is not required, however, at least one hour advance notice of arrival must be furnished.
LRA—Landing Rights Airport—Application for permission to land must be submitted in advance to U.S. Customs. At least one hour advance notice of arrival must be furnished.
NOTE: Advance notice of arrival at both an AOE and LRA airport may be included in the flight plan when filed in Canada or Mexico, where Flight Notification Service (ADCUS) is available the airport remark will indicate this service. This notice will also be treated as an application for permission to land in the case of an LRA. Although advance notice of arrival may be relayed to Customs through Mexico, Canadian, and U.S. Communications facilities by flight plan, the aircraft operator is solely responsible for insuring that Customs receives the notification. (See Customs, Immigration and Naturalization, Public Health and Agriculture Department requirements in the International Flight Information Manual for further details.)

⑯ CERTIFICATED AIRPDRT (FAR 139)

Airports serving Department of Transportation certified carriers and certified under FAR, Part 139, are indicated by the ARFF index; i.e., ARFF Index A, which relates to the availability of crash, fire, rescue equipment.

FAR–PART 139 CERTIFICATED AIRPORTS
INDICES AND AIRCRAFT RESCUE AND FIRE FIGHTING EQUIPMENT REQUIREMENTS

Airport Index	Required No. Vehicles	Aircraft Length		Scheduled Departures	Agent + Water for Foam
A	1	<90'		≥1	500#DC or HALON 1211 or 450#DC + 100 gal H$_2$O
B	1 or 2	≥90',	<126'	≥5	Index A + 1500 gal H$_2$O
		≥126',	<159'	<5	
C	2 or 3	≥126',	<159'	≥5	Index A + 3000 gal H$_2$O
		≥159',	<200'	<5	
D	3	≥159',	<200'	≥5	Index A + 4000 gal H$_2$O
		>200'		<5	
E	3	≥200'		≥5	Index A + 6000 gal H$_2$O

> Greater Than; < Less Than; ≥ Equal or Greater Than; ≤ Equal or Less Than;   H$_2$O–Water; DC–Dry Chemical.

NOTE: The listing of ARFF index does not necessarily assure coverage for non-air carrier operations or at other than prescribed times for air carrier. ARFF Index Ltd.—indicates ARFF coverage may or may not be available, for information contact airport manager prior to flight.

LEGEND 5.—Airport/Facility Directory.

DIRECTORY LEGEND

⑰ FAA INSPECTION

All airports not inspected by FAA will be identified by the note: Not insp. This indicates that the airport information has been provided by the owner or operator of the field.

⑱ RUNWAY DATA

Runway information is shown on two lines. That information common to the entire runway is shown on the first line while information concerning the runway ends are shown on the second or following line. Lengthy information will be placed in the Airport Remarks.

Runway direction, surface, length, width, weight bearing capacity, lighting, slope and appropriate remarks are shown for each runway. Direction, length, width, lighting and remarks are shown for sealanes. The full dimensions of helipads are shown, i.e., 50X150.

RUNWAY SURFACE AND LENGTH

Runway lengths prefixed by the letter "H" indicate that the runways are hard surfaced (concrete, asphalt). If the runway length is not prefixed, the surface is sod, clay, etc. The runway surface composition is indicated in parentheses after runway length as follows:

(AFSC)—Aggregate friction seal coat	(GRVD)—Grooved	(RFSC)—Rubberized friction seal coat
(ASPH)—Asphalt	(GRVL)—Gravel, or cinders	(TURF)—Turf
(CONC)—Concrete	(PFC)—Porous friction courses	(TRTD)—Treated
(DIRT)—Dirt	(PSP)—Pierced steel plank	(WC)—Wire combed

RUNWAY WEIGHT BEARING CAPACITY

Runway strength data shown in this publication is derived from available information and is a realistic estimate of capability at an average level of activity. It is not intended as a maximum allowable weight or as an operating limitation. Many airport pavements are capable of supporting limited operations with gross weights of 25-50% in excess of the published figures. Permissible operating weights, insofar as runway strengths are concerned, are a matter of agreement between the owner and user. When desiring to operate into any airport at weights in excess of those published in the publication, users should contact the airport management for permission. Add 000 to figure following S, D, DT, DDT, AUW, etc., for gross weight capacity:

S—Single-wheel type landing gear. (DC-3), (C-47), (F-15), etc.
D—Dual-wheel type landing gear. (DC-6), etc.
T—Twin-wheel type landing gear. (DC-6), (C-9A), etc.
ST—Single-tandem type landing gear. (C-130).
SBTT—Single-belly twin tandem landing gear (KC-10).
DT—Dual-tandem type landing gear, (707), etc.
TT—Twin-tandem type (includes quadricycle) landing gear (707), (B-52), (C-135), etc.
TRT—Triple-tandem landing gear, (C-17)
DDT—Double dual-tandem landing gear. (E4A/747).
TDT—Twin delta-tandem landing gear. (C-5, Concorde).
AUW—All up weight. Maximum weight bearing capacity for any aircraft irrespective of landing gear configuration.
SWL—Single Wheel Loading. (This includes information submitted in terms of Equivalent Single Wheel Loading (ESWL) and Single Isolated Wheel Loading). SWL figures are shown in thousands of pounds with the last three figures being omitted.
PSI—Pounds per square inch. PSI is the actual figure expressing maximum pounds per square inch runway will support, e.g., (SWL 000/PSI 535).

Quadricycle and dual-tandem are considered virtually equal for runway weight bearing consideration, as are single-tandem and dual-wheel. Omission of weight bearing capacity indicates information unknown.

The ACN/PCN System is the ICAO method of reporting pavement strength for pavements with bearing strengths greater than 12,500 pounds. The Pavement Classification Number (PCN) is established by an engineering assessment of the runway. The PCN is for use in conjunction with an Aircraft Classification Number (ACN). Consult the Aircraft Flight Manual or other appropriate source for ACN tables or charts. Currently, ACN data may not be available for all aircraft. If an ACN table or chart is available, the ACN can be calculated by taking into account the aircraft weight, the pavement type, and the subgrade category. For runways that have been evaluated under the ACN/PCN system, the PCN will be shown as a five part code (e.g. PCN 80 R/B/W/T). Details of the coded format are as follows:

(1) The PCN NUMBER—The reported PCN indicates that an aircraft with an ACN equal or less than the reported PCN can operate on the pavement subject to any limitation on the tire pressure.

(2) The type of pavement:
  R — Rigid
  F — Flexible

(3) The pavement subgrade category:
  A — High
  B — Medium
  C — Low
  D — Ultra-low

(4) The maximum tire pressure authorized for the pavement:
  W — High, no limit
  X — Medium, limited to 217 psi
  Y — Low, limited to 145 psi
  Z — Very low, limited to 73 psi

(5) Pavement evaluation method:
  T — Technical evaluation
  U — By experience of aircraft using the pavement

NOTE: Prior permission from the airport controlling authority is required when the ACN of the aircraft exceeds the published PCN or aircraft tire pressure exceeds the published limits.

LEGEND 6.—Airport/Facility Directory.

8   **DIRECTORY LEGEND**

RUNWAY DECLARED DISTANCE INFORMATION

TORA—Take-off Run Available
TODA—Take-off Distance Available
ASDA—Accelerate-Stop Distance Available
LDA—Landing Distance Available

⑲ AIRPORT REMARKS

Landing Fee indicates landing charges for private or non-revenue producing aircraft, in addition, fees may be charged for planes that remain over a couple of hours and buy no services, or at major airline terminals for all aircraft.
Remarks—Data is confined to operational items affecting the status and usability of the airport.
Parachute Jumping.—See "PARACHUTE" tabulation for details.
Unless otherwise stated, remarks including runway ends refer to the runway's approach end.

⑳ WEATHER DATA SOURCES

ASOS—Automated Surface Observing System. Reports the same as an AWOS-3 plus precipitation identification and intensity, and freezing rain occurrence (future enhancement).
AWOS—Automated Weather Observing System
  AWOS-A—reports altimeter setting.
  AWOS-1—reports altimeter setting, wind data and usually temperature, dewpoint and density altitude.
  AWOS-2—reports the same as AWOS-1 plus visibility.
  AWOS-3—reports the same as AWOS-1 plus visibility and cloud/ceiling data.
  See AIM, Basic Flight Information and ATC Procedures for detailed description of AWOS.
HIWAS—See RADIO AIDS TO NAVIGATION
LAWRS—Limited Aviation Weather Reporting Station where observers report cloud height, weather, obstructions to vision, temperature and dewpoint (in most cases), surface wind, altimeter and pertinent remarks.
LLWAS—indicates a Low Level Wind Shear Alert System consisting of a center field and several field perimeter anemometers.
SAWRS—identifies airports that have a Supplemental Aviation Weather Reporting Station available to pilots for current weather information.
SWSL—Supplemental Weather Service Location providing current local weather information via radio and telephone.
TDWR—indicates airports that have Terminal Doppler Weather Radar.

㉑ COMMUNICATIONS

Communications will be listed in sequence in the order shown below:
Common Traffic Advisory Frequency (CTAF), Automatic Terminal Information Service (ATIS) and Aeronautical Advisory Stations (UNICOM) along with their frequency is shown, where available, on the line following the heading "COMMUNICATIONS." When the CTAF and UNICOM is the same frequency, the frequency will be shown as CTAF/UNICOM freq.
Flight Service Station (FSS) information. The associated FSS will be shown followed by the identifier and information concerning availability of telephone service, e.g., Direct Line (DL), Local Call (LC-384-2341), Toll free call, dial (TF 800–852–7036 or TF 1–800–227–7160), Long Distance (LD 202-426-8800 or LD 1-202-555-1212) etc. The airport NOTAM file identifier will be shown as "NOTAM FILE IAD." Where the FSS is located on the field it will be indicated as "on arpt" following the identifier. Frequencies available will follow. The FSS telephone number will follow along with any significant operational information. FSS's whose name is not the same as the airport on which located will also be listed in the normal alphabetical name listing for the state in which located. Remote Communications Outlet (RCO) providing service to the airport followed by the frequency and name of the Controlling FSS.
FSS's provide information on airport conditions, radio aids and other facilities, and process flight plans. Local Airport Advisory Service is provided on the CTAF by FSS's located at non-tower airports or airports where the tower is not in operation.
(See AIM, Par. 157/158 Traffic Advisory Practices at airports where a tower is not in operation or AC 90 - 42C.)
Aviation weather briefing service is provided by FSS specialists. Flight and weather briefing services are also available by calling the telephone numbers listed.
Remote Communications Outlet (RCO)—An unmanned air/ground communications facility, remotely controlled and providing UHF or VHF communications capability to extend the service range of an FSS.
Civil Communications Frequencies—Civil communications frequencies used in the FSS air/ground system are now operated simplex on 122.0, 122.2, 122.3, 122.4, 122.6, 123.6; emergency 121.5; plus receive-only on 122.05, 122.1, 122.15, and 123.6.
  a.   122.0 is assigned as the Enroute Flight Advisory Service channel at selected FSS's,
  b.   122.2 is assigned to most FSS's as a common enroute simplex service.
  c.   123.6 is assigned as the airport advisory channel at non-tower FSS locations, however, it is still in commission at some FSS's collocated with towers to provide part time Local Airport Advisory Service.
  d.   122.1 is the primary receive-only frequency at VOR's. 122.05, 122.15 and 123.6 are assigned at selected VOR's meeting certain criteria.
  e.   Some FSS's are assigned 50 kHz channels for simplex operation in the 122-123 MHz band (e.g. 122.35). Pilots using the FSS A/G system should refer to this directory or appropriate charts to determine frequencies available at the FSS or remoted facility through which they wish to communicate.
Part time FSS hours of operation are shown in remarks under facility name.

  Emergency frequency 121.5 is available at all Flight Service Stations, Towers, Approach Control and RADAR facilities, unless indicated as not available.
Frequencies published followed by the letter "T" or "R", indicate that the facility will only transmit or receive respectively on that frequency. All radio aids to navigation frequencies are transmit only.

LEGEND 7.—Airport/Facility Directory.

DIRECTORY LEGEND   9

TERMINAL SERVICES

CTAF—A program designed to get all vehicles and aircraft at uncontrolled airports on a common frequency.

ATIS—A continuous broadcast of recorded non-control information in selected areas of high activity.

UNICOM—A non-government air/ground radio communications facility utilized to provide general airport advisory service.

APP CON —Approach Control. The symbol ⓡ indicates radar approach control.

TOWER—Control tower.

GND CON—Ground Control.

GCO—GROUND COMMUNICATION OUTLET—An unstaffed, remotely controlled, ground/ground communications facility. Pilots at uncontrolled airports may contact ATC and FSS via VHF to a telephone connection to obtain an instrument clearance or close a VFR or IFR flight plan. They may also get an updated weather briefing prior to takeoff. Pilots will use four "key clicks" on the VHF radio to contact the appropriate ATC facility or six "key clicks" to contact the FSS. The GCO system is intended to be used only on the ground.

DEP CON—Departure Control. The symbol ⓡ indicates radar departure control.

CLNC DEL—Clearance Delivery.

PRE TAXI CLNC—Pre taxi clearance.

VFR ADVSY SVC—VFR Advisory Service. Service provided by Non-Radar Approach Control.

  Advisory Service for VFR aircraft (upon a workload basis) ctc APP CON.

TOWER, APP CON and DEP CON RADIO CALL will be the same as the airport name unless indicated otherwise.

㉒ NOTAM SERVICE

All public use landing areas are provided NOTAM "D" (distant dissemination) and NOTAM "L" (local dissemination) service. Airport NOTAM file identifier is shown following the associated FSS data for individual airports, e.g. "NOTAM FILE IAD". See AIM, Basic Flight Information and ATC Procedures for detailed description of NOTAM's.

㉓ AIRSPACE

CLASS B—Radar Sequencing and Separation Service for all aircraft in CLASS B airspace

TRSA—Radar Sequencing and Separation Service for participating VFR Aircraft within a Terminal Radar Service Area

Class C, D, and E airspace described in this publication is that airspace usually consisting of a 5 NM radius core surface area that begins at the surface and extends upward to an altitude above the airport elevation (charted in MSL for Class C and Class D).

When CLASS C airspace defaults to CLASS E, the core surface area becomes CLASS E. This will be formatted as: **AIRSPACE: CLASS C** svc "times" ctc **APP CON** other times CLASS E.

When Class C airspace defaults to Class G, the core surface area becomes Class G up to but not including the overlying controlled airspace. There are Class E airspace areas beginning at either 700' or 1200' AGL used to transition to/from the terminal or enroute environment. This will be formatted as: **AIRSPACE: CLASS C** svc "times" ctc **APP CON** other times CLASS G, CLASS E 700' (or 1200') AGL & abv.

NOTE: AIRSPACE SVC "TIMES" INCLUDE ALL ASSOCIATED EXTENSIONS. Arrival extensions for instrument approach procedures become part of the primary core surface area. These extensions may be either Class D or Class E airspace and are effective concurrent with the times of the primary core surface area.

(See CLASS AIRSPACE in the Aeronautical Information Manual for further details)

㉔ RADIO AIDS TO NAVIGATION

The Airport Facility Directory lists by facility name all Radio Aids to Navigation, except Military TACANS, that appear on National Ocean Service Visual or IFR Aeronautical Charts and those upon which the FAA has approved an Instrument Approach Procedure. All VOR, VORTAC ILS and MLS equipment in the National Airspace System has an automatic monitoring and shutdown feature in the event of malfunction. Unmonitored, as used in this publication for any navigational aid, means that FSS or tower personnel cannot observe the malfunction or shutdown signal. The NAVAID NOTAM file identifier will be shown as "NOTAM FILE IAD" and will be listed on the Radio Aids to Navigation line. When two or more NAVAIDS are listed and the NOTAM file identifier is different than shown on the Radio Aids to Navigation line, then it will be shown with the NAVAID listing. NOTAM file identifiers for ILS's and their components (e.g., NDB (LOM) are the same as the identifiers for the associated airports and are not repeated. Hazardous Inflight Weather Advisory Service (HIWAS) will be shown where this service is broadcast over selected VOR's.

NAVAID information is tabulated as indicated in the following sample:

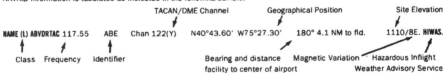

NAME (L) ABVDRTAC 117.55   ABE   Chan 122(Y)   N40°43.60' W75°27.30'   180° 4.1 NM to fld.   1110/8E. **HIWAS.**

Class   Frequency   Identifier | TACAN/DME Channel   Geographical Position   Bearing and distance facility to center of airport   Magnetic Variation   Site Elevation   Hazardous Inflight Weather Advisory Service

VOR unusable 020°-060° byd 26 NM blo 3,500'

Restriction within the normal altitude/range of the navigational aid (See primary alphabetical listing for restrictions on VORTAC and VOR/DME).

Note: Those DME channel numbers with a (Y) suffix require TACAN to be placed in the "Y" mode to receive distance information.

LEGEND 8.—Airport/Facility Directory.

10   **DIRECTORY LEGEND**

HIWAS—Hazardous Inflight Weather Advisory Service is a continuous broadcast of inflight weather advisories including summarized SIGMETs, convective SIGMETs, AIRMETs and urgent PIREPs. HIWAS is presently broadcast over selected VOR's and will be implemented throughout the conterminous U.S.

ASR/PAR—Indicates that Surveillance (ASR) or Precision (PAR) radar instrument approach minimums are published in the U.S. Terminal Procedures. Only part-time hours of operation will be shown.

RADIO CLASS DESIGNATIONS

VOR/DME/TACAN Standard Service Volume (SSV) Classifications

SSV Class	Altitudes	Distance (NM)
(T) Terminal	1000' to 12,000'	25
(L) Low Altitude	1000' to 18,000'	40
(H) High Altitude	1000' to 14,500'	40
	14,500' to 18,000'	100
	18,000' to 45,000'	130
	45,000' to 60,000'	100

NOTE: Additionally, (H) facilities provide (L) and (T) service volume and (L) facilities provide (T) service. Altitudes are with respect to the station's site elevation. Coverage is not available in a cone of airspace directly above the facility.

The term VOR is, operationally, a general term covering the VHF omnidirectional bearing type of facility without regard to the fact that the power, the frequency protected service volume, the equipment configuration, and operational requirements may vary between facilities at different locations.

AB	Automatic Weather Broadcast.
DF	Direction Finding Service.
DME	UHF standard (TACAN compatible) distance measuring equipment.
DME(Y)	UHF standard (TACAN compatible) distance measuring equipment that require TACAN to be placed in the "Y" mode to receive DME.
GS	Glide slope.
H	Non-directional radio beacon (homing), power 50 watts to less than 2,000 watts (50 NM at all altitudes).
HH	Non-directional radio beacon (homing), power 2,000 watts or more (75 NM at all altitudes).
H-SAB	Non-directional radio beacons providing automatic transcribed weather service.
ILS	Instrument Landing System (voice, where available, on localizer channel).
IM	Inner marker.
ISMLS	Interim Standard Microwave Landing System.
LDA	Localizer Directional Aid.
LMM	Compass locator station when installed at middle marker site (15 NM at all altitudes).
LOM	Compass locator station when installed at outer marker site (15 NM at all altitudes).
MH	Non-directional radio beacon (homing) power less than 50 watts (25 NM at all altitudes).
MLS	Microwave Landing System.
MM	Middle marker.
OM	Outer marker.
S	Simultaneous range homing signal and/or voice.
SABH	Non-directional radio beacon not authorized for IFR or ATC. Provides automatic weather broadcasts.
SDF	Simplified Direction Facility.
TACAN	UHF navigational facility-omnidirectional course and distance information.
VOR	VHF navigational facility-omnidirectional course only.
VOR/DME	Collocated VOR navigational facility and UHF standard distance measuring equipment.
VORTAC	Collocated VOR and TACAN navigational facilities.
W	Without voice on radio facility frequency.
Z	VHF station location marker at a LF radio facility.

LEGEND 9.—Airport/Facility Directory.

TERMS/LANDING MINIMA DATA

IFR LANDING MINIMA

The United States Standard for Terminal Instrument Procedures (TERPS) is the approved criteria for formulating instrument approach procedures. Landing minima are established for six aircraft approach categories (ABCDE and COPTER). In the absence of COPTER MINIMA, helicopters may use the CAT A minimums of other procedures. The standard format for RNAV minima and landing minima portrayal follows:

RNAV MINIMA

CATEGORY	A	B	C	D
GLS PA DA	1382/24 200 (200-½)			
LNAV/ DA VNAV	1500/24 318 (400-½)			1500/40 318 (400-¾)
LNAV MDA	1700/24 518 (600-½)		1700/50 518 (600-1)	1700/60 518 (600-1¼)
CIRCLING	1760-1 578 (600-1)		1760-1½ 578 (600-1½)	1760-2 578 (600-2)

RNAV minimums are dependent on navigation equipment capability, as stated in the applicable AFM or AFMS and as outlined below.

GLS (GLobal Navigation System (GNSS) Landing System)

Must have WAAS (Wide Area Augmentation System) equipment approved for precise approach.
Note: "PA" indicates that the runway environment, i.e., runway markings, runway lights, parallel taxiway, etc., meets precision approach requirements. If the GLS minimums line does not contain "PA", then the runway environment does not support precision requirements.

LNAV/VNAV (Lateral Navigation/Vertical Navigation)

Must have WAAS equipment approved for precision approach, or RNP-0.3 system based on GPS or DME/DME, with an IFR approach approved Baro-VNAV system. Other RNAV approach systems require special approval.
Use of Baro-VNAV systems is limited by temperature, i.e., "Baro-VNAV NA below -20 C(-4 F)".
(Not applicable if chart is annotated "Baro-VNAV NA".)
NOTE: DME/DME based RNP-0.3 systems may be used only when a chart note indicates DME/DME availability, for example, "DME/DME RNP-0.3 Authorized." Specific DME facilities may be required, for example: "DME/DME RNP-0.3 Authorized. ABC, XYZ required."

LNAV (Lateral Navigation)

Must have IFR approach approved WAAS, GPS, GPS based FMS systems, or RNP-0.3 systems based on GPS or DME/DME. Other RNAV approach systems require special approval.
NOTE: DME/DME based RNP-0.3 systems may be used only when a chart note indicates DME/DME availability, for example, "DME/DME RNP-0.3 Authorized." Specific DME facilities may be required, for example: "DME/DME RNP-0.3 Authorized. ABC, XYZ required."

LANDING MINIMA FORMAT

In this example airport elevation is 1179, and runway touchdown zone elevation is 1152.

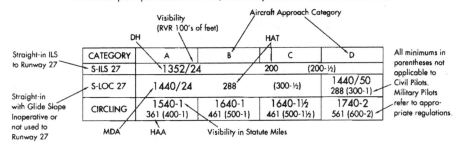

TERMS/LANDING MINIMA DATA

A1

LEGEND 10.—Instrument Approach Procedures Explanation of Terms.

SC-1, 24 FEB 2000　　　　　　　　　　　A2

00055
TERMS/LANDING MINIMA DATA

COPTER MINIMA ONLY

CATEGORY	COPTER		
H-176°	680-½	363	(400-½)

Copter Approach Direction　　　　　　　Height of MDA/DH
　　　　　　　　　　　　　　　　　　Above Landing Area (HAL)

No circling minimums are provided

RADAR MINIMA

										Visibility (RVR 100's of feet)
PAR (c)	10	2.5°/42/1000	ABCDE	**195**/16	100	(100-¼)				
(d)	28	2.5°/48/1068	ABCDE	**187**/16	100	(100-¼)				
ASR	10		ABC	**560**/40	463	(500-¾)	D	**560**/50	463	(500-1)
			E	**580**/60	463	(500-1¼)				
	28		AB	**600**/50	513	(600-1)	C	**600**/60	513	(600-1¼)
			DE	**600**-1½	513	(600-1½)				
CIR (b)	10		AB	**560**-1¼	463	(500-1¼)	C	**560**-1½	463	(500-1½)
	28		AB	**600**-1¼	503	(600-1¼)	C	**600**-1½	503	(600-1½)
	10, 28		DE	**660**-2	563	(600-2)				

All minimums in parentheses not applicable to Civil Pilots.
Military Pilots refer to appropriate regulations.

Visibility in Statute Miles

Radar Minima:

1. Minima shown are the lowest permitted by established criteria. Pilots should consult applicable directives for their category of aircraft.
2. The circling MDA and weather minima to be used are those for the runway to which the final approach is flown - not the landing runway. In the above RADAR MINIMA example, a category C aircraft flying a radar approach to runway 10, circling to land on runway 28, must use an MDA of 560 feet with weather minima of 500-1½ .

⚠ Alternate Minimums not standard. Civil users refer to tabulation. USA/USN/USAF pilots refer to appropriate regulations.

⚠ NA　Alternate minimums are Not Authorized due to unmonitored facility or absence of weather reporting service.

▼ Take-off Minimums not standard and/or Departure Procedures are published. Refer to tabulation.

AIRCRAFT APPROACH CATEGORIES

Speeds are based on 1.3 times the stall speed in the landing configuration of maximum gross landing weight. An aircraft shall fit in only one category. If it is necessary to maneuver at speeds in excess of the upper limit of a speed range for a category, the minimums for the next higher category should be used. For example, an aircraft which falls in Category A, but is circling to land at a speed in excess of 91 knots, should use the approach Category B minimums when circling to land. See following category limits:

MANEUVERING TABLE

Approach Category	A	B	C	D	E
Speed (Knots)	0-90	91-120	121-140	141-165	Abv 165

RVR/ Meteorological Visibility Comparable Values

The following table shall be used for converting RVR to meteorological visibility when RVR is not reported for the runway of intended operation. Adjustments of landing minima may be required - see Inoperative Components Table.

RVR (feet)	Visibility (statute miles)	RVR (feet)	Visibility (statute miles)
1600	¼	4000	¾
2000	⅜	4500	⅞
2400	½	5000	1
3200	⅝	6000	1¼

TERMS/ NDING MINIM DATA

LEGEND 11.—Instrument Approach Procedures Explanation of Terms.

F1

99252
GENERAL INFO

GENERAL INFORMATION

This publication includes Instrument Approach Procedures (IAPs), Departure Procedures (DPs), and Standard Terminal Arrivals (STARs) for use by both civil and military aviation and is issued every 56 days.

STANDARD TERMINAL ARRIVALS AND DEPARTURE PROCEDURES

The use of the associated codified STAR/DP and transition identifiers are requested of users when filing flight plans via teletype and are required for users filing flight plans via computer interface. It must be noted that when filing a STAR/DP with a transition, the first three coded characters of the STAR and the last three coded characters of the DP are replaced by the transition code. Examples: ACTON SIX ARRIVAL, file (AQN.AQN6); ACTON SIX ARRIVAL, EDNAS TRANSITION, file (EDNAS.AQN6). FREEHOLD THREE DEPARTURE, file (FREH3.RBV), FREEHOLD THREE DEPARTURE, ELWOOD CITY TRANSITION, file (FREH3.EWC).

PILOT CONTROLLED AIRPORT LIGHTING SYSTEMS

Available pilot controlled lighting (PCL) systems are indicated as follows:
1. Approach lighting systems that bear a system identification are symbolized using negative symbology, e.g., ⬤, ⬤, ⊗
2. Approach lighting systems that do not bear a system identification are indicated with a negative "⬤" besides the name.
A star (*) indicates non-standard PCL, consult Directory/Supplement, e.g., ⬤*
To activate lights use frequency indicated in the communication section of the chart with a ⬤ or the appropriate lighting system identification e.g., UNICOM 122.8 ⬤, ⬤, ⬤

KEY MIKE	FUNCTION
7 times within 5 seconds	Highest intensity available
5 times within 5 seconds	Medium or lower intensity (Lower REIL or REIL-off)
3 times within 5 seconds	Lowest intensity available (Lower REIL or REIL-off)

CHART CURRENCY INFORMATION

FAA procedure amendment number ——— ⟍ Amdt 11A 99365 ⟋ ——— Date of latest change
                                      ⟍ Orig 00365 ⟋

The Chart Date identifies the Julian date the chart was added to the volume or last revised for any reason. The first two digits indicate the year, the last three digits indicate the day of the year (001 to 365/6) in which the latest addition or change was first published.
The Procedure Amendment Number precedes the Chart Date, and changes any time instrument information (e.g., DH, MDA, approach routing, etc.) changes. Procedure changes also cause the Chart Date to change.

MISCELLANEOUS

★ Indicates a non-continuously operating facility, see A/FD or flight supplement.
# Indicates control tower temporarily closed UFN.
"Radar required" on the chart indicates that radar vectoring is required for the approach.
Distances in nautical miles (except visibility in statute miles and Runway Visual Range in hundreds of feet). Runway Dimensions in feet. Elevations in feet. Mean Sea Level (MSL). Ceilings in feet above airport elevation. Radials/ bearings/headings/courses are magnetic. Horizontal Datum: Unless otherwise noted on the chart, all coordinates are referenced to North American Datum 1983 (NAD 83), which for charting purposes is considered equivalent to World Geodetic System 1984 (WGS 84).

LEGEND 12.—General Information.

99140
GENERAL INFO

ABBREVIATIONS

ADF	Automatic Direction Finder
ALS	Approach Light System
ALSF	Approach Light System with Sequenced Flashing Lights
APP CON	Approach Control
ARR	Arrival
ASOS	Automated Surface Observing System
ASR/PAR	Published Radar Minimums at this Airport
ATIS	Automatic Terminal Information Service
AWOS	Automated Weather Observing System
AZ	Azimuth
BC	Back Course
C	Circling
CAT	Category
CCW	Counter Clockwise
Chan	Channel
CLNC DEL	Clearance Delivery
CNF	Computer Navigation Fix
CTAF	Common Traffic Advisory Frequency
CW	Clockwise
DH	Decision Height
DME	Distance Measuring Equipment
DR	Dead Reckoning
ELEV	Elevation
FAF	Final Approach Fix
FM	Fan Marker
FMS	Flight Management System
GCO	Ground Communications Outlet
GPI	Ground Point of Interception
GPS	Global Positioning System
GS	Glide Slope
HAA	Height above Airport
HAL	Height above Landing
HAT	Height above Touchdown
HIRL	High Intensity Runway Lights
IAF	Initial Approach Fix
ICAO	International Civil Aviation Organization
IM	Inner Marker
Intcp	Intercept
INT	Intersection
LDA	Localizer Type Directional Aid
Ldg	Landing
LDIN	Lead in Light System
LIRL	Low Intensity Runway Lights
LOC	Localizer
LR	Lead Radial. Provides at least 2 NM (Copter 1 NM) of lead to assist in turning onto the intermediate/final course.
MALS	Medium Intensity Approach Light System

MALSR	Medium Intensity Approach Light System with RAIL
MAP	Missed Approach Point
MDA	Minimum Descent Altitude
MIRL	Medium Intensity Runway Lights
MLS	Microwave Landing System
MM	Middle Marker
NA	Not Authorized
NDB	Non-directional Radio Beacon
NM	Nautical Mile
NoPT	No Procedure Turn Required (Procedure Turn shall not be executed without ATC clearance)
ODALS	Omnidirectional Approach Light System
OM	Outer Marker
R	Radial
RA	Radio Altimeter setting height
RAIL	Runway Alignment Indicator Lights
RBn	Radia Beacon
RCLS	Runway Centerline Light System
REIL	Runway End Identifier Lights
RNAV	Area Navigation
RNP	Required Navigation Performance
RPI	Runway Point of Intercept(ion)
RRL	Runway Remaining Lights
Rwy	Runway
RVR	Runway Visual Range
S	Straight-in
SALS	Short Approach Light System
SSALR	Simplified Short Approach Light System with RAIL
SDF	Simplified Directional Facility
TA	Transition Altitude
TAC	TACAN
TCH	Threshold Crossing Height (height in feet Above Ground level)
TDZ	Touchdown Zone
TDZE	Touchdown Zone Elevation
TDZ/CL	Touchdown Zone and Runway Centerline Lighting
TDZL	Touchdown Zone Lights
TLv	Transition Level
VASI	Visual Approach Slope Indicator
VDP	Visual Descent Point
VGSI	Visual Glide Slope Indicator
WP/WPT	Waypoint (RNAV)
X	Radar Only Frequency

GENERAL INFO
99140

F2   SW-1, 4 NOV 1999

LEGEND 13.—Abbreviations.

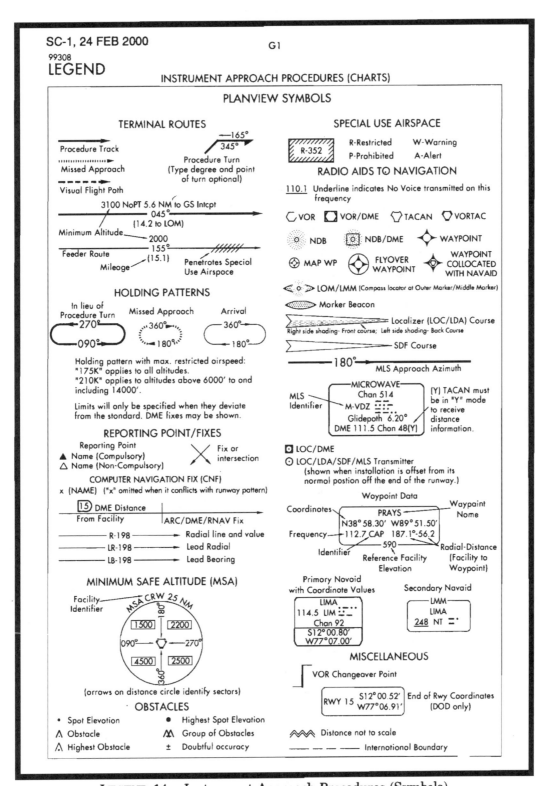

LEGEND 14.—Instrument Approach Procedures (Symbols).

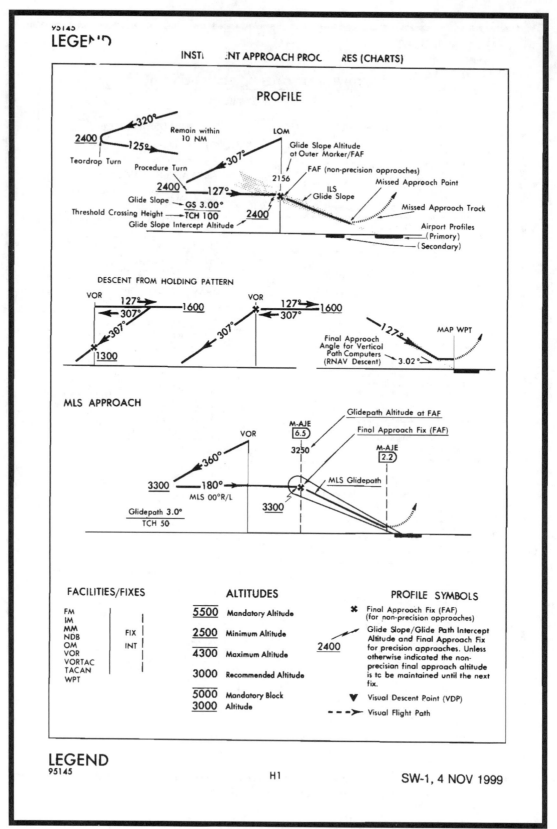

LEGEND 15.—Instrument Approach Procedures (Profile).

INSTRUMENT TAKEOFF PROCEDURE CHARTS
RATE-OF-CLIMB TABLE
(ft. per min.)

A rate-of-climb table is provided for use in planning and executing
takeoff procedures under known or approximate ground speed conditions.

REQUIRED CLIMB RATE (ft. per NM)	GROUND SPEED (KNOTS)						
	30	60	80	90	100	120	140
200	100	200	267	300	333	400	467
250	125	250	333	375	417	500	583
300	150	300	400	450	500	600	700
350	175	350	467	525	583	700	816
400	200	400	533	600	667	800	933
450	225	450	600	675	750	900	1050
500	250	500	667	750	833	1000	1167
550	275	550	733	825	917	1100	1283
600	300	600	800	900	1000	1200	1400
650	325	650	867	975	1083	1300	1516
700	350	700	933	1050	1167	1400	1633

REQUIRED CLIMB RATE (ft. per NM)	GROUND SPEED (KNOTS)					
	150	180	210	240	270	300
200	500	600	700	800	900	1000
250	625	750	875	1000	1125	1250
300	750	900	1050	1200	1350	1500
350	875	1050	1225	1400	1575	1750
400	1000	1200	1400	1600	1700	2000
450	1125	1350	1575	1800	2025	2250
500	1250	1500	1750	2000	2250	2500
550	1375	1650	1925	2200	2475	2750
600	1500	1800	2100	2400	2700	3000
650	1625	1950	2275	2600	2925	3250
700	1750	2100	2450	2800	3150	3500

LEGEND 16.—Instrument Takeoff Procedure Charts, Rate-of-Climb Table.

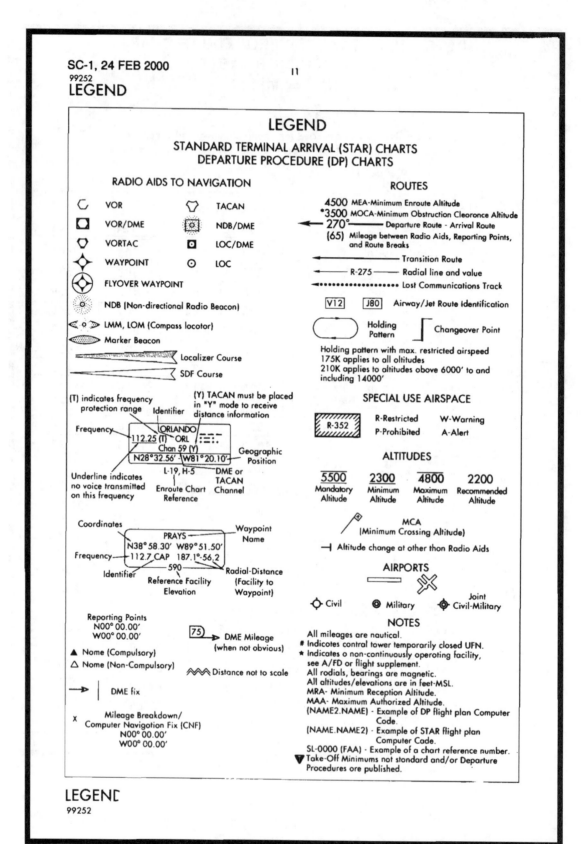

K1   SW-1, 4 NOV 1999

95201
LEGEND   INSTRUMENT APPROACH PROCEDURES (CHARTS)

AIRPORT DIAGRAM/AIRPORT SKETCH

Runways

Hard Surface | Other Than Hard Surface | Stopways, Taxiways, Parking Areas | Displaced Threshold

Closed Runway | Closed Taxiway | Under Construction | Metal Surface | Runway Centerline Lighting

ARRESTING GEAR: Specific arresting gear systems; e.g., BAK-12, MA-1A etc., shown on airport diagrams, not applicable to Civil Pilots. Military Pilots Refer to Appropriate DOD Publications.

uni-directional | bi-directional | Jet Barrier

REFERENCE FEATURES

Buildings.. ■

Tanks... ●

Obstruction.. ⋀

Airport Beacon #.. ☆

Runway Radar Reflectors................................ ⏳

Control Tower #... ▪

\# When Control Tower and Rotating Beacon are co-located, Beacon symbol will be used and further identified as TWR.

Runway length depicted is the physical length of the runway (end-to-end, including displaced thresholds if any) but excluding areas designated as stopways. Where a displaced threshold is shown and/or part of the runway is otherwise not available for landing, an annotation is added to indicate the landing length of the runway; e.g., RWY 13 ldg 5000'.

Runway Weight Bearing Capacity/or PCN Pavement Classification Number is shown as a codified expression.
Refer to the appropriate Supplement/Directory for applicable codes; e.g.,
RWY 14-32 S75, T185, ST175, TT325
PCN 80 F/D/X/U

Helicopter Alighting Areas Ⓗ ⊞ Ⓗ ⚠ ⊞

Negative Symbols used to identify Copter Procedures

landing point.................. Ⓗ ⊕ Ⓗ ⚠ ⊞

Runway TDZ elevation.................... TDZE 123

←—0.3% DOWN

Runway Slope.............................. 0.8% UP—→

(shown when runway slope exceeds 0.3%)

NOTE:
Runway Slope measured to midpoint on runways 8000 feet or longer.

◨ U.S. Navy Optical Landing System (OLS) "OLS" location is shown because of its height of approximately 7 feet and proximity to edge of runway may create an obstruction for some types of aircraft.

Approach light symbols are shown in the Flight Information Handbook.

Airport diagram scales are variable.

True/magnetic North orientation may vary from diagram to diagram.

Coordinate values are shown in 1 or ½ minute increments. They are further broken down into 6 second ticks, within each 1 minute increment.

Positional accuracy within ±600 feet unless otherwise noted on the chart.

NOTE:
All new and revised airport diagrams are shown referenced to the World Geodetic System (WGS) (noted on appropriate diagram), and may not be compatible with local coordinates published in FLIP. (Foreign Only)

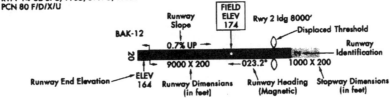

SCOPE

Airport diagrams are specifically designed to assist in the movement of ground traffic at locations with complex runway/taxiway configurations and provide information for updating Computer Based Navigation Systems (I.E., INS, GPS) aboard aircraft. Airport diagrams are not intended to be used for approach and landing or departure operations. For revisions to Airport Diagrams: Consult FAA Order 7910.4B.

LEGE
95201

LEGEND 18.—Airport Diagram.

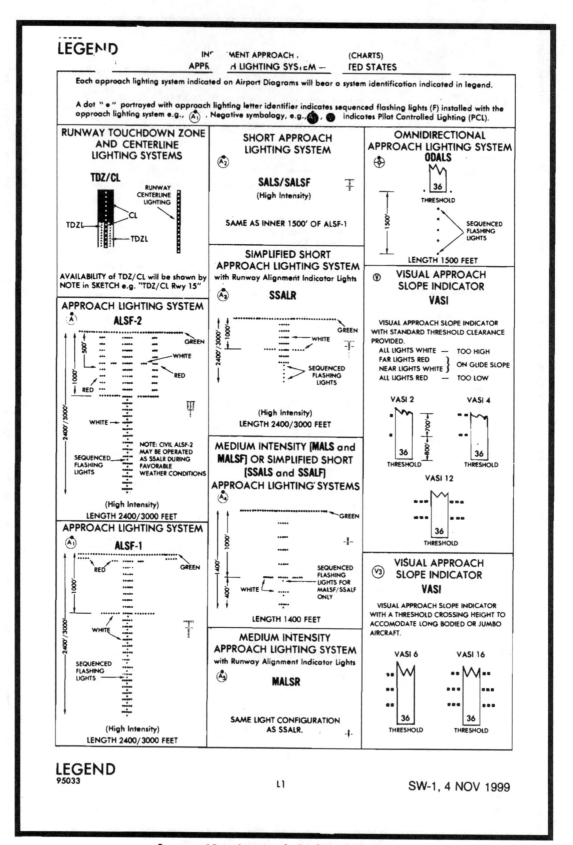

LEGEND

INSTRUMENT APPROACH . (CHARTS)
APPROACH LIGHTING SYSTEM — UNITED STATES

Each approach lighting system indicated on Airport Diagrams will bear a system identification indicated in legend.

A dot " • " portrayed with approach lighting letter identifier indicates sequenced flashing lights (F) installed with the approach lighting system e.g., (A₁) . Negative symbology, e.g., (A₁), ● indicates Pilot Controlled Lighting (PCL).

RUNWAY TOUCHDOWN ZONE AND CENTERLINE LIGHTING SYSTEMS

TDZ/CL

RUNWAY CENTERLINE LIGHTING
CL
TDZL
TDZL

AVAILABILITY of TDZ/CL will be shown by NOTE in SKETCH e.g. "TDZ/CL Rwy 15"

APPROACH LIGHTING SYSTEM
(A) **ALSF-2**

GREEN
WHITE
RED
RED
WHITE
SEQUENCED FLASHING LIGHTS

NOTE: CIVIL ALSF-2 MAY BE OPERATED AS SSALR DURING FAVORABLE WEATHER CONDITIONS

(High Intensity)
LENGTH 2400/3000 FEET

APPROACH LIGHTING SYSTEM
(A₁) **ALSF-1**

RED   GREEN

WHITE

SEQUENCED FLASHING LIGHTS

(High Intensity)
LENGTH 2400/3000 FEET

SHORT APPROACH LIGHTING SYSTEM
(A₂)

SALS/SALSF
(High Intensity)

SAME AS INNER 1500' OF ALSF-1

SIMPLIFIED SHORT APPROACH LIGHTING SYSTEM
with Runway Alignment Indicator Lights
(A₃) **SSALR**

GREEN
WHITE
SEQUENCED FLASHING LIGHTS

(High Intensity)
LENGTH 2400/3000 FEET

MEDIUM INTENSITY [MALS and MALSF] OR SIMPLIFIED SHORT [SSALS and SSALF] APPROACH LIGHTING SYSTEMS
(A₄)

GREEN
SEQUENCED FLASHING LIGHTS FOR MALSF/SSALF ONLY
WHITE

LENGTH 1400 FEET

MEDIUM INTENSITY APPROACH LIGHTING SYSTEM
with Runway Alignment Indicator Lights
(A₅) **MALSR**

SAME LIGHT CONFIGURATION AS SSALR.

OMNIDIRECTIONAL APPROACH LIGHTING SYSTEM
ODALS

36
THRESHOLD
SEQUENCED FLASHING LIGHTS
LENGTH 1500 FEET

VISUAL APPROACH SLOPE INDICATOR
(V) **VASI**

VISUAL APPROACH SLOPE INDICATOR WITH STANDARD THRESHOLD CLEARANCE PROVIDED.
ALL LIGHTS WHITE — TOO HIGH
FAR LIGHTS RED } ON GLIDE SLOPE
NEAR LIGHTS WHITE
ALL LIGHTS RED — TOO LOW

VASI 2   VASI 4
36   36
THRESHOLD   THRESHOLD

VASI 12
36
THRESHOLD

VISUAL APPROACH SLOPE INDICATOR
(V₃) **VASI**

VISUAL APPROACH SLOPE INDICATOR WITH A THRESHOLD CROSSING HEIGHT TO ACCOMODATE LONG BODIED OR JUMBO AIRCRAFT.

VASI 6   VASI 16
36   36
THRESHOLD   THRESHOLD

LEGEND
95033

L1

SW-1, 4 NOV 1999

LEGEND 19.—Approach Lighting Systems.

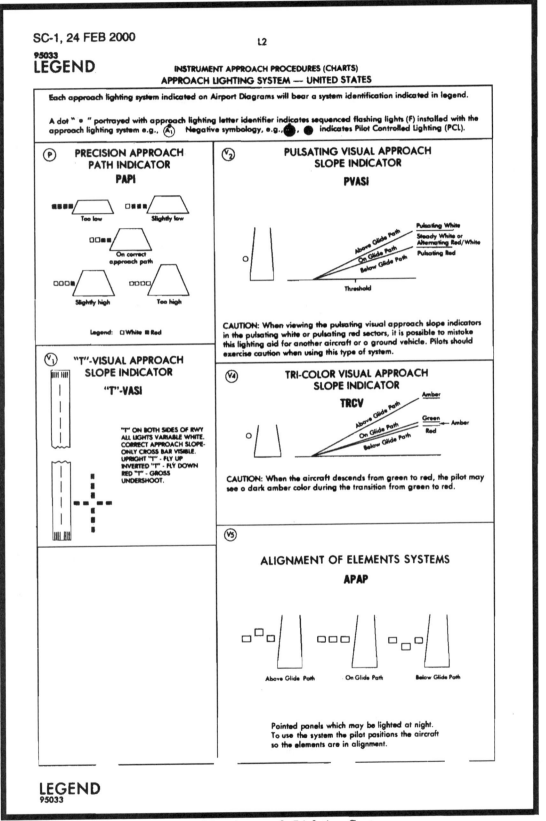

LEGEND 20.—Approach Lighting System.

RATE OF DESCENT TABLE

A rate of descent table is provided for use in planning and executing precision descents under known or approximate ground speed conditions. It will be especially useful for approaches when the localizer only is used for course guidance. A best speed, power, altitude combination can be programmed which will result in a stable glide rate and altitude favorable for executing a landing if minimums exist upon breakout. Care should always be exercised so that minimum descent altitude and missed approach point are not exceeded.

ANGLE OF DESCENT (degrees and tenths)	FEET /NM	GROUND SPEED (knots)										
		30	45	60	75	90	105	120	135	150	165	180
2.0	210	105	160	210	265	320	370	425	475	530	585	635
2.5	265	130	200	265	330	395	465	530	595	665	730	795
2.7	287	143	215	287	358	430	501	573	645	716	788	860
2.8	297	149	223	297	371	446	520	594	669	743	817	891
2.9	308	154	231	308	385	462	539	616	693	769	846	923
3.0	318	159	239	318	398	478	557	637	716	796	876	955
3.1	329	165	247	329	411	494	576	658	740	823	905	987
3.2	340	170	255	340	425	510	594	679	764	849	934	1019
3.3	350	175	263	350	438	526	613	701	788	876	963	1051
3.4	361	180	271	361	451	541	632	722	812	902	993	1083
3.5	370	185	280	370	465	555	650	740	835	925	1020	1110
4.0	425	210	315	425	530	635	740	845	955	1060	1165	1270
4.5	475	240	355	475	595	715	835	955	1075	1190	1310	1430
5.0	530	265	395	530	660	795	925	1060	1190	1325	1455	1590
5.5	580	290	435	580	730	875	1020	1165	1310	1455	1600	1745
6.0	635	315	475	635	795	955	1110	1270	1430	1590	1745	1950
6.5	690	345	515	690	860	1030	1205	1375	1550	1720	1890	2065
7.0	740	370	555	740	925	1110	1295	1480	1665	1850	2035	2220
7.5	795	395	595	795	990	1190	1390	1585	1785	1985	2180	2380
8.0	845	425	635	845	1055	1270	1480	1690	1905	2115	2325	2540
8.5	900	450	675	900	1120	1345	1570	1795	2020	2245	2470	2695
9.0	950	475	715	950	1190	1425	1665	1900	2140	2375	2615	2855
9.5	1005	500	750	1005	1255	1505	1755	2005	2255	2510	2760	3010
10.0	1055	530	790	1055	1320	1585	1845	2110	2375	2640	2900	3165
10.5	1105	555	830	1105	1385	1660	1940	2215	2490	2770	3045	3320
11.0	1160	580	870	1160	1450	1740	2030	2320	2610	2900	3190	3480
11.5	1210	605	910	1210	1515	1820	2120	2425	2725	3030	3335	3635
12.0	1260	630	945	1260	1575	1890	2205	2520	2835	3150	3465	3780

(Rows 2.7 through 3.4 are grouped under the label VERTICAL PATH ANGLE)

DESCENT TABLE 99028

LEGEND 21.—Instrument Approach Procedure Charts, Rate-of-Descent Table.

INOP COMPONENTS
99084

INOPERATIVE COMPONENTS OR VISUAL AIDS TABLE

Landing minimums published on instrument approach procedure charts are based upon full operation of all components and visual aids associated with the particular instrument approach chart being used. Higher minimums are required with inoperative components or visual aids as indicated below. If more than one component is inoperative, each minimum is raised to the highest minimum required by any single component that is inoperative. ILS glide slope inoperative minimums are published on the instrument approach charts as localizer minimums. This table may be amended by notes on the approach chart. Such notes apply only to the particular approach catergory(ies) as stated. See legend page for description of components indicated below.

(1) ILS, MLS, and PAR

Inoperative Component or Aid	Approach Category	Increase Visibility
ALSF 1 & 2, MALSR, & SSALR	ABCD	1/4 mile

(2) ILS with visibility minimum of 1,800 RVR

ALSF 1 & 2, MALSR, & SSALR	ABCD	To 4000 RVR
TDZL RCLS	ABCD	To 2400 RVR
RVR	ABCD	To 1/2 mile

(3) VOR, VOR/DME, VORTAC, VOR (TAC), VOR/DME (TAC), LOC, LOC/DME, LDA, LDA/DME, SDF, SDF/DME, GPS, RNAV, and ASR

Inoperative Visual Aid	Approach Category	Increase Visibility
ALSF 1 & 2, MALSR, & SSALR	ABCD	1/2 mile
SSALS, MALS, & ODALS	ABC	1/4 mile

(4) NDB

ALSF 1 & 2, MALSR, & SSALR	C	1/2 mile
	ABD	1/4 mile
MALS, SSALS, ODALS	ABC	1/4 mile

CORRECTIONS, COMMENTS AND/OR PROCUREMENT

FOR CHARTING ERRORS CONTACT:
National Ocean Service/NOAA
N/ACC1, SSMC-4, Sta. #2335
1305 East-West Highway
Silver Spring, MD 20910-3281
Telephone Toll-Free (800) 626-3677
Internet/E-Mail: Aerochart@NOAA.GOV

FOR CHANGES, ADDITIONS, OR RECOMMENDATIONS ON PROCEDURAL ASPECTS:
Contact Federal Aviation Administration, ATA 110
800 Independence Avenue, SW
Washington, DC 20591
Telephone Toll Free (800) 457-6656

TO PURCHASE CHARTS CONTACT:
National Ocean Service
NOAA, N/ACC3
Distribution Division
Riverdale, MD 20737
Telephone Toll Free (800) 638-8972

Requests for the creation or revisions to Airport Diagrams should be in accordance with FAA Order 7910.4B.

LEGEND 22.—Inoperative Components or Visual Aids Table.

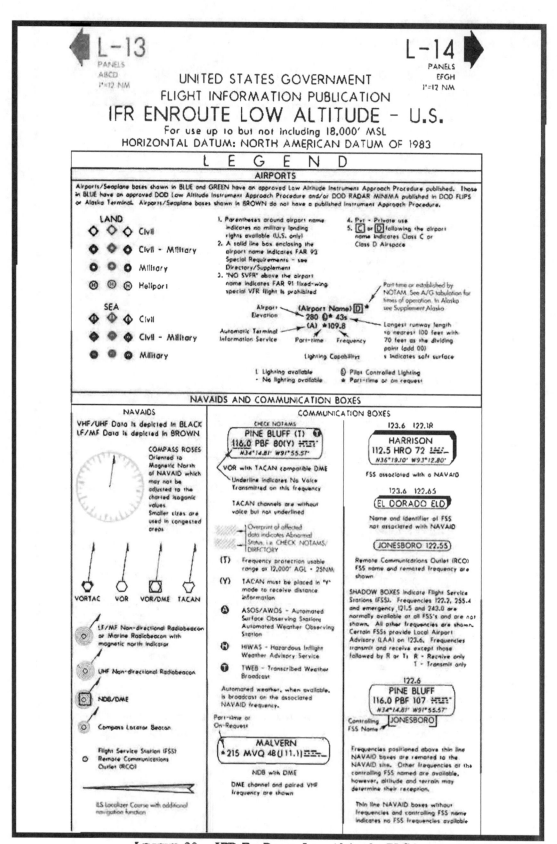

LEGEND 23.—IFR En Route Low Altitude (U.S.).

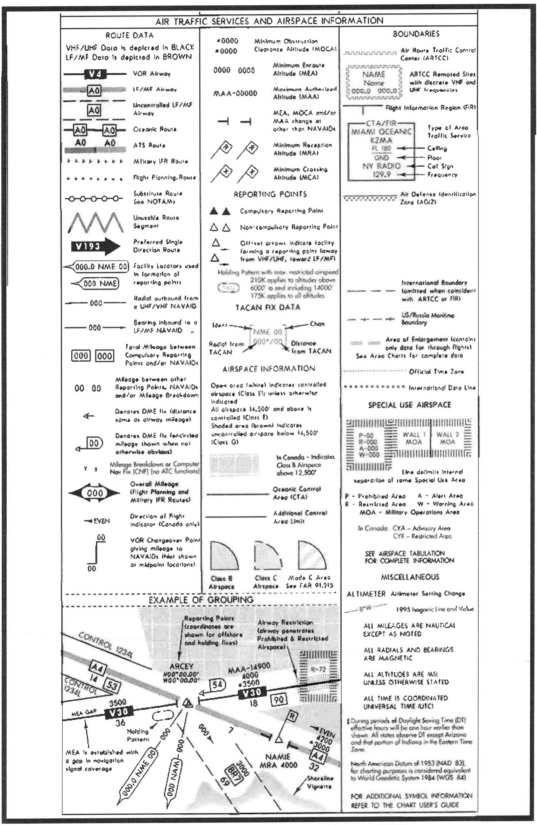

LEGEND 24.—IFR En Route Low Altitude (U.S.).

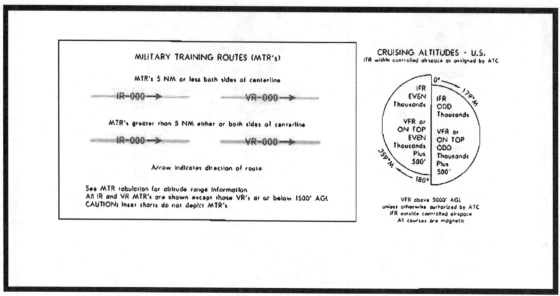

LEGEND 25.—IFR En Route Low Altitude (U.S.).

AIRCRAFT EQUIPMENT SUFFIXES

Suffix	Aircraft Equipment Suffixes
	NO DME
/X	No transponder
/T	Transponder with no Mode C
/U	Transponder with Mode C
	DME
/D	No transponder
/B	Transponder with no Mode C
/A	Transponder with Mode C
	TACAN ONLY
/M	No transponder
/N	Transponder with no Mode C
/P	Transponder with Mode C
	AREA NAVIGATION (RNAV)
/Y	LORAN, VOR/DME, or INS with no transponder
/C	LORAN, VOR/DME, or INS, transponder with no Mode C
/I	LORAN, VOR/DME, or INS, transponder with Mode C
	ADVANCED RNAV WITH TRANSPONDER AND MODE C (If an aircraft is unable to operate with a transponder and/or Mode C, it will revert to the appropriate code listed above under Area Navigation.)
/E	Flight Management System (FMS) with en route, terminal, and approach capability. Equipment requirements are: (a) Dual FMS which meets the specifications of AC 25-15, Approval of Flight Management Systems in Transport Category Airplanes; AC 20-129, Airworthiness Approval of Vertical Navigation (VNAV) Systems for use in the U.S. NAS and Alaska; AC 20-130A, Airworthiness Approval of Navigation or Flight Management Systems Integrating Multiple Navigation Sensors; or equivalent criteria as approved by Flight Standards. (b) A flight director and autopilot control system capable of following the lateral and vertical FMS flight path. (c) At least dual inertial reference units (IRU's). (d) A database containing the waypoints and speed/altitude constraints for the route and/or procedure to be flown that is automatically loaded into the FMS flight plan. (e) An electronic map. (U.S. and U.S. territories only unless otherwise authorized.)
/F	A single FMS with en route, terminal, and approach capability that meets the equipment requirements of /E, (a) through (d), above. (U.S. and U.S. territories only unless otherwise authorized.)
/G	Global Positioning System (GPS)/Global Navigation Satellite System (GNSS) equipped aircraft with en route and terminal capability
/R	Required Navigational Performance (Denotes capability to operate in RNP designated airspace and routes)
/W	Reduced Vertical Separation Minima (RVSM)

LEGEND 26.—Aircraft Equipment Suffixes.

AIR NAVIGATION RADIO AIDS

STANDARD HIGH ALTITUDE SERVICE VOLUME

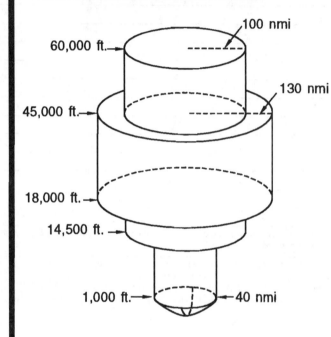

STANDARD LOW ALTITUDE SERVICE VOLUME

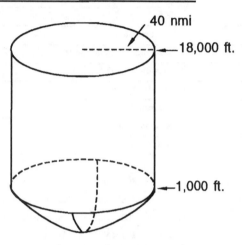

NOTE: All elevations shown are with respect to the station's site elevation (AGL). Coverage is not available in a cone of airspace directly above the facility.

STANDARD TERMINAL SERVICE VOLUME

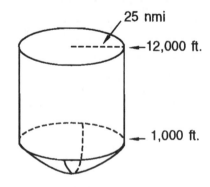

LEGEND 27.—Air Navigation Radio Aids.

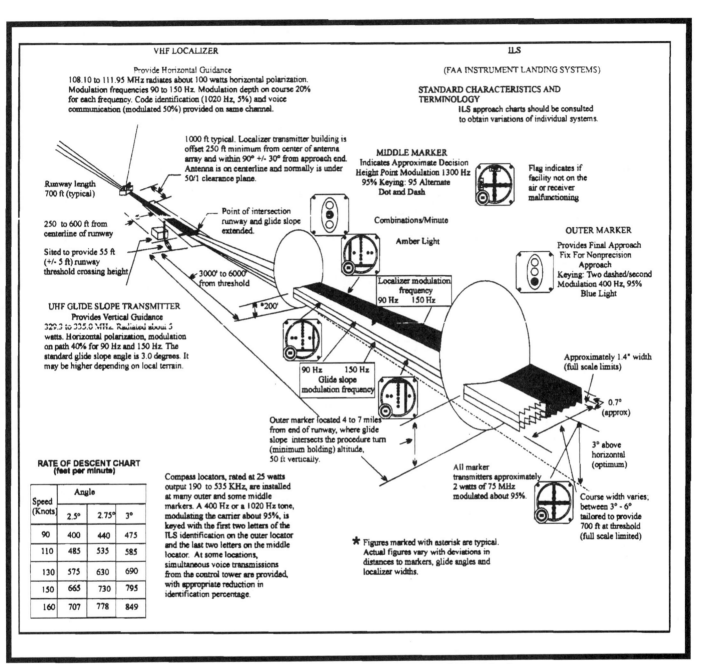

VHF LOCALIZER

Provide Horizontal Guidance
108.10 to 111.95 MHz radiates about 100 watts horizontal polarization. Modulation frequencies 90 to 150 Hz. Modulation depth on course 20% for each frequency. Code identification (1020 Hz, 5%) and voice communication (modulated 50%) provided on same channel.

1000 ft typical. Localizer transmitter building is offset 250 ft minimum from center of antenna array and within 90° +/- 30° from approach end. Antenna is on centerline and normally is under 50/1 clearance plane.

Runway length 700 ft (typical)

250 to 600 ft from centerline of runway

Sited to provide 55 ft (+/- 5 ft) runway threshold crossing height

Point of intersection runway and glide slope extended.

UHF GLIDE SLOPE TRANSMITTER

Provides Vertical Guidance
329.3 to 335.0 MHz. Radiated about 5 watts. Horizontal polarization, modulation on path 40% for 90 Hz and 150 Hz. The standard glide slope angle is 3.0 degrees. It may be higher depending on local terrain.

3000' to 6000' from threshold

*200'

ILS

(FAA INSTRUMENT LANDING SYSTEMS)

STANDARD CHARACTERISTICS AND TERMINOLOGY

ILS approach charts should be consulted to obtain variations of individual systems.

MIDDLE MARKER

Indicates Approximate Decision Height Point Modulation 1300 Hz 95% Keying: 95 Alternate Dot and Dash

Combinations/Minute

Amber Light

Flag indicates if facility not on the air or receiver malfunctioning

OUTER MARKER

Provides Final Approach Fix For Nonprecision Approach Keying: Two dashed/second Modulation 400 Hz, 95% Blue Light

Localizer modulation frequency
90 Hz   150 Hz

90 Hz   150 Hz
Glide slope modulation frequency

Outer marker located 4 to 7 miles from end of runway, where glide slope intersects the procedure turn (minimum holding) altitude, 50 ft vertically.

All marker transmitters approximately 2 watts of 75 MHz modulated about 95%.

Approximately 1.4° width (full scale limits)

0.7° (approx)

3° above horizontal (optimum)

Course width varies: between 3° - 6° tailored to provide 700 ft at threshold (full scale limited)

RATE OF DESCENT CHART
(feet per minute)

Speed (Knots)	Angle		
	2.5°	2.75°	3°
90	400	440	475
110	485	535	585
130	575	630	690
150	665	730	795
160	707	778	849

Compass locators, rated at 25 watts output 190 to 535 KHz, are installed at many outer and some middle markers. A 400 Hz or a 1020 Hz tone, modulating the carrier about 95%, is keyed with the first two letters of the ILS identification on the outer locator and the last two letters on the middle locator. At some locations, simultaneous voice transmissions from the control tower are provided, with appropriate reduction in identification percentage.

★ Figures marked with asterisk are typical. Actual figures vary with deviations in distances to markers, glide angles and localizer widths.

LEGEND 28.—ILS Standard Characteristics and Terminology.

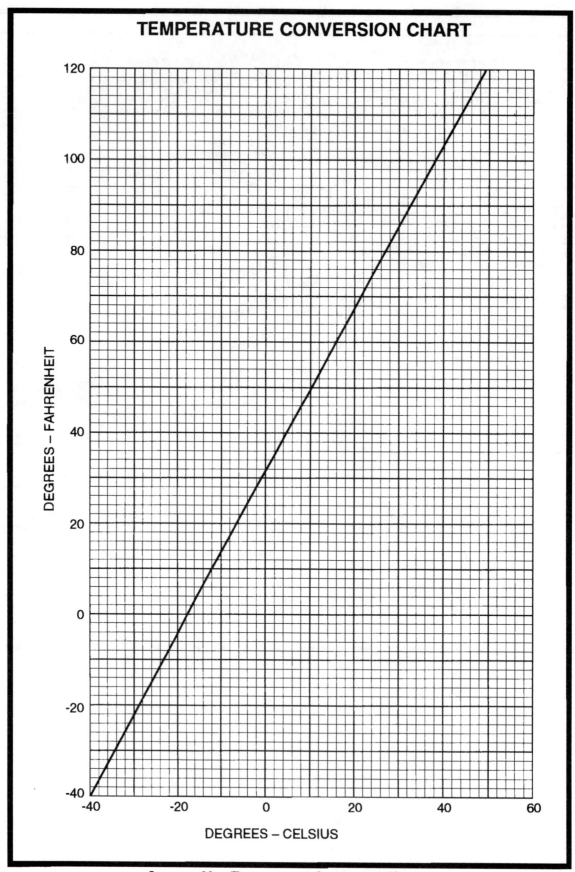

LEGEND 29.—Temperature Conversion Chart.

APPENDIX
2

FAA FIGURES

				Form Approved: OMB No. 2120-0034

U.S. DEPARTMENT OF TRANSPORTATION FEDERAL AVIATION ADMINISTRATION **FLIGHT PLAN**	(FAA USE ONLY)	☐ PILOT BRIEFING ☐ STOPOVER	☐ VNR	TIME STARTED	SPECIALIST INITIALS

| 1. TYPE
☐ VFR
☐ IFR
☐ DVFR | 2. AIRCRAFT
IDENTIFICATION | 3. AIRCRAFT TYPE/
SPECIAL EQUIPMENT | 4. TRUE
AIRSPEED

KTS | 5. DEPARTURE POINT | 6. DEPARTURE TIME
PROPOSED (Z) / ACTUAL (Z) | 7. CRUISING
ALTITUDE |

8. ROUTE OF FLIGHT

9. DESTINATION (Name of airport and city)	10. EST. TIME ENROUTE HOURS / MINUTES	11. REMARKS

12. FUEL ON BOARD HOURS / MINUTES	13. ALTERNATE AIRPORT(S)	14. PILOT'S NAME, ADDRESS & TELEPHONE NUMBER & AIRCRAFT HOME BASE	15. NUMBER ABOARD

17. DESTINATION CONTACT/TELEPHONE (OPTIONAL)

16. COLOR OF AIRCRAFT	CIVIL AIRCRAFT PILOTS. FAR Part 91 requires you file an IFR flight plan to operate under instrument flight rules in controlled airspace. Failure to file could result in a civil penalty not to exceed $1,000 for each violation (Section 901 of the Federal Aviation Act of 1958, as amended). Filing of a VFR flight plan is recommended as a good operating practice. See also Part 99 for requirements concerning DVFR flight plans.

FAA Form 7233-1 (8-82)   CLOSE VFR FLIGHT PLAN WITH _____ FSS ON ARRIVAL

FIGURE 1.—Flight Plan.

VALID 141200Z FOR USE 0900-1500Z. TEMPS NEG ABV 24000

FT	3000	6000	9000	12000	18000	24000	30000	34000	39000
EMI	2807	2715-07	2728-10	2842-13	2867-21	2891-30	751041	771150	780855
ALB	0210	9900-07	2714-09	2728-12	2656-19	2777-28	781842	760150	269658
PSB		1509+04	2119+01	2233-04	2262-14	2368-26	781939	760850	780456
STL	2308	2613+02	2422-03	2431-08	2446-19	2461-30	760142	782650	760559

FIGURE 2.—Winds and Temperatures Aloft Forecast.

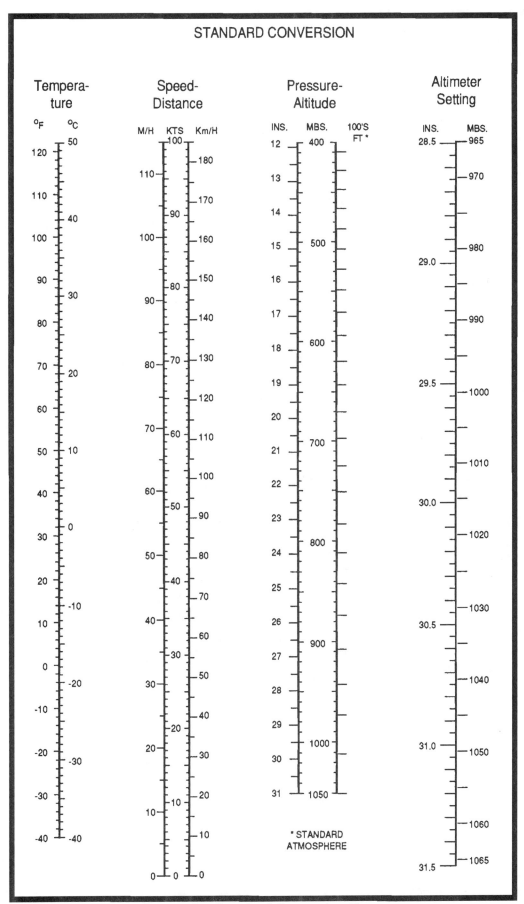

FIGURE 3.—Standard Conversion Chart.

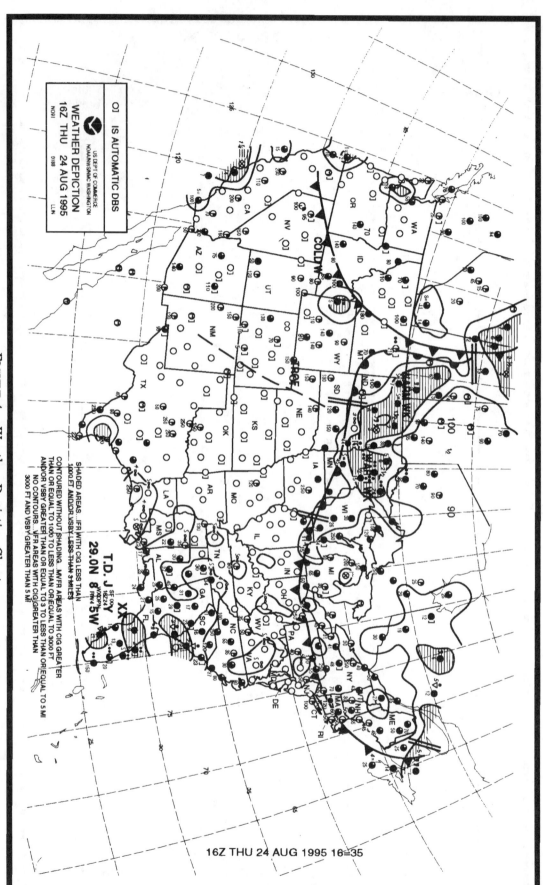

FIGURE 4.—Weather Depiction Chart.

16Z THU 24 AUG 1995 16=35

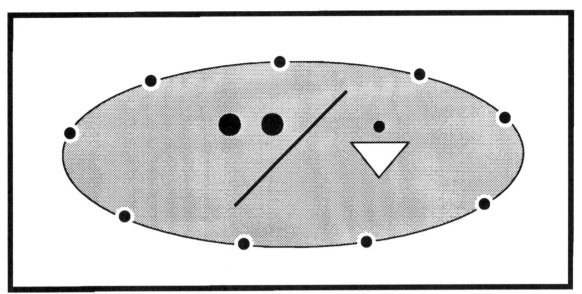

FIGURE 5.—Symbol Used on Low-Level Significant Weather Prognostic Chart.

FIGURE 6.—Deleted.

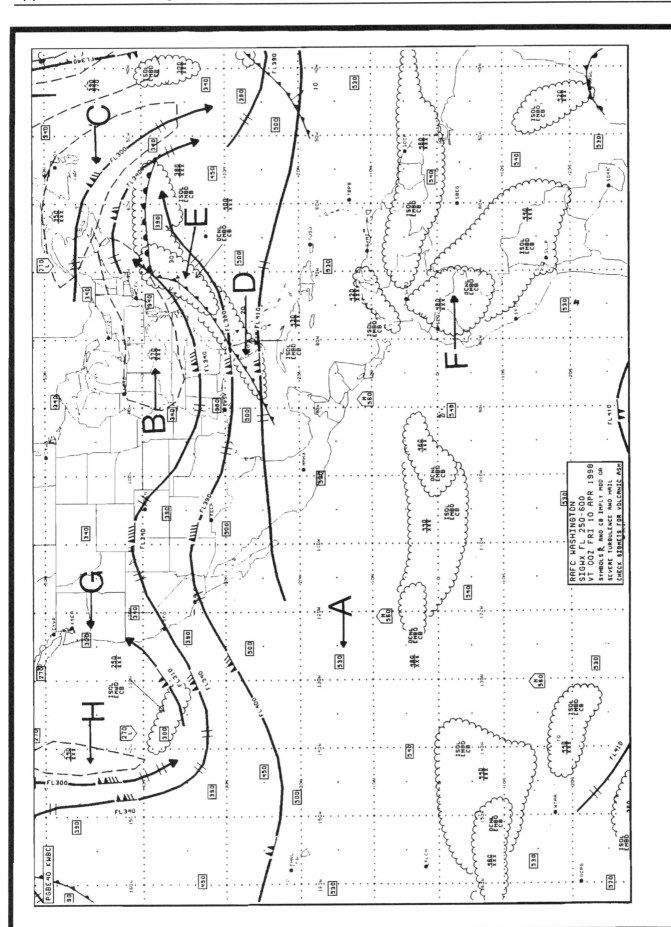

FIGURE 7.—High-Level Significant Weather Prognostic Chart.

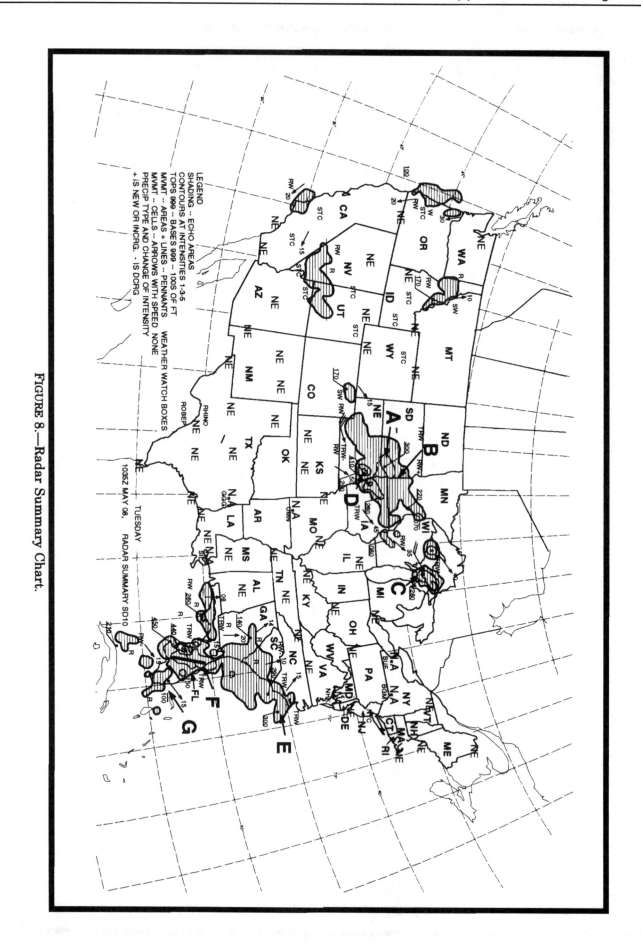

FIGURE 8.—Radar Summary Chart.

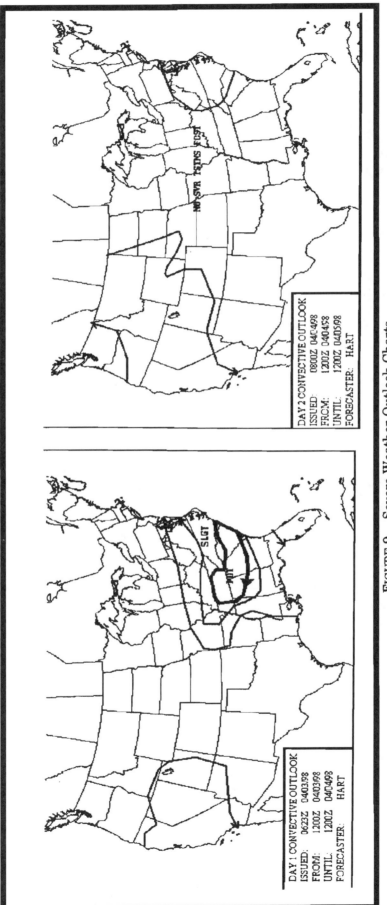

FIGURE 9.—Severe Weather Outlook Charts.

FIGURE 10.—Deleted.

FIGURE 11.—Deleted.

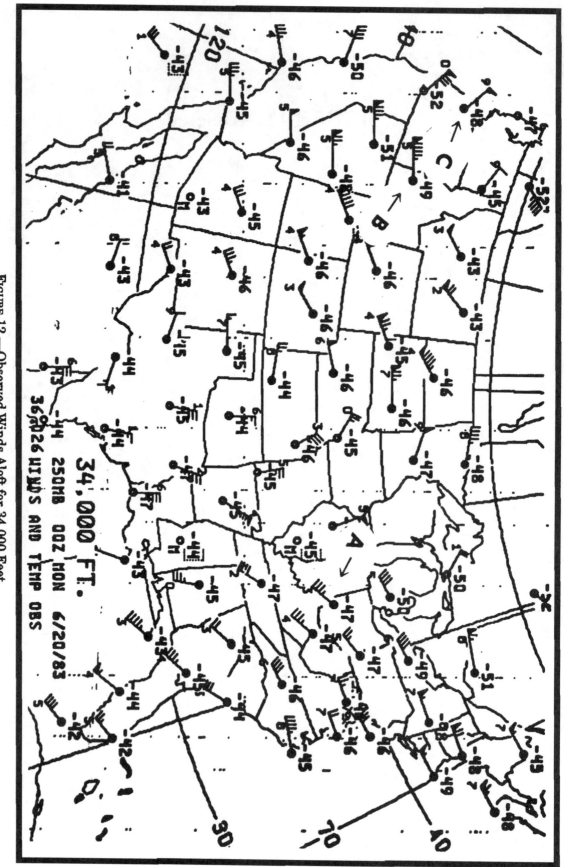

Figure 12.—Observed Winds Aloft for 34,000 Feet.

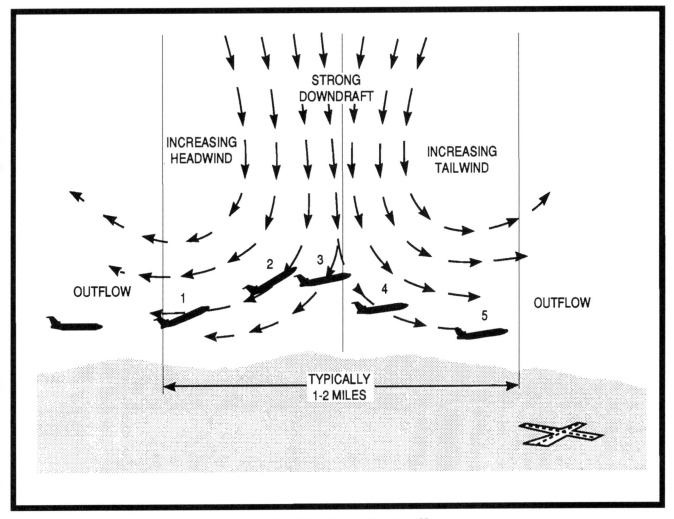

FIGURE 13.—Microburst Section Chart.

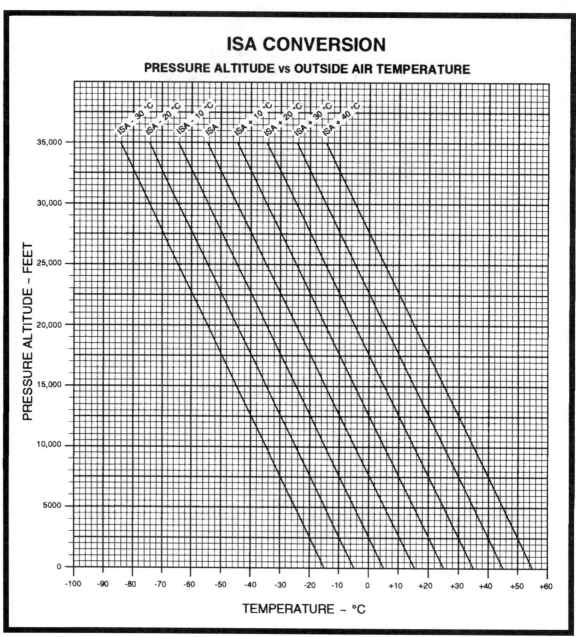

FIGURE 14.—ISA Conversion Chart.

FIGURE 15.—Deleted.

FIGURE 16.—Deleted.

FIGURE 17.—Deleted.

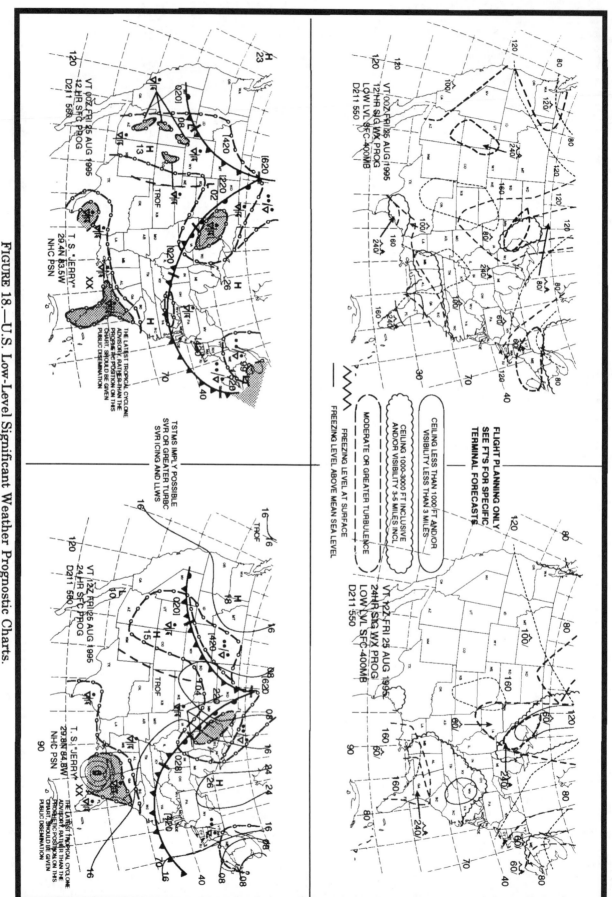

FIGURE 18.—U.S. Low-Level Significant Weather Prognostic Charts.

FIGURE 19.—Deleted.

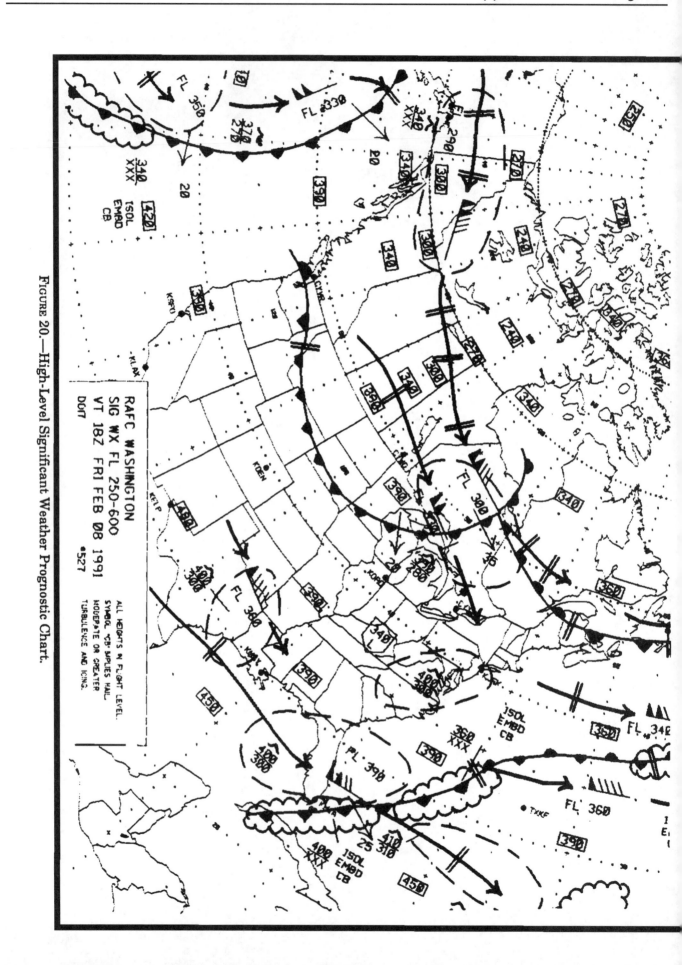

FIGURE 20.—High-Level Significant Weather Prognostic Chart.

Form Approved: OMB No. 2120-0034

U.S. DEPARTMENT OF TRANSPORTATION FEDERAL AVIATION ADMINISTRATION **FLIGHT PLAN**	(FAA USE ONLY)	☐ PILOT BRIEFING ☐ STOPOVER	☐ VNR	TIME STARTED	SPECIALIST INITIALS

1. TYPE	2. AIRCRAFT IDENTIFICATION	3. AIRCRAFT TYPE/ SPECIAL EQUIPMENT	4. TRUE AIRSPEED	5. DEPARTURE POINT	6. DEPARTURE TIME		7. CRUISING ALTITUDE
VFR					PROPOSED (Z)	ACTUAL (Z)	
X IFR DVFR	N 123RC	T210N/	175 KTS	GJT			15,000

8. ROUTE OF FLIGHT

JNC9, JNC, V187, MANCA, V211

9. DESTINATION (Name of airport and city)	10. EST. TIME ENROUTE		11. REMARKS
	HOURS	MINUTES	
DRO			

12. FUEL ON BOARD		13. ALTERNATE AIRPORT(S)	14. PILOT'S NAME, ADDRESS & TELEPHONE NUMBER & AIRCRAFT HOME BASE	15. NUMBER ABOARD
HOURS	MINUTES			
4	30	GJT	17. DESTINATION CONTACT/TELEPHONE (OPTIONAL)	2

16. COLOR OF AIRCRAFT	CIVIL AIRCRAFT PILOTS. FAR Part 91 requires you file an IFR flight plan to operate under instrument flight rules in controlled airspace. Failure to file could result in a civil penalty not to exceed $1,000 for each violation (Section 901 of the Federal Aviation Act of 1958, as amended). Filing of a VFR flight plan is recommended as a good operating practice. See also Part 99 for requirements concerning DVFR flight plans.
RED/WHITE/BLUE	

FAA Form 7233-1 (8-82)   CLOSE VFR FLIGHT PLAN WITH _____ FSS ON ARRIVAL

AIRCRAFT INFORMATION

MAKE Cessna   MODEL T210N

N 123RC   Vso 58 ____

AIRCRAFT EQUIPMENT/STATUS**

**NOTE: X= OPERATIVE   INOP= INOPERATIVE   N/A= NOT APPLICABLE
TRANSPONDER: X (MODE C) X ILS: (LOCALIZER) X (GLIDE SLOPE) X
VOR NO. 1 X (NO. 2) X ADF: X RNAV: X
VERTICAL PATH COMPUTER: N/A DME: X
MARKER BEACON: X (AUDIO) X (VISUAL) X

FIGURE 21.—Flight Plan and Aircraft Information.

Form Approved: OMB No. 2120-0034

U.S. DEPARTMENT OF TRANSPORTATION FEDERAL AVIATION ADMINISTRATION **FLIGHT PLAN**	(FAA USE ONLY)	☐ PILOT BRIEFING ☐ STOPOVER	☐ VNR	TIME STARTED	SPECIALIST INITIALS

1. TYPE	2. AIRCRAFT IDENTIFICATION	3. AIRCRAFT TYPE/ SPECIAL EQUIPMENT	4. TRUE AIRSPEED	5. DEPARTURE POINT	6. DEPARTURE TIME		7. CRUISING ALTITUDE
VFR					PROPOSED (Z)	ACTUAL (Z)	
X IFR DVFR	N 123RC	T210N/	175 KTS	DRO			16,000

8. ROUTE OF FLIGHT

V211, MANCA, V187, HERRM, V187, JNC

9. DESTINATION (Name of airport and city) GJT	10. EST. TIME ENROUTE		11. REMARKS
	HOURS	MINUTES	

12. FUEL ON BOARD		13. ALTERNATE AIRPORT(S)	14. PILOT'S NAME, ADDRESS & TELEPHONE NUMBER & AIRCRAFT HOME BASE	15. NUMBER ABOARD
HOURS	MINUTES			
			17. DESTINATION CONTACT/TELEPHONE (OPTIONAL)	2

16. COLOR OF AIRCRAFT RED/WHITE/BLUE	CIVIL AIRCRAFT PILOTS. FAR Part 91 requires you file an IFR flight plan to operate under instrument flight rules in controlled airspace. Failure to file could result in a civil penalty not to exceed $1,000 for each violation (Section 901 of the Federal Aviation Act of 1958, as amended). Filing of a VFR flight plan is recommended as a good operating practice. See also Part 99 for requirements concerning DVFR flight plans.

FAA Form 7233-1 (8-82)   CLOSE VFR FLIGHT PLAN WITH _____ FSS ON ARRIVAL

AIRCRAFT INFORMATION

MAKE Cessna   MODEL T210N

N 123RC   Vso 58____

AIRCRAFT EQUIPMENT/STATUS**

**NOTE: X= OPERATIVE   INOP= INOPERATIVE   N/A= NOT APPLICABLE
TRANSPONDER: X (MODE C) X ILS: (LOCALIZER) X   (GLIDE SLOPE) X
VOR NO. 1 X (NO. 2) X ADF: X RNAV: X
VERTICAL PATH COMPUTER: N/A DME: X
MARKER BEACON: X (AUDIO) X   (VISUAL) X

FIGURE 21A.—Flight Plan and Aircraft Information.

FLIGHT LOG

GRAND JUNCTION (GJT) TO DURANGO (DRO)

CHECK POINTS		ROUTE		WIND	SPEED-KTS		DIST	TIME		FUEL	
FROM	TO	ALTITUDE	COURSE	TEMP	TAS	GS	NM	LEG	TOT	LEG	TOT
GJT	JNC	JNC9JNC CLIMB		230 08				✕			
	HERRM	V187 15,000	151°		175			:24:0			
	MANCA	V187	151°								
APPROACH & LANDING		V211 DESENT	092°					:18:30			
	DRO										

OTHER DATA:

NOTE: TAKEOFF RUNWAY 29. MAG VAR, 14° E.

FLIGHT SUMMARY

TIME	FUEL (LB)	
		EN ROUTE
		RESERVE
		MISSED APPR.
		TOTAL

FIGURE 22.—Flight Planning Log.

FLIGHT LOG

DURANGO (DRO) TO GRAND JUNCTION, WALKER FIELD (GJT)

CHECK POINTS		ROUTE	COURSE	WIND	SPEED-KTS		DIST	TIME		FUEL	
FROM	TO	ALTITUDE		TEMP	TAS	GS	NM	LEG	TOT	LEG	TOT
DRO	MANCA	V211 CLIMB	272°	230 08				:14:30			
	HERRM	V187 16,000	333°		174						
	JNC	V187	331°								
APPROACH & LANDING		DESCENT						:12:00			
	GJT										

OTHER DATA:
NOTE: MAG. VAR. 14° E.

FLIGHT SUMMARY

TIME	FUEL (LB)	
		EN ROUTE
		RESERVE
		MISSED APPR.
		TOTAL

FIGURE 22A.—Flight Planning Log.

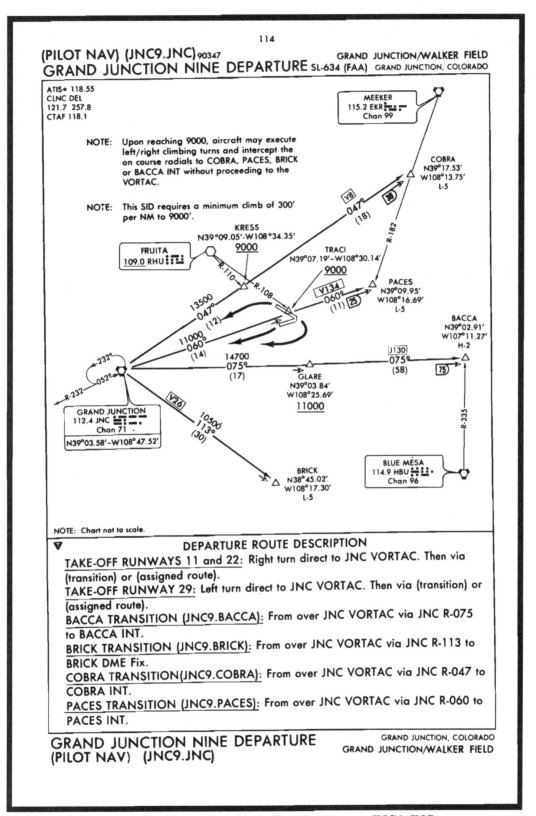

114

(PILOT NAV) (JNC9.JNC) 90347   GRAND JUNCTION/WALKER FIELD
GRAND JUNCTION NINE DEPARTURE SL-634 (FAA)   GRAND JUNCTION, COLORADO

ATIS* 118.55
CLNC DEL
121.7 257.8
CTAF 118.1

NOTE: Upon reaching 9000, aircraft may execute left/right climbing turns and intercept the on course radials to COBRA, PACES, BRICK or BACCA INT without proceeding to the VORTAC.

NOTE: This SID requires a minimum climb of 300' per NM to 9000'.

NOTE: Chart not to scale.

DEPARTURE ROUTE DESCRIPTION

TAKE-OFF RUNWAYS 11 and 22: Right turn direct to JNC VORTAC. Then via (transition) or (assigned route).

TAKE-OFF RUNWAY 29: Left turn direct to JNC VORTAC. Then via (transition) or (assigned route).

BACCA TRANSITION (JNC9.BACCA): From over JNC VORTAC via JNC R-075 to BACCA INT.

BRICK TRANSITION (JNC9.BRICK): From over JNC VORTAC via JNC R-113 to BRICK DME Fix.

COBRA TRANSITION(JNC9.COBRA): From over JNC VORTAC via JNC R-047 to COBRA INT.

PACES TRANSITION (JNC9.PACES): From over JNC VORTAC via JNC R-060 to PACES INT.

GRAND JUNCTION NINE DEPARTURE   GRAND JUNCTION, COLORADO
(PILOT NAV) (JNC9.JNC)   GRAND JUNCTION/WALKER FIELD

FIGURE 23.—Grand Junction Nine Departure (JNC9.JNC).

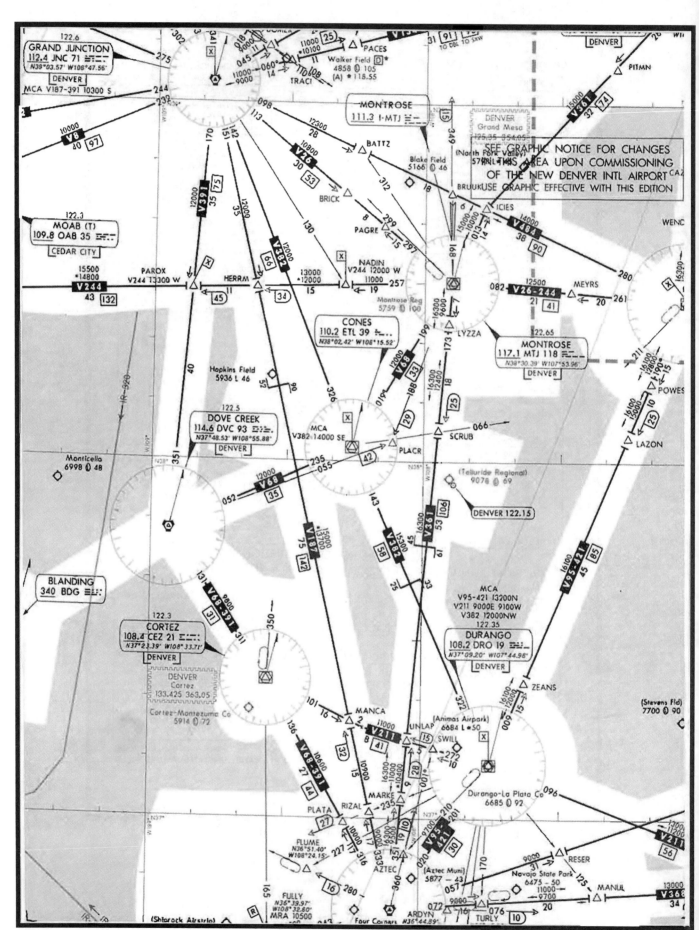

FIGURE 24.—En Route Low-Altitude Chart Segment.

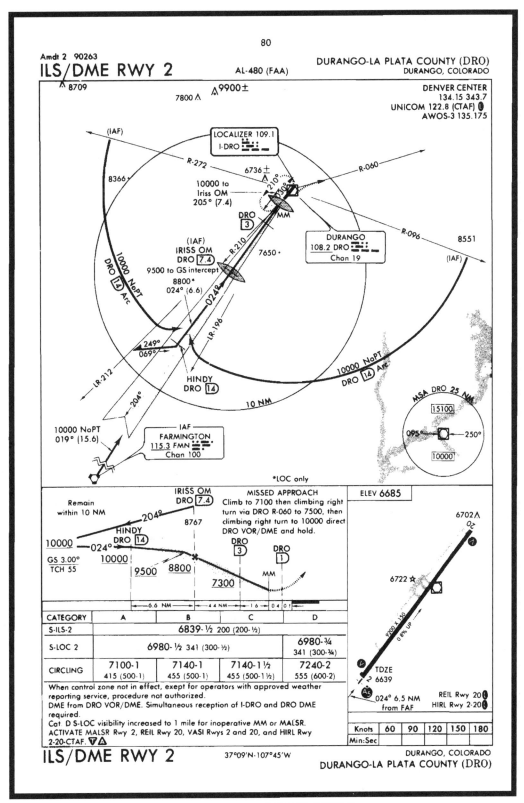

FIGURE 25.—ILS/DME RWY 2.

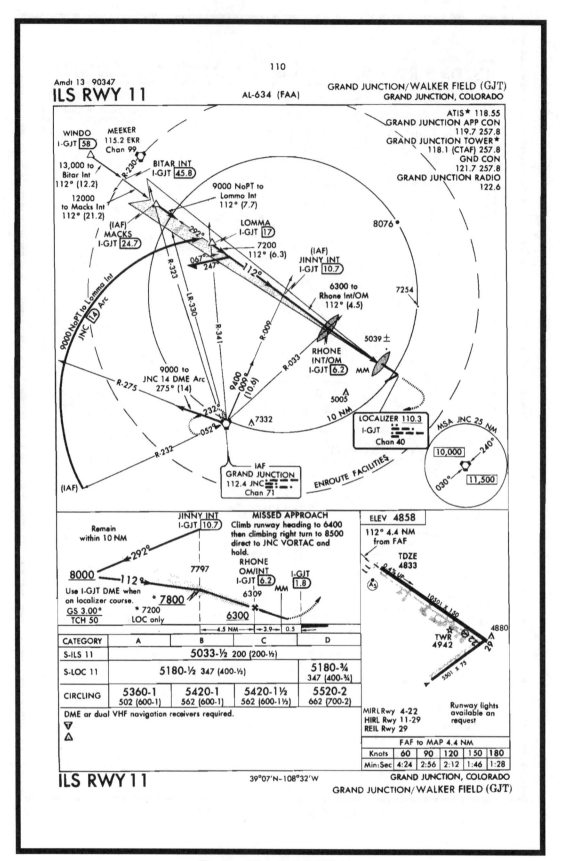

FIGURE 26.—ILS RWY 11.

Form Approved: OMB No. 2120-0034

U.S. DEPARTMENT OF TRANSPORTATION FEDERAL AVIATION ADMINISTRATION **FLIGHT PLAN**	(FAA USE ONLY)	☐ PILOT BRIEFING ☐ STOPOVER	☐ VNR	TIME STARTED	SPECIALIST INITIALS

1. TYPE	2. AIRCRAFT IDENTIFICATION	3. AIRCRAFT TYPE/ SPECIAL EQUIPMENT	4. TRUE AIRSPEED	5. DEPARTURE POINT	6. DEPARTURE TIME		7. CRUISING ALTITUDE
					PROPOSED (Z)	ACTUAL (Z)	
VFR							
X IFR	N132SM	C 182/	155 KTS	MFR			8,000
DVFR							

8. ROUTE OF FLIGHT

GNATS 6 , MOURN, V121 EUG

9. DESTINATION (Name of airport and city)	10. EST. TIME ENROUTE		11. REMARKS
	HOURS	MINUTES	
MAHLON/SWEET FIELD, EUGENE, OR.			INSTRUMENT TRAINING FLIGHT

12. FUEL ON BOARD		13. ALTERNATE AIRPORT(S)	14. PILOT'S NAME, ADDRESS & TELEPHONE NUMBER & AIRCRAFT HOME BASE	15. NUMBER ABOARD
HOURS	MINUTES			
			17. DESTINATION CONTACT/TELEPHONE (OPTIONAL)	

16. COLOR OF AIRCRAFT	N/R	CIVIL AIRCRAFT PILOTS. FAR Part 91 requires you file an IFR flight plan to operate under instrument flight rules in controlled airspace. Failure to file could result in a civil penalty not to exceed $1,000 for each violation (Section 901 of the Federal Aviation Act of 1958, as amended). Filing of a VFR flight plan is recommended as a good operating practice. See also Part 99 for requirements concerning DVFR flight plans.

FAA Form 7233-1 (8-82)

CLOSE VFR FLIGHT PLAN WITH _____ FSS ON ARRIVAL

AIRCRAFT INFORMATION

MAKE CESSNA   MODEL 182

N 132SM   Vso 57

AIRCRAFT EQUIPMENT/STATUS**

**NOTE: X= OPERATIVE   INOP= INOPERATIVE   N/A= NOT APPLICABLE
TRANSPONDER: X (MODE C) X ILS: (LOCALIZER) X (GLIDE SLOPE) N/A
VOR NO. 1 X (NO. 2) X ADF: X RNAV: N/A
VERTICAL PATH COMPUTER: NA DME: X
MARKER BEACON: (AUDIO) INOP (VISUAL) Inop.

FIGURE 27.—Flight Plan and Aircraft Information.

FLIGHT LOG

MEDFORD - JACKSON CO. AIRPORT TO HAHLON/SWEET FIELD, EUGENE, OR.

| CHECK POINTS | | ROUTE | COURSE | WIND | SPEED-KTS | | DIST | TIME | | FUEL | |
FROM	TO	ALTITUDE		TEMP	TAS	GS	NM	LEG	TOT	LEG	TOT
MFR	MERLI	GNATS 6 CLIMB	270°		155			:11:0			
	MOURN	V121 8000	333°			AVER. 135					
	RBG	V121 8000	287°								
	OTH	V121 8000	272°								
	EUG	APPROACH DESCENT	026°								
APPROACH & LANDING								:10:0			
	SWEET FIELD										

OTHER DATA:
　　NOTE:

　　　　MAG. VAR. 20' E.
　　　　AVERAGE G.S. 135 KTS. FOR GNATS 1
　　　　DEPARTURE CLIMB.

FLIGHT SUMMARY

TIME	FUEL (LB)	
		EN ROUTE
		RESERVE
		MISSED APPR.
		TOTAL

FIGURE 28.—Flight Planning Log.

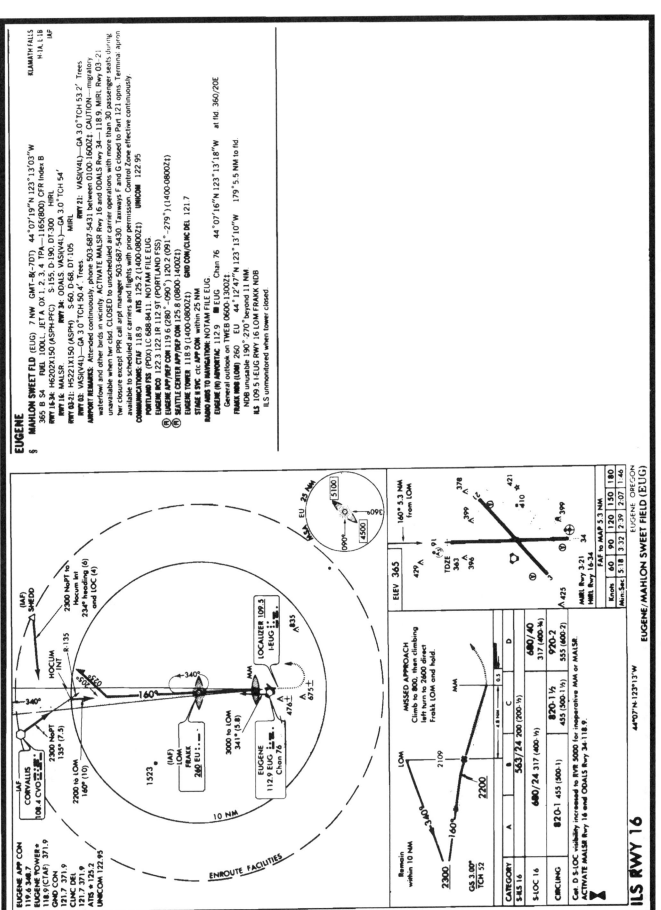

FIGURE 29.—ILS RWY 16 (EUG) and Excerpt from Airport/Facility Directory.

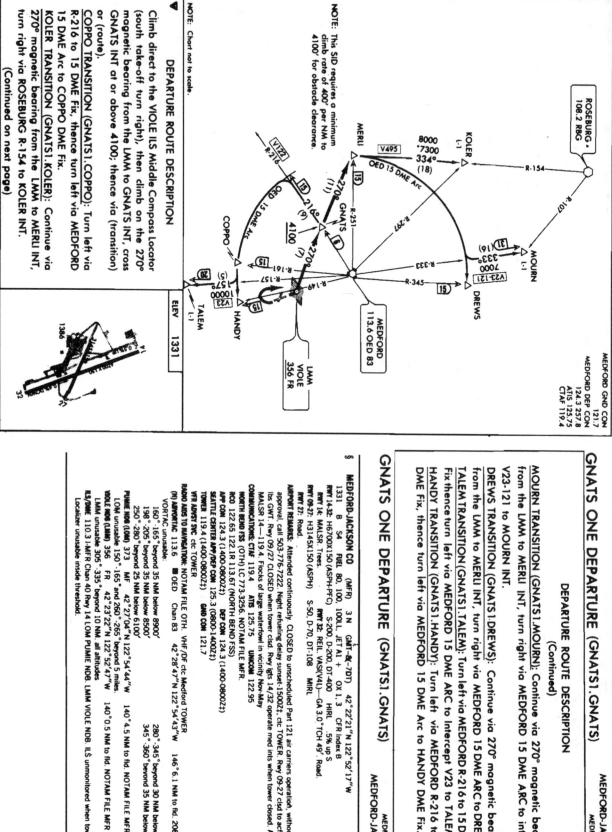

GNATS ONE DEPARTURE (GNATS1.GNATS)

DEPARTURE ROUTE DESCRIPTION

Climb direct to the VIOLE ILS Middle Compass Locator (south take-off turn right), then climb on the 270° magnetic bearing from the LMM to GNATS INT, cross GNATS INT at or above 4100; thence via (transition) or (route).

COPPO TRANSITION (GNATS1.COPPO): Turn left via R-216 to 15 DME Fix, thence turn left via MEDFORD 15 DME Arc to COPPO DME Fix.

KOLER TRANSITION (GNATS1.KOLER): Continue via 270° magnetic bearing from the LMM to MERLI INT, turn right via ROSEBURG R-154 to KOLER INT.

(Continued on next page)

FIGURE 30.—GNATS One Departure and Excerpt from Airport/Facility Directory.

NOTE: Chart not to scale.

▲ DEPARTURE ROUTE DESCRIPTION

NOTE: This SID requires a minimum climb rate of 400' per NM to 4100' for obstacle clearance.

GNATS ONE DEPARTURE (GNATS1.GNATS)

DEPARTURE ROUTE DESCRIPTION
(Continued)

MOURN TRANSITION (GNATS1.MOURN): Continue via 270° magnetic bearing from the LMM to MERLI INT, turn right via MEDFORD 15 DME ARC to intercept V23-121 to MOURN INT.

DREWS TRANSITION (GNATS1.DREWS): Continue via 270° magnetic bearing from the LMM to MERLI INT, turn right via MEDFORD 15 DME ARC to DREWS INT.

TALEM TRANSITION (GNATS1.TALEM): Turn left via MEDFORD R-216 to 15 DME Fix thence turn left via MEDFORD 15 DME ARC to intercept V23 to TALEM INT.

HANDY TRANSITION (GNATS1.HANDY): Turn left via MEDFORD R-216 to 15 DME Fix, thence turn left via MEDFORD 15 DME Arc to HANDY DME Fix.

MEDFORD-JACKSON CO
MEDFORD, OREGON

GNATS ONE DEPARTURE (GNATS1.GNATS)

MEDFORD-JACKSON CO
MEDFORD, OREGON

§ **MEDFORD-JACKSON CO**   (MFR)   3 N   GMT−8(−7DT)   42°22'21"N 122°52'17"W   KLAMATH FALLS
1331 B S4 FUEL 80, 100, 100LL, JET A1 + OX 1, 3 CFR Index B   H-1A, L-1A
RWY 14-32: H6700X150 (ASPH-PFC). S-200, D-200, DT-400   HIRL   .5% up S   IAP
RWY 14: MALSR. Trees.   RWY 32: REIL VASI(V4L)—GA 3.0° TCH 49'. Road.
RWY 09-27: H3145X150 (ASPH)   S-50, D-70, DT-108   MIRL
RWY 27: Road.
AIRPORT REMARKS: Attended continuously. CLOSED to unscheduled Part 121 air carriers operation, without prior approval, call 503-776-7222. Night refueling delay sunset-1500‡, ctc TOWER. Rwy lgts 14/32 operate med ints when tower closed. ACTIVATE its GWT. Rwy 09/27 CLOSED when tower clsd. Flocks of large waterfowl in vicinity Nov-May.
COMMUNICATIONS: CTAF 119.4 ATIS 125.75   UNICOM 122.95
NORTH BEND FSS (OTH) LC 773-3256. NOTAM FILE MFR.
RCO 122.65 122.1R 113.6T (NORTH BEND FSS)
APP CON 124.3 (1400-0800‡)   DEP CON 125.3 (0800-1400‡)
SEATTLE CENTER APP/DEP CON 125.3 (1400-0800‡)
TOWER 119.4 (1400-0800‡)   GND CON 121.7
VFR ADVSY SVC ctc TOWER
RADIO AIDS TO NAVIGATION: NOTAM FILE OTH. VHF/DF ctc Medford TOWER
(N) AIRPORT/VORTAC 113.6   ® OED   Chan 83   42°28'47"N 122°54'43"W   146° 6.1 NM to fld. 2080/19E
   VORTAC unusable:
      160°-165° beyond 35 NM below 8900'   280°-345° beyond 30 NM below 6500'
      198°-205° beyond 35 NM below 8500'   345°-360° beyond 35 NM below 6800'
      250°-280° beyond 25 NM below 6100'
PUMIE NDB (LOM) 373   MF   42°27'04"N 122°54'44"w   140° 4.5 NM to fld. NOTAM FILE MFR
   LOM unusable 150°-165° and 260°-265° beyond 5 miles.
VIOLE NDB (LMM) 356   FR   42°23'22"N 122°52'47"W   140° 0.5 NM to fld. NOTAM FILE MFR
   LMM unusable 305°-335° beyond 10 NM all altitudes
ILS/DME 110.31-MFR Chan 40 Rwy 14 LOM PUMIE NDB. LMM VIOLE NDB. ILS unmonitored when tower closed.
   Localizer unusable inside threshold.

MEDFORD, OREGON
MEDFORD-JACKSON CO

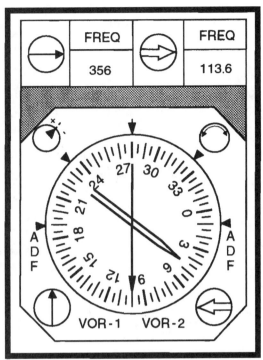

FIGURE 30A.—RMI Indicator.

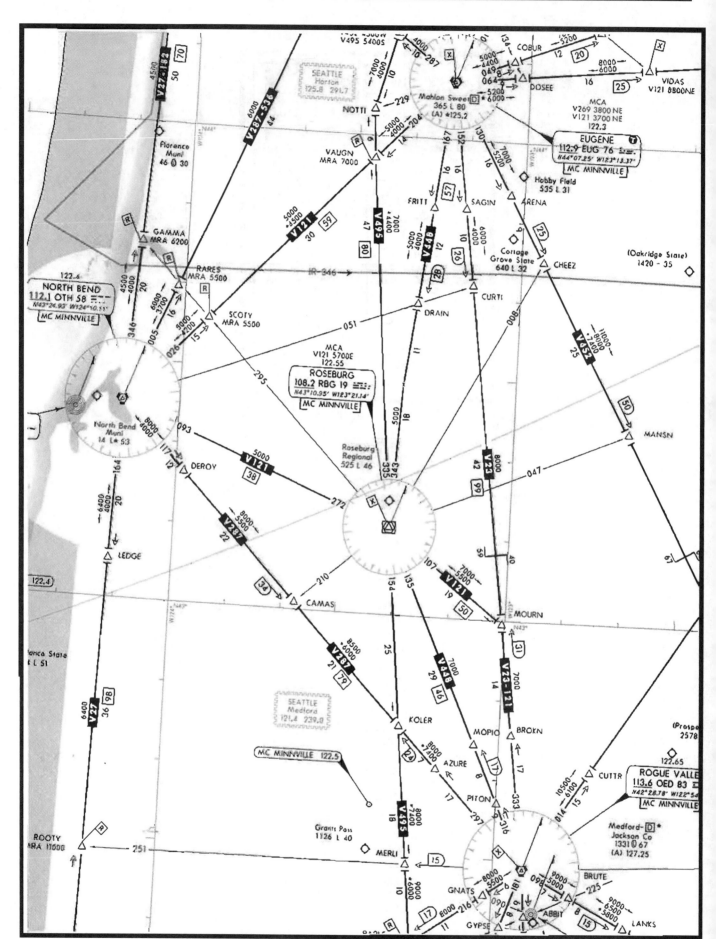

FIGURE 31.—En Route Low-Altitude Chart Segment.

Form Approved: OMB No. 2120-0034

U.S. DEPARTMENT OF TRANSPORTATION FEDERAL AVIATION ADMINISTRATION **FLIGHT PLAN**	(FAA USE ONLY)	☐ PILOT BRIEFING ☐ STOPOVER	☐ VNR	TIME STARTED	SPECIALIST INITIALS

1. TYPE	2. AIRCRAFT IDENTIFICATION	3. AIRCRAFT TYPE/ SPECIAL EQUIPMENT	4. TRUE AIRSPEED	5. DEPARTURE POINT	6. DEPARTURE TIME		7. CRUISING ALTITUDE
VFR					PROPOSED (Z)	ACTUAL (Z)	
X IFR DVFR	N4078A	PA 31/	180 KTS	HOT			8,000

8. ROUTE OF FLIGHT

HOT V573, TXK, TXK.BUJ3

9. DESTINATION (Name of airport and city)	10. EST. TIME ENROUTE		11. REMARKS
DALLAS ADDISON AIRPORT DALLAS, TX	HOURS	MINUTES	

12. FUEL ON BOARD		13. ALTERNATE AIRPORT(S)	14. PILOT'S NAME, ADDRESS & TELEPHONE NUMBER & AIRCRAFT HOME BASE	15. NUMBER ABOARD
HOURS	MINUTES			
		N/A	17. DESTINATION CONTACT/TELEPHONE (OPTIONAL)	2

16. COLOR OF AIRCRAFT TAN/WHITE	CIVIL AIRCRAFT PILOTS. FAR Part 91 requires you file an IFR flight plan to operate under instrument flight rules in controlled airspace. Failure to file could result in a civil penalty not to exceed $1,000 for each violation (Section 901 of the Federal Aviation Act of 1958, as amended). Filing of a VFR flight plan is recommended as a good operating practice. See also Part 99 for requirements concerning DVFR flight plans.

FAA Form 7233-1 (8-82)   CLOSE VFR FLIGHT PLAN WITH _____ FSS ON ARRIVAL

AIRCRAFT INFORMATION

MAKE Piper   MODEL PA-31

N 4078A   Vso 74

AIRCRAFT EQUIPMENT/STATUS**

**NOTE: X= OPERATIVE   INOP= INOPERATIVE   N/A= NOT APPLICABLE
TRANSPONDER: X (MODE C) X ILS: (LOCALIZER) X (GLIDE SLOPE) X
VOR NO. 1 X (NO. 2) X ADF: X RNAV: X
VERTICAL PATH COMPUTER: N/A DME: X
MARKER BEACON: X (AUDIO) X (VISUAL) X

FIGURE 32.—Flight Plan and Aircraft Information.

FLIGHT LOG

HOT SPRINGS, MEMORIAL FIELD TO DALLAS, ADDISON, TX.

CHECK POINTS		ROUTE		WIND	SPEED-KTS		DIST	TIME		FUEL	
FROM	TO	ALTITUDE	COURSE	TEMP	TAS	GS	NM	LEG	TOT	LEG	TOT
HOT	MARKI	V573 CLIMB	221°					:12:00			
	TXK	V573 8000	210°		180						
	TXK BUJ3	BUJ3 8000	272°								
	BUJ3	BUJ3 DESCENT	239°								
APPROACH & LANDING								:10:00			
	DALLAS ADDISON										

OTHER DATA:
NOTE: MAG. VAR. 4° E.

FLIGHT SUMMARY

TIME	FUEL (LB)	
		EN ROUTE
		RESERVE
		MISSED APPR.
		TOTAL

FIGURE 33.—Flight Planning Log.

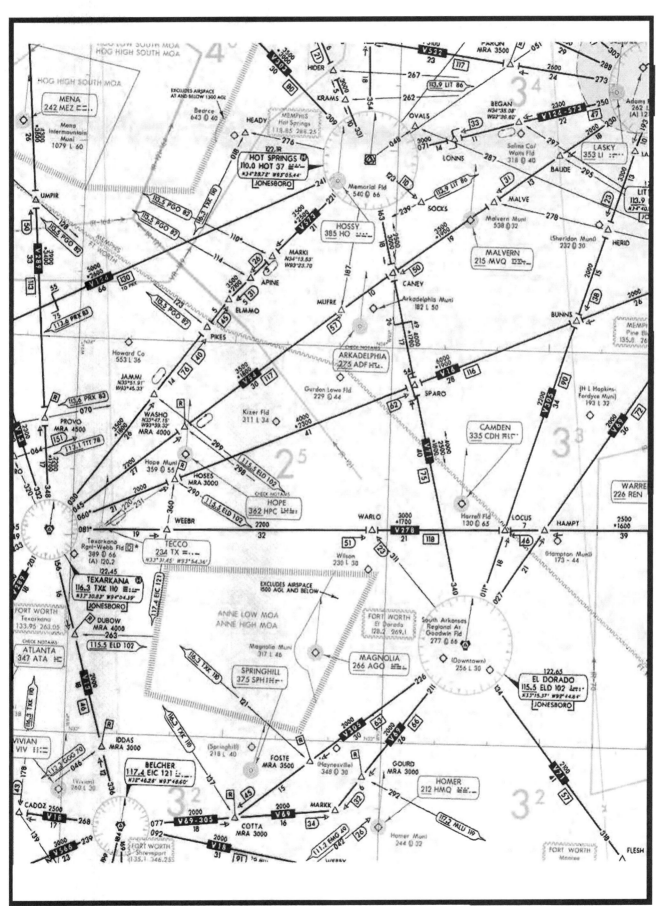

FIGURE 34.—En Route Chart.

ARKANSAS

HOT SPRINGS
   MEMORIAL FLD   (HOT)   3 SW   UTC–6(–5DT)   34°28′41″N 93°05′46″W   **MEMPHIS**
    540   B   S4   FUEL 100LL, JET A   ARFF Index Ltd.   **H-4G, L-14E**
   RWY 05-23: H6595X150 (ASPH-GRVD)   S-75, D-125, DT-210, DDT-400.   HIRL   0.6% up NE   **IAP**
    RWY 05: MALSR. Tree.   **RWY 23:** REIL. Thld dsplcd 490′. Tree.
   RWY 13-31: H4099X150 (ASPH)   S-28, D-36, DT-63   MIRL
    RWY 13: REIL. Road/Trees.   **RWY 31:** Pole.
   AIRPORT REMARKS: Attended 1130-0400Z‡. CLOSED to unscheduled air carrier ops with more than 30 passenger
    seats except PPR, call arpt manager 501–624–3306. Last 500′ Rwy 05 CLOSED to takeoffs. Rwy 13-31 fair
    with extensive loose grvl-pavement debris. ACTIVATE HIRL Rwy 05–23 and MALSR Rwy 05—CTAF. Rwy 23 REIL
    out of svc indefinitely. Control Zone effective 1200–0400Z‡.
   COMMUNICATIONS: CTAF/UNICOM 123.0
    JONESBORO FSS (JBR) TF 1–800–WX–BRIEF. NOTAM FILE HOT.
    HOT SPRINGS RCO 122.1R 110.0T (LITTLE ROCK FSS)
    MEMPHIS CENTER APP/DEP CON: 118.85
   RADIO AIDS TO NAVIGATION: NOTAM FILE HOT.
    HOT SPRINGS (L) VOR/DME 110.0   HOT   Chan 37   34°28′43″N 93°05′26″W   at fld. 530/4E.
    HOSSY NDB (HW/LOM) 385   HO   34°25′21″N 93°11′22″W   050° 5.7 NM to fld.
    ILS/DME 111.5 I-HOT Chan 52 Rwy 05 LOM HOSSY NDB. Unmonitored.

Figure 34A.—Airport/Facility Directory (HOT).

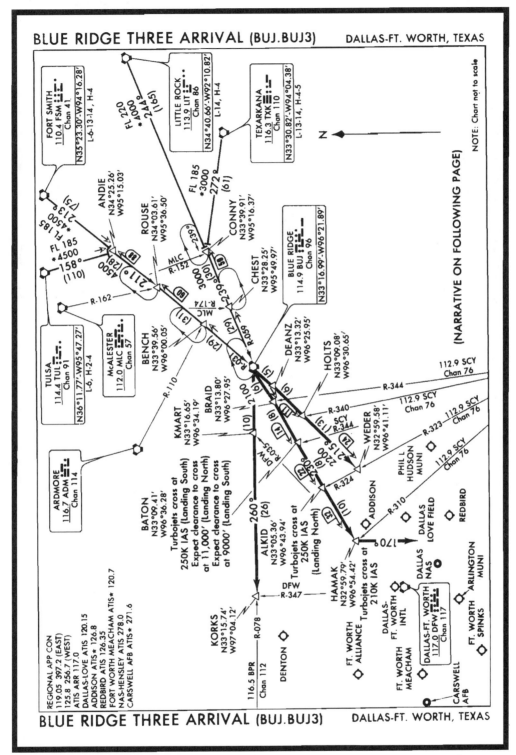

FIGURE 35.—En Route Chart Segment and Blue Ridge Three Arrival.

91094   SL-6039 (FAA)
BLUE RIDGE THREE ARRIVAL (BUJ.BUJ3)   DALLAS-FT. WORTH, TEXAS

ARRIVAL DESCRIPTION

<u>FORT SMITH TRANSITION (FSM.BUJ3):</u> From over FSM VORTAC via FSM R-213
and BUJ R-031 to BUJ VORTAC. Thence . . . .
<u>LITTLE ROCK TRANSITION (LIT.BUJ3):</u> From over LIT VORTAC via LIT R-244
and BUJ R-059 to BUJ VORTAC. Thence . . . .
<u>TEXARKANA TRANSITION (TXK.BUJ3):</u> From over TXK VORTAC via TXK R-272
and BUJ R-059 to BUJ VORTAC. Thence . . . .
<u>TULSA TRANSITION (TUL.BUJ3):</u> From over TUL VORTAC via TUL R-158 and
BUJ R-031 to BUJ VORTAC. Thence . . . .
<u>TURBOJETS LANDING DALLAS-FT WORTH INTL:</u> (Landing South): From over
BUJ VORTAC via BUJ R-230 to HAMAK INT. Expect vectors at BATON INT.
(Landing North): From over BUJ VORTAC via BUJ R-230 to HAMAK INT, thence
heading 170° for vector to final approach course.
<u>NON-TURBOJETS LANDING DALLAS-FT WORTH INTL:</u> (Landing South): From
over BUJ VORTAC via BUJ R-230 to HAMAK INT. Expect vectors at BATON
INT. (Landing North): From over BUJ VORTAC via BUJ R-215 to WEDER INT.
Expect vectors to final approach course.
<u>ALL AIRCRAFT LANDING DALLAS-LOVE FIELD, ADDISON, REDBIRD, NAS
DALLAS, and PHIL L. HUDSON:</u> (Landing South/North): From over BUJ VORTAC
via BUJ R-215 to WEDER INT. Expect vectors to final approach course.
<u>ALL AIRCRAFT LANDING MEACHAM, CARSWELL AFB, ALLIANCE, ARL-
INGTON, DENTON and FT. WORTH SPINKS:</u> (Landing South/North): From over
BUJ VORTAC via BUJ R-260 to KORKS INT. Expect vectors to final approach
course.

FIGURE 35A.—Blue Ridge Three Arrival Description.

TEXAS   1·15

DALLAS
ADDISON (ADS) 9 N UTC–6(–5DT) 32°58'06"N 96°50'10"W   DALLAS-FT. WORTH
  643 B S4 FUEL 100LL, JET A   H-2K, 4F, 5B, L-13C, A
  RWY 15-33: H7201X100 (ASPH) S-80, D-100, DT-160 MIRL   IAP
    RWY 15: MALSR. VASI(V4R)—GA 3.0°TCH 51'. Thld dsplcd 980'. Ground.
    RWY 33: REIL. Thld dsplcd 468'. Road.
    AIRPORT REMARKS: Attended continuously. Numerous flocks of birds on and in vicinity of arpt. Use extreme care:
      numerous 200' AGL buildings within 1 mile East, and South of arpt, transmission towers and water tanks West of
      arpt. Rwy 33 REIL out of svc indefinitely. ACTIVATE MALSR Rwy 15—CTAF. Rwy limited to maximum gross
      weight 120,000 pounds. Control Zone effective 1200-0400Z‡.
    WEATHER DATA SOURCES: LAWRS
    COMMUNICATIONS: CTAF 121.1   ATIS 126.8 (1200-0400Z‡)   UNICOM 122.95
      FORT WORTH FSS (FTW) TF 1–800–WX–BRIEF. NOTAM FILE ADS.
    ®REGIONAL APP CON 123.9   ® REGIONAL DEP CON 124.3
      TOWER 121.1 (1200-0400Z‡)   GND CON 121.6   CLNC DEL 119.55
    RADIO AIDS TO NAVIGATION: NOTAM FILE DAL.
      LOVE (L) VORW/DME 114.3   LUE   Chan 90   32°50'51"N 96°51'42"W   002° 7.4 NM to fld. 490/08E.
      BRONS NDB (LOM) 407   AD   33°02'40"N 96°52'13"W   153° 4.9 NM to fld.
      ILS/DME 110.1 I-ADS Chan 38 Rwy 15. LOM BRONS NDB. Unmonitored when tower closed.
      ILS 110.1 I-TBQ Rwy 33 LOC only. Unmonitored when twr clsd.

FIGURE 36.—Excerpt from Airport/Facility Directory.

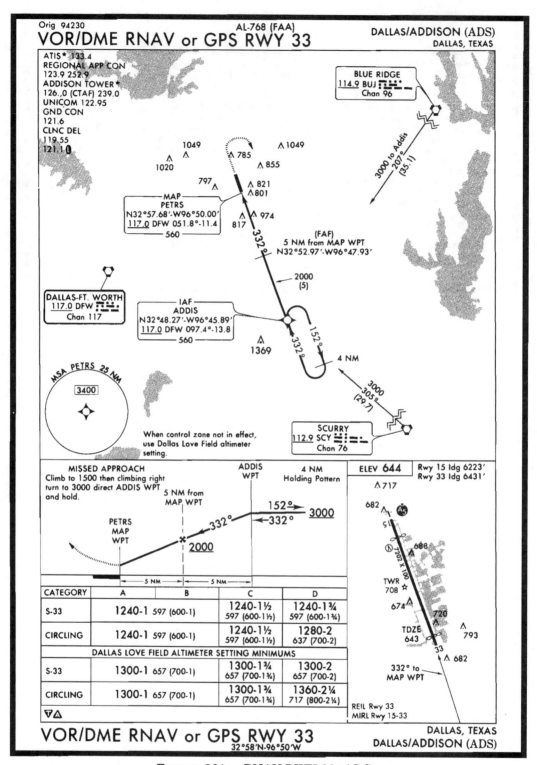

FIGURE 36A.—RNAV RWY 33 (ADS).

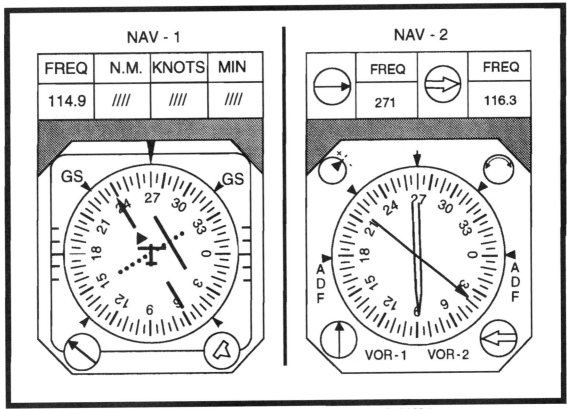

FIGURE 37.—CDI and RMI — NAV 1 and NAV 2.

Form Approved: OMB No. 2120-0034

U.S. DEPARTMENT OF TRANSPORTATION FEDERAL AVIATION ADMINISTRATION **FLIGHT PLAN**	(FAA USE ONLY)	□ PILOT BRIEFING □ STOPOVER	□ VNR	TIME STARTED	SPECIALIST INITIALS

1. TYPE	2. AIRCRAFT IDENTIFICATION	3. AIRCRAFT TYPE/ SPECIAL EQUIPMENT	4. TRUE AIRSPEED	5. DEPARTURE POINT	6. DEPARTURE TIME		7. CRUISING ALTITUDE
					PROPOSED (Z)	ACTUAL (Z)	
VFR							
X IFR	N4321P	C402/	156 KTS	BGS			11000
DVFR							

8. ROUTE OF FLIGHT

DIRECT BGS, V16 ABI, ABI.AQN2

9. DESTINATION (Name of airport and city) DALLAS FT. WORTH DFW	10. EST. TIME ENROUTE		11. REMARKS
	HOURS	MINUTES	

12. FUEL ON BOARD		13. ALTERNATE AIRPORT(S)	14. PILOT'S NAME, ADDRESS & TELEPHONE NUMBER & AIRCRAFT HOME BASE	15. NUMBER ABOARD
HOURS	MINUTES		17. DESTINATION CONTACT/TELEPHONE (OPTIONAL)	2
		N/A		

16. COLOR OF AIRCRAFT RED/BLUE/WHITE	CIVIL AIRCRAFT PILOTS. FAR Part 91 requires you file an IFR flight plan to operate under instrument flight rules in controlled airspace. Failure to file could result in a civil penalty not to exceed $1,000 for each violation (Section 901 of the Federal Aviation Act of 1958, as amended). Filing of a VFR flight plan is recommended as a good operating practice. See also Part 99 for requirements concerning DVFR flight plans.

FAA Form 7233-1 (8-82)   CLOSE VFR FLIGHT PLAN WITH _____ FSS ON ARRIVAL

AIRCRAFT INFORMATION

MAKE Cessna   MODEL 402C

N 4321P   Vso 71

AIRCRAFT EQUIPMENT/STATUS**

**NOTE: X= OPERATIVE   INOP= INOPERATIVE   N/A= NOT APPLICABLE
TRANSPONDER: X (MODE C) X ILS: (LOCALIZER) X (GLIDE SLOPE) X
VOR NO. 1 X (NO. 2) X ADF: X RNAV: X
VERTICAL PATH COMPUTER: N/A DME: X
MARKER BEACON: X (AUDIO) X (VISUAL) X

FIGURE 38.—Flight Plan and Aircraft Information.

FLIGHT LOG

BIG SPRING McMAHON-WRINKLE TO DALLAS FT. WORTH (DFW)

CHECK POINTS		ROUTE		WIND	SPEED-KTS		DIST	TIME		FUEL	
FROM	TO	ALTITUDE	COURSE	TEMP	TAS	GS	NM	LEG	TOT	LEG	TOT
21XS	BGS	DIRECT CLIMB	DIRECT					:06:0			
	LORAN	V16 11,000	075°								
	ABI	V16 11,000	076°		156						
	COTTN	DIRECT 11,000	087°								
	AQN	AQN2	075°								
	CREEK	AQN2	040°								
APPROACH & LANDING		RADAR VEC-						:08:0			
	DFW AIRPORT	DESCENT									

OTHER DATA: NOTE:	MAG. VAR. 11° E. (STAR) ACTON TWO ARRIVAL (AQN2)	FLIGHT SUMMARY		
		TIME	FUEL (LB)	
				EN ROUTE
				RESERVE
				MISSED APPR.
				TOTAL

BIG SPRING McMAHON-WRINKLE   (21XS) 2SW UTC-6(-5DT).   **DALLAS-FT. WORTH**
H-21, 5A, L-13A, 15B
IAP

   32°12'45"N 101°31"17"W
2572 B S4FUEL 100LL, JET A
RWY 17-35: H8803X100 (ASPH-CONC) S-44, D-62, DDT-101 MIRL
   RWY 17:SSALS.PVASI(ASPH)-GA3.0°TCH 41'.
RWY 06-24:H4600X75(ASPH) MIRL
   RWY 24:PVASI(PSIL)-GA3.55°TCH31'. P-line.
AIRPORT REMARKS: Attended 1400-2300Z . For fuel after hours call 915-263-3958. ACTIVATE MIRL Rwy 06-24
   and Rwy 17-35, SSALS Rwy 17 and PVASI Rwy 17 and 24-CTAF.
COMMUNICATIONS:CTAF/UNICOM 122.8
   SAN ANGELOSFSS (SJT) TF 1-800-WX-BRIEF. NOTAM FILE SJT.
   RCO 122.4(SAN ANGELOFSS)
   FORT WORTH CENTER APP/DEP CON 133.7
RADIO AIDS TO NAVIGATION: NOTAM FILE SJT.
   (L) VORTACW 144.3 BGS Chan 90 32°23'08"N 101°10.5NM to fld. 2670/11E.

EXCERPT FROM AIRPORT/FACILITY DIRECTORY (21 XS)

FIGURE 39.—Flight Log and Excerpt from Airport/Facility Directory (21 XS).

HELENA REGIONAL   (HLN)   2 NE   UTC–7(–6DT)   46°36'25"N 111°58'55"W   **GREAT FALLS**
  3873   B   S4   FUEL 100LL, JET A   OX 1,3   AOE   ARFF Index B   **H–1C, L–9B**
  RWY 09-27: H9000X150 (ASPH-PFC)   S-100, D-160, DT-250   HIRL   IAP
    RWY 09: VASI(V4L)—GA 3.0°TCH 45'. Ground.   **RWY 27:** MALSR. VASI(V4L)—GA 3.0°TCH 55'. Rgt tfc.
  RWY 05-23: H4599X75 (ASPH-PFC)   S-21, D-30
    RWY 05: Road.   **RWY 23:** Fence. Rgt tfc.
  RWY 16-34: H2979X75 (ASPH)   S-21, D-30   MIRL
    RWY 34: Ground. Rgt tfc.
  AIRPORT REMARKS: Attended 1200-0800Z‡. East 2400' Taxiway C and first 900' Rwy 27 not visible from tower.
    Prior permission for unscheduled FAR 121 operations, Call 406-442-2821. AOE, 1 hour prior notice required,
    phone 449–1569 1500–0000Z‡, 0000–1500Z‡ 449–1024. Twys A;B; high speed and C (between A and D)
    not available for air carrier use by acft with greater than 30 passenger seats. Rwy 16–34 and Rwy 05–23 (except
    between Rwy 09–27 and Twy D) not available for air carrier use by acft with greater than 30 passenger seats.
    When tower closed, ACTIVATE HIRL Rwy 09–27 and MALSR Rwy 27—CTAF, when twr closed MIRL Rwy 16–34
    are off. Ldg fee for all acft over 12,500 lbs. NOTE: See SPECIAL NOTICE—Simultaneous Operations on
    Intersecting Runways.
  COMMUNICATIONS: CTAF 118.3   **ATIS** 120.4 (Mon-Fri 1300–0700Z‡, Sat-Sun 1300–0500Z‡)
    UNICOM 122.95
    GREAT FALLS FSS (GTF) TF 1-800-WX-BRIEF. NOTAM FILE HLN.
    RCO 122.2 122.1R 117.7T (GREAT FALLS FSS)
    APP/DEP CON 119.5 (Mon–Fri 1300–0700Z‡, Sat-Sun 1300–0500Z‡)
    SALT LAKE CENTER APP/DEP CON 133.4 (Mon–Fri 0700–1300Z‡, Sat-Sun 0500–1300Z‡)
    TOWER 118.3 (Mon–Fri 1300–0700Z‡, Sat-Sun 1300–0500Z‡)   **GND CON** 121.9
  RADIO AIDS TO NAVIGATION: NOTAM FILE HLN.
    (H) VORTAC 117.7   HLN   Chan 124   46°36'25"N 111°57'10"W   254° 1.2 NM to fld. 3810/16E.
      VORTAC unusable:
        006°-090° beyond 25 NM below 11,000'   091°-120° beyond 20 NM below 16,000'
        121°-240° beyond 25 NM below 10,000'   355°-006° beyond 15 NM below 17,500'
        241°-320° beyond 25 NM below 10,000'
    CAPITOL NDB (HW) 317   CVP   46°36'24"N 111°56'11"W   254° 1.9 NM to fld.
      NDB unmonitored when tower closed.
    HAUSER NDB (MHW) 386   HAU   46°34'08"N 111°45'26"W   268° 9.6 NM to fld.
    ILS 110.1 I-HLN Rwy 27 ILS unmonitored when tower closed.

Excerpt from Airport/Facility Directory (21 XS)

BIG SPRING McMAHON-WRINKLE   (21XS)   2 SW   UTC–6(–5DT).   **DALLAS-FT WORTH**
    32°12'45"N 101°31'17"W   **H-21, 5A, L-13A, 15B**
  2572   B   S4   FUEL 100LL, JET A   IAP
  RWY 17-35: H8803X100 (ASPH-CONC)   S–44, D–62, DDT–101   MIRL
    RWY 17: SSALS. PVASI (PSIL)—GA 3.0° TCH 41'.
  RWY 06-24: H4600X75 (ASPH)   MIRL
    RWY 24: PVASI (PSIL)—GA 3.55°TCH 31'. P-line.
  AIRPORT REMARKS: Attended 1400-2300Z‡. For fuel after hours call 915-263-3958. ACTIVATE MIRL Rwy 06–24
    and Rwy 17–35, SSALS Rwy 17 and PVASI Rwy 17 and 24—CTAF.
  COMMUNICATIONS: CTAF/UNICOM 122.8
    SAN ANGELO FSS (SJT) TF 1-800-WX-BRIEF. NOTAM FILE SJT.
    RCO 122.4 (SAN ANGELO FSS)
    FORT WORTH CENTER APP/DEP CON 133.7
  RADIO AIDS TO NAVIGATION: NOTAM FILE SJT.
    (L) VORTACW 114.3   BGS   Chan 90   32°23'08"N 101°29'00"W   180° 10.5 NM to fld. 2670/11E.

FIGURE 39A.—Excerpt from Airport/Facility Directory (21 XS).

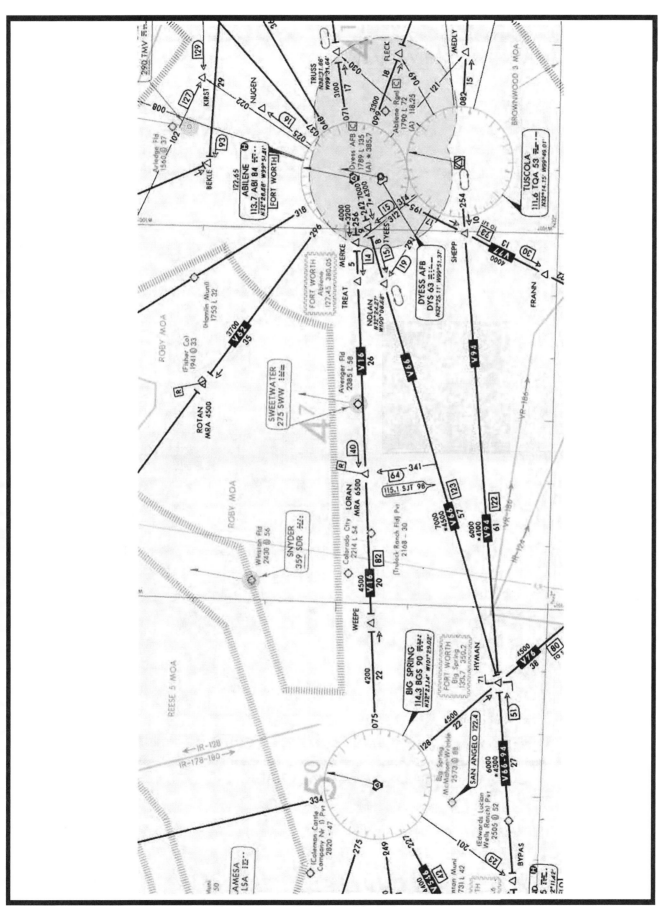

FIGURE 40.—En Route Chart Segment.

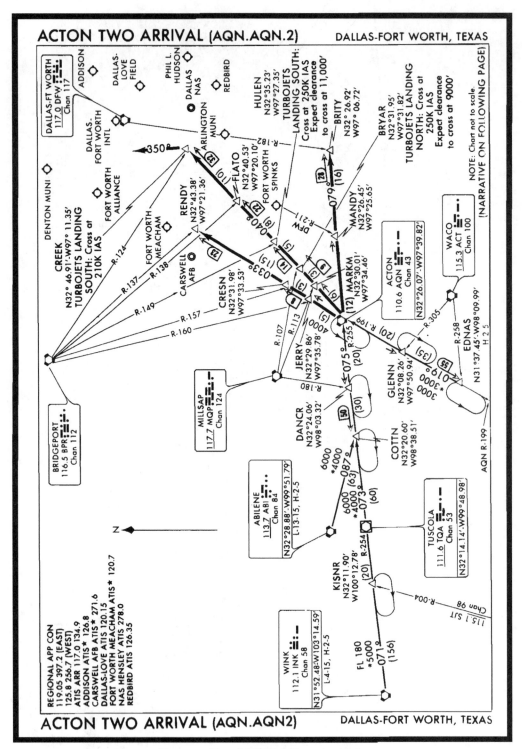

FIGURE 41.—ACTON Two Arrival.

ACTON TWO ARRIVAL (AQN.AQN2)

DALLAS-FORT WORTH, TEXAS

ARRIVAL DESCRIPTION

<u>ABILENE TRANSITION (ABI.AQN2)</u>: From over ABI VORTAC via ABI R-087 and AQN R-255 to AQN VORTAC. Thence . . . .
<u>EDNAS TRANSITION (EDNAS.AQN2)</u>: From over EDNAS INT via AQN R-199 to AQN VORTAC. Thence . . . .
<u>WINK TRANSITION (INK.AQN2)</u>: From over INK VORTAC via INK R-071, TQA R-254, TQA R-073 and AQN R-255 to AQN VORTAC. Thence . . . .
<u>TURBOJETS LANDING DALLAS-FT. WORTH INTL, MEACHAM, CARSWELL AFB, DENTON, ALLIANCE:</u> (Landing South): From over AQN VORTAC via AQN R-040 to CREEK INT, thence heading 350° for vector to final approach course. (Landing North): From over AQN VORTAC via AQN R-040 to CREEK INT. Expect vectors at BRYAR INT.
<u>NON-TURBOJETS LANDING DALLAS-FT. WORTH INTL, MEACHAM, CARSWELL AFB, DENTON, ALLIANCE:</u> (Landing South): From over AQN VORTAC via AQN R-033 to RENDY INT. Expect vectors to final approach course. (Landing North): From over AQN VORTAC via AQN R-040 to CREEK INT. Expect vector at BRYAR INT.
<u>TURBOJETS LANDING DALLAS-LOVE FIELD and ADDISON:</u> (Landing South): From over AQN VORTAC via AQN R-040 to CREEK INT, thence heading 350° for vector to final approach course. (Landing North): From over AQN VORTAC via AQN R-079 to BRITY INT. Expect vector to final approach course.
<u>NON-TURBOJETS LANDING DALLAS-LOVE FIELD and ADDISON:</u> (Landing South/North): From over AQN VORTAC via AQN R-079 to BRITY INT. Expect vector to final approach course.
<u>ALL AIRCRAFT LANDING FORT WORTH SPINKS, ARLINGTON, NAS DALLAS, REDBIRD, and PHIL L. HUDSON:</u> (Landing South/North): From over AQN VORTAC via AQN R-079 to BRITY INT. Expect vectors to final approach course.

FIGURE 41A.—ACTON Two Arrival Description.

TEXAS

- -

DALLAS-FORT WORTH INTL   (DFW)   12 NW   UTC–6(–5DT)32°53'47"N 97°02'28"W   'DALLAS–FT. WORTH
  603   B   FUEL   100LL, JET A   OX 1, 3   LRA   ARFF Index E   H-2K, 4F, 5B, L-13C, A
  RWY 17L-35R: H11,388X150 (CONC-GRVD)   S-120, D-200, DT-600, DDT-850   HIRL CL   IAP
    RWY 17L: ALSF2. TOZ.   RWY 35R: MALSR. TDZ.
  RWY 17R-35L: H11,388X200 (CONC-GRVD)   S-120, D-200, DT-600, DDT-850   HIRL CL
    RWY 17R: MALSR. TDZ.   RWY 35L: TDZ. VASI(V6L).
  RWY 18R-36L: H11,388X150(CONC-GRVD)   S-120, D-200, DT-600, DDT-850   HIRL CL
    RWY 18R: ALSF2. TDZ   RWY 36L: MALSR. TDZ
  RWY 18L-36R: H11,387X200 (CONC-GRVD)   S-120, D-200, DT-600, DDT-850   HIRL CL
    RWY 18L: MALSR. TDZ.   RWY 36R: TDZ. VASI(V6L).
  RWY 13R-31L: H9300X150(CONC-GRVD)   S-120, D-220, DT-600, DDT-850   HIRL CL
    RWY 13R: MALSR. TDZ.   RWY 31L: TDZ.
  RWY 13L-31R: H9000X200 (CONC-GRVD)   S-120, D-200, DT-600, DDT-850   HIRL CL   0,5% up NW
    RWY 13L: TDZ. VASI(V6L)—Upper GA 3.25° TCH 93'. Lower GA 3.0° TCH 47'.   RWY 31R: MALSR. TDZ.
  RWY 18S-36S: H4000X100 (CONC)
  AIRPORT REMARKS: Attended continuously. Rwy 18S–36S CLOSED indefinitely. Arpt under construction, men and
    equipment in movement areas. Partial outages of arpt lgt circuits will occur daily. Prior Permission Required from
    arpt ops for General Aviation acft to proceed to airline terminal gate except to General Aviation Facility. Rwy
    18S-36S located on taxiway G, 4000' long 100' wide restricted to prop acft 12,500 lbs. & below and stol acft
    daylight VFR plus IFR departures. Prior permission required from the primary tenant airlines to operate within
    central terminal area, CAUTION: proper minimum clearance may not be maintained within the central terminal
    area. Landing fee. Helipad H1 on apt 104X104 (CONC) Heliport located at Twy G and Twy 24 intersection,
    daylight VFR. Clearways 500X1000 each end Rwy 17L–35R, Rwy 17R–35L, Rwy 18L–36R and Rwy 18R–36L.
    Flight Notification Service (ADCUS) available.
  WEATHER DATA SOURCES: LLWAS.
  COMMUNICATIONS: ATIS 117.0 134.9 (ARR) 135.5 (DEP)   UNICOM 122.95
    FORT WORTH FSS (FTW) LC 429–6434. TF 1–800–WX–BRIEF. NOTAM FILE DFW
  ®REGIONAL APP CON 119.05(E) 119.4(E) 125.8(W) 132.1(W)
    REGIONAL TOWER 126.55 (E) 124.15 (W)   GND CON 121.65 133.15(E) 121.8 (W)   CLNC DEL 128.25 127.5
  ®REGIONAL DEP CON 118.55 (E) 124.25 (WEST) 127.75 (NORTH–SOUTH)
  TCA: See VFR Terminal Area chart.
  RADIO AIDS TO NAVIGATION: NOTAM FILE DFW.
    (H) VORTACW 117.0   DFW   Chan 117   32°51'57"N 97°01'40"W   at fld. 560/08E.
      VOR Portion unusable 045°-050° all altitudes and distances, 350°–100° beyond 30 NM below 2100'.
    ISSUE NDB (LOM) 233   PK   32°47'35"N 97°01'49"W   348° 6.2 NM to fld.
    JIFFY NDB (LOM) 219   FL   32°59'44"N 97°01'46"W   179° 6.0 NM to fld.
    ILS/DME 109.5 I-LWN Chan 32 Rwy 13R.
    ILS/DME 109.1 I-FLQ Chan 28 Rwy 17L. LOM JIFFY NDB.
    ILS 111.5 I-JHZ Rwy 17R. LOM JIFFY NDB.
    ILS 111.3 I-CIX Rwy 18L.
    ILS/DME 111.9 I-VYN Chan 56 Rwy 18R.
    ILS 110.9 I-RRA Rwy 31R.
    ILS/DME 109.1 I-PKQ Chan 28 Rwy 35R. LOM ISSUE NDB.
    ILS/DME 111.9 I-BXN Chan 56 Rwy 36L.

FIGURE 42.—ILS-1 RWY 36L, Dallas-Fort Worth Intl.

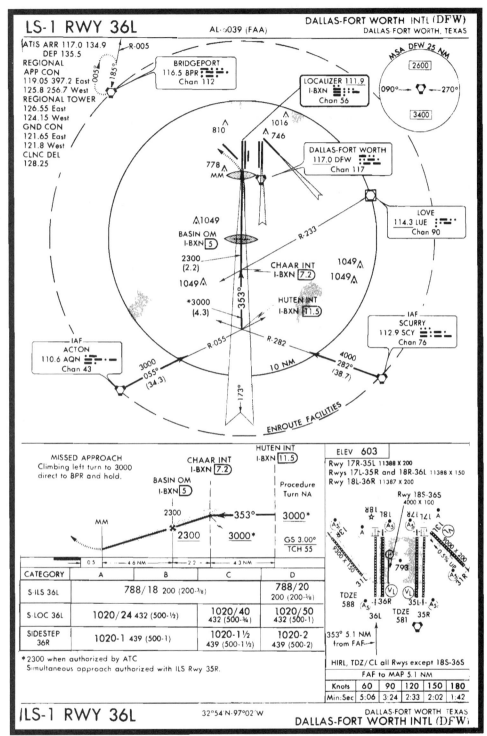

FIGURE 42A.—ILS RWY 36L.

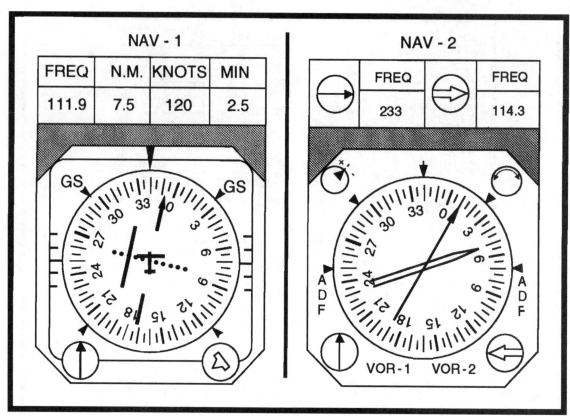

FIGURE 43.—CDI and RMI – NAV 1 and NAV 2.

Form Approved: OMB No. 2120-0034

U.S. DEPARTMENT OF TRANSPORTATION FEDERAL AVIATION ADMINISTRATION **FLIGHT PLAN**	(FAA USE ONLY)	☐ PILOT BRIEFING ☐ STOPOVER	☐ VNR	TIME STARTED	SPECIALIST INITIALS

1. TYPE	2. AIRCRAFT IDENTIFICATION	3. AIRCRAFT TYPE/ SPECIAL EQUIPMENT	4. TRUE AIRSPEED	5. DEPARTURE POINT	6. DEPARTURE TIME		7. CRUISING ALTITUDE
VFR					PROPOSED (Z)	ACTUAL (Z)	
X IFR DVFR	N3678A	PA31/	180 KTS	YKM			12000

8. ROUTE OF FLIGHT

GROMO 3, HITCH, V468 BTG, DIRECT

9. DESTINATION (Name of airport and city) PORTLAND INTL. AIRPORT PDX	10. EST. TIME ENROUTE		11. REMARKS
	HOURS	MINUTES	INSTRUMENT TRAINING FLIGHT

12. FUEL ON BOARD		13. ALTERNATE AIRPORT(S)	14. PILOT'S NAME, ADDRESS & TELEPHONE NUMBER & AIRCRAFT HOME BASE	15. NUMBER ABOARD
HOURS	MINUTES			
			17. DESTINATION CONTACT/TELEPHONE (OPTIONAL)	2
		N/A		

16. COLOR OF AIRCRAFT GOLD/WHITE	CIVIL AIRCRAFT PILOTS. FAR Part 91 requires you file an IFR flight plan to operate under instrument flight rules in controlled airspace. Failure to file could result in a civil penalty not to exceed $1,000 for each violation (Section 901 of the Federal Aviation Act of 1958, as amended). Filing of a VFR flight plan is recommended as a good operating practice. See also Part 99 for requirements concerning DVFR flight plans.

FAA Form 7233-1 (8-82)   CLOSE VFR FLIGHT PLAN WITH _____ FSS ON ARRIVAL

AIRCRAFT INFORMATION

MAKE Piper   MODEL PA-31

N 3678A   Vso 77

AIRCRAFT EQUIPMENT/STATUS**

**NOTE: X= OPERATIVE   INOP= INOPERATIVE   N/A= NOT APPLICABLE
TRANSPONDER: X (MODE C) X ILS: (LOCALIZER) X (GLIDE SLOPE) X
VOR NO. 1 X (NO. 2) X ADF: X RNAV: X
VERTICAL PATH COMPUTER: N/A DME: X
MARKER BEACON: X (AUDIO) INOP (VISUAL) X

FIGURE 44.—Flight Plan and Aircraft Information.

FLIGHT LOG

YAKIMA AIR TERMINAL TO PORTLAND, INTL.

| CHECK POINTS | | ROUTE | | WIND | SPEED-KTS | | DIST | TIME | | FUEL | |
FROM	TO	ALTITUDE	COURSE	TEMP	TAS	GS	NM	LEG	TOT	LEG	TOT
YKM	HITCH	GROMO 3 CLIMB	206°					:10.			
	VOR C.O.P.	V468 12,000	206°		180						
	BTG	V468 12,000	234°								
	PDX	DIRECT	160°								
APPROACH & LANDING								:13.			
	PDX AIRPORT										

OTHER DATA:
  NOTE: MAG. VAR. 20° E.

FLIGHT SUMMARY

TIME	FUEL (LB)	
		EN ROUTE
		RESERVE
		MISSED APPR.
		TOTAL

FIGURE 45.—Flight Planning Log.

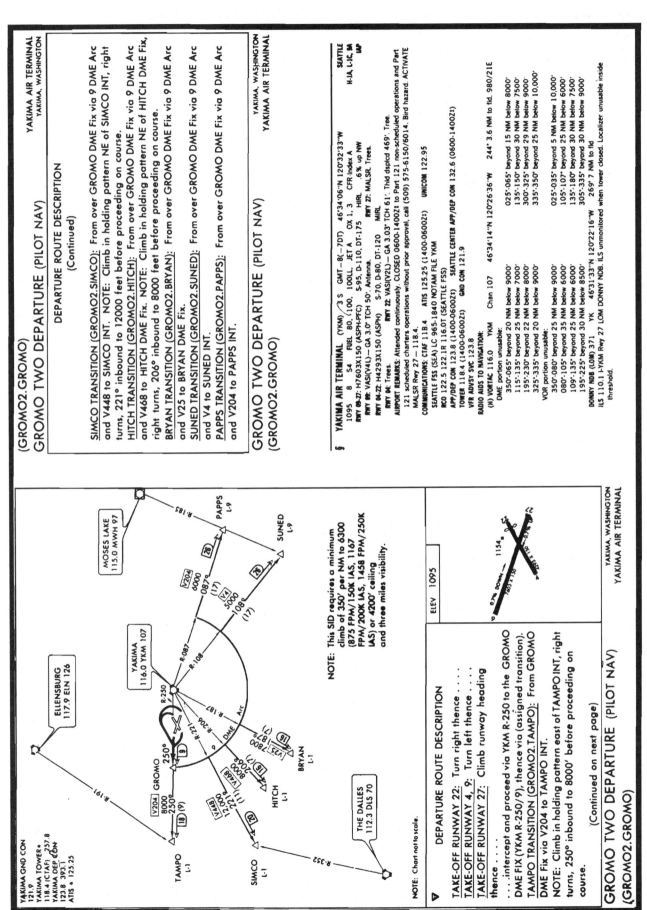

(GROMO2.GROMO)
GROMO TWO DEPARTURE (PILOT NAV)

DEPARTURE ROUTE DESCRIPTION
(Continued)

SIMCO TRANSITION (GROMO2.SIMCO): From over GROMO DME Fix via 9 DME Arc and V448 to SIMCO INT. NOTE: Climb in holding pattern NE of SIMCO INT, right turns, 221° inbound to 12000 feet before proceeding on course.
HITCH TRANSITION (GROMO2.HITCH): From over GROMO DME Fix via 9 DME Arc and V468 to HITCH DME Fix. NOTE: Climb in holding pattern NE of HITCH DME Fix, right turns, 206° inbound to 8000 feet before proceeding on course.
BRYAN TRANSITION (GROMO2.BRYAN): From over GROMO DME Fix via 9 DME Arc and V25 to BRYAN DME Fix.
SUNED TRANSITION (GROMO2.SUNED): From over GROMO DME Fix via 9 DME Arc and V4 to SUNED INT.
PAPPS TRANSITION (GROMO2.PAPPS): From over GROMO DME Fix via 9 DME Arc and V204 to PAPPS INT.

GROMO TWO DEPARTURE (PILOT NAV)
(GROMO2.GROMO)

---

§ **YAKIMA AIR TERMINAL** (YKM) /3 S GMT−8(−7DT) 46°34'06"N 120°32'33"W **SEATTLE**
1095 8 S4 FUEL 80, (100, 100LL, JET A OX 1, 3 CFR Index A H-1A, L-1C, 9A
RWY 09-27: H7603X150 (ASPH+PFC) S-95, D-110, DT-175 HIRL 6% up NW LAP
RWY 09: VASI(V4L) − GA 3.0° TCH 50'. Antenna. RWY 27: MALSR. Trees.
RWY 04-22: H4293X150 (ASPH) S-70, D-80, DT-120 MIRL
RWY 04: Trees. RWY 22: VASI(V2L) − GA 3.03° TCH 61'. Thld dsplcd 469'. Tree.
AIRPORT REMARKS: Attended continuously. CLOSED 0600-1400Z‡ to Part 121 non-scheduled operations and Part
121 scheduled charters operations without prior approval, call (509) 575-6150/6014. Bird hazard. ACTIVATE
MALSR Rwy 27 − 118.4.
COMMUNICATIONS: CTAF 118.4 ATIS 125.25 (1400-0600Z‡) UNICOM 122.95
SEATTLE FSS (SEA) LC 965-1840 NOTAM FILE YKM
RCO 122.5 122.1R 116.0T (SEATTLE FSS)
APP/DEP CON 123.8 (1400-0600Z‡) SEATTLE CENTER APP/DEP CON 132.6 (0600-1400Z‡)
TOWER 118.4 (1400-0600Z‡) GND CON 121.9
VFR ADVSY SVC 123.8
RADIO AIDS TO NAVIGATION:
(H) VORTAC 116.0 YKM Chan 107 46°34'14"N 120°26'36"W 244° 3.6 NM to fld. 980/21E
DME portion unusable:
350°-065° beyond 20 NM below 9000' 025°-065° beyond 15 NM below 8000'
115°-135° beyond 25 NM below 7000' 135°-150° beyond 30 NM below 7500'
195°-230° beyond 22 NM below 8000' 300°-325° beyond 29 NM below 9000'
325°-335° beyond 20 NM below 9000' 335°-350° beyond 25 NM below 10,000'
VOR portion unusable:
350°-080° beyond 20 NM below 9000' 025°-035° beyond 5 NM below 10,000'
080°-105° beyond 35 NM below 6000' 105°-107° beyond 25 NM below 6000'
109°-135° beyond 25 NM below 6000' 135°-180° beyond 30 NM below 7500'
195°-225° beyond 30 NM below 8500' 305°-335° beyond 30 NM below 9000'
DONNY NDB (LOM) 371 YK 46°31'33"N 120°22'16"W 269° 7 NM to fld
ILS 110.1 I-YKM Rwy 27 LOM DONNY NDB. ILS unmonitored when tower closed. Localizer unusable inside
threshold.

YAKIMA GND CON
121.9
YAKIMA TOWER*
118.4 (CTAF) 257.8
YAKIMA DEP CON
123.8 * 125.25
ATIS * 125.25

ELEV 1095

NOTE: This SID requires a minimum climb of 350' per NM to 6300 (875 FPM/150K IAS, 1167 FPM/200K IAS, 1458 FPM/250K IAS) or 4200' ceiling and three miles visibility.

NOTE: Chart not to scale.

▽ DEPARTURE ROUTE DESCRIPTION

TAKE-OFF RUNWAY 22: Turn right thence . . . . .
TAKE-OFF RUNWAY 4, 9: Turn left thence . . . . .
TAKE-OFF RUNWAY 27: Climb runway heading thence . . . .
. . . intercept and proceed via YKM R-250 to the GROMO DME FIX (YKM R-250/9), thence via (assigned transition).
TAMPO TRANSITION (GROMO2.TAMPO): From GROMO DME Fix via V204 to TAMPO INT.
NOTE: Climb in holding pattern east of TAMPO INT, right turns, 250° inbound to 8000' before proceeding on course.
(Continued on next page)

GROMO TWO DEPARTURE (PILOT NAV)
(GROMO2.GROMO)

FIGURE 46.—GROMO Two Departure and Excerpt from Airport/Facility Directory.

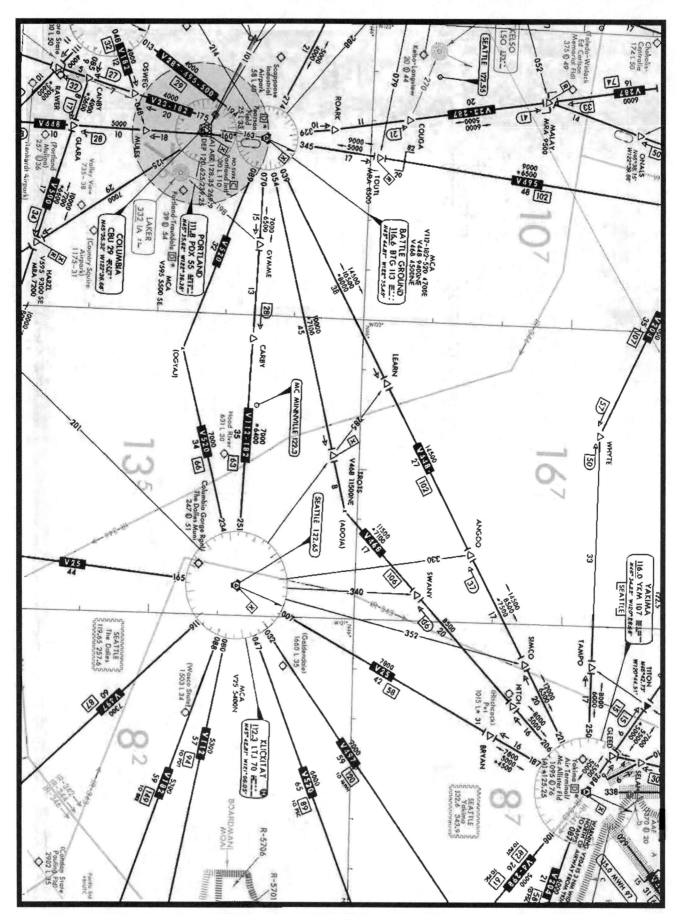

FIGURE 47.—En Route Chart Segment.

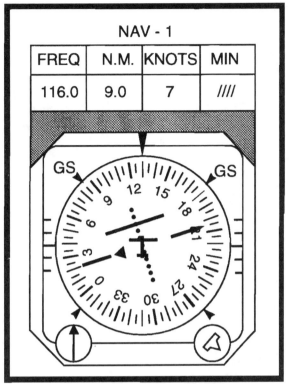

FIGURE 48.—CDI — NAV 1.

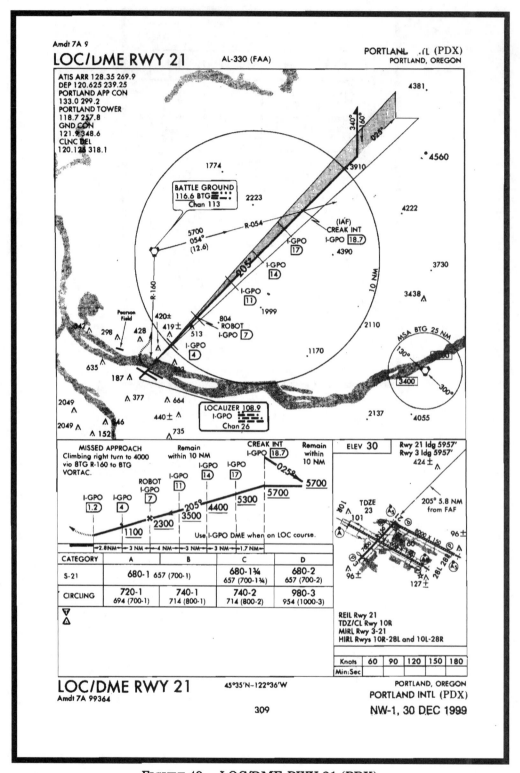

FIGURE 49.—LOC/DME RWY 21 (PDX).

Form Approved: OMB No. 2120-0034

U.S. DEPARTMENT OF TRANSPORTATION FEDERAL AVIATION ADMINISTRATION **FLIGHT PLAN**	(FAA USE ONLY)	☐ PILOT BRIEFING ☐ STOPOVER	☐ VNR	TIME STARTED	SPECIALIST INITIALS

1. TYPE		2. AIRCRAFT IDENTIFICATION	3. AIRCRAFT TYPE/ SPECIAL EQUIPMENT	4. TRUE AIRSPEED	5. DEPARTURE POINT	6. DEPARTURE TIME		7. CRUISING ALTITUDE
	VFR					PROPOSED (Z)	ACTUAL (Z)	
X	IFR	N2468	A36/	158 KTS	SBA			8000
	DVFR							

8. ROUTE OF FLIGHT

HABUT4 GVO, V27 MQO, V113 PRB

9. DESTINATION (Name of airport and city) PASO ROBLES MUNI PRB	10. EST. TIME ENROUTE		11. REMARKS
	HOURS	MINUTES	IFR TRAINING FLIGHT

12. FUEL ON BOARD		13. ALTERNATE AIRPORT(S)	14. PILOT'S NAME, ADDRESS & TELEPHONE NUMBER & AIRCRAFT HOME BASE	15. NUMBER ABOARD
HOURS	MINUTES			
		N/A	17. DESTINATION CONTACT/TELEPHONE (OPTIONAL)	2

16. COLOR OF AIRCRAFT GOLD/WHITE	CIVIL AIRCRAFT PILOTS. FAR Part 91 requires you file an IFR flight plan to operate under instrument flight rules in controlled airspace. Failure to file could result in a civil penalty not to exceed $1,000 for each violation (Section 901 of the Federal Aviation Act of 1958, as amended). Filing of a VFR flight plan is recommended as a good operating practice. See also Part 99 for requirements concerning DVFR flight plans.

FAA Form 7233-1 (8-82)   CLOSE VFR FLIGHT PLAN WITH _____ FSS ON ARRIVAL

AIRCRAFT INFORMATION

MAKE Beechcraft   MODEL A-36

N 2468   Vso 52

AIRCRAFT EQUIPMENT/STATUS**

**NOTE: X= OPERATIVE   INOP= INOPERATIVE   N/A= NOT APPLICABLE
TRANSPONDER: X (MODE C) X ILS: (LOCALIZER) X (GLIDE SLOPE) X
VOR NO. 1 X (NO. 2) X ADF: X RNAV: X
VERTICAL PATH COMPUTER: N/A DME: X
MARKER BEACON: X (AUDIO) X (VISUAL) INOP

FIGURE 50.—Flight Plan and Aircraft Information.

FLIGHT LOG

SANTA BARBARA MUNI TO PASO ROBLES MUNI

CHECK POINTS		ROUTE		WIND	SPEED-KTS		DIST	TIME		FUEL	
FROM	TO	ALTITUDE	COURSE	TEMP	TAS	GS	NM	LEG	TOT	LEG	TOT
SBA	HABUT	HABUT 4 CLIMB	253°					:08:00			
	GVO	163°R 8000	343°		158						
	MQO	V27 8000	306°								
	PRB	V113	358°								
APPROACH & LANDING		DESCENT						:10:00			
	PRB AIRPORT										

OTHER DATA:
NOTE: MAG. VAR. 16° E.

FLIGHT SUMMARY

TIME	FUEL (LB)	
		EN ROUTE
		RESERVE
		MISSED APPR.
		TOTAL

FIGURE 51.—Flight Planning Log.

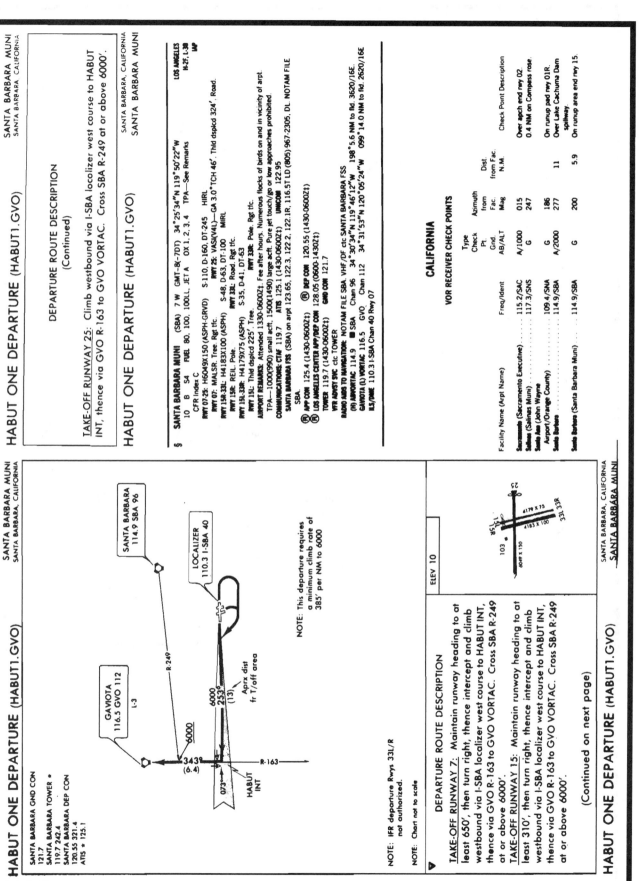

FIGURE 52.—HABUT One Departure and Excerpt from Airport/Facility Directory.

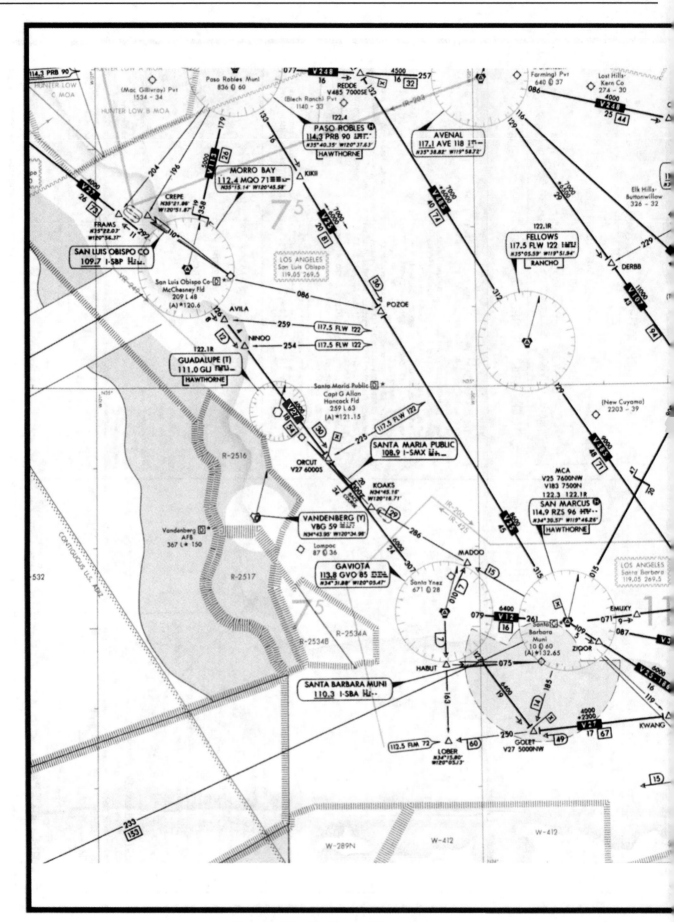

FIGURE 53.—En Route Chart Segment.

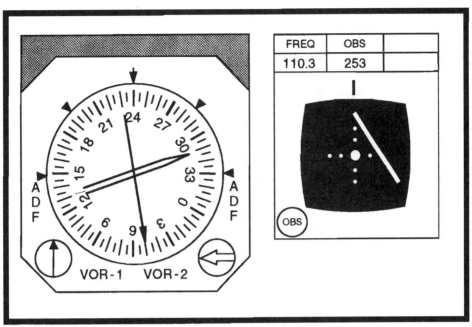

FIGURE 54.—RMI and CDI Indicators.

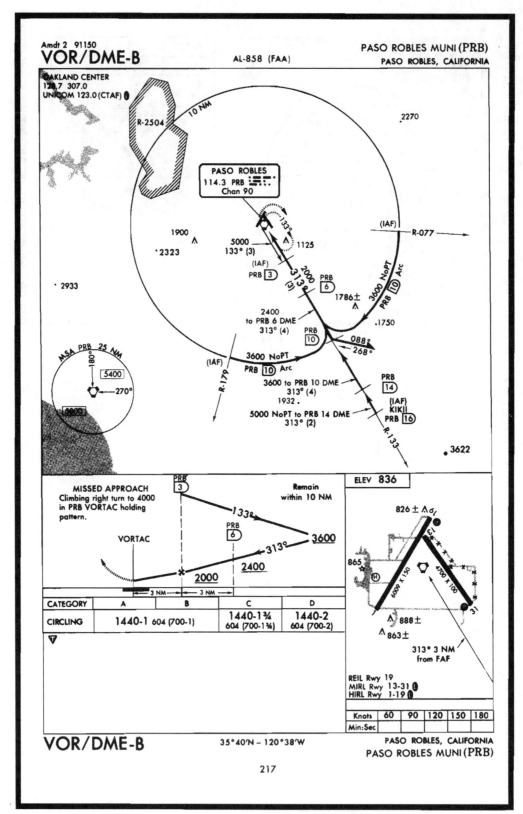

FIGURE 55.—VOR/DME-B (PRB).

Form Approved: OMB No. 2120-0034

U.S. DEPARTMENT OF TRANSPORTATION FEDERAL AVIATION ADMINISTRATION **FLIGHT PLAN**	(FAA USE ONLY)	☐ PILOT BRIEFING	☐ VNR	TIME STARTED	SPECIALIST INITIALS
		☐ STOPOVER			

1. TYPE	2. AIRCRAFT IDENTIFICATION	3. AIRCRAFT TYPE/ SPECIAL EQUIPMENT	4. TRUE AIRSPEED	5. DEPARTURE POINT	6. DEPARTURE TIME		7. CRUISING ALTITUDE
VFR					PROPOSED (Z)	ACTUAL (Z)	
X IFR	N12193	BH 206/	110 KTS	EASTERWOOD FIELD			7000
DVFR							

8. ROUTE OF FLIGHT

DIRECT CLL, V15 TNV, V571 IAH, DIRECT

9. DESTINATION (Name of airport and city)	10. EST. TIME ENROUTE		11. REMARKS
WILLIAM P HOBBY AIRPORT HOUSTON, TX	HOURS	MINUTES	

12. FUEL ON BOARD		13. ALTERNATE AIRPORT(S)	14. PILOT'S NAME, ADDRESS & TELEPHONE NUMBER & AIRCRAFT HOME BASE	15. NUMBER ABOARD
HOURS	MINUTES			
		N/A	17. DESTINATION CONTACT/TELEPHONE (OPTIONAL)	2

16. COLOR OF AIRCRAFT	CIVIL AIRCRAFT PILOTS. FAR Part 91 requires you file an IFR flight plan to operate under instrument flight rules in controlled airspace. Failure to file could result in a civil penalty not to exceed $1,000 for each violation (Section 901 of the Federal Aviation Act of 1958, as amended). Filing of a VFR flight plan is recommended as a good operating practice. See also Part 99 for requirements concerning DVFR flight plans.
TAN/GOLD/WHITE	

FAA Form 7233-1 (8-82)   CLOSE VFR FLIGHT PLAN WITH _____ FSS ON ARRIVAL

AIRCRAFT INFORMATION

MAKE Bell   MODEL 206L

N 12193   Vso N/A

AIRCRAFT EQUIPMENT/STATUS**

**NOTE: X= OPERATIVE   INOP= INOPERATIVE   N/A= NOT APPLICABLE
TRANSPONDER: X (MODE C) X ILS: (LOCALIZER) X (GLIDE SLOPE) X
VOR NO. 1 X (NO. 2) X ADF: X RNAV: X
VERTICAL PATH COMPUTER: N/A DME: X
MARKER BEACON: X (AUDIO) X (VISUAL) X

FIGURE 56.—IFR Flight Plan and Aircraft Information.

FLIGHT LOG

EASTERWOOD FIELD TO WILLIAM P HOBBY AIRPORT

CHECK POINTS		ROUTE	COURSE	WIND	SPEED-KTS		DIST	TIME		FUEL	
FROM	TO	ALTITUDE		TEMP	TAS	GS	NM	LEG	TOT	LEG	TOT
EASTER WOOD	CLL	DIRECT CLIMB	DIRECT					:05:			
	TNV	V15 7000	127°		110		27				
	IAH	V571 7000	110°				42				
	HUB	DIRECT 7000	161°				18				
APPROACH & LANDING								:15:			
	HOBBY AIRPORT										

OTHER DATA:
NOTE: MAG. VAR. 6° E.

FLIGHT SUMMARY

TIME	FUEL (LB)	
		EN ROUTE
		RESERVE
		MISSED APPR.
		TOTAL

FIGURE 57.—Flight Planning Log.

140   **TEXAS**

COLLEGE STATION

EASTERWOOD FLD   (CLL)   3 SW   UTC-6(-5DT)   30°35'18"N 96°21'49"W   HOUSTON
320   B   S4   **FUEL** 100LL, JET A   **OX** 2   ARFF Index A   H-2K, 5B, L-17A
RWY 16-34: H7000X150 (ASPH–GRVD)   S-70, D-90, DT-150   MIRL   IAP
   RWY 16: VASI(V4R)—GA 3.0°TCH 51'. Tree.   **RWY 34:** MALSR.
RWY 10-28: H5160X150 (CONC)   S-27, D-50, DT-87   MIRL
   RWY 10: VASI(V4L)—GA 3.0°TCH 50'. Tree.   **RWY 28:** REIL VASI(V4L)—GA 3.0° TCH 54'. Tree.
RWY 04-22: H5149X150 (CONC)   S-27, D-50, DT-87
   RWY 04: Tree.   **RWY 22:** Tree.
AIRPORT REMARKS: Attended 1200-0500Z‡. CAUTION: deer on rwys. CAUTION: Rwy 10-28 taxiway B and taxiway E
   have uneven surfaces. Birds on and in vicinity of arpt. MIRL Rwy 10-28 preset medium ints when twr clsd, to
   increase ints and ACTIVATE MIRL Rwy 16-34 and MALSR Rwy 34—CTAF. CLOSED to unscheduled air carrier
   ops with more than 30 passenger seats except 24 hours PPR call, arpt manager 409-845-4811. Rwy 04-22
   day VFR ops only. Itinerant acft park North of twr, overnight parking fee. Ldg fee scheduled FAR 135 and all FAR
   121 ops. For fuel after hours PPR call 409-845-4811/823-0690 or ctc Texas A and M University police
   409-845-2345; late ngt fee. Rwy 16-34 grvd except south 200'. Rwy 04-22 deteriorating and vegetation
   growing through cracks. NOTE: See SPECIAL NOTICE—Simultaneous Operations on Intersecting Runways.
COMMUNICATIONS: CTAF 118.5   **ATIS** 126.85 (1200-0400Z‡)   **UNICOM** 122.95
   MONTGOMERY COUNTY FSS (CXO) TF 1-800-WX-BRIEF. NOTAM FILE CLL.
   COLLEGE STATION RCO 122.65 122.2 (MONTGOMERY COUNTY FSS).
®HOUSTON CENTER APP/DEP CON: 120.4
   TOWER: 118.5 (1200-0400Z‡) (VFR only)   **GND CON:** 121.7
RADIO AIDS TO NAVIGATION: NOTAM FILE CLL. VHF/DF ctc FSS
   COLLEGE STATION (L) **VORTACW** 113.3   CLL   Chan 80   30°36'17"N 96°25'13"W   100° 3.1 NM to fld.
   370/08E. **HIWAS.**
   ROWDY NDB (LOM) 260   CL   30°29'36"N 96°20'16"W   341° 5.9 NM to fld.
   ILS 111.7 I-CLL Rwy 34 LOM ROWDY NDB. ILS unmonitored when twr closed.

COLLEGE STATION   30°36'17"N 96°25'13"W   NOTAM FILE CLL.   HOUSTON
   (L) **VORTACW** 113.3   CLL   Chan 80   100° 3.1 NM to Easterwood Fld. 370/08E. **HIWAS.**   H-2K, 5B, L-17A
   RCO 122.65 122.2 (MONTGOMERY COUNTY FSS)

VOR RECEIVER CHECK   259

TEXAS

VOR RECEIVER CHECK POINTS

Facility Name (Arpt Name)	Freq/Ident	Type Check Pt. Gnd. AB/ALT	Azimuth from Fac. Mag	Dist. from Fac. N.M.	Check Point Description
Abilene (Abilene Regional)	113.7/ABI	A/2800	047	10.1	Over silos in center of Ft Phantom Lake.
Alice (Alice International)	114.5/ALI	G	270	0.5	On twy N of hangar.
Amarillo (Amarillo Internationl)	117.2/AMA	G	210	4.5	On east runup pad Rwy 22
Austin (Robert Mueller Muni)	114.6/AUS	G	118	0.6	On runup area on twy to Rwy 31L.
Beaumont (Jefferson County)	114.5/BPT	G	310	1.0	On runup area for Rwy 12
Big Spring (Big Spring McMahon-Wrinkle)	114.3/BGS	A/3500	107	10.5	Over red and white water tank.
Borger (Hutchinson Co)	108.6/BGD	G	175	6.7	On intersecting twy in front of terminal.
Brownsville (Brownsville/South Padre Island Intl)	116.3/BRO	G	248	3.2	On NE corner of parking ramp.
Brownwood (Brownwood Muni)	108.6/BWD	A/2600	169	6.2	Over rotating bcn.
Childress (Childress Muni)	117.6/CDS	G	353	3.7	At intersection of edge of ramp at center twy.
College Station (Easterwood Field)	113.3/CLL	G	097	3.2	On W edge of parking ramp
Corpus Christi (Corpus Christi Intl)	115.5/CRP	A/1100	187	7.5	Over grain elevator.
Corpus Christi (San Patricio County)	115.5/CRP	A/1000	318	9.5	Over rotating beacon on arpt.
Daisetta (Liberty Muni)	116.9/DAS	A/1200	195	7.5	Over hangar S of arpt.
Dalhart (Dalhart Muni)	112.0/DHT	G	170	3.9	On SE corner of main ra--
Eagle Lake (Eagle Lake)	116.4/ELA	A/1200	180	4.5	Over water tank 0.4 NM S--

FIGURE 58.—Excerpts from Airport/Facility Directory.

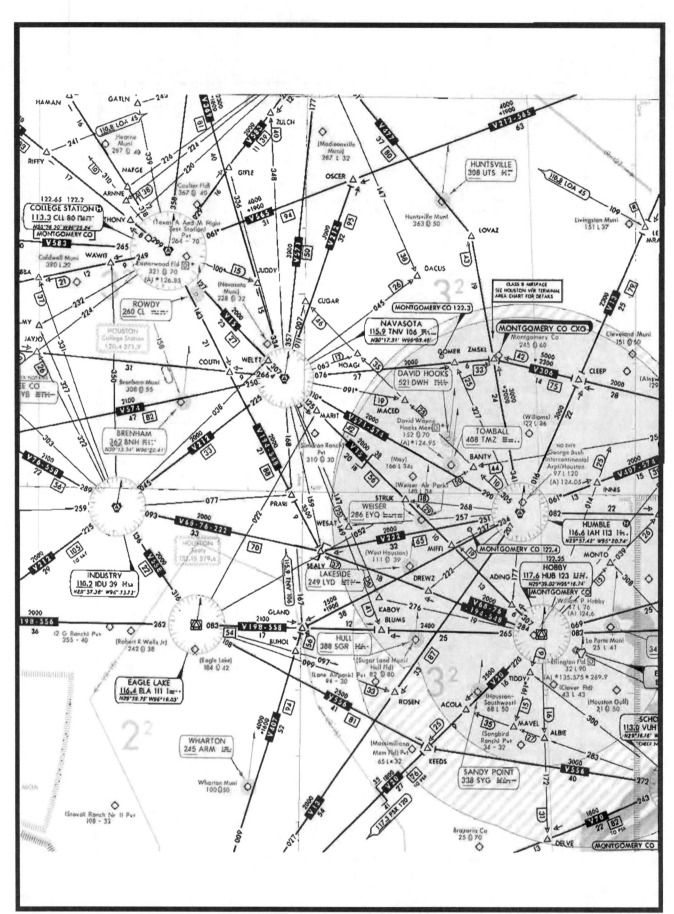

FIGURE 59.—En Route Chart Segment.

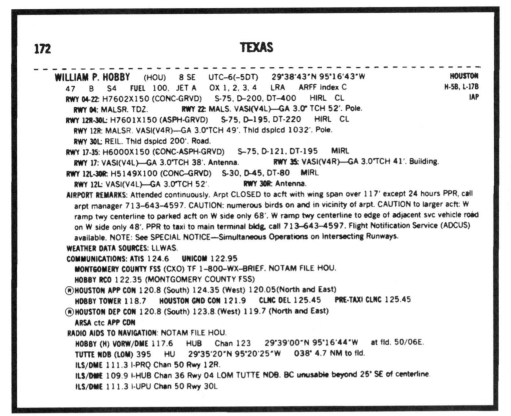

172 **TEXAS**

WILLIAM P. HOBBY (HOU) 8 SE UTC–6(–5DT) 29°38'43"N 95°16'43"W **HOUSTON**
 47 B S4 FUEL 100, JET A OX 1, 2, 3, 4 LRA ARFF Index C H–5B, L–17B
 RWY 04-22: H7602X150 (CONC–GRVD) S–75, D–200, DT–400 HIRL CL IAP
  RWY 04: MALSR. TDZ. RWY 22: MALS. VASI(V4L)—GA 3.0° TCH 52'. Pole.
 RWY 12R-30L: H7601X150 (ASPH–GRVD) S–75, D–195, DT–220 HIRL CL
  RWY 12R: MALSR. VASI(V4R)—GA 3.0°TCH 49'. Thld dsplcd 1032'. Pole.
  RWY 30L: REIL. Thld dsplcd 200'. Road.
 RWY 17-35: H6000X150 (CONC–ASPH–GRVD) S–75, D–121, DT–195 MIRL
  RWY 17: VASI(V4L)—GA 3.0°TCH 38'. Antenna. RWY 35: VASI(V4R)—GA 3.0°TCH 41'. Building.
 RWY 12L-30R: H5149X100 (CONC–GRVD) S–30, D–45, DT–80 MIRL
  RWY 12L: VASI(V4L)—GA 3.0°TCH 52'. RWY 30R: Antenna.
 AIRPORT REMARKS: Attended continuously. Arpt CLOSED to acft with wing span over 117' except 24 hours PPR, call
  arpt manager 713–643–4597. CAUTION: numerous birds on and in vicinity of arpt. CAUTION to larger acft: W
  ramp twy centerline to parked acft on W side only 68'. W ramp twy centerline to edge of adjacent svc vehicle road
  on W side only 48'. PPR to taxi to main terminal bldg, call 713–643–4597. Flight Notification Service (ADCUS)
  available. NOTE: See SPECIAL NOTICE—Simultaneous Operations on Intersecting Runways.
 WEATHER DATA SOURCES: LLWAS.
 COMMUNICATIONS: ATIS 124.6 UNICOM 122.95
  MONTGOMERY COUNTY FSS (CXO) TF 1–800–WX–BRIEF. NOTAM FILE HOU.
  HOBBY RCO 122.35 (MONTGOMERY COUNTY FSS)
 ®HOUSTON APP CON 120.8 (South) 124.35 (West) 120.05(North and East)
  HOBBY TOWER 118.7 HOUSTON GND CON 121.9 CLNC DEL 125.45 PRE-TAXI CLNC 125.45
 ®HOUSTON DEP CON 120.8 (South) 123.8 (West) 119.7 (North and East)
  ARSA ctc APP CON
 RADIO AIDS TO NAVIGATION: NOTAM FILE HOU.
  HOBBY (H) VORW/DME 117.6 HUB Chan 123 29°39'00"N 95°16'44"W at fld. 50/06E.
  TUTTE NDB (LOM) 395 HU 29°35'20"N 95°20'25"W 038° 4.7 NM to fld.
  ILS/DME 111.3 I-PRQ Chan 50 Rwy 12R.
  ILS/DME 109.9 I-HUB Chan 36 Rwy 04 LOM TUTTE NDB. BC unusable beyond 25° SE of centerline.
  ILS/DME 111.3 I-UPU Chan 50 Rwy 30L

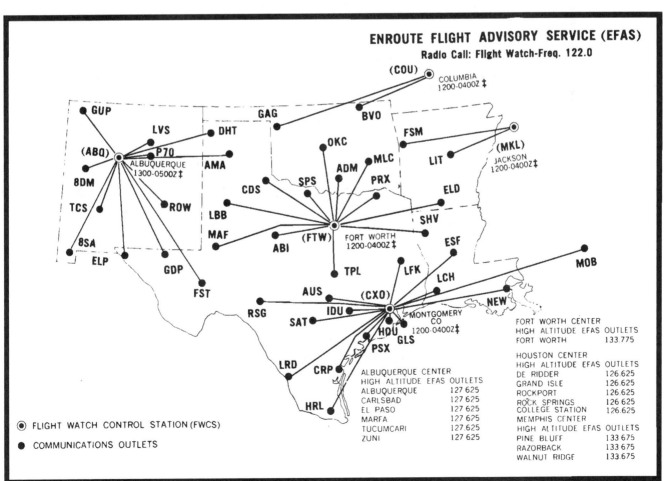

FIGURE 60.—Airport/Facility Directory and Enroute Flight Advisory Service (EFAS).

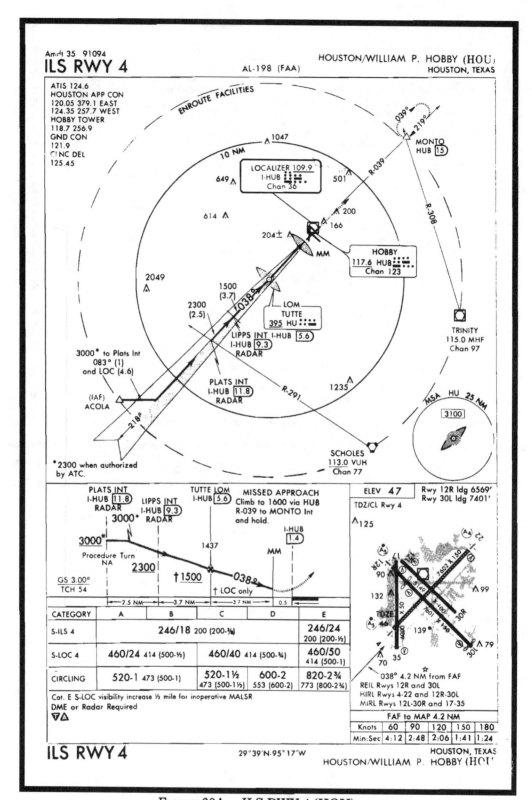

FIGURE 60A.—ILS RWY 4 (HOU).

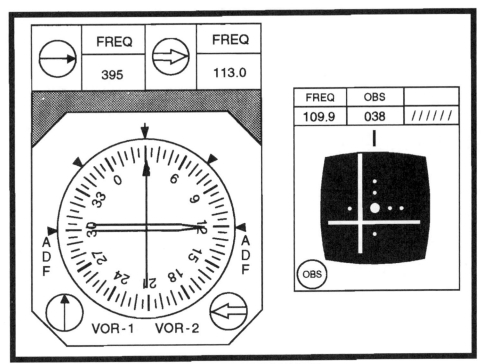

FIGURE 61.—RMI and CDI Indicators.

Form Approved: OMB No. 2120-0034

U.S. DEPARTMENT OF TRANSPORTATION FEDERAL AVIATION ADMINISTRATION **FLIGHT PLAN**	(FAA USE ONLY)	☐ PILOT BRIEFING	☐ VNR	TIME STARTED	SPECIALIST INITIALS
		☐ STOPOVER			

1. TYPE	2. AIRCRAFT IDENTIFICATION	3. AIRCRAFT TYPE/ SPECIAL EQUIPMENT	4. TRUE AIRSPEED	5. DEPARTURE POINT	6. DEPARTURE TIME		7. CRUISING ALTITUDE
VFR					PROPOSED (Z)	ACTUAL (Z)	
X IFR	N321JL	HU369/	105 KTS	LFT			5000
DVFR							

8. ROUTE OF FLIGHT

DIRECT LFT, V552 TBD

9. DESTINATION (Name of airport and city)	10. EST. TIME ENROUTE		11. REMARKS
HOUMA TERREBONNE LA (HUM)	HOURS	MINUTES	

12. FUEL ON BOARD		13. ALTERNATE AIRPORT(S)	14. PILOT'S NAME, ADDRESS & TELEPHONE NUMBER & AIRCRAFT HOME BASE	15. NUMBER ABOARD
HOURS	MINUTES			
		N/A	17. DESTINATION CONTACT/TELEPHONE (OPTIONAL)	2

16. COLOR OF AIRCRAFT	CIVIL AIRCRAFT PILOTS. FAR Part 91 requires you file an IFR flight plan to operate under instrument flight rules in controlled airspace. Failure to file could result in a civil penalty not to exceed $1,000 for each violation (Section 901 of the Federal Aviation Act of 1958, as amended). Filing of a VFR flight plan is recommended as a good operating practice. See also Part 99 for requirements concerning DVFR flight plans.
ORANGE/BLACK/WHITE	

FAA Form 7233-1 (8-82)   CLOSE VFR FLIGHT PLAN WITH _____ FSS ON ARRIVAL

AIRCRAFT INFORMATION

MAKE Hughes   MODEL 369

N 321JL   Vso N/A

AIRCRAFT EQUIPMENT/STATUS**

**NOTE: X= OPERATIVE   INOP= INOPERATIVE   N/A= NOT APPLICABLE
TRANSPONDER: X (MODE C) X ILS: (LOCALIZER) X (GLIDE SLOPE) X
VOR NO. 1 X (NO. 2) X ADF: X RNAV: X
VERTICAL PATH COMPUTER: N/A DME: X
MARKER BEACON: X (AUDIO) X (VISUAL) X

FIGURE 62.—Flight Plan and Aircraft Information.

FLIGHT LOG

LAFAYETTE REGIONAL TO HOUMA TERREBONNE (HUM)

CHECK POINTS		ROUTE		WIND	SPEED-KTS		DIST	TIME		FUEL	
FROM	TO	ALTITUDE	COURSE	TEMP	TAS	GS	NM	LEG	TOT	LEG	TOT
LFT AIRPORT	LFT VOR	DIRECT CLIMB						:05:0			
	HATCH	V552 5000	114°		105						
	GRICE	V552 5000	116°								
	TBD	V552 5000	116°								
APPROACH & LANDING		DESCENT	117°					:10:0			
	HUM AIRPORT										

OTHER DATA:
NOTE: MAG. VAR. 6° E.

FLIGHT SUMMARY

TIME	FUEL (LB)	
		EN ROUTE
		RESERVE
		MISSED APPR.
		TOTAL

FIGURE 63.—Flight Planning Log.

LOUISIANA

VOR RECEIVER CHECK POINTS

Facility Name (Arpt Name)	Freq/Ident	Type Check Pt. Gnd AB/ALT	Azimuth from Fac. Mag	Dist. from Fac. N.M.	Check Point Description
Baton Rouge (Baton Rouge Metro, Ryan) . . .	116.5/BTR	A/1500	063	7.7	Over water tank W side of arpt.
Downtown	108.6/DTN	A/1500	290	10	Over white water tower.
Esler (Esler Regional)	108.8/ESF	G	151	3.5	On ramp in front of admin bldg.
Hammond (Hammond Muni)	109.6/HMU	G	342	.6	On twy W side app end Rwy 18.
Lafayette (Lafayette Regional)	110.8/LFT	A/1000	340	25	Over rotating beacon
Lake Charles (Lake Charles Muni)	113.4/LCH	A/1000	253	6.2	Over rotg bcn on atct.
Monroe (Monroe Muni)	117.2/MLU	G	209	0.9	On ramp SE of atct.
Natchez (Concordia Parish)	110.0/HEZ	A/1000	247	10.5	Over hangar NW end of field.
New Orleans (Lakefront)	113.2/MSY	A/1000	081	7.7	Over lakefront atct.
Ruston	112.8/RSN	A/2000	343	14	Over hwy & RR crossing at Dubash.
Shreveport (Shreveport Downtown)	108.6/DTN	G	307	.5	On runup area N side of rwy 14.
Shreveport (Shreveport Regional)	117.4/SHV	A/1200	175	19.3	Over old terminal building.
Tibby (Thibodaux Muni)	112.0/TBD	A/1000	006	5.0	Over railroad bridge off apch end rwy 26.
	112.0/TBD	A/1000	117	10.0	Over intersection of rwys 17-35 and 12-30

LAFAYETTE REGIONAL   (LFT)   2 SE   GMT–6(–5DT)   30°12′14″N 91°59′16″W   **HOUSTON**
42   B   S4   **FUEL** 100LL, JET A   OX 1   CFR Index B   **H-4F, L-17C**
RWY 03-21: H7651X150 (ASPH-GRVD)   S-75, D-170, DT-290   HIRL   **IAP**
  RWY 03: REIL. VASI(V4L)—GA 3.0°TCH 35′. Tree.
  RWY 21: MALSR. VASI(V4L)—GA 3.0°TCH 44′. Tree.
RWY 10-28: H5401X150 (ASPH)   S-85, D-110, DT-175   MIRL
  RWY 10: REIL (out of svc indefinitely). VASI(V4L)—GA 3.0° TCH 35.33′. Tree.
  RWY 28: REIL. VASI(V4L)—GA 3.0° TCH 55′. Thld dsplcd 202′. Tree.
RWY 01-19: H5069X150 (ASPH)   S-25, D-45
  RWY 01: VASI(V4R)—GA 3.0°TCH 50′. Tree.
AIRPORT REMARKS: Attended continuously. Rwy 01-19 closed to air carriers. ACTIVATE MALSR Rwy 21—118.5.
COMMUNICATIONS: CTAF 118.5   **ATIS** 120.5 Opr 1200-0500Z‡   **UNICOM** 122.95
  LAFAYETTE FSS (LFT) on arpt. 122.35, 122.2, 122.1R, 110.8T LD 318-233-4952 NOTAM FILE LFT.
Ⓡ **APP/DEP CON** 121.1 (011°-190°) 124.0 (191°-010°) (1200-0400Z‡)
  HOUSTON CENTER APP/DEP CON 133.65 (0400-1200Z‡)
  TOWER 118.5, 121.35 (Helicopter ops) (1200-0400Z‡)   **GND CON** 121.8   **CLNC DEL** 125.55
  STAGE III ctc **APP CON** within 25 NM below 7000′
RADIO AIDS TO NAVIGATION: NOTAM FILE LFT. VHF/DF ctc LAFAYETTE FSS
  (L) VORTAC 110.8   LFT   Chan 45   30°08′45″N 91°59′00″W   344°3.0 NM to fld. 40/06E
  LAFFS NDB (LOM) 375   LF   30°17′21″N 91°54′29″W   215° 5.8 NM to fld
  LAKE MARTIN NDB (MHW) 362   LKM   30°11′33″N 91°52′58″W   270°5.2 NM to fld
  ILS/DME 109.5 I-LFT Chan 32 Rwy 21 LOM LAFFS NDB. Unmonitored when twr clsd.
  ASR

FIGURE 64.—Excerpt from Airport/Facility Directory (LFT).

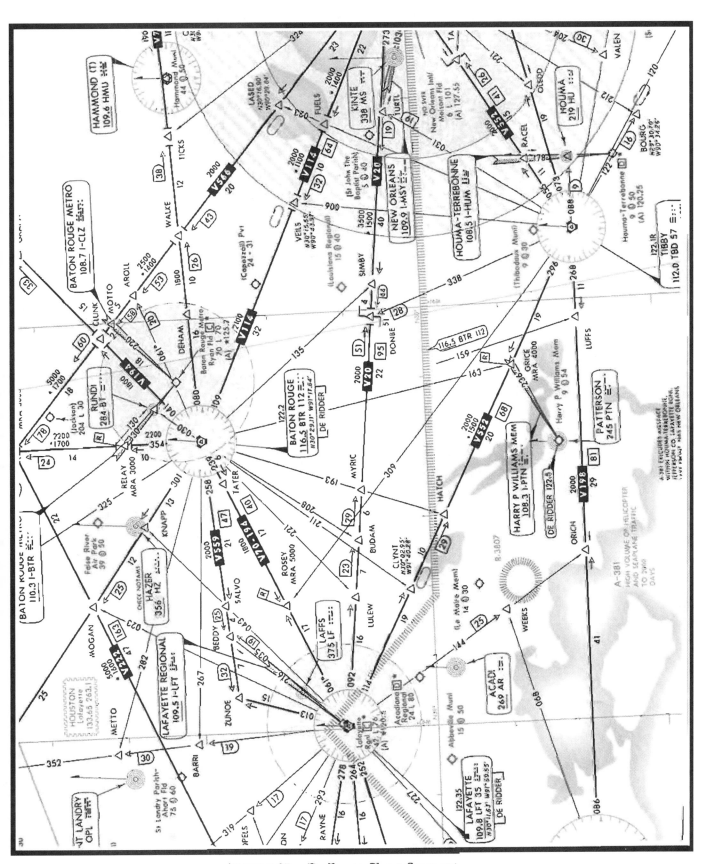

FIGURE 65.—En Route Chart Segment.

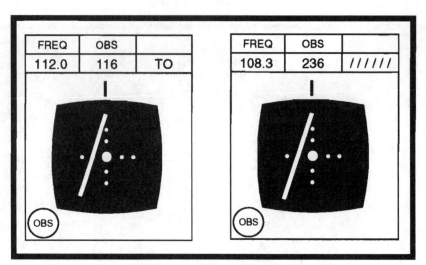

FIGURE 66.—CDI and OBS Indicators.

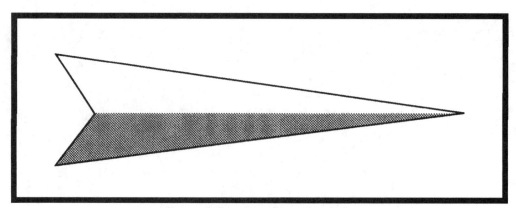

FIGURE 67.—Localizer Symbol.

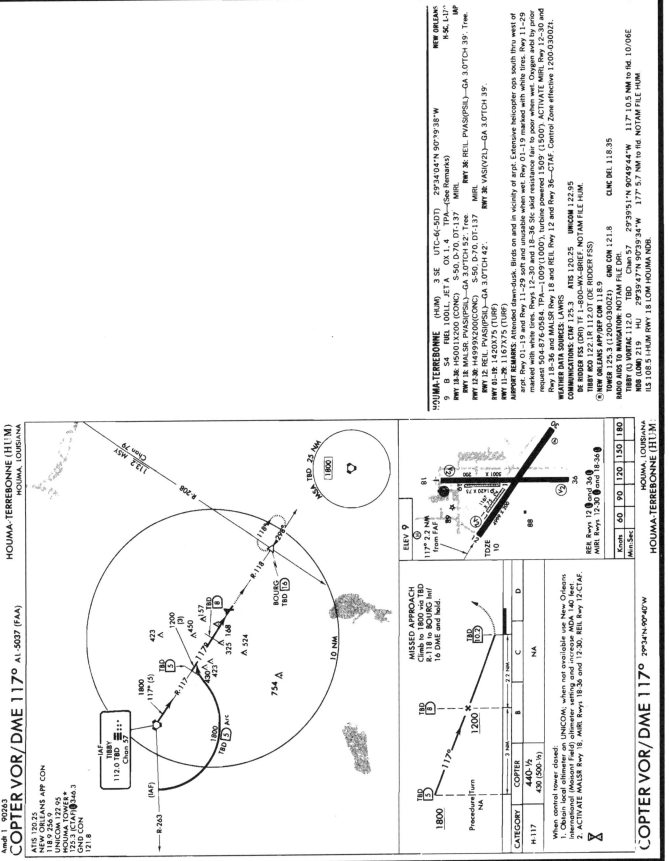

FIGURE 68.—COPTER VOR DME-117 Degrees (HUM).

Form Approved: OMB No. 2120-0034

| U.S. DEPARTMENT OF TRANSPORTATION FEDERAL AVIATION ADMINISTRATION **FLIGHT PLAN** | (FAA USE ONLY) ☐ PILOT BRIEFING ☐ STOPOVER | | ☐ VNR | TIME STARTED | | SPECIALIST INITIALS |

1. TYPE	2. AIRCRAFT IDENTIFICATION	3. AIRCRAFT TYPE/ SPECIAL EQUIPMENT	4. TRUE AIRSPEED	5. DEPARTURE POINT	6. DEPARTURE TIME		7. CRUISING ALTITUDE
VFR					PROPOSED (Z)	ACTUAL (Z)	
X IFR	N2142S	C172/	128 KTS	GREENWOOD LAKE 4N1			5000
DVFR							

8. ROUTE OF FLIGHT

DIRECT SHAFF INT., V213 HELON INT., V58 JUDDS INT., JUDDS2

9. DESTINATION (Name of airport and city)	10. EST. TIME ENROUTE		11. REMARKS
	HOURS	MINUTES	
BRADLEY INTL. BDL			INSTRUMENT TRAINING FLIGHT

12. FUEL ON BOARD		13. ALTERNATE AIRPORT(S)	14. PILOT'S NAME, ADDRESS & TELEPHONE NUMBER & AIRCRAFT HOME BASE	15. NUMBER ABOARD
HOURS	MINUTES			
			17. DESTINATION CONTACT/TELEPHONE (OPTIONAL)	
		N/A		2

| 16. COLOR OF AIRCRAFT BROWN/TAN/WHITE | CIVIL AIRCRAFT PILOTS. FAR Part 91 requires you file an IFR flight plan to operate under instrument flight rules in controlled airspace. Failure to file could result in a civil penalty not to exceed $1,000 for each violation (Section 901 of the Federal Aviation Act of 1958, as amended). Filing of a VFR flight plan is recommended as a good operating practice. See also Part 99 for requirements concerning DVFR flight plans. |

FAA Form 7233-1 (8-82)   CLOSE VFR FLIGHT PLAN WITH _____ FSS ON ARRIVAL

AIRCRAFT INFORMATION

MAKE   Cessna   MODEL 172

N 2142S   Vso 33

AIRCRAFT EQUIPMENT/STATUS**

**NOTE: X= OPERATIVE   INOP= INOPERATIVE   N/A= NOT APPLICABLE
TRANSPONDER: X (MODE C) X ILS: (LOCALIZER) X   (GLIDE SLOPE) X
VOR NO. 1 X (NO. 2) X ADF: X RNAV: N/A
VERTICAL PATH COMPUTER: N/A DME: X
MARKER BEACON: X (AUDIO) INOP (VISUAL) X

FIGURE 69.—Flight Plan and Aircraft Information.

FLIGHT LOG

GREENWOOD LAKE (4N1) TO BRADLEY INTL. (BDL)

CHECK POINTS		ROUTE		WIND	SPEED-KTS		DIST	TIME		FUEL	
FROM	TO	ALTITUDE	COURSE	TEMP	TAS	GS	NM	LEG	TOT	LEG	TOT
4N1	SHAFF	DIRECT CLIMB	350°					:08:0			
	HELON	V213 5000	029°		128						
	IGN	V58 5000	102°								
		JUDDS2	112°								
	JUDDS	JUDDS2	100°								
	BRISS	JUDDS2	057°								
APPROACH & LANDING								:12:0			
	BDL INTL										

OTHER DATA:
NOTE: MAG. VAR. 14° W.

FLIGHT SUMMARY

TIME	FUEL (LB)	
		EN ROUTE
		RESERVE
		MISSED APPR.
		TOTAL

FIGURE 70.—Flight Planning Log.

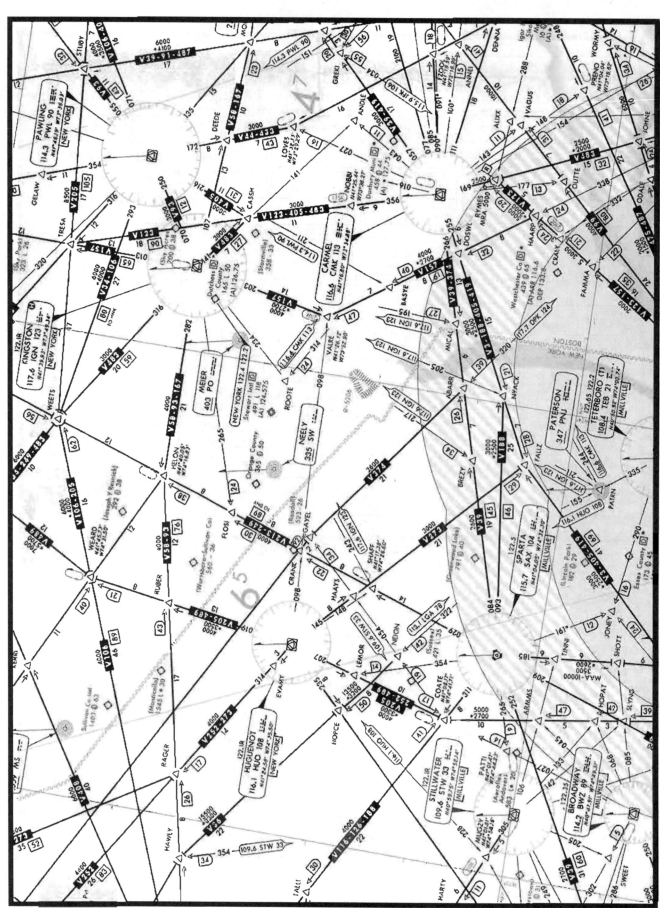

FIGURE 71.—En Route Chart Segment.

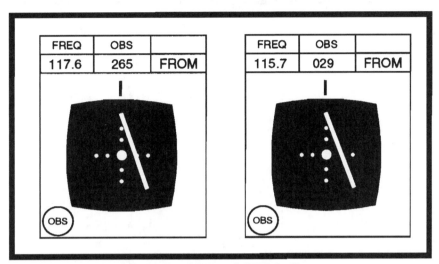

FIGURE 71A.—CDI and OBS Indicators.

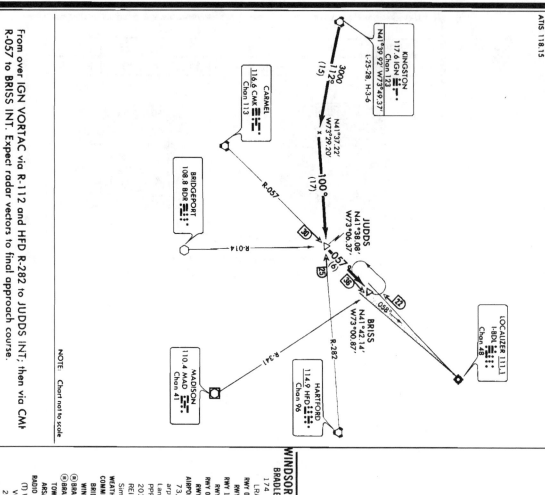

P1150

JUDDS TWO ARRIVAL (IGN.JUDDS2)

ST-460 (FAA)

ATIS 118.15

BRADLEY INTERNATIONAL
WINDSOR LOCKS, CONNECTICUT

KINGSTON
117.6 IGN
Chan 123
N41°39.92' W73°49.37'
L-25-28, H-3-6

3000
112°
(15)

CARMEL
116.6 CMK
Chan 113
N41°37.22'
W73°29.20'
x

100°
(17)

R-057

BRIDGEPORT
108.8 BDR

R-014

JUDDS
N41°38.08'
W73°06.37'

30

057

25

058

36

21

BRISS
N41°42.14'
W73°00.87'

R-282

R-341

LOCALIZER 111.1
I-BDL
Chan 48

MADISON
110.4 MAD
Chan 41

HARTFORD
114.9 HFD
Chan 96

NOTE: Chart not to scale

JUDDS TWO ARRIVAL (IGN.JUDDS2)

From over IGN VORTAC via R-112 and HFD R-282 to JUDDS INT; then via CMK
R-057 to BRISS INT. Expect radar vectors to final approach course.

WINDSOR LOCKS, CONNECTICUT
BRADLEY INTERNATIONAL

FIGURE 72.— JUDDS TWO ARRIVAL.

CONNECTICUT

WINDSOR LOCKS
BRADLEY INTL   (BDL)   3 W   UTC−5(−4DT)   41°56'20"N 72°41'01"W   **NEW YORK**
174   B   S4   FUEL 100LL, JET A   OX 1, 2, 3, 4   TPA—See Remarks   H-3D, 6J, L-25C, 28I
LRA   ARFF Index D   IAP
RWY 06-24: H9502X200 (ASPH-GRVD)   S-200, D-200, DT-350,DDT-710   HIRL CL
RWY 06: ALSF2 TDZ. Trees.   RWY 24: MALSR. VASI(V4L)—GA 3.0°TCH 56'.
RWY 15-33: H6846X200 (ASPH)   S-200, D-200, DT-350   HIRL
RWY 15: REIL. VASI(V4L)—GA 3.5°TCH 59'. Trees.   RWY 33: MALSF. VASI(V4R)—GA 3.0°TCH 59'. Trees
RWY 01-19: H5141X100 (ASPH)   S-60, D-190, DT-328   MIRL
RWY 01: Building.   RWY 19: Trees.
AIRPORT REMARKS: Attended continuously. Rwy 01-19 restricted to ldg and tkf with maximum tkf gross weight of
73,000 pounds. This restriction does not apply to acft emergency. Numerous birds frequently on or in vicinity or
arpt. Portions of taxiway Alpha not visible from tower. TPA—1174(1000) light acft, 1874(1700) heavy acft.
Landing fee for business, corporate and revenue producing aircraft. 24 hours ARFF level D svc avbl. 24 hours
PPR for unscheduled air carrier ops with more than 30 passenger seats call arpt manager
203-627-3001/3008. This does not include delayed regularly schedule air carrier ops or diversions. Rwy 15
REIL out of svc indefinitely. Flight Notification Service (ADCUS) available. NOTE: See SPECIAL NOTICE—
Simultaneous Operations on Intersecting Runways.
WEATHER DATA SOURCES: LLWAS.
COMMUNICATIONS: ATIS 118.15   UNICOM 122.95
BRIDGEPORT FSS (BDR) TF 1-800-WX-BRIEF. NOTAM FILE BDL.
WINDSOR LOCKS RCO 122.3 (BRIDGEPORT FSS)
Ⓡ BRADLEY APP CON 125.8 (within 20 miles)
Ⓡ BRADLEY DEP CON 121.05 (South) 125.35 (North and West) 123.95 (Northeast)
TOWER 120.3   GND CON 121.9   CLNC DEL 121.75
ARSA ctc APP CON
RADIO AIDS TO NAVIGATION: NOTAM FILE BDL.
(T) VORTACW 109.0   BDL   Chan 27   41°56'27"N 72°41'21"W   at fld. 165/14W.
VOR portion unusable 090°-103° beyond 24 NM below 5000', 104°-170° beyond 10 NM below 6000'.
260°-290° beyond 15 NM below 6000'.
DME portion unusable:
040°-085° beyond 13 NM below 2000'.
130°-150° beyond 10 NM below 3000'.
170°-195° beyond 14 NM below 3000'.
250°-290° beyond 18 NM below 6000'.
CHUPP NDB (LOM) 388   BD   41°52'38"N 72°46'00"W   058° 5.2 NM to fld.
ILS/DME 111.1 I-BDL Chan 48 Rwy 06. LOM CHUPP NDB
ILS/DME 108.55 I-IKX Chan 22Y Rwy 33
ILS/DME 111.1 I-MYQ Chan 48 Rwy 24

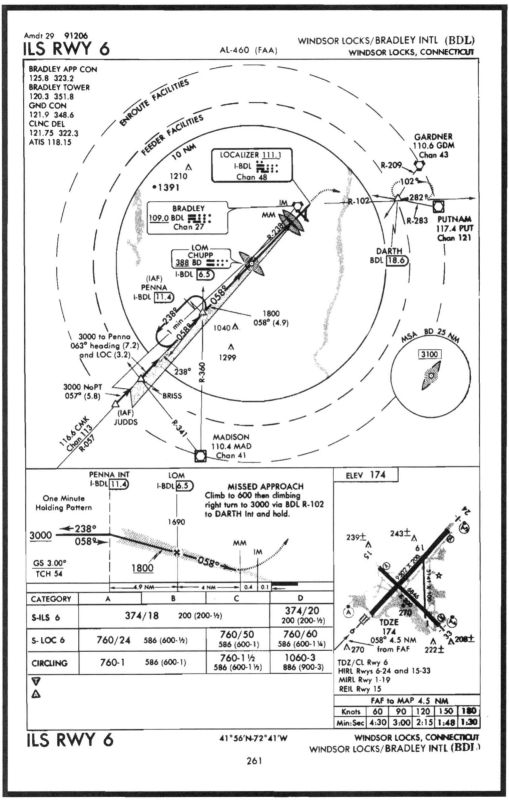

FIGURE 73.—ILS RWY 6 (BDL).

Form Approved: OMB No. 2120-0034

U.S. DEPARTMENT OF TRANSPORTATION FEDERAL AVIATION ADMINISTRATION **FLIGHT PLAN**	(FAA USE ONLY)	☐ PILOT BRIEFING ☐ STOPOVER	☐ VNR	TIME STARTED	SPECIALIST INITIALS

1. TYPE	2. AIRCRAFT IDENTIFICATION	3. AIRCRAFT TYPE/ SPECIAL EQUIPMENT	4. TRUE AIRSPEED	5. DEPARTURE POINT	6. DEPARTURE TIME		7. CRUISING ALTITUDE
VFR					PROPOSED (Z)	ACTUAL (Z)	
X IFR DVFR	N242T	C310/	160 KTS	HLN			11000

8. ROUTE OF FLIGHT

STAKK3, V365 BZN, V86

9. DESTINATION (Name of airport and city)	10. EST. TIME ENROUTE		11. REMARKS
LOGAN INTL. AIRPORT (BIL)	HOURS	MINUTES	

12. FUEL ON BOARD		13. ALTERNATE AIRPORT(S)	14. PILOT'S NAME, ADDRESS & TELEPHONE NUMBER & AIRCRAFT HOME BASE	15. NUMBER ABOARD
HOURS	MINUTES			
		N/A	17. DESTINATION CONTACT/TELEPHONE (OPTIONAL)	2

16. COLOR OF AIRCRAFT	CIVIL AIRCRAFT PILOTS. FAR Part 91 requires you file an IFR flight plan to operate under instrument flight rules in controlled airspace. Failure to file could result in a civil penalty not to exceed $1,000 for each violation (Section 901 of the Federal Aviation Act of 1958, as amended). Filing of a VFR flight plan is recommended as a good operating practice. See also Part 99 for requirements concerning DVFR flight plans.
RED/BLACK/WHITE	

FAA Form 7233-1 (8-82)   CLOSE VFR FLIGHT PLAN WITH _____ FSS ON ARRIVAL

AIRCRAFT INFORMATION

MAKE Cessna   MODEL 310R

N 242T   Vso 72

AIRCRAFT EQUIPMENT/STATUS**

**NOTE: X= OPERATIVE   INOP= INOPERATIVE   N/A= NOT APPLICABLE
TRANSPONDER: X (MODE C) X ILS: (LOCALIZER) X (GLIDE SLOPE) INOP
VOR NO. 1 X (NO. 2) X ADF: X RNAV: N/A
VERTICAL PATH COMPUTER: N/A DME: X
MARKER BEACON: X (AUDIO) X (VISUAL) X

FIGURE 74.—Flight Plan and Aircraft Information.

FLIGHT LOG

HELENA REGIONAL AIRPORT TO BILLINGS LOGAN INTL.

CHECK POINTS		ROUTE		WIND		SPEED-KTS		DIST	TIME		FUEL	
FROM	TO	ALTITUDE	COURSE	TEMP		TAS	GS	NM	LEG	TOT	LEG	TOT
HLN	SWEDD	STAKK 3 CLIMB	103°						:15:0			
	BZN	V365 11000	140°			160						
	LVM	V86 11000	110° / 063°									
	REEPO	V86 11000	067°									
	BIL	V86	069°									
APPROACH & LANDING									:15:0			
	LOGAN INTL											

OTHER DATA:
NOTE: MAG. VAR. 18° E.

FLIGHT SUMMARY

TIME	FUEL (LB)	
		EN ROUTE
		RESERVE
		MISSED APPR.
		TOTAL

FIGURE 75.—Flight Planning Log.

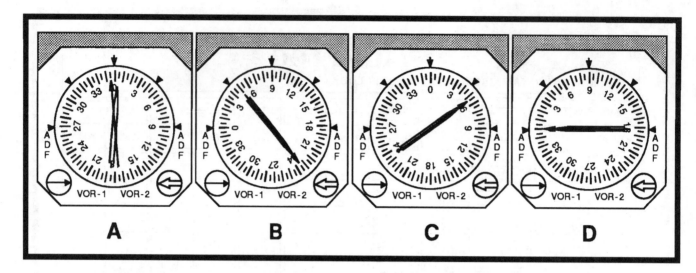

HELENA REGIONAL   (HLN)   2 NE   UTC–7(–6DT)   46°36'25"N 111°58'55"W   GREAT FALLS
3,873   B   S4   FUEL 100LL, JET A   OX 1,3 AOE   ARFF Index B   H-1C, L-9B
RWY 09-27: H9000X150 (ASPH-PFC)   S-100, D-160, DT-250   HIRL   IAP
   RWY 09: VASI(V4L)—GA 3.0°TCH 45'. Ground.   RWY 27: MALSR. VASI(V4L)—GA 3.0°TCH 55'. Rgt tfc.
RWY 05-23: H4599X75 (ASPH-PFC)   S-21, D-30
   RWY 05: Road.   RWY 23: Fence. Rgt tfc.
RWY 16-34: H2979X75 (ASPH)   S-21, D-30   MIRL
   RWY 34: Ground. Rgt tfc.
AIRPORT REMARKS: Attended 1200-0800Z‡. East 2400' Taxiway C and first 900' Rwy 27 not visible from tower.
   Prior permission for unscheduled FAR 121 operations, Call 406-442-2821. AOE, 1 hour prior notice required,
   phone 449-1569 1500-0000Z‡; 0000-1500Z‡ 449-1024. Twys A;B; high speed and C (between A and D)
   not available for air carrier use by acft with greater than 30 passenger seats. Rwy 16-34 and Rwy 05-23 (except
   between Rwy 09-27 and Twy D) not available for air carrier use by acft with greater than 30 passenger seats.
   When tower closed, ACTIVATE HIRL Rwy 09-27 and MALSR Rwy 27—CTAF, when twr closed MIRL Rwy 16-34
   are off. Ldg fee for all acft over 12,500 lbs. NOTE: See SPECIAL NOTICE—Simultaneous Operations on
   Intersecting Runways.
COMMUNICATIONS: CTAF 118.3   ATIS 120.4 (Mon-Fri 1300-0700Z‡, Sat-Sun 1300-0500Z‡)
   UNICOM 122.95
   GREAT FALLS FSS (GTF) TF 1-800-WX-BRIEF. NOTAM FILE HLN.
   RCO 122.2 122.1R 117.7T (GREAT FALLS FSS)
   APP/DEP CON 119.5 (Mon-Fri 1300-0700Z‡, Sat-Sun 1300-0500Z‡)
   SALT LAKE CENTER APP/DEP CON 133.4 (Mon-Fri 0700-1300Z‡, Sat-Sun 0500-1300Z‡)
   TOWER 118.3 (Mon-Fri 1300-0700Z‡, Sat-Sun 1300-0500Z‡)   GND CON 121.9
RADIO AIDS TO NAVIGATION: NOTAM FILE HLN.
   (H) VORTAC 117.7   HLN   Chan 124   46°36'25"N 111°57'10"W   254° 1.2 NM to fld. 3810/16E.
      VORTAC unusable:
      006°-090° beyond 25 NM below 11,000'   091°-120° beyond 20 NM below 16,000'
      121°-240° beyond 25 NM below 10,000'   355°-006° beyond 15 NM below 17,500'
      241°-320° beyond 25 NM below 10,000'
   CAPITOL NDB (HW) 317   CVP   46°36'24"N 111°56'11"W   254° 1.9 NM to fld.
      NDB unmonitored when tower closed.
   HAUSER NDB (MHW) 386   HAU   46°34'08"N 111°45'26"W   268° 9.6 NM to fld.
   ILS 110.1 I-HLN Rwy 27 ILS unmonitored when tower closed.

VOR RECEIVER CHECK

Facility Name (Arpt Name)	Freq/Ident	Type Check Pt. Gnd. AB/ALT	Azimuth from Fac. Mag	Dist. from Fac. N.M.	Check Point Description
Helena (Helena Regional)	117.7/HLN	G	237	0.7	On Twy E midway between Twy C and Rwy 27.
Kalispell (Glacier Park Intl)	108.4/FCA	A/4000	316	6.4	Over apch end Rwy 29.
Lewistown (Lewistown Muni)	112.0/LWT	A/5200	072	5.4	Over apch end Rwy 07.
Livingston	116.1/LVM	A/6500	234	5.5	Over northern most radio twr NE of city.
Miles City (Frank Wiley Field)	112.1/MLS	G	036	4.2	On twy leading to Rwy 30.
Missoula (Missoula Intl)	112.8/MSO	G	340	0.6	On edge of ramp in front of Admin Building.

FIGURE 76.— VOR Indications and Excerpts from Airport/Facility Directory (HLN).

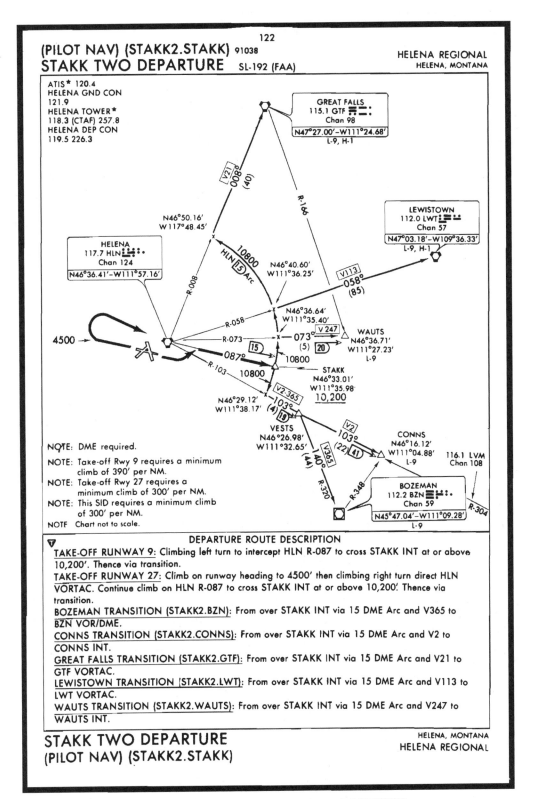

FIGURE 77.— STAKK TWO DEPARTURE.

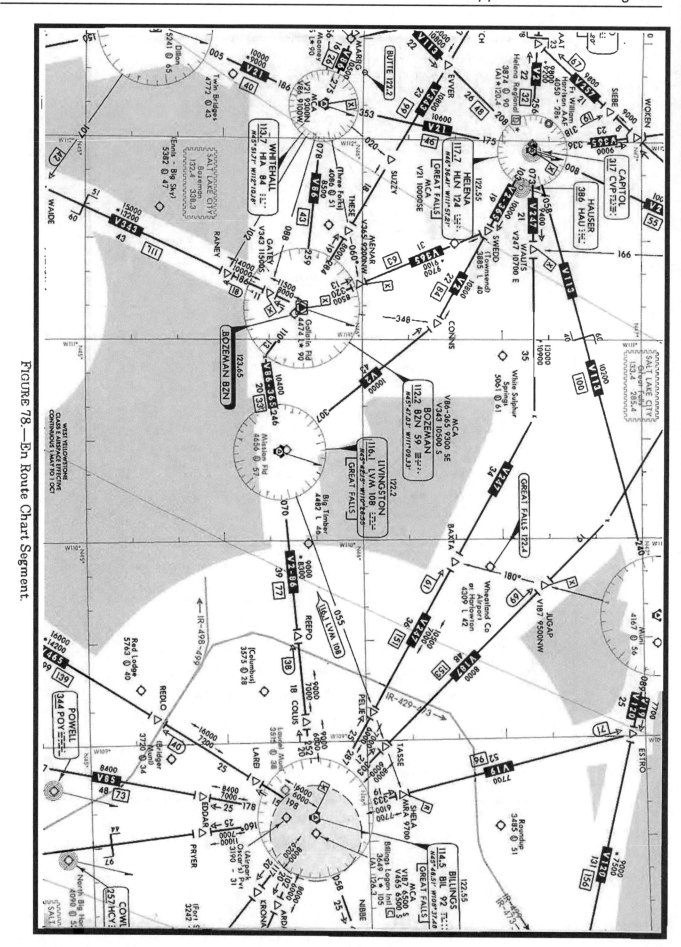

FIGURE 78.—En Route Chart Segment.

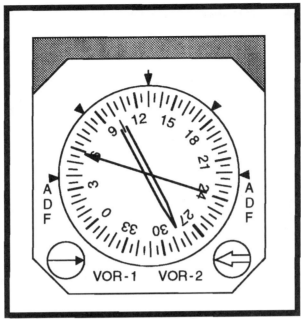

FIGURE 79.—RMI Indicator.

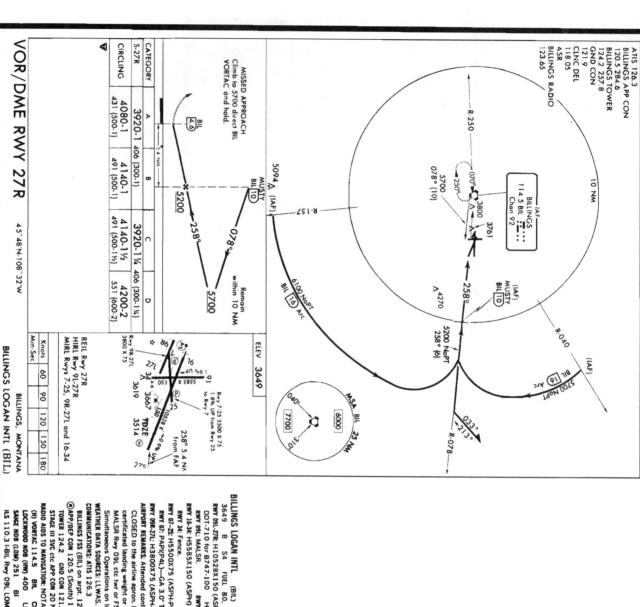

FIGURE 80.—VOR/DME RWY 27R and Airport/Facility Directory (BIL).

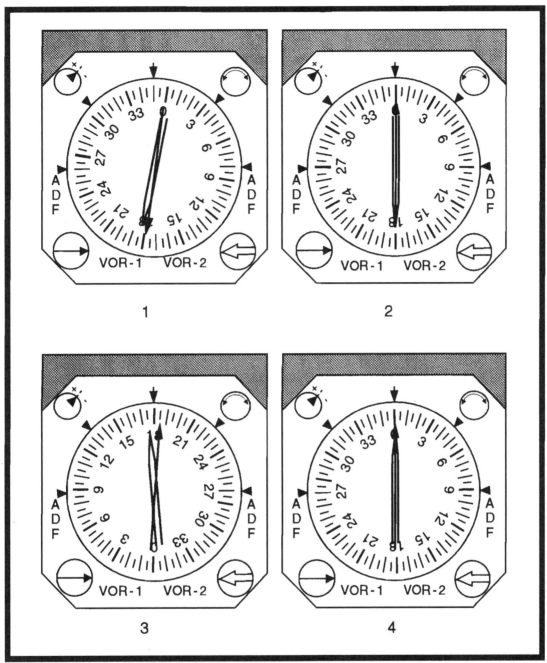

FIGURE 81.—Dual VOR System, VOT Check.

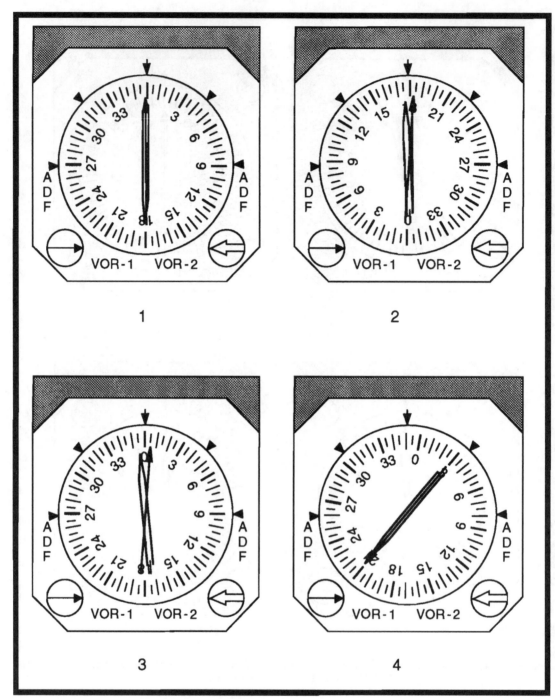

FIGURE 82.—Dual VOR System, Accuracy Check.

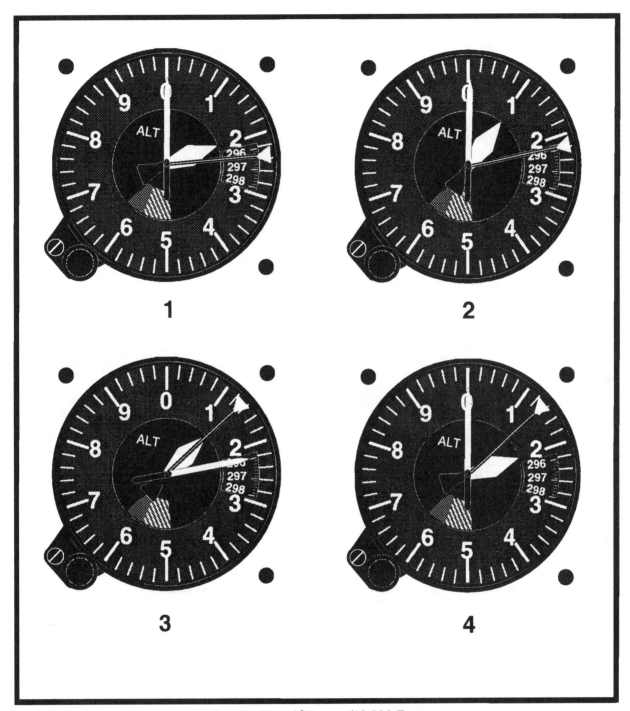

FIGURE 83.—Altimeter/12,000 Feet.

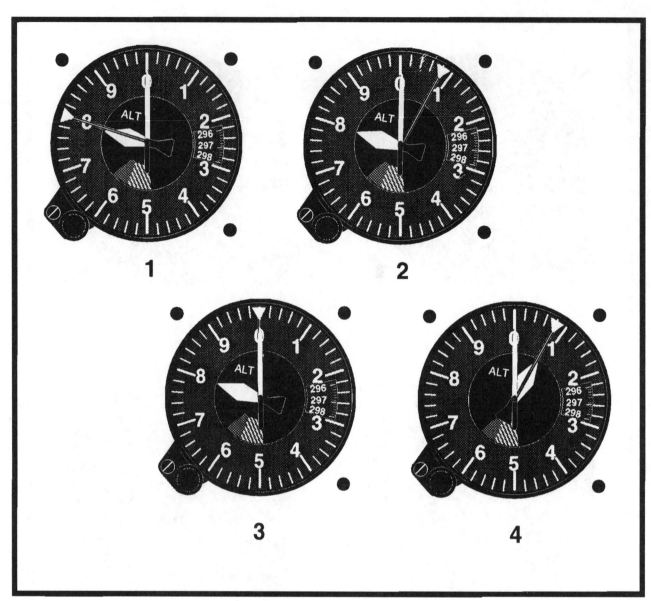

FIGURE 84.—Altimeter/8,000 Feet.

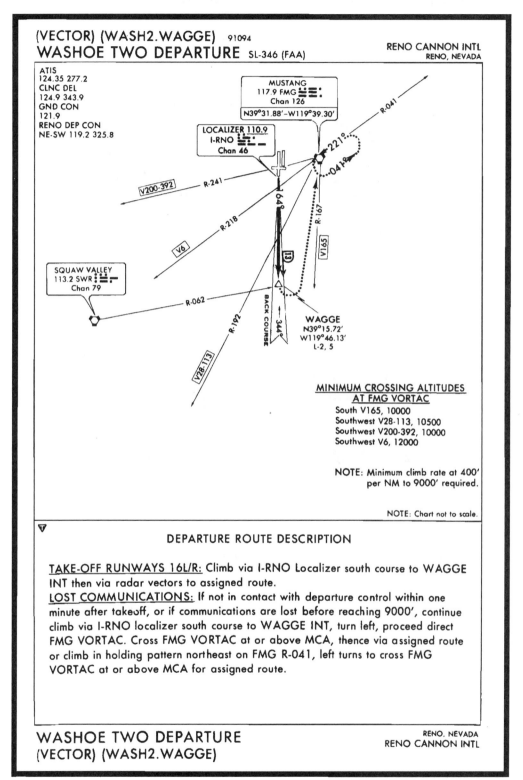

(VECTOR) (WASH2.WAGGE) 91094
WASHOE TWO DEPARTURE SL-346 (FAA)

RENO CANNON INTL
RENO, NEVADA

ATIS
124.35 277.2
CLNC DEL
124.9 343.9
GND CON
121.9
RENO DEP CON
NE-SW 119.2 325.8

MINIMUM CROSSING ALTITUDES
AT FMG VORTAC
South V165, 10000
Southwest V28-113, 10500
Southwest V200-392, 10000
Southwest V6, 12000

NOTE: Minimum climb rate at 400'
per NM to 9000' required.

NOTE: Chart not to scale.

DEPARTURE ROUTE DESCRIPTION

TAKE-OFF RUNWAYS 16L/R: Climb via I-RNO Localizer south course to WAGGE
INT then via radar vectors to assigned route.
LOST COMMUNICATIONS: If not in contact with departure control within one
minute after takeoff, or if communications are lost before reaching 9000', continue
climb via I-RNO localizer south course to WAGGE INT, turn left, proceed direct
FMG VORTAC. Cross FMG VORTAC at or above MCA, thence via assigned route
or climb in holding pattern northeast on FMG R-041, left turns to cross FMG
VORTAC at or above MCA for assigned route.

WASHOE TWO DEPARTURE
(VECTOR) (WASH2.WAGGE)

RENO, NEVADA
RENO CANNON INTL

FIGURE 85.—WASHOE TWO DEPARTURE.

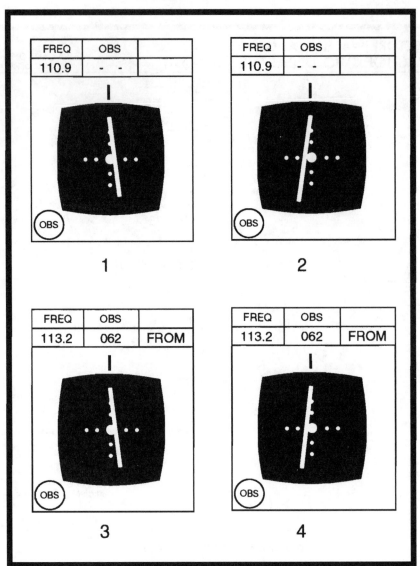

FIGURE 86.—CDI and OBS Indicators.

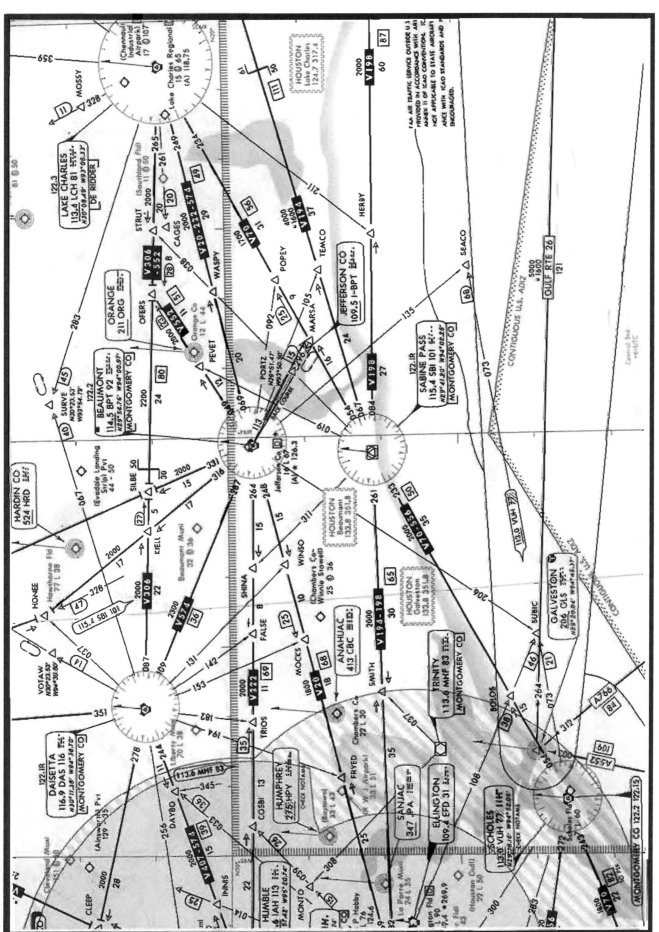

FIGURE 87.—En Route Chart Segment.

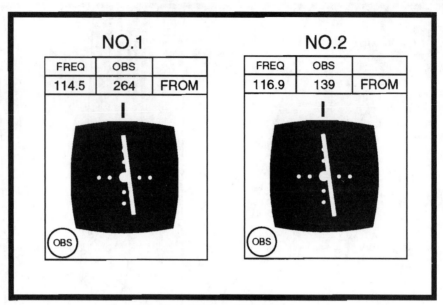

FIGURE 88.—CDI and OBS Indicators.

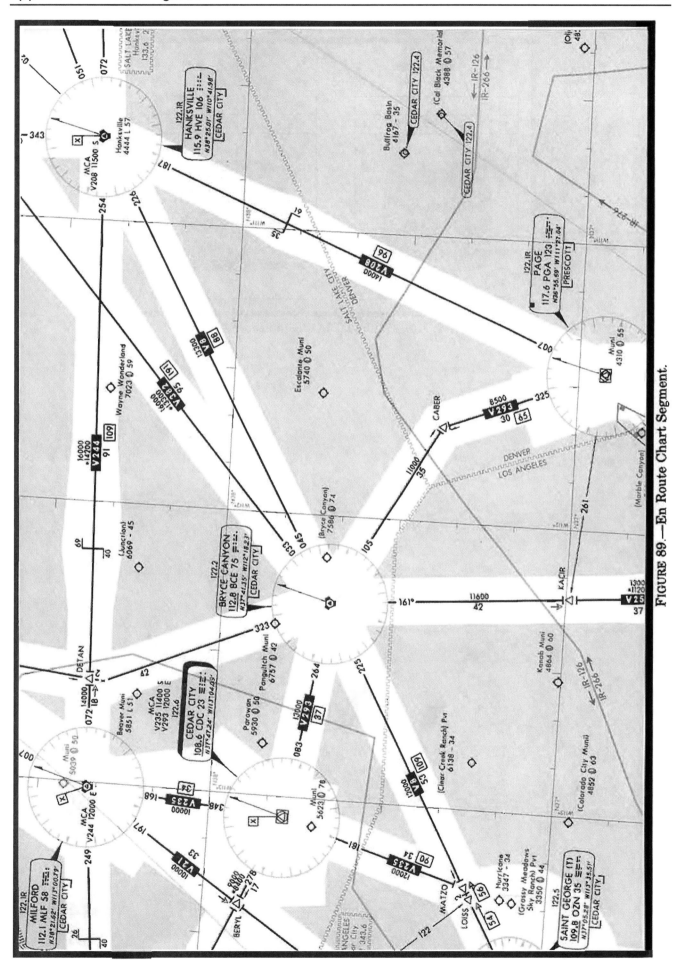

FIGURE 89.—En Route Chart Segment.

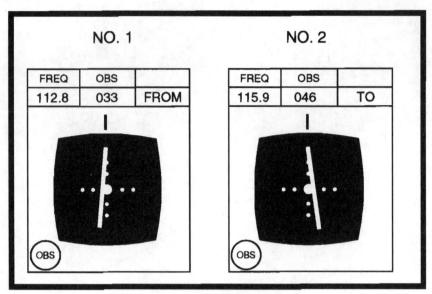

FIGURE 90.—CDI/OBS Indicators.

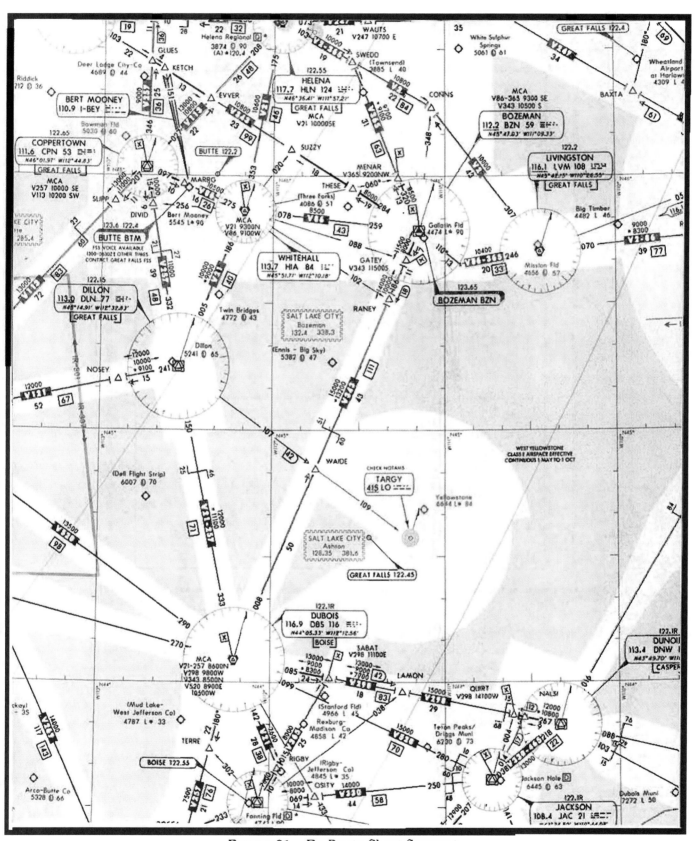

FIGURE 91.—En Route Chart Segment.

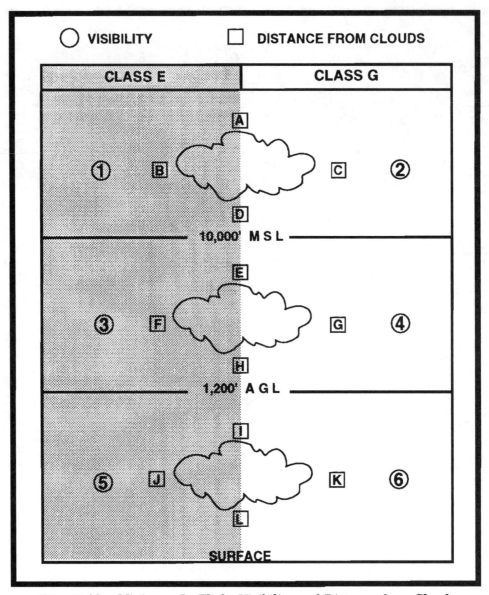

FIGURE 92.—Minimum In-Flight Visibility and Distance from Clouds.

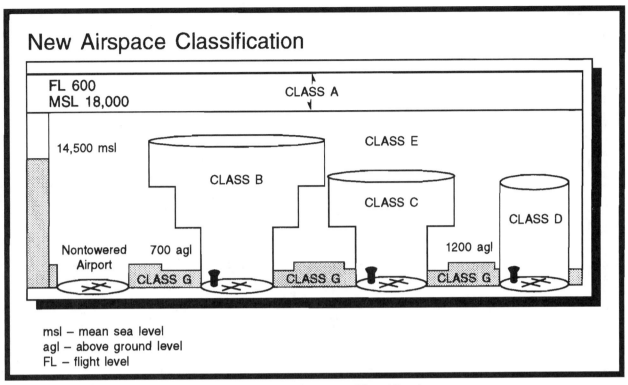

FIGURE 93.—New Airspace Classification.

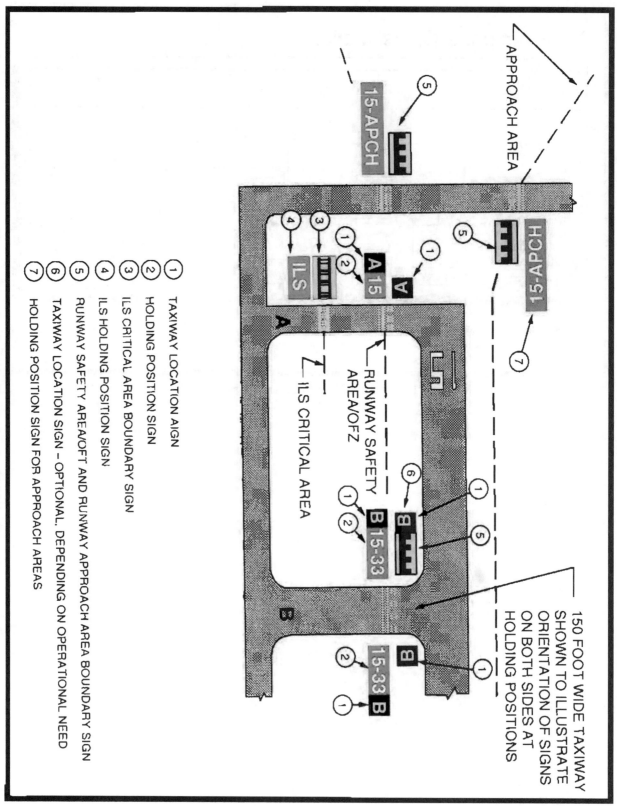

FIGURE 94.—Application Examples for Holding Positions.

① TAXIWAY LOCATION SIGN

② HOLDING POSITION SIGN

③ ILS CRITICAL AREA BOUNDARY SIGN

④ ILS HOLDING POSITION SIGN

⑤ RUNWAY SAFETY AREA/OFT AND RUNWAY APPROACH AREA BOUNDARY SIGN

⑥ TAXIWAY LOCATION SIGN – OPTIONAL, DEPENDING ON OPERATIONAL NEED

⑦ HOLDING POSITION SIGN FOR APPROACH AREAS

FREQ	N.M.	KNOTS	MIN
115.0	60.0	180	20.0

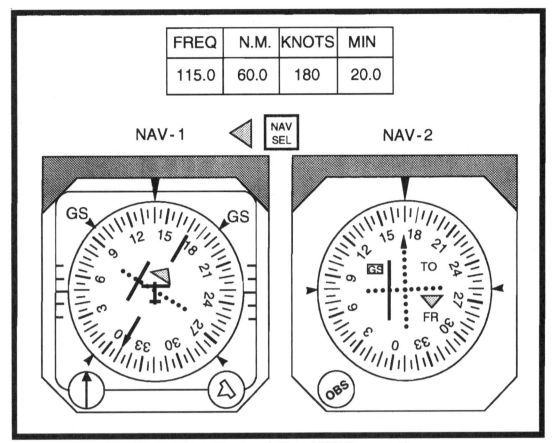

FIGURE 95.—No. 1 and No. 2 NAV Presentation.

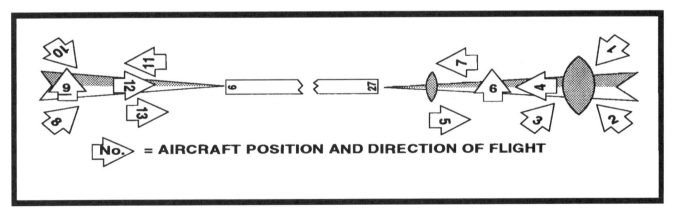

FIGURE 96.—Aircraft Position and Direction of Flight.

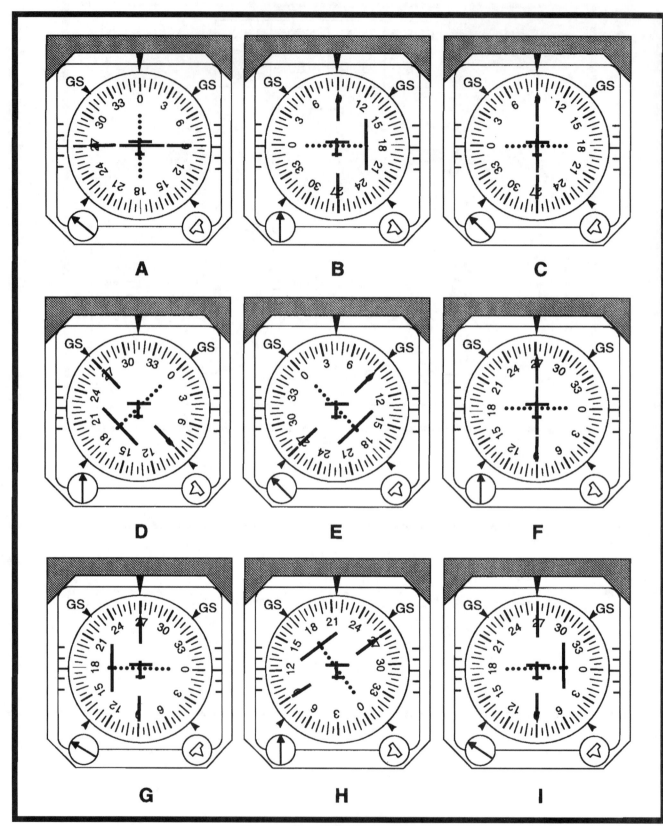

FIGURE 97.—HSI Presentation.

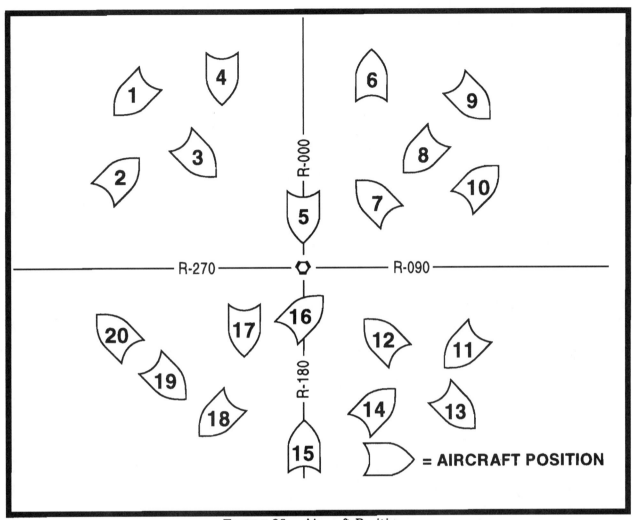

FIGURE 98.—Aircraft Position.

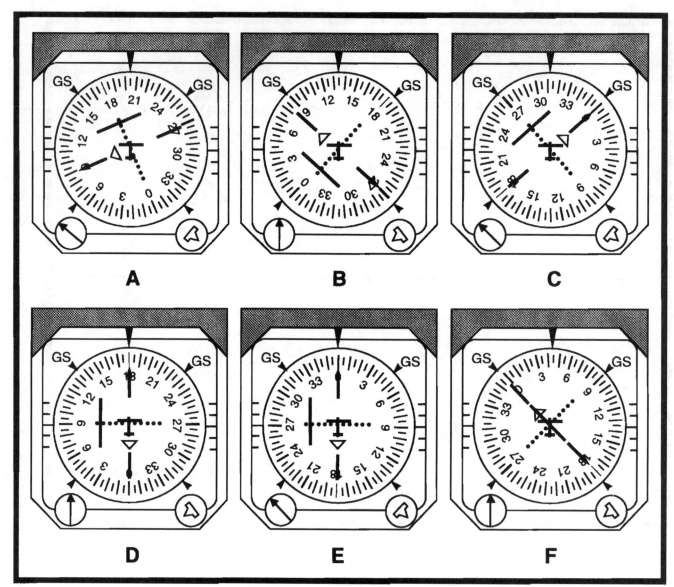

FIGURE 99.—HSI Presentation.

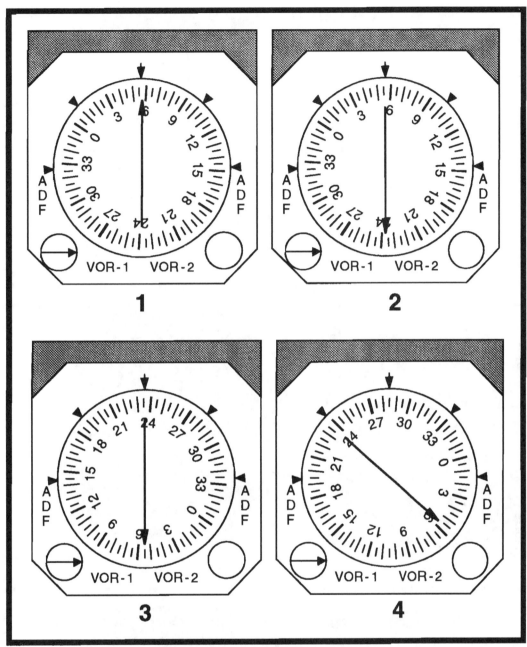

FIGURE 100.—RMI Illustrations.

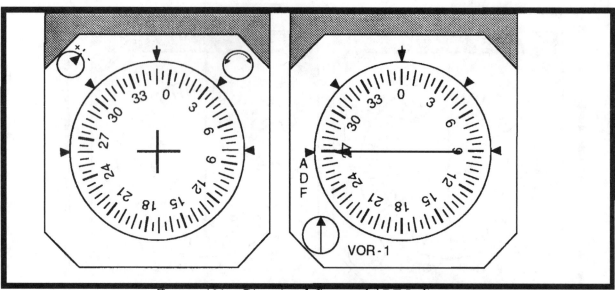

FIGURE 101.—Directional Gyro and ADF Indicator.

FIGURE 102.—Directional Gyro and ADF Indicator.

FIGURE 103.—Directional Gyro and ADF Indicator.

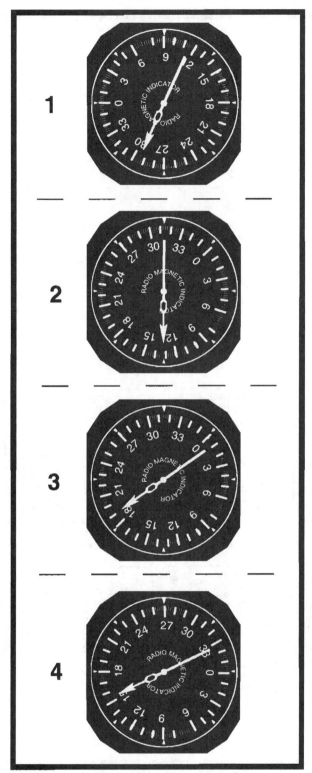

FIGURE 104.—Radio Magnetic Indicator.

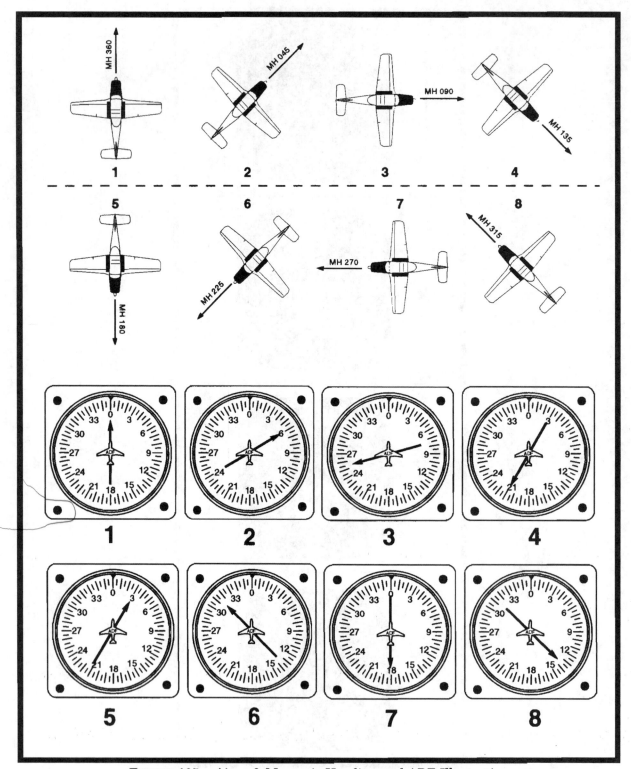

FIGURE 105.—Aircraft Magnetic Heading and ADF Illustration.

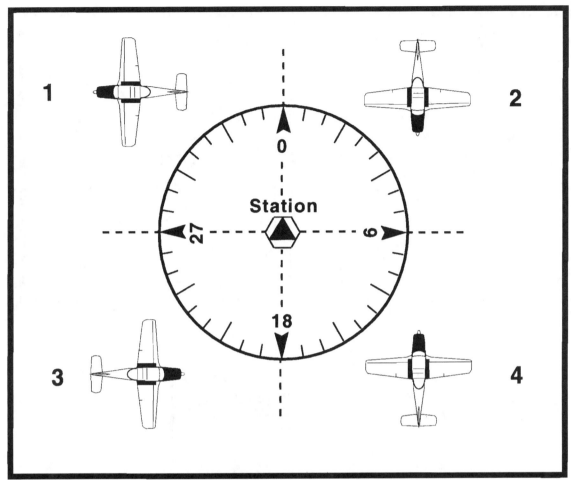

FIGURE 106.—Aircraft Location Relative to VOR.

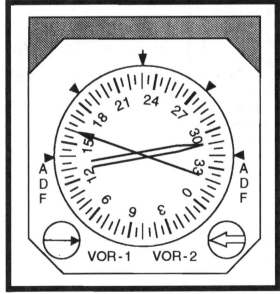

FIGURE 107.—RMI — DME — ARC
Illustration Wind Component.

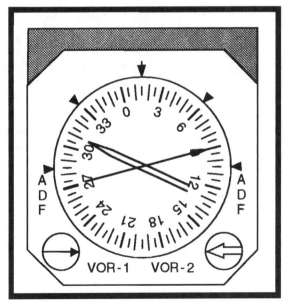

FIGURE 108.—RMI — DME — ARC
Illustration Wind Component.

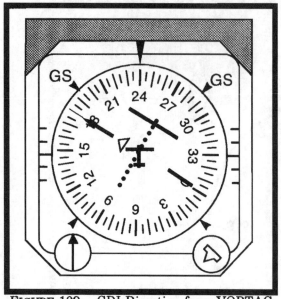

FIGURE 109.—CDI Direction from VORTAC.

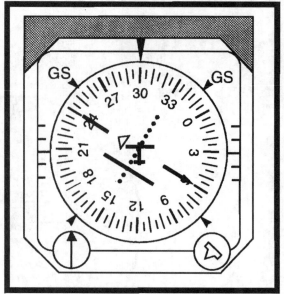

FIGURE 110.—CDI Direction from VORTAC.

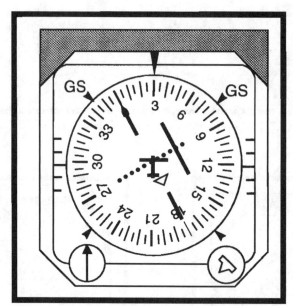

FIGURE 111.—CDI Direction from VORTAC.

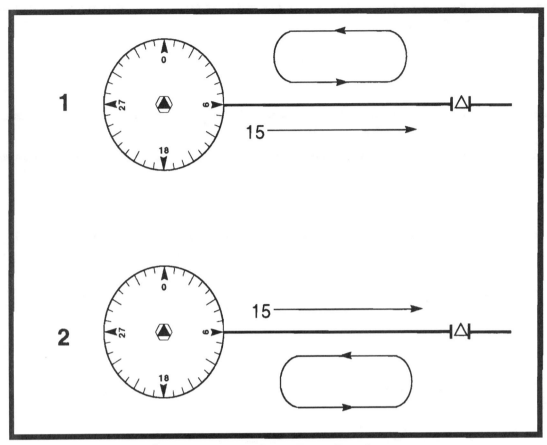

FIGURE 112.—Holding Entry Pocedure.

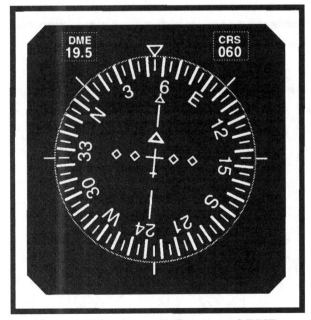

FIGURE 113.—Aircraft Course and DME
Indicator.

FIGURE 114.—Aircraft Course and DME
Indicator.

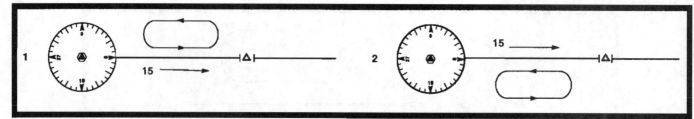

FIGURE 115.—DME Fix with Holding Pattern.

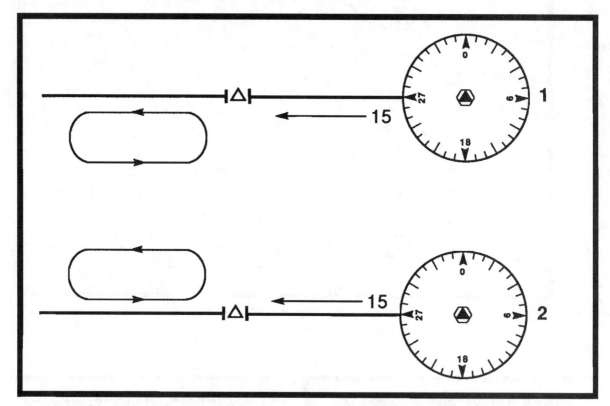

FIGURE 116.—Holding Entry Procedure.

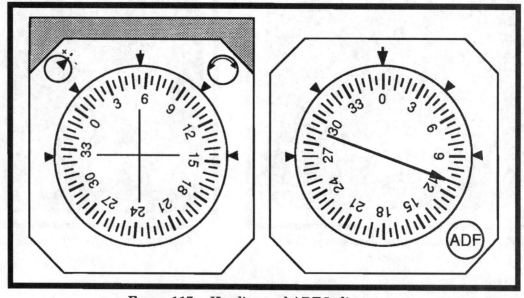

FIGURE 117.—Heading and ADF Indicators.

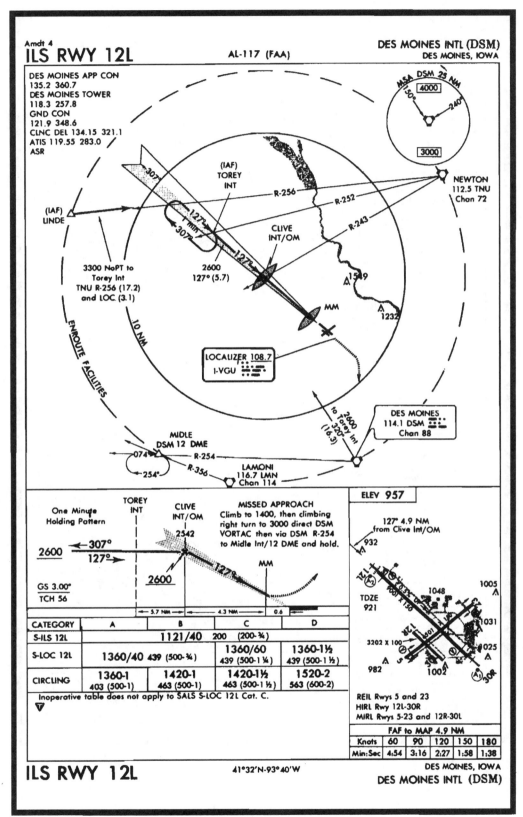

FIGURE 118.—ILS RWY 12L (DSM).

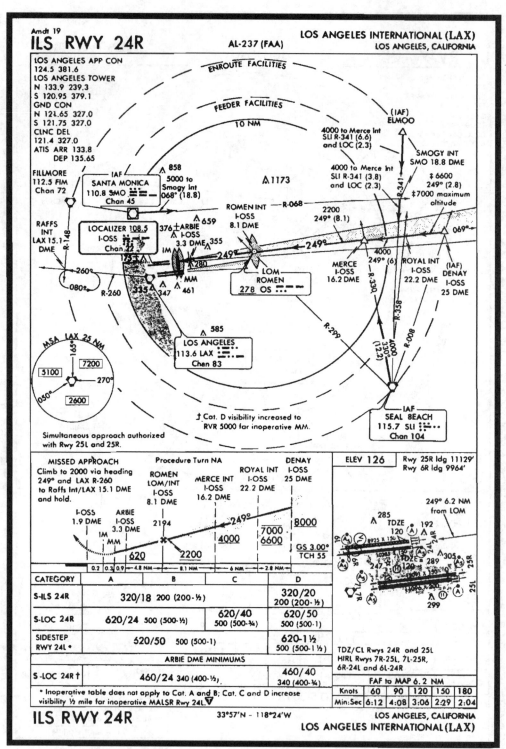

FIGURE 119.—ILS RWY 24R (LAX).

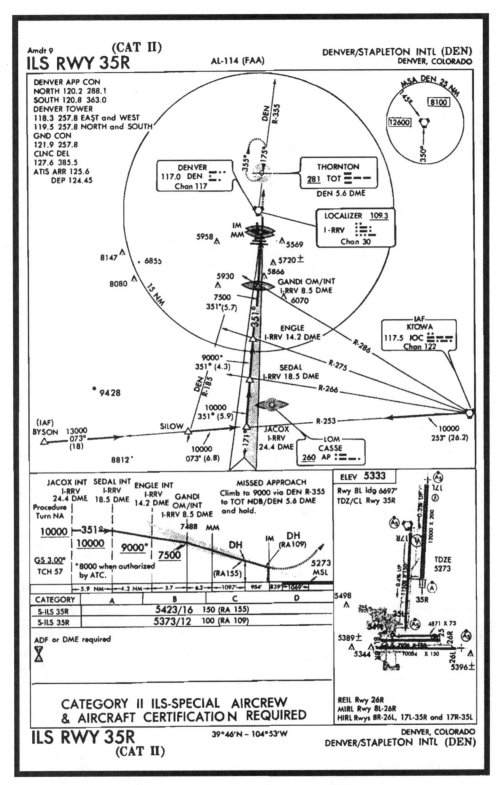

FIGURE 120.—ILS RWY 35R (DEN).

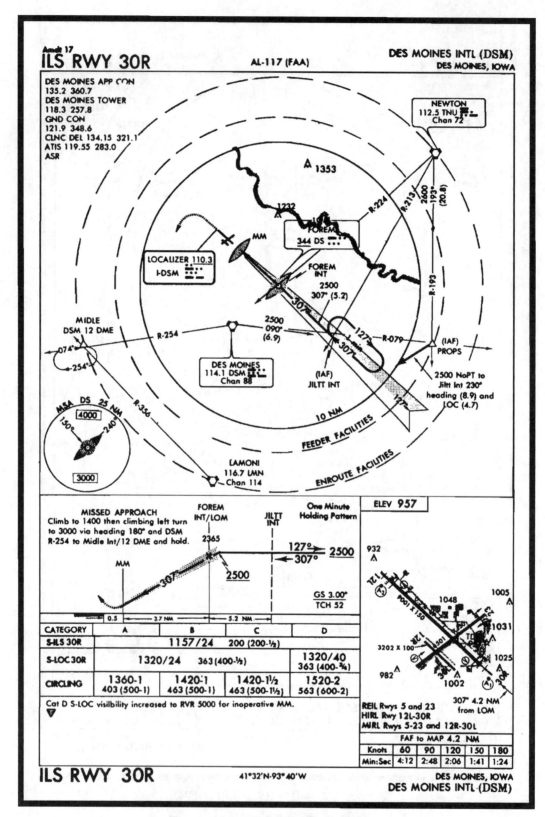

FIGURE 121.—ILS RWY 30R (DSM).

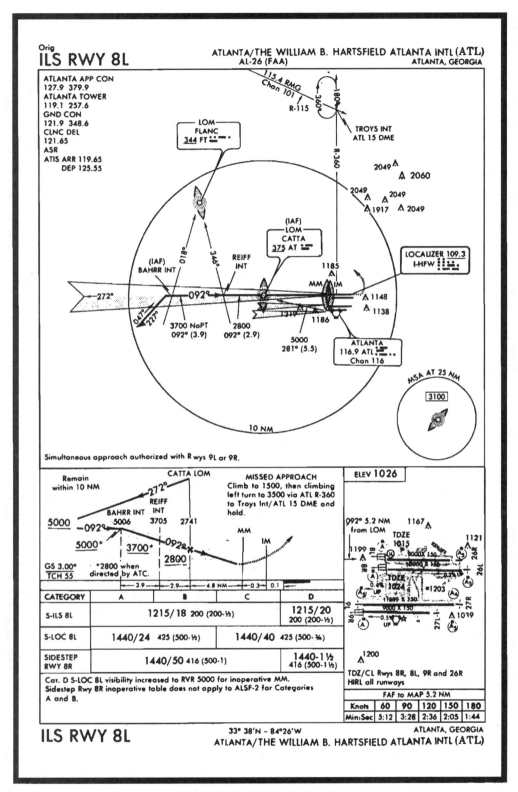

FIGURE 122.—ILS RWY 8L (ATL).

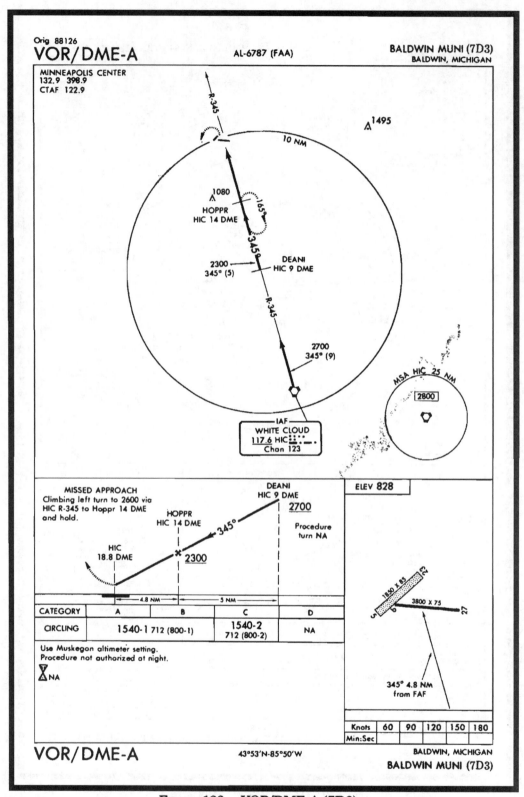

Orig 88126
VOR/DME-A   AL-6787 (FAA)   **BALDWIN MUNI (7D3)**
                                                              BALDWIN, MICHIGAN

MINNEAPOLIS CENTER
132.9 398.9
CTAF 122.9

R-345

△ 1495

10 NM

△ 1080

HOPPR
HIC 14 DME

165°

345°

2300
345° (5)

DEANI
HIC 9 DME

R-345

2700
345° (9)

MSA HIC 25 NM
2800

IAF
WHITE CLOUD
117.6 HIC
Chan 123

MISSED APPROACH   DEANI
Climbing left turn to 2600 via   HIC 9 DME
HIC R-345 to Hoppr 14 DME   **2700**
and hold.   HOPPR
                                   HIC 14 DME   Procedure
                                        345°   turn NA
          HIC
          18.8 DME   ✕ **2300**

ELEV 828

1850 X 85
3800 X 75
5
23
27

345° 4.8 NM
from FAF

	4.8 NM	5 NM	
CATEGORY	**A**	**B**	**C**	**D**
CIRCLING	1540-1 712 (800-1)		1540-2 712 (800-2)	NA

Use Muskegon altimeter setting.
Procedure not authorized at night.

⊠ NA

Knots	60	90	120	150	180
Min:Sec					

VOR/DME-A   43°53'N-85°50'W   **BALDWIN, MICHIGAN**
                                                       BALDWIN MUNI (7D3)

FIGURE 123.—VOR/DME-A (7D3).

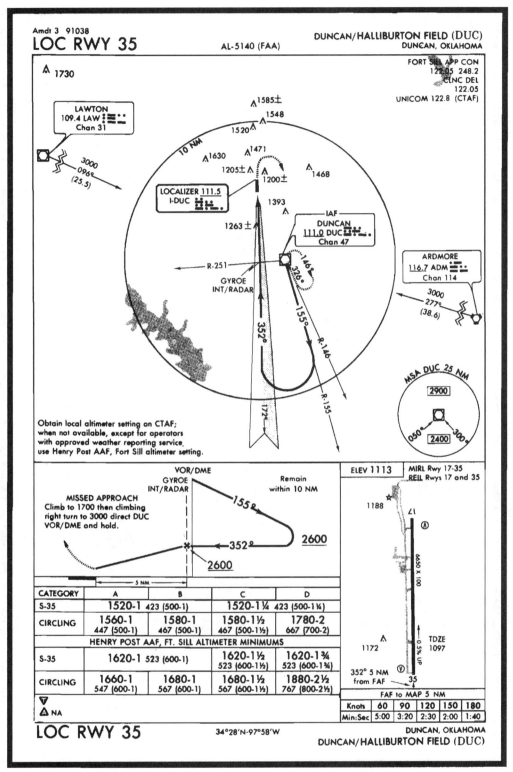

FIGURE 124.—LOC RWY 35, Duncan, Oklahoma.

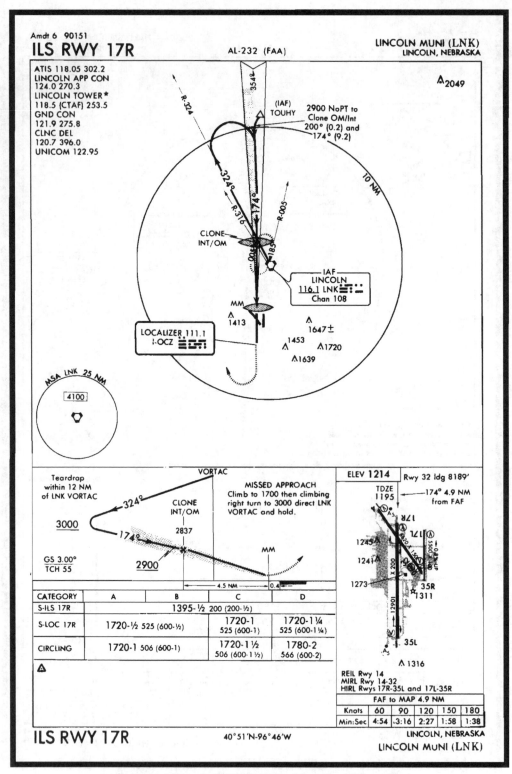

FIGURE 125.—ILS RWY 17R, Lincoln, Nebraska.

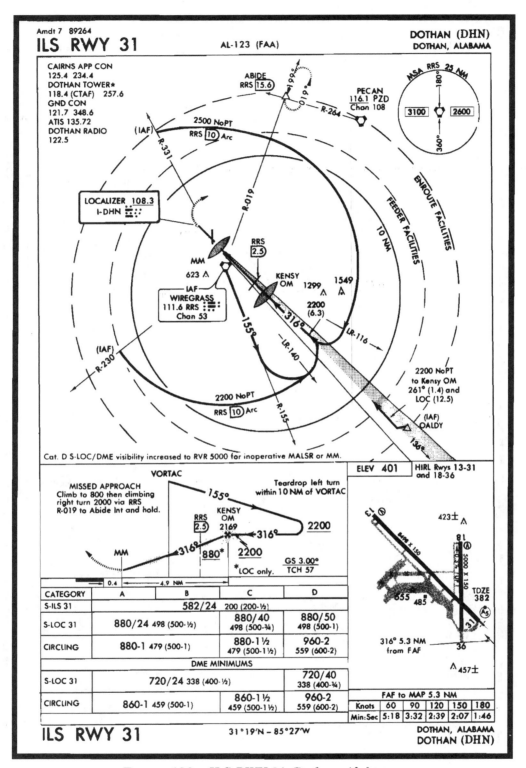

FIGURE 126.—ILS RWY 31, Dothan, Alabama.

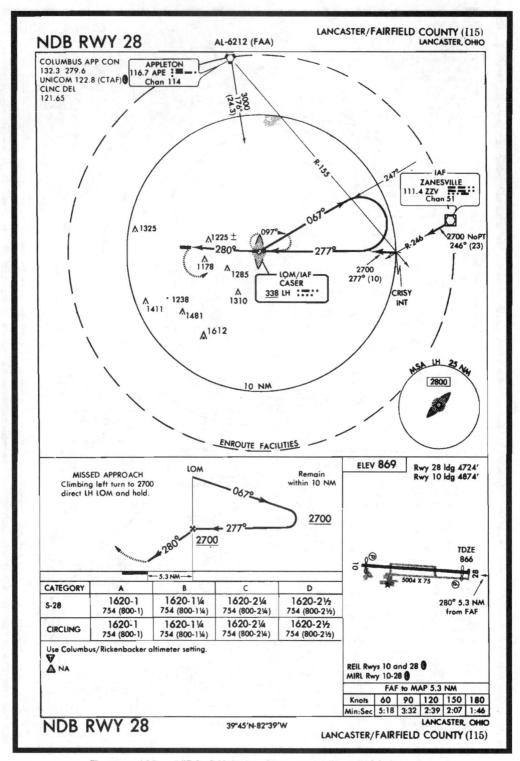

FIGURE 127.—NDB RWY 28, Lancaster/Fairfield County.

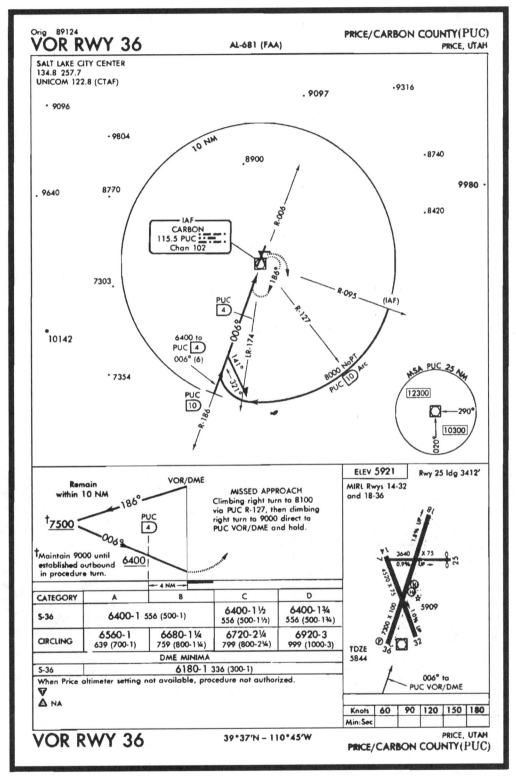

FIGURE 128.—VOR RWY 36 (PUC).

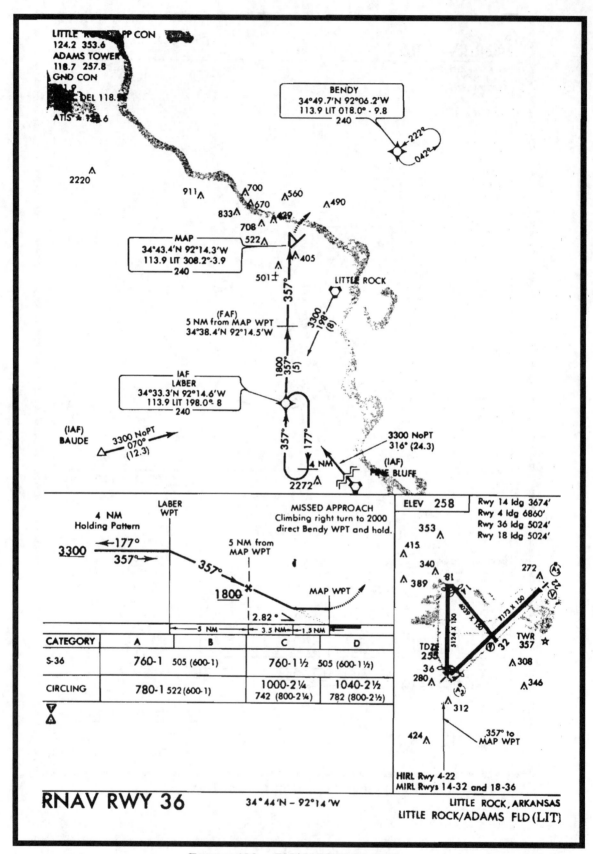

FIGURE 129.—RNAV RWY 36 (LIT).

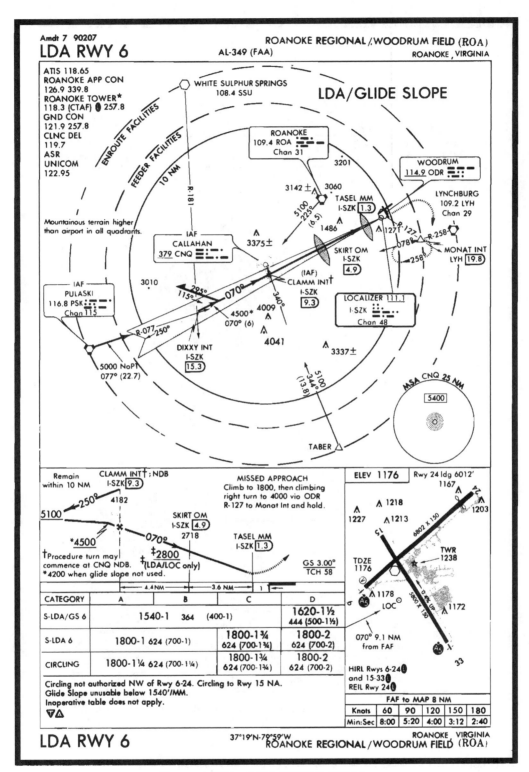

FIGURE 130.—LDA RWY 6 (ROA).

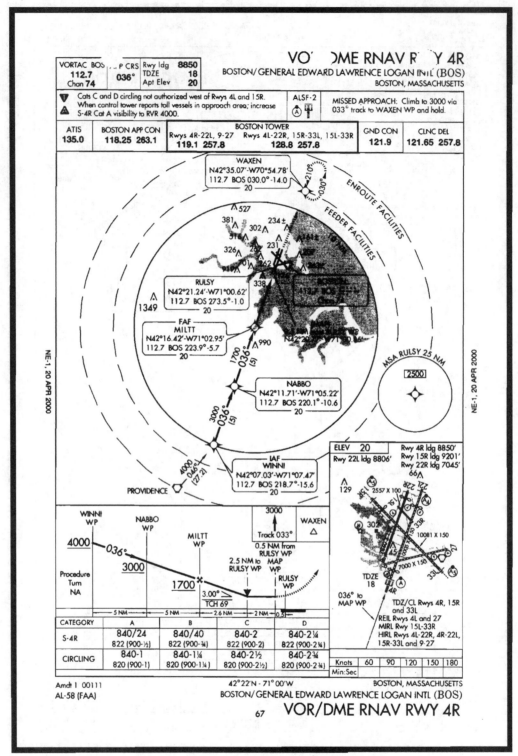

FIGURE 131.—VOR/DME RNAV RWY 4R.

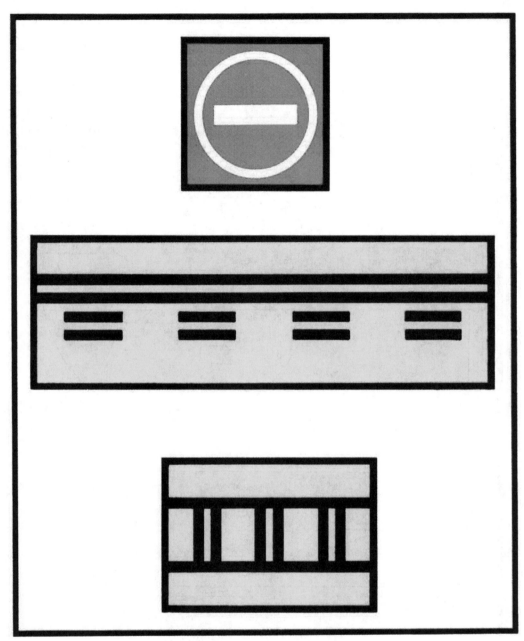

Figure 132 — Airport Signs.

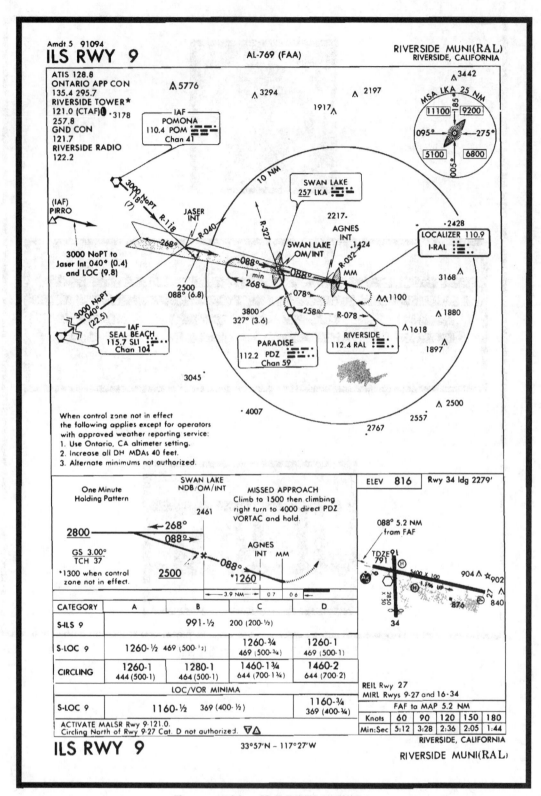

FIGURE 133.—ILS RWY 9 (RAL).

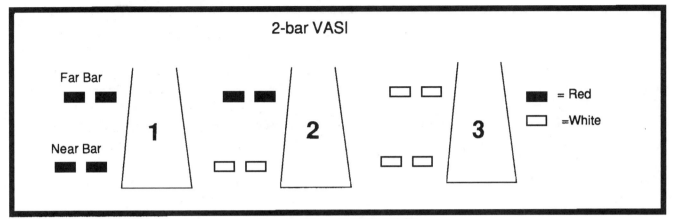

FIGURE 134.—2-BAR VASI.

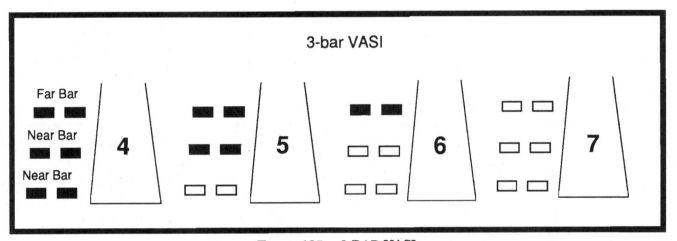

FIGURE 135.—3-BAR VASI.

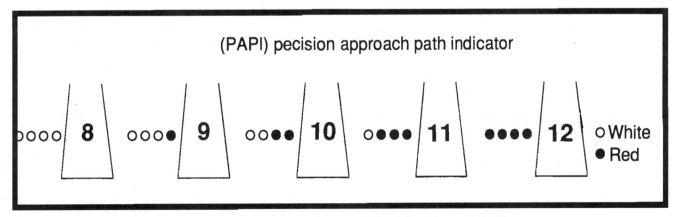

FIGURE 136.—Precision Approach Path Indicator (PAPI).

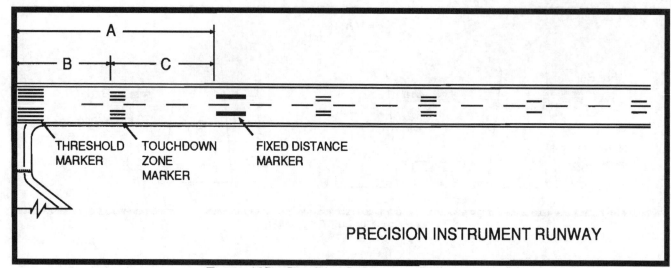

FIGURE 137.—Precision Instrument Runway.

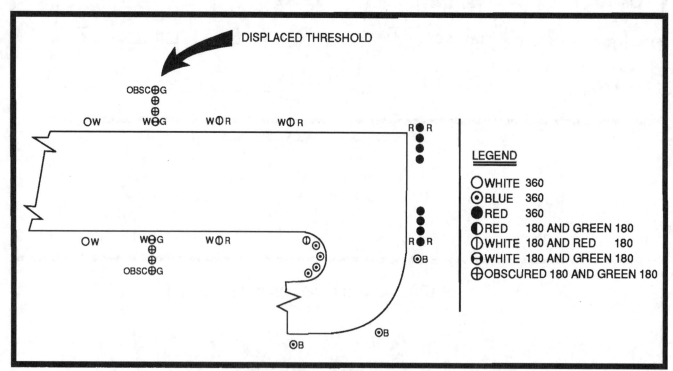

FIGURE 138.—Runway Legend.

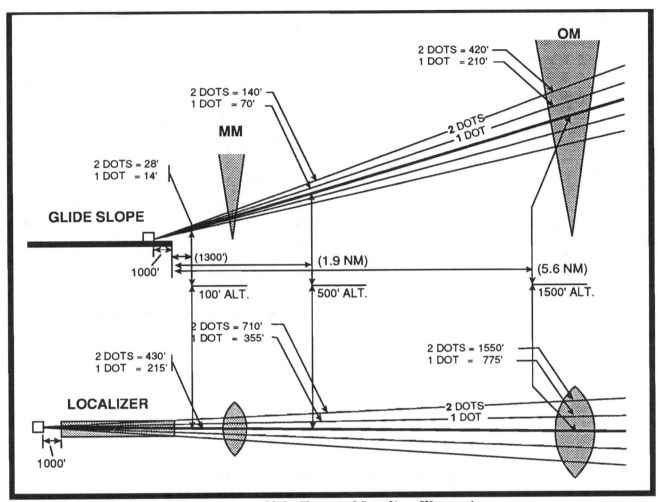

FIGURE 139.—Glide Slope and Localizer Illustration.

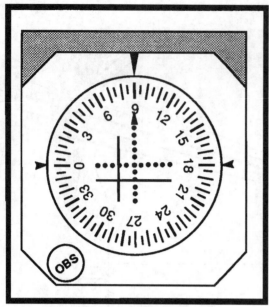

FIGURE 140.—OBS, ILS, and
GS Displacement.

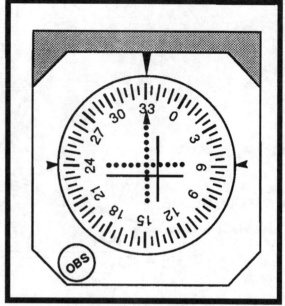

FIGURE 141.—OBS, ILS, and
GS Displacement.

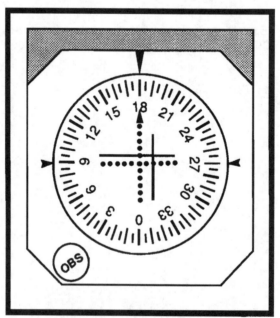

FIGURE 142.—OBS, ILS, and
GS Displacement.

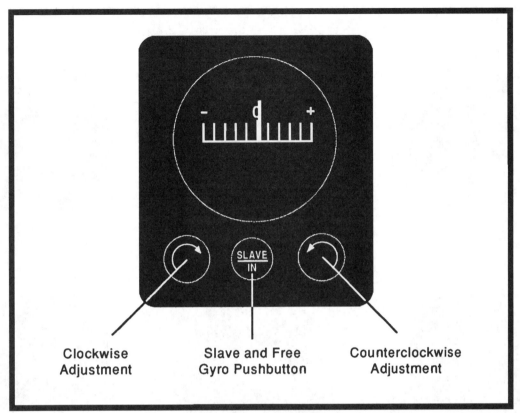

FIGURE 143.—Slaved Gyro Illustration.

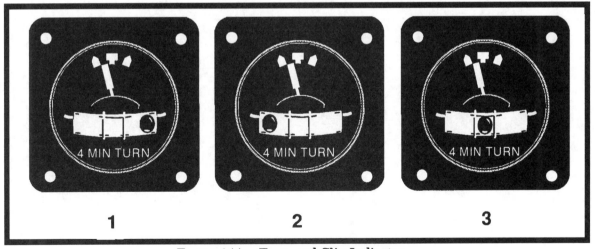

FIGURE 144.—Turn-and-Slip Indicator.

FIGURE 145.—Instrument Sequence (Unusual Attitude).

FIGURE 146.—Instrument Sequence (System Failed).

FIGURE 147.—Instrument Sequence (Unusual Attitude).

FIGURE 148.—Instrument Interpretation (System Malfunction).

FIGURE 149.—Instrument Interpretation (System Malfunction).

FIGURE 150.—Instrument Interpretation (Instrument Malfunction).

FIGURE 151.—Instrument Interpretation (Instrument Malfunction).

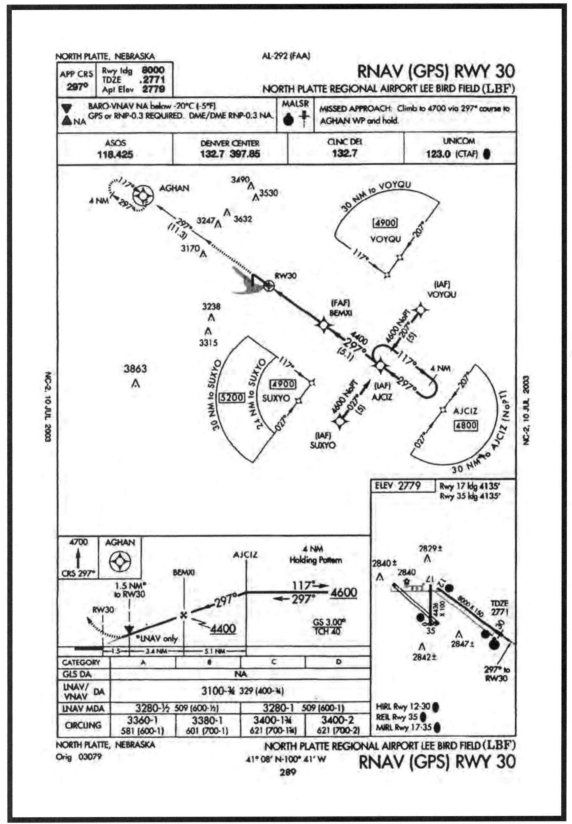

FIGURE 152.—RNAV (GPS) RWY 30, North Plate Regional Airport Lee Bird Field (LBF).

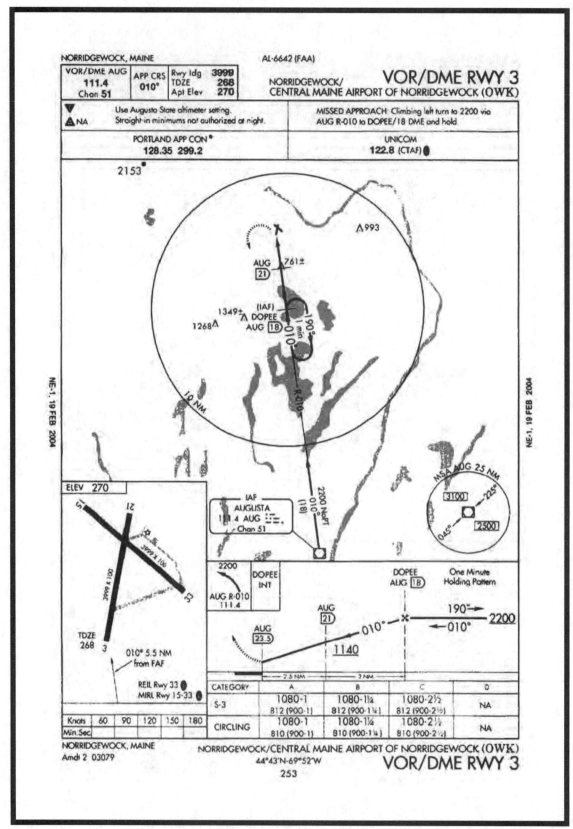

FIGURE 153.—VOR/DME RWY 3, Norridgewock/Central Maine Airport of Norridgewock (OWK).

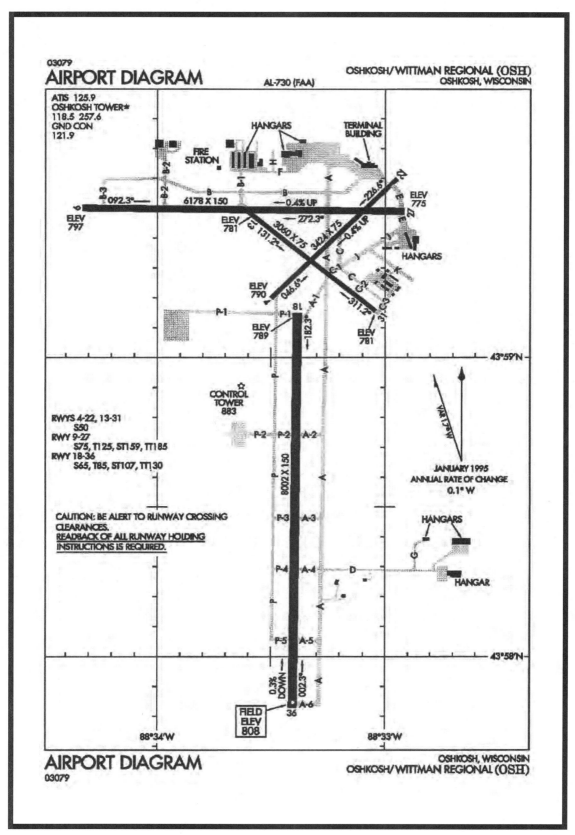

FIGURE 154.—Osh Kosh/Wittman Regional (OSH).

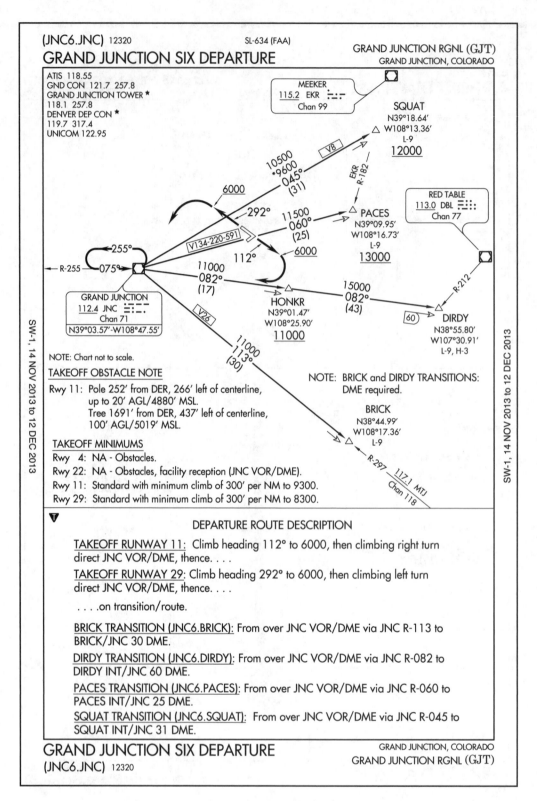

GRAND JUNCTION SIX DEPARTURE

(JNC6.JNC) 12320 · SL-634 (FAA) · GRAND JUNCTION RGNL (GJT) · GRAND JUNCTION, COLORADO

ATIS 118.55
GND CON 121.7 257.8
GRAND JUNCTION TOWER ★
118.1 257.8
DENVER DEP CON ★
119.7 317.4
UNICOM 122.95

NOTE: Chart not to scale.

TAKEOFF OBSTACLE NOTE

Rwy 11: Pole 252' from DER, 266' left of centerline,
up to 20' AGL/4880' MSL.
Tree 1691' from DER, 437' left of centerline,
100' AGL/5019' MSL.

TAKEOFF MINIMUMS

Rwy 4: NA - Obstacles.
Rwy 22: NA - Obstacles, facility reception (JNC VOR/DME).
Rwy 11: Standard with minimum climb of 300' per NM to 9300.
Rwy 29: Standard with minimum climb of 300' per NM to 8300.

NOTE: BRICK and DIRDY TRANSITIONS:
DME required.

DEPARTURE ROUTE DESCRIPTION

<u>TAKEOFF RUNWAY 11:</u> Climb heading 112° to 6000, then climbing right turn
direct JNC VOR/DME, thence. . . .

<u>TAKEOFF RUNWAY 29:</u> Climb heading 292° to 6000, then climbing left turn
direct JNC VOR/DME, thence. . . .

. . . .on transition/route.

<u>BRICK TRANSITION (JNC6.BRICK):</u> From over JNC VOR/DME via JNC R-113 to
BRICK/JNC 30 DME.

<u>DIRDY TRANSITION (JNC6.DIRDY):</u> From over JNC VOR/DME via JNC R-082 to
DIRDY INT/JNC 60 DME.

<u>PACES TRANSITION (JNC6.PACES):</u> From over JNC VOR/DME via JNC R-060 to
PACES INT/JNC 25 DME.

<u>SQUAT TRANSITION (JNC6.SQUAT):</u> From over JNC VOR/DME via JNC R-045 to
SQUAT INT/JNC 31 DME.

GRAND JUNCTION SIX DEPARTURE   GRAND JUNCTION, COLORADO
(JNC6.JNC) 12320   GRAND JUNCTION RGNL (GJT)

SW-1, 14 NOV 2013 to 12 DEC 2013

Figure 155

13178

14 NOV 2013 to 12 DEC 2013

14 NOV 2013 to 12 DEC 2013

HOT SPOTS

An "airport surface hot spot" is a location on an aerodrome movement area with a history or potential risk of collision or runway incursion, and where heightened attention by pilots/drivers is necessary.

A "hot spot" is a runway safety related problem area on an airport that presents increased risk during surface operations. Typically it is a complex or confusing taxiway/taxiway or taxiway/runway intersection. The area of increased risk has either a history of or potential for runway incursions or surface incidents, due to a variety of causes, such as but not limited to: airport layout, traffic flow, airport marking, signage and lighting, situational awareness, and training. Hot spots are depicted on airport diagrams as open circles or polygons designated as "HS 1", "HS 2", etc. and tabulated in the list below with a brief description of each hot spot. Hot spots will remain charted on airport diagrams until such time the increased risk has been reduced or eliminated.

CITY/AIRPORT	HOT SPOT	DESCRIPTION*
ALAMOGORDO, NM		
HOLLOMAN AFB (HMN)	HS1	Twy R, Twy G, and Twy L have multiple hold lines for Rwy 07-25 and Rwy 04-22. Contact tower if confused or lost.
	HS2	Hold line on Twy /EOR A and Twy/EOR H have multiple POV access roads, possibility of high vehicle traffic.
	HS3	Hold line on Twy /EOR B and Twy C for Rwy 07-25 have multiple POV access roads, possibility of high vehicle traffic.
	HS4	Multiple hold lines at intersecting rwys. Landing/departing aircraft disregard hold lines, taxiing aircraft contact tower prior to crossing hold lines.
	HS5	Multiple hold lines where rwys intersect. Hold line also at Twy D. Contact tower if confused or lost.
	HS6	POV crossing controlled by tower. Hold line located on each side of Rwy 07-25. Possibility of high vehicular traffic.
ALBUQUERQUE, NM		
ALBUQUERQUE INTL		
SUNPORT (ABQ)	HS 1	Hold Position Marking on Twy E1 for Rwy 08 and Rwy 12.
	HS 2	Twy G1 from Cutter Aviation ramp and Rwy 12-30.
	HS 3	Complex int at Twy F, Twy C, Twy G. Twy G and Rwy 03-21
ASPEN, CO		
ASPEN-PITKIN COUNTY /		
SARDY FIELD (ASE)	HS 1	Twy A2. Short taxi distance from ramp to rwy.
	HS 2	Twy A3. Short taxi distance from ramp to rwy.
	HS 3	Twy A4. Short taxi distance from ramp to rwy.
COLORADO SPRINGS, CO		
CITY OF COLORADO		
SPRINGS (COS)	HS 1	The apch ends of Rwy 13 and Rwy 17R; and Twy A1.
	HS 2	Twy A4 and Twy G at Rwy 17R-35L.
	HS 3	Int of Twy E4, Twy G, Twy H and Twy E.
	HS 4	Apch ends of Rwy 35R and Rwy 35L.
DENVER, CO		
CENTENNIAL (APA)	HS 1	Rwy 17L at Twy A1.
	HS 2	Twy A, Twy A8, Twy A9 and Twy C1 congested INT.
	HS 3	Twy C1 and Twy D1 close proximity to Rwy 10.
DENVER, CO		
DENVER INTL (DEN)	HS 1	Rwy 35L hold signs may not be visible from Twy SC or Twy A until entering Twy M, pilots sometimes enter Rwy 35L without authorization.
	HS 2	Rwy 17R Apch Hold Position.
DENVER, CO		
ROCKY MOUNTAIN		
METROPOLITAN (BJC)	HS 1	Frequent helicopter operations.
	HS 2	Multiple hold lines in close proximity. Hold line on Twy B south of Rwy 11R-29L is prior to Twy D.
EAGLE, CO		
EAGLE COUNTY RGNL (EGE)	HS 1	High density parking area.
GRAND JUNCTION, CO		
GRAND JUNCTION RGNL (GJT)	HS 1	Rwy 22 and Rwy 29 close proximity, wrong rwy departure risk.

13178

Figure 156

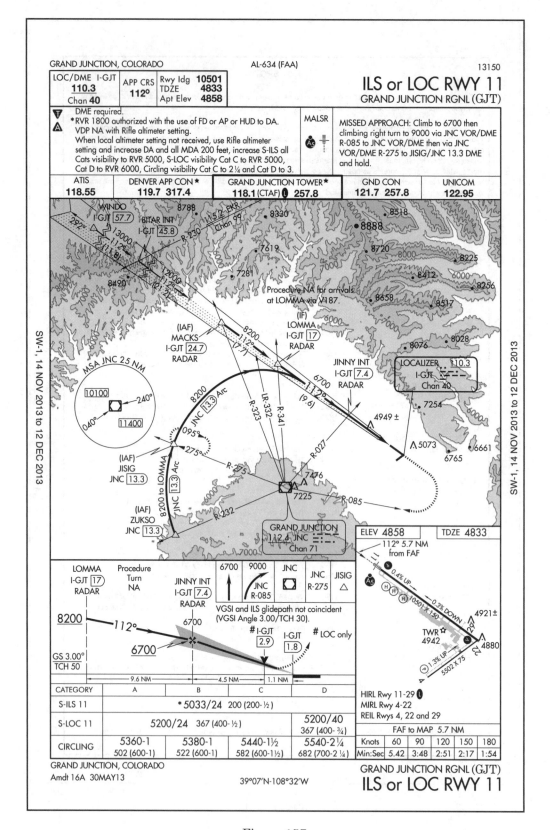

Figure 157

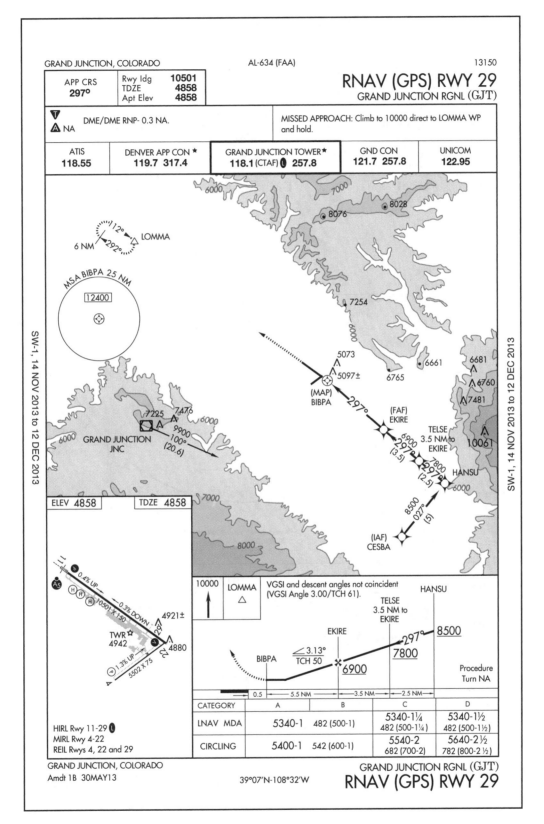

Figure 158

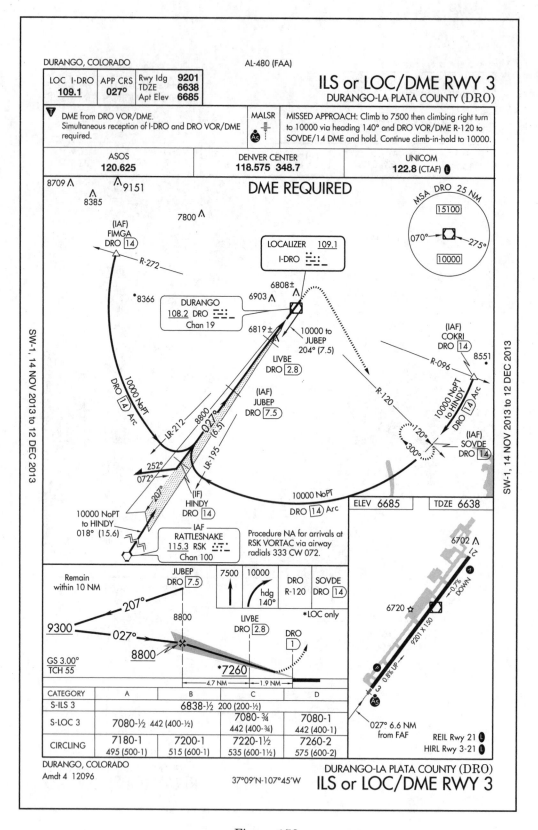

Figure 159

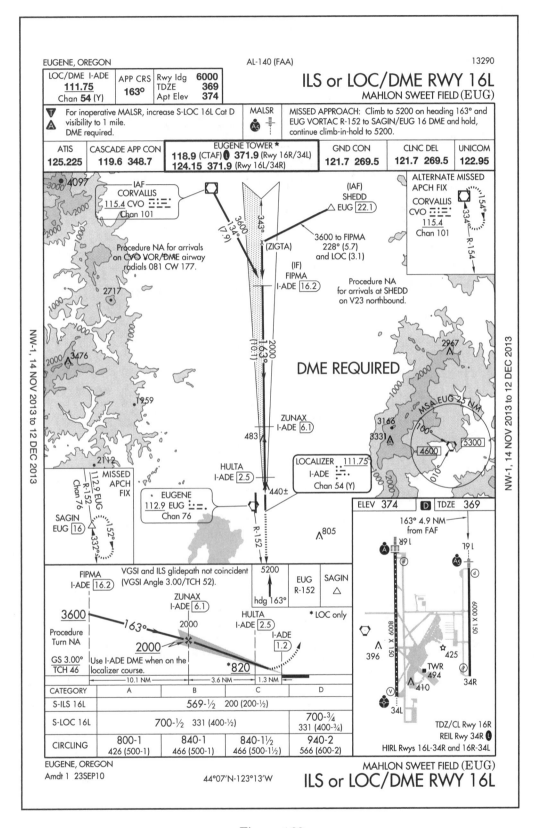

Figure 160

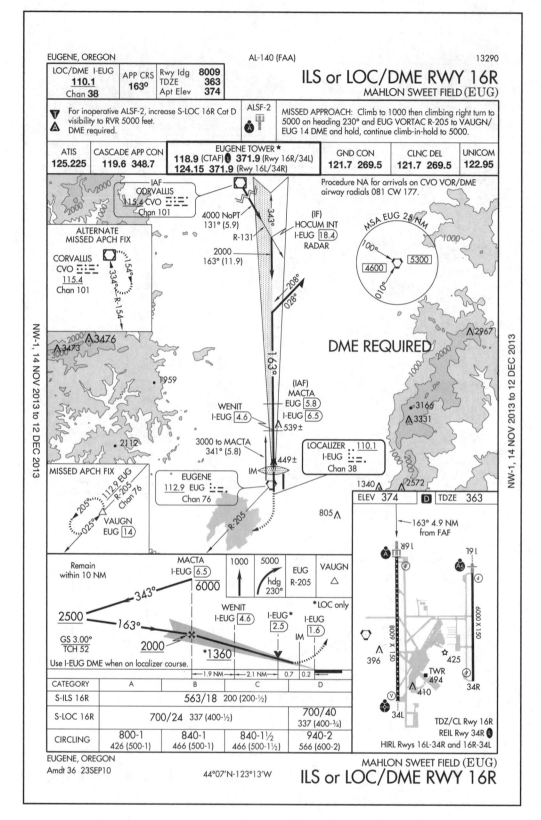

Figure 161

OREGON   119

EUGENE

MAHLON SWEET FLD (EUG) 7 NW UTC–8(–7DT) N44°07.48´ W123°12.72´

KLAMATH FALLS
H–1B, L–1B
IAP, AD

374 B S4 **FUEL** 100LL, JET A OX 1, 2, 3, 4 TPA—1174(800) Class I, ARFF Index B
NOTAM FILE EUG

RWY 16R–34L: H8009X150 (ASPH–GRVD) S–75, D–200, 2D–400
HIRL CL

RWY 16R: ALSF2. TDZL. PAPI(P4L)—GA 3.0° TCH 50´.

RWY 34L: ODALS. VASI(V4L)—GA 3.0° TCH 53´.

RWY 16L–34R: H6000X150 (ASPH–GRVD) S–105, D–175, 2D–240
HIRL

RWY 16L: MALSR. PAPI(P4L)—GA 3.0° TCH 52´.

RWY 34R: REIL. PAPI(P4L)—GA 3.0° TCH 50´.

RUNWAY DECLARED DISTANCE INFORMATION

RWY 16L: TORA–6000 TODA–6000   ASDA–6000   LDA–6000

RWY 16R: TORA–8009 TODA–8009   ASDA–8009   LDA–8009

RWY 34L: TORA–8009 TODA–8009   ASDA–8009   LDA–8009

RWY 34R: TORA–6000 TODA–6000   ASDA–6000   LDA–6000

AIRPORT REMARKS: Attended continuously. Migratory waterfowl and other birds on and invof arpt. PPR for unscheduled air carrier ops with more than 30 passenger seats call 541–682–5430. ARFF svcs unavailable 0000–0500 local except PPR 541–682–5430. No access to Rwy 34L byd Twy A9. Helicopters ldg and departing avoid overflying the airline passenger terminal and ramp located E of Rwy 16R–34L. Helipad west of Rwy 16R restricted, PPR phone 541–682–5430. Twys H and K unavailable to acft 21,000 pounds single weight and 40,000 pounds dual gross weight. Terminal apron closed to acft except scheduled air carriers and flights with prior permission. PAPI Rwy 16R and Rwy 16L and 34R and VASI Rwy 34L opr 24 hrs. When twr clsd HIRL Rwy 16L–34R and Rwy 16R–34L preset medium ints. When twr clsd ACTIVATE ALSF2 Rwy 16R, ODALS Rwy 34L MALSR Rwy 16L and REIL Rwy 34R—CTAF.

WEATHER DATA SOURCES: ASOS (541) 461–3114 **HIWAS** 112.9 EUG.

COMMUNICATIONS: CTAF 118.9 **ATIS** 125.225 541–607–4699 **UNICOM** 122.95

EUGENE RCO 122.3 (MC MINNVILLE RADIO)

Ⓡ **CASCADE APP/DEP CON** 119.6 (340°–159°) 120.25 (160°–339°) (1400–0730Z‡)

Ⓡ **SEATTLE CENTER APP/DEP CON** 125.8 (0730–1400Z‡)

EUGENE TOWER 118.9 (Rwy 16R– 34L) 124.15 (Rwy 16L– 34R) (1400–0730Z‡) **GND CON** 121.7 **CLNC DEL** 121.7

AIRSPACE: CLASS D svc 1400–0730Z‡ other times CLASS E.

RADIO AIDS TO NAVIGATION: NOTAM FILE EUG.

EUGENE (H) VORTACW 112.9   EUG Chan 76 N44°07.25´ W123°13.37´ at fld. 364/20E. **HIWAS.**

ILS/DME 111.75 I–ADE Chan 54(Y) Rwy 16L. Class IE.

ILS/DME 110.1 I–EUG Chan 38 Rwy 16R. Class IIIE. Unmonitored when ATCT clsd.

FLORENCE

FLORENCE MUNI (6S2) 1 N UTC–8(–7DT) N43°58.97´ W124°06.68´

KLAMATH FALLS
L–1A

51 B **FUEL** 100LL, JET A TPA—1051(1000) NOTAM FILE MMV

RWY 15–33: H3000X60 (ASPH) S–12.5 MIRL 0.4% up NW

RWY 15: Hill. Rgt tfc.

RWY 33: PAPI(P2L)—GA 3.0° TCH 40´. Trees.

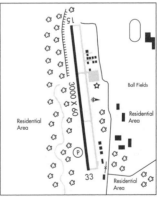

AIRPORT REMARKS: Attended 1630–0030Z‡. Birds, deer and wildlife on and invof arpt. ACTIVATE MIRL Rwy 15–33—CTAF. PAPI Rwy 33 opr 24 hrs.

WEATHER DATA SOURCES: AWOS–3 118.225 (541) 997–8664.

COMMUNICATIONS: CTAF/UNICOM 122.8

RADIO AIDS TO NAVIGATION: NOTAM FILE OTH.

NORTH BEND (L) VORTACW 112.1   OTH Chan 58 N43°24.93´ W124°10.11´ 346° 34.1 NM to fld. 707/18E. **HIWAS.**

VORTAC unusable:
012°–087° byd 30 NM blo 5,000´

Figure 162

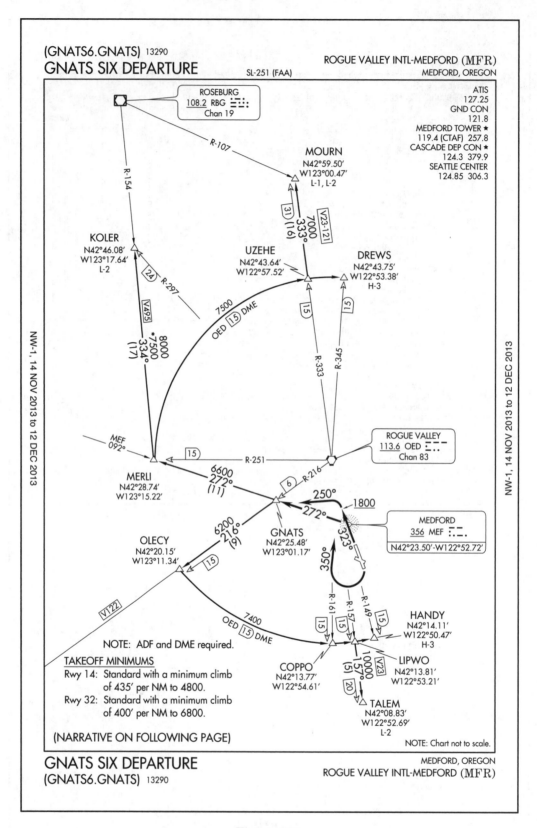

Figure 163

(GNATS6.GNATS) 13290
GNATS SIX DEPARTURE
SL-251 (FAA)

ROGUE VALLEY INTL-MEDFORD (MFR)
MEDFORD, OREGON

DEPARTURE ROUTE DESCRIPTION

<u>TAKEOFF RUNWAY 14</u>: Climbing right turn on heading 350° to intercept bearing 272° from MEF NDB to GNATS INT. Thence . . . .

<u>TAKEOFF RUNWAY 32</u>: Climb on heading 323° to 1800 then climbing left turn on heading 250° to intercept bearing 272° from MEF NDB to GNATS INT. Thence . . . .

. . . . via (transition) or (assigned route). Maintain 11000 or assigned lower altitude.

<u>COPPO TRANSITION (GNATS6.COPPO)</u>: From over GNATS INT via OED VORTAC R-216 to OLECY DME, then via the OED VORTAC 15 DME Arc CCW to COPPO DME.

<u>DREWS TRANSITION (GNATS6.DREWS)</u>: From over GNATS INT via MEF NDB 272° to MERLI INT, then via the OED VORTAC 15 DME Arc CW to DREWS DME.

<u>HANDY TRANSITION (GNATS6.HANDY)</u>: From over GNATS INT via the OED VORTAC R-216 to OLECY DME, then via the OED VORTAC 15 DME Arc CCW to HANDY DME.

<u>KOLER TRANSITION (GNATS6.KOLER)</u>: From over GNATS INT via MEF NDB 272° to MERLI INT, then via RBG VOR/DME R-154 to KOLER INT.

<u>MOURN TRANSITION (GNATS6.MOURN)</u>: From over GNATS INT via MEF NDB 272° to MERLI INT, then via the OED VORTAC 15 DME Arc CW to UZEHE DME, then via OED VORTAC R-333 to MOURN INT.

<u>TALEM TRANSITION (GNATS6.TALEM)</u>: From over GNATS INT via OED VORTAC R-216 to OLECY DME, then via the OED VORTAC 15 DME Arc CCW to LIPWO DME, then via OED VORTAC R-157 to TALEM DME.

NW-1, 14 NOV 2013 to 12 DEC 2013

NW-1, 14 NOV 2013 to 12 DEC 2013

GNATS SIX DEPARTURE
(GNATS6.GNATS) 13290

MEDFORD, OREGON
ROGUE VALLEY INTL-MEDFORD (MFR)

Figure 164

OREGON   129

MEDFORD

ROGUE VALLEY INTL – MEDFORD (MFR) 3 N UTC–8(–7DT) N42°22.45′ W122°52.41′   KLAMATH FALLS
  1335 B S4 **FUEL** 100LL, JET A OX 1, 3 TPA—See Remarks Class I, ARFF Index B   H–3B, L–2I
  NOTAM FILE MFR   IAP, AD
  RWY 14–32: H8800X150 (ASPH–GRVD) S–200, D–200, 2S–175,
    2D–400 HIRL CL
    RWY 14: MALSR. TDZL. PAPI(P4L)—GA 3.0° TCH 73′. 0.4% up.
    RWY 32: REIL. PAPI(P4R)—GA 3.0° TCH 50′. 0.5% down.
  RUNWAY DECLARED DISTANCE INFORMATION
    RWY 14: TORA–8800 TODA–8800 ASDA–8800 LDA–8800
    RWY 32: TORA–8800 TODA–8800 ASDA–8800 LDA–8800
  AIRPORT REMARKS: Attended 1300–0800Z‡. For fuel after hrs call
    541–779–5451, or 541–842–2254. Bird haz large flocks of
    migratory waterfowl in vicinity Nov–May. Terminal apron clsd to acft
    exc scheduled air carrier and flts with prior permission. PPR for
    unscheduled ops with more than 30 passenger seats, call arpt ops
    541–776–7228. Tran tie–downs avbl thru FBOs only. Rwy 32
    preferred for tkfs and ldgs when twr clsd. TPA—2304(969) for
    propeller acft, 2804(1469) for turbo acft. PAPI Rwy 14 and VASI
    Rwy 32 on continuously. ACTIVATE HIRL Rwy 14–32, MALSR Rwy
    14, REIL Rwy 32, TDZL Rwy 14, centerline lgts Rwy 14 and Rwy
    32, and twy lgts—CTAF. Ldg fee applies to all corporate acft and all
    other acft with weight exceeding 12,500 lbs.
  WEATHER DATA SOURCES: ASOS (541) 776–1238 SAWRS.
  COMMUNICATIONS: CTAF 119.4 **ATIS** 127.25 **UNICOM** 122.95
    MEDFORD RCO 122.65 (MC MINNVILLE RADIO)
  ® **CASCADE APP/DEP CON** 124.3 (1400–0730Z‡)
    SEATTLE CENTER APP/DEP CON 124.85 (0730–1400Z‡)
    TOWER 119.4 (1400–0500Z‡) **GND CON** 121.8
  AIRSPACE: CLASS D svc 1400–0500Z‡ other times CLASS E.
  VOR TEST FACILITY (VOT) 117.2
  RADIO AIDS TO NAVIGATION: NOTAM FILE MFR.
    (H) VORTACW 113.6 OED Chan 83 N42°28.77′ W122°54.78′   145° 6.6 NM to fld. 2083/19E. **HIWAS.**
    VOR portion unusable:
      260°–270° byd 35 NM blo 9,000′
      290°–300° byd 35 NM blo 8,500′
    MEDFORD NDB (MHW) 356 MEF N42°23.50′ W122°52.73′   151° 1.1 NM to fld.
    NDB unusable:
      220°–240° byd 15 NM
    PUMIE NDB (LOM) 373 MF N42°27.06′ W122°54.80′ 143° 4.9 NM to fld. LOM unusable 260°–270° beyond 10 NM.
      Unmonitored when ATCT closed.
    ILS/DME 110.3 I–MFR Chan 40 Rwy 14. Class IA. LOM PUMIE NDB. LOM unusable 260°–270° beyond 10 NM.
      Unmonitored when ATCT closed. Localizer backcourse unusable byd 11 NM blo 7,000′, byd 13 NM blo 8,300′, byd
      17 NM blo 8,700′. Localizer backcourse unusable byd 20° left of course.

MEMALOOSE (See IMNAHA on page 122)

MILLER MEM AIRPARK (See VALE on page 145)

MONUMENT MUNI (12S) 1 NW UTC–8(–7DT) N44°49.89′ W119°25.78′   SEATTLE
  2323 TPA—3323(1000) NOTAM FILE MMV
  RWY 14–32: H2104X29 (ASPH)
    RWY 14: Hill.
  AIRPORT REMARKS: Unattended. Intermittently clsd winters due to snow. Wildlife on and invof arpt. Rwy ends marked at each
    corner by a single white tire.
  COMMUNICATIONS: CTAF 122.9

MULINO STATE (See PORTLAND–MULINO on page 137)

NW, 17 OCT 2013 to 12 DEC 2013

Figure 165

ARKANSAS 43

HOSSY N34º25.35´ W93º11.38´ NOTAM FILE HOT. MEMPHIS
   NDB (HW/LOM) 385 HO 050º 5.7 NM to Mem Fld. L–17E

HOT SPRINGS
  MEMORIAL FLD (HOT) 3 SW UTC–6(–5DT) N34º28.68´ W93º05.77´ MEMPHIS
    540 B S4 **FUEL** 100LL, JET A Class II, ARFF Index A NOTAM FILE HOT H–6I, L–17E
    RWY 05–23: H6595X150 (ASPH–GRVD) S–75, D–125, 2S–158, IAP
      2D–210, 2D/2D2–400 HIRL 0.6% up NE
     RWY 05: MALSR. Rgt tfc.
     RWY 23: PAPI(P4L)—GA 3.0º TCH 40´. Pole.
    RWY 13–31: H4098X100 (ASPH) S–28, D–36, 2D–63 MIRL
     0.4% up NW
     RWY 13: REIL. Trees. Rgt tfc.
     RWY 31: Pole.
    RUNWAY DECLARED DISTANCE INFORMATION
     RWY 05: TORA–6595 TODA–6595 ASDA–6595 LDA–6595
     RWY 13: TORA–4100 TODA–4100 ASDA–4100 LDA–4100
     RWY 23: TORA–6595 TODA–6595 ASDA–6595 LDA–6595
     RWY 31: TORA–4100 TODA–4100 ASDA–4100 LDA–4100
    AIRPORT REMARKS: Attended 1100–0400Z‡. For fuel after hrs call
     501–617–0324 or 501–617–4908. Rwy 23 PAPI OTS indef.
     ACTIVATE HIRL Rwy 05–23, MIRL Rwy 13–31, MALSR Rwy 05,
     PAPI Rwy 23 and REIL Rwy 13—CTAF.
    WEATHER DATA SOURCES: ASOS 119.925 (501) 624–7633. **HIWAS** 110.0
     HOT.
    COMMUNICATIONS: CTAF/UNICOM 123.0
     RCO 122.1R 110.0T (JONESBORO RADIO)
  Ⓡ**MEMPHIS CENTER APP/DEP CON** 128.475
    AIRSPACE: CLASS E svc 1200–0400Z‡ other times **CLASS G.**
    RADIO AIDS TO NAVIGATION: NOTAM FILE HOT.
     HOT SPRINGS (L) VOR/DME 110.0 HOT Chan 37 N34º28.72´ W93º05.44´ at fld. 529/4E. **HIWAS.**
      VOR unusable:
       056º–140º byd 20 NM blo 6,500´
       141º–227º byd 20 NM blo 3,500´
       141º–227º byd 26 NM blo 5,500´
       228º–311º byd 20 NM blo 3,500´
       312º–345º byd 15 NM blo 5,500´
       312º–345º byd 32 NM blo 9,500´
       346º–055º byd 20 NM blo 3,500´
      DME unusable:
       310º–035º byd 10 NM blo 11,000´
       310º–035º byd 25 NM blo 12,000´
       310º–035º byd 30 NM blo 17,000´
     HOSSY NDB (LOM) 385 HO N34º25.36´ W93º11.38´ 050º 5.7 NM to fld. Unmonitored.
     ILS/DME 111.5 I–HOT Chan 52 Rwy 05. Class IT. LOM HOSSY NDB. ILS and LOM unmonitored.

HOWARD CO (See NASHVILLE on page 55)

Figure 166

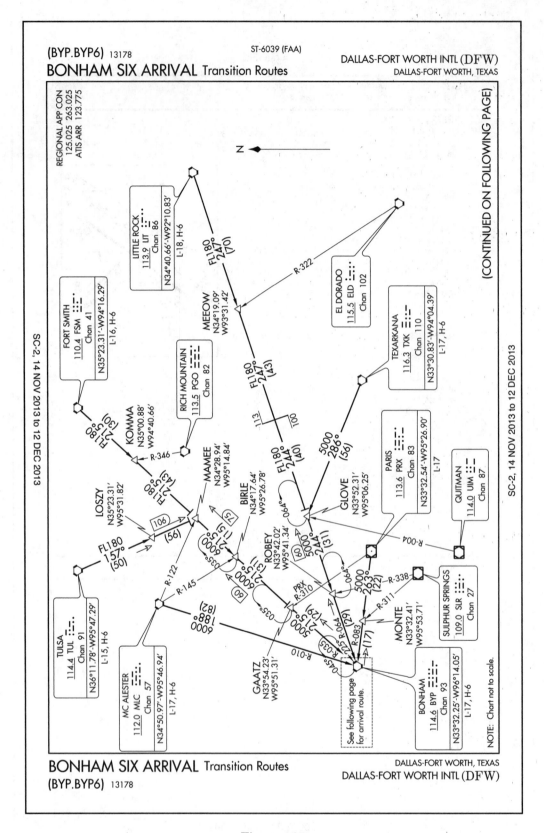

Figure 167

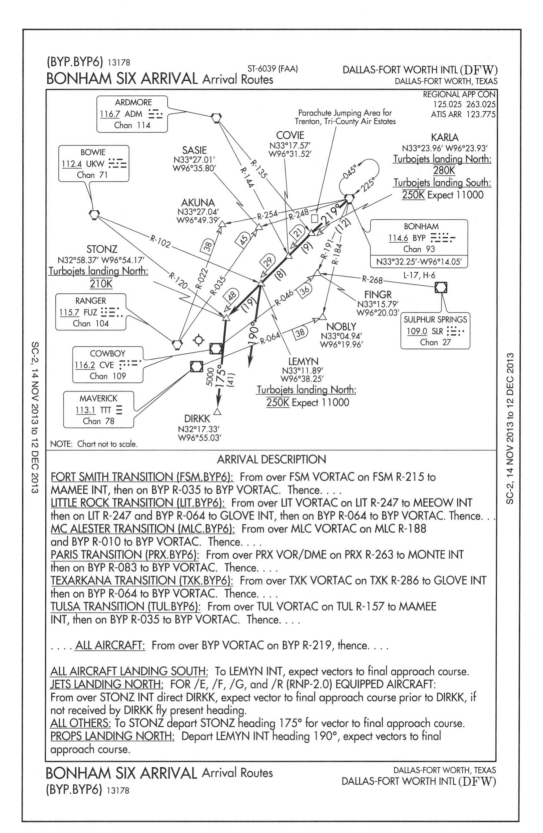

(BYP.BYP6) 13178
BONHAM SIX ARRIVAL Arrival Routes
ST-6039 (FAA)
DALLAS-FORT WORTH INTL (DFW)
DALLAS-FORT WORTH, TEXAS

REGIONAL APP CON
125.025 263.025
ATIS ARR 123.775

ARDMORE
116.7 ADM
Chan 114

BOWIE
112.4 UKW
Chan 71

SASIE
N33°27.01'
W96°35.80'

AKUNA
N33°27.04'
W96°49.39'

STONZ
N32°58.37' W96°54.17'
Turbojets landing North:
210K

RANGER
115.7 FUZ
Chan 104

COWBOY
116.2 CVE
Chan 109

MAVERICK
113.1 TTT
Chan 78

Parachute Jumping Area for
Trenton, Tri-County Air Estates

COVIE
N33°17.57'
W96°31.52'

KARLA
N33°23.96' W96°23.93'
Turbojets landing North:
280K
Turbojets landing South:
250K Expect 11000

BONHAM
114.6 BYP
Chan 93
N33°32.25'-W96°14.05'

L-17, H-6

FINGR
N33°15.79'
W96°20.03'

SULPHUR SPRINGS
109.0 SLR
Chan 27

NOBLY
N33°04.94'
W96°19.96'

LEMYN
N33°11.89'
W96°38.25'
Turbojets landing North:
250K Expect 11000

DIRKK
N32°17.33'
W96°55.03'

NOTE: Chart not to scale.

ARRIVAL DESCRIPTION

FORT SMITH TRANSITION (FSM.BYP6): From over FSM VORTAC on FSM R-215 to
MAMEE INT, then on BYP R-035 to BYP VORTAC. Thence....
LITTLE ROCK TRANSITION (LIT.BYP6): From over LIT VORTAC on LIT R-247 to MEEOW INT
then on LIT R-247 and BYP R-064 to GLOVE INT, then on BYP R-064 to BYP VORTAC. Thence...
MC ALESTER TRANSITION (MLC.BYP6): From over MLC VORTAC on MLC R-188
and BYP R-010 to BYP VORTAC. Thence....
PARIS TRANSITION (PRX.BYP6): From over PRX VOR/DME on PRX R-263 to MONTE INT
then on BYP R-083 to BYP VORTAC. Thence....
TEXARKANA TRANSITION (TXK.BYP6): From over TXK VORTAC on TXK R-286 to GLOVE INT
then on BYP R-064 to BYP VORTAC. Thence....
TULSA TRANSITION (TUL.BYP6): From over TUL VORTAC on TUL R-157 to MAMEE
INT, then on BYP R-035 to BYP VORTAC. Thence....

.... ALL AIRCRAFT: From over BYP VORTAC on BYP R-219, thence....

ALL AIRCRAFT LANDING SOUTH: To LEMYN INT, expect vectors to final approach course.
JETS LANDING NORTH: FOR /E, /F, /G, and /R (RNP-2.0) EQUIPPED AIRCRAFT:
From over STONZ INT direct DIRKK, expect vector to final approach course prior to DIRKK, if
not received by DIRKK fly present heading.
ALL OTHERS: To STONZ depart STONZ heading 175° for vector to final approach course.
PROPS LANDING NORTH: Depart LEMYN INT heading 190°, expect vectors to final
approach course.

BONHAM SIX ARRIVAL Arrival Routes
(BYP.BYP6) 13178
DALLAS-FORT WORTH, TEXAS
DALLAS-FORT WORTH INTL (DFW)

SC-2, 14 NOV 2013 to 12 DEC 2013

SC-2, 14 NOV 2013 to 12 DEC 2013

Figure 168

240   TEXAS

DALLAS

ADDISON (ADS)   9 N   UTC–6(–5DT)   N32°58.11´ W96°50.19´   DALLAS–FT WORTH
  645   B S4 **FUEL** 100LL, JET A   OX 2, 3   TPA—See Remarks LRA   NOTAM FILE ADS   COPTER
  RWY 15–33: H7203X100 (ASPH–GRVD)   S–60, D–120   HIRL   H–6H, L–17C, A
    RWY 15: MALSR. PAPI(P4R)—GA 3.0° TCH 60´. Thld dsplcd 979´.   IAP, AD
  Pole.
    RWY 33: REIL. PAPI(P4L)—GA 3.0° TCH 60´. Thld dsplcd 772´. Bldg.
  RUNWAY DECLARED DISTANCE INFORMATION
    RWY 15: TORA–7202   TODA–7202   ASDA–6592   LDA–5613
    RWY 33: TORA–7202   TODA–7202   ASDA–7202   LDA–6431
  AIRPORT REMARKS: Attended continuously. Birds on and invof arpt. No touch
    and go landings without arpt managers approval. Numerous 200´
    buildings within 1 mile East, and South of arpt, transmission towers and
    water tanks West of arpt. Noise sensitive areas surround arpt. Pilots
    requested to use NBAA std noise procedures. TPA—1600 (956) for light
    acft, 2000 (1356) for large acft. Be alert: Rwy holding position
    markings located at the west edge of Twy A. ACTIVATE HIRL Rwy
    15–33 and MALSR Rwy 15—CTAF. Flight Notification Service (ADCUS)
    available.
  WEATHER DATA SOURCES: AWOS–3 (972) 386–4855 LAWRS.
  COMMUNICATIONS: CTAF 126.0   **ATIS** 133.4 972–628–2439
    UNICOM 122.95
  Ⓡ**REGIONAL APP/DEP CON** 124.3
    TOWER 126.0 (1200–0400Z‡)   **GND CON** 121.6   **CLNC DEL** 119.55
  AIRSPACE: CLASS D svc 1200–0400Z‡, other times CLASS G.
  RADIO AIDS TO NAVIGATION: NOTAM FILE FTW.
    MAVERICK (H) VORW/DME 113.1   TTT   Chan 78   N32°52.15´ W97°02.43´   054° 11.9 NM to fld. 540/6E.
    All acft arriving DFW are requested to turn DME off until departure due to traffic overload of Maverick DME
    ILS/DME 110.1   I–ADS   Chan 38   Rwy 15.   Class IT.   Unmonitored when ATCT closed. DME also serves Rwy 33.
    ILS/DME 110.1   I–TBQ   Chan 38   Rwy 33.   Class IB.   Localizer unmonitored when ATCT closed. DME also serves
      Rwy 15.

- -

AIR PARK–DALLAS (F69)   16 NE   UTC–6(–5DT)   N33°01.41´ W96°50.22´   DALLAS–FT WORTH
  695   S4   **FUEL** 100LL   TPA—1890(1195)   NOTAM FILE FTW   COPTER
  RWY 16–34: H3080X30 (ASPH)   LIRL(NSTD)   L–17C, A
    RWY 16: Thld dsplcd 300´. Pole.
    RWY 34: Tree. Rgt tfc.
  AIRPORT REMARKS: Uattended. For fuel call 972–248–4265 prior to arrival. Rwy 16–34 extensive cracking, loose asph and
    stones rwy. Rwy 16–34 NSTD LIRL, south 2780´ of rwy lgtd. Rwy 16 and Rwy 34 NSTD centerline marking incorrect
    size and spacing, dsplcd thld yellow. Rwy numbers 25´ tall. ACTIVATE LIRL Rwy 16–34—CTAF.
  COMMUNICATIONS: CTAF 122.9
  RADIO AIDS TO NAVIGATION: NOTAM FILE FTW.
    MAVERICK (H) VORW/DME 113.1   TTT   Chan 78   N32°52.15´ W97°02.43´   042° 13.8 NM to fld. 540/6E.
    All acft arriving DFW are requested to turn DME off until departure due to traffic overload of Maverick DME

- -

AIRPARK EAST (1F7)   23 E   UTC–6(–5DT)   N32°48.78´ W96°21.12´   DALLAS–FT WORTH
  510   B S4   NOTAM FILE FTW   COPTER
  RWY 13–31: H2630X30 (ASPH)   LIRL
    RWY 13: Tree. Rgt tfc.
    RWY 31: Tree.
  AIRPORT REMARKS: Unattended. ACTIVATE LIRL Rwy 13–31—122.9.
  COMMUNICATIONS: CTAF/UNICOM 122.7

- -

SC, 17 OCT 2013 to 12 DEC 2013

Figure 169

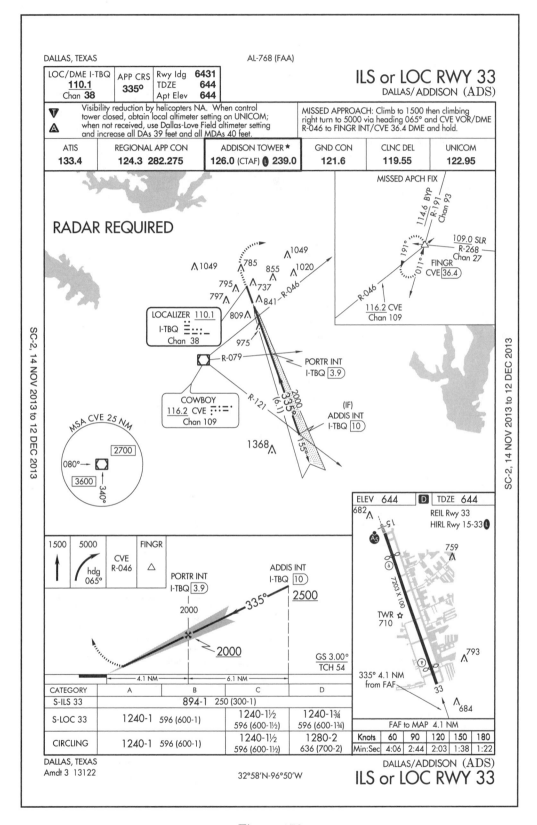

Figure 170

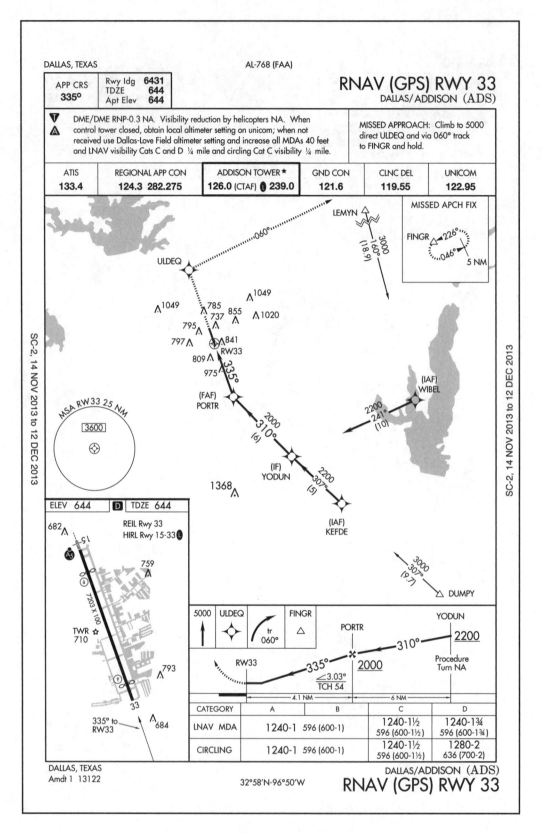

DALLAS, TEXAS   AL-768 (FAA)

| APP CRS 335° | Rwy Idg 6431 TDZE 644 Apt Elev 644 | **RNAV (GPS) RWY 33** DALLAS/ADDISON (ADS) |

DME/DME RNP-0.3 NA. Visibility reduction by helicopters NA. When control tower closed, obtain local altimeter setting on unicom; when not received use Dallas-Love Field altimeter setting and increase all MDAs 40 feet and LNAV visibility Cats C and D ¼ mile and circling Cat C visibility ¼ mile.

MISSED APPROACH: Climb to 5000 direct ULDEQ and via 060° track to FINGR and hold.

| ATIS 133.4 | REGIONAL APP CON 124.3 282.275 | ADDISON TOWER ★ 126.0 (CTAF) 239.0 | GND CON 121.6 | CLNC DEL 119.55 | UNICOM 122.95 |

MISSED APCH FIX

FINGR 226° 046° 5 NM

LEMYN 3000 160° (18.9)

060°

ULDEQ

∧1049   785   ∧1049
∧1049 737 855 ∧1020
795∧
797∧   ⊕841
       RW33
809∧   335°
975∧

(FAF) PORTR   2000 310° (6)

(IF) YODUN   2200 307° (5)

(IAF) KEFDE

(IAF) WIBEL   2200 241° (10)

1368∧

3000 307° (9.7)   △ DUMPY

MSA RW33 25 NM   3600

ELEV 644 | **D** | TDZE 644

682∧

REIL Rwy 33
HIRL Rwy 15-33 Ⓛ

759∧

793∧

TWR 710

7203 X 100

33

335° to RW33   ∧684

5000 ↑	ULDEQ ◇	tr 060°	FINGR △	PORTR	YODUN 2200
					Procedure Turn NA
↙	RW33	335° ⟋3.03° TCH 54	2000	310°	
		◄— 4.1 NM —►	◄— 6 NM —►	

CATEGORY	A	B	C	D
LNAV MDA	1240-1	596 (600-1)	1240-1½ 596 (600-1½)	1240-1¾ 596 (600-1¾)
CIRCLING	1240-1	596 (600-1)	1240-1½ 596 (600-1½)	1280-2 636 (700-2)

DALLAS, TEXAS
Amdt 1 13122

32°58'N-96°50'W

DALLAS/ADDISON (ADS)
RNAV (GPS) RWY 33

Figure 171

84   **MONTANA**

HELENA RGNL   (HLN)(KHLN) P (ARNG)   2 NE   UTC–7(–6DT)   N46°36.41′ W111°58.97′   **GREAT FALLS**
  3877   B   S4   **FUEL** 80, 100, 100LL, JET A   OX 1, 3   LRA   Class I, ARFF Index B   NOTAM FILE HLN   **H–1D, L–13C**
  RWY 09–27: H9000X150 (ASPH–PFC)   S–100, D–160, 2S–175,   **IAP, DIAP, AD**
    2D–250   HIRL
    RWY 09: REIL. VASI(V4L)—GA 3.0° TCH 45′. Ground. 0.3% down.
    RWY 27: MALSR. VASI(V4L)—GA 3.0° TCH 47′. Rgt tfc.
  RWY 05–23: H4644X75 (ASPH–PFC)   S–21, D–30   MIRL   1.2% up SW
    RWY 05: Road.
    RWY 23: PAPI(P2L)—GA 3.0° TCH 49′. Fence. Rgt tfc.
  RWY 17–35: H2989X75 (ASPH–PFC)   S–21, D–30   MIRL   1.7% up SE
    RWY 35: Ground. Rgt tfc.
  MILITARY SERVICE: LGT When twr clsd, ACTIVATE–HIRL Rwy 09–27, MIRL
    Rwy 05–23 and 16–34, REIL Rwy 09, MALSR Rwy 27 – CTAF.   **FUEL**
    A+, J8 (C406–442–2190. Opr 1200–0600Z‡, OT $150 fee, 90 min
    PPR.) (NC–80, 100, 100LL)
  AIRPORT REMARKS: Attended 1200–0800Z‡. ARFF coverage provided for
    scheduled Part 121 air carriers only exc with prior approval, call
    406–442–2821. Ldg rights customs avbl call 406–449–5506. Rwy
    17–35 and Rwy 05–23 (exc between Twy F and Rwy 09–27) not avbl
    for air carrier use by acft with greater than 30 passenger seats. Twy A,
    Twy B, and Twy C between Twy A and Rwy 35 not avbl for air carrier
    use by acft with greater than 30 passenger seats. When twr clsd
    ACTIVATE HIRL Rwy 09–27, MIRL Rwy 05–23 and Rwy 17–35, REIL Rwy 09, MALSR Rwy 27—CTAF. Ldg fee for all
    commercial acft and all acft over 10,000 lbs. Flight Notification Service (ADCUS) avbl. NOTE: See SPECIAL NOTICE.
  MILITARY REMARKS: ARNG Opr Mon–Fri 1400–0030Z‡, exc holidays. Exercise caution while taxiing, AASF ramp not stressed
    for large acft. Ctc flt ops for ramp advisory 126.2, DSN 324–3055/56, C406–324–3055/56. No tran svc Sat, Sun,
    holidays or after 2300Z‡ Mon–Fri.
  WEATHER DATA SOURCES: ASOS (406) 443–4317
  COMMUNICATIONS: CTAF 118.3 **ATIS** 120.4 **UNICOM** 122.95
    RCO 122.55 255.4 (GREAT FALLS RADIO)
    APP/DEP CON 119.5 229.4 (1300–0500Z‡)
    SALT LAKE CENTER APP/DEP CON 133.4 285.4 (0500–1300Z‡)
    TOWER 118.3 257.8 (1300–0500Z‡) **GND CON** 121.9
    ARNG OPS 40.65 126.2 321.45
  AIRSPACE: CLASS D svc 1300–0500Z‡ other times CLASS E.
  RADIO AIDS TO NAVIGATION: NOTAM FILE HLN.
    (H) VORTACW 117.7   HLN   Chan 124   N46°36.41′ W111°57.21′   254° 1.2 NM to fld. 3823/16E.
    VOR portion unusable:
      035°–050° byd 35 NM blo 12,000′
      105°–165° byd 25 NM blo 17,000′
      165°–185° byd 25 NM blo 13,500′
      185°–230° byd 25 NM blo 17,500′
      203°–213° byd 22 NM blo 13,000′
      230°–270° byd 25 NM blo 12,500′
    TACAN AZIMUTH and DME unusable:
      035°–070° byd 35 NM blo 13,000′
      165°–185° byd 25 NM blo 13,500′
      250°–300° byd 25 NM blo 14,000′
      320°–035° byd 25 NM blo 13,000′
    TACAN DME unusable:
      035°–070° byd 35 NM blo 13,000′
      105°–150° byd 25 NM
      105°–210° byd 15 NM blo 11,100′
      105°–210° byd 20 NM blo 12,000′
      150°–165° byd 25 NM blo 17,000′
      165°–185° byd 25 NM blo 13,500′
      185°–210° byd 25 NM
      203°–213° byd 22 NM blo 13,000′
      210°–250° byd 15 NM blo 12,000′
      210°–250° byd 25 NM blo 17,500′
      250°–300° byd 25 NM blo 14,000′
      320°–035° byd 25 NM blo 13,000′
    TACAN AZIMUTH unusable:
      105°–150° byd 15 NM
      150°–165° byd 15 NM blo 17,000′
      185°–210° byd 15 NM
      210°–250° byd 15 NM blo 17,500′

Rwy 17-35: 2989 X 75

CONTINUED ON NEXT PAGE

NW, 17 OCT 2013 to 12 DEC 2013

Figure 172

MONTANA   85
CONTINUED FROM PRECEDING PAGE

CAPITOL NDB (HW) 335   CVP   N46°36.40′ W111°56.23′   258° 1.9 NM to fld. NDB unmonitored when ATCT clsd.
HAUSER NDB (MHW) 386   HAU   N46°34.13′ W111°45.48′   268° 9.6 NM to fld. NDB unmonitored when HLN
    ATCT clsd.
ILS 110.1 I–HLN Rwy 27. Unmonitored when ATCT closed. Localizer backcourse unusable byd 22° rgt of course,
    unusable within 2.7 DME.

HINSDALE (6U5)   0 SE   UTC–7(–6DT)   N48°23.28′ W107°05.00′   BILLINGS
2220   NOTAM FILE GTF
RWY 07–25: 2200X75 (TURF)   LIRL(NSTD)   0.7% up W
    RWY 07: Road.
RWY 10–28: 2160X200 (TURF)   0.3% up W
    RWY 10: Road.
RWY 16–34: 1960X75 (TURF)   1.5% up S
    RWY 16: P–line.
    RWY 34: Fence.
AIRPORT REMARKS: Unattended. Rwys soft when wet. Hay bales and farm equipment adjacent to rwy. Rwys not clearly defined.
    Rwy 16–34, Rwy 07–25 and Rwy 10–28 marked with white cones full length of rwy. Rwy 16 p–lines marked with globes.
    Rwy 07–25 NSTD LIRL 335′ spacing between lgts, one thld lgt each end. For rwy lgts phone 406–364–2272/2387.
COMMUNICATIONS: CTAF 122.9

HOGELAND (6U6)   1 NW   UTC–7(–6DT)   N48°51.61′ W108°39.66′   BILLINGS
3139   B   NOTAM FILE GTF
RWY 07–25: 3140X60 (TRTD)   0.6% up W
RWY 16–34: 1230X50 (TURF)
    RWY 34: Bldg.
AIRPORT REMARKS: Unattended. Rwy 16–34 for emerg use only, road and drainage ditch parallel rwy on east side. Rwy 07–25
    patches of loose aggregate and grvl.
COMMUNICATIONS: CTAF 122.9

HOT SPRINGS (SØ9)   2 E   UTC–7(–6DT)   N47°36.75′ W114°36.81′   GREAT FALLS
2763   B   NOTAM FILE GTF
RWY 06–24: H3550X45 (ASPH–TRTD)   MIRL
    RWY 24: Thld dsplcd 411′. Road.
AIRPORT REMARKS: Unattended. Ultralights on and in vicinity of arpt. Occasional snow removal. Rwy 06–24 asph grvl
    composition full length. Rwy 24 has 411′ unlighted, 2169′ lgtd at ngt. Rwy 06–24 cones adjacent to MIRL full length
    and dsplcd thld marked with white cones. Rwy 06 and Rwy 24 numbers 4′x 8′ in measure, thld line and rwy lines NSTD.
COMMUNICATIONS: CTAF 122.9

HYSHAM (6U7)   2 E   UTC–7(–6DT)   N46°17.61′ W107°11.60′   BILLINGS
2624   B   NOTAM FILE GTF
RWY 07–25: H3060X45 (ASPH–TRTD)   LIRL
AIRPORT REMARKS: Unattended. 1030′ dirt extension east of Rwy 07 thld soft when wet. Rwy 07 basic markings NSTD
    numbers and stripes, markings are faded. Rwy 25 basic markings NSTD small numbers and stripes, markings are faded.
    Numerous rwy lgts inop. ACTIVATE LIRL Rwy 07–25—CTAF.
COMMUNICATIONS: CTAF 122.9

JORDAN (JDN)   2 NW   UTC–7(–6DT)   N47°19.73′ W106°57.16′   BILLINGS
2662   B   NOTAM FILE JDN   L–13D
RWY 10–28: H4300X75 (ASPH–PFC)   S–12.5   MIRL
    RWY 28: PAPI(P2L)—GA 3.0° TCH 29′.
AIRPORT REMARKS: Unattended. ACTIVATE MIRL Rwy 10–28 and PAPI Rwy 28—CTAF.
COMMUNICATIONS: CTAF 122.9
RADIO AIDS TO NAVIGATION: NOTAM FILE GGW.
    GLASGOW (H) VORW/DME 113.9   GGW   Chan 86   N48°12.92′ W106°37.53′   180° 54.8 NM to fld. 2283/14E.
    NDB (MHW) 263   JDN   N47°20.00′ W106°56.29′   at fld.   NOTAM FILE JDN. VFR only.

JUDITH MOUNTAIN   N47°13.03′ W109°13.31′   GREAT FALLS
RCO 122.2 (GREAT FALLS RADIO)   L–13D

Figure 172A

216   **TEXAS**

BIG SPRING MC MAHON—WRINKLE (BPG)   2 SW   UTC–6(–5DT)   N32°12.76′ W101°31.30′   DALLAS–FT WORTH
   2573   B S4 **FUEL** 100LL, JET A   NOTAM FILE BPG   H–6G, L–6H
   RWY 17–35: H8802X100 (CONC)   S–60, D–150, 2D–200   MIRL   IAP
      RWY 17: SSALS. PAPI(P4L)—GA 3.0° TCH 45′. Rgt tfc.
      RWY 35: PAPI(P4L)—GA 3.0° TCH 36′.
   RWY 06–24: H4601X75 (ASPH)   MIRL   0.6% up NE
      RWY 06: PVASI(PSIL)—GA 2.97° TCH 47′. Rgt tfc.
      RWY 24: PVASI(PSIL)—GA 3.55° TCH 35′.
   AIRPORT REMARKS: Attended Mon–Sat 1400–2300Z‡. For fuel after hours
      call 432–267–8952 or 432–935–3395. Prairie dogs on rwys and twys.
      Extensive agricultural ops invof arpt. Sandhill Cranes crossing in the
      spring and fall. MIRL Rwy 06–24 and Rwy 17–35 preset low ints, to
      increase ints and ACTIVATE SSALS Rwy 17 and PVASI Rwy 06, Rwy
      24, and PAPI Rwy 17 and Rwy 35—CTAF.
   WEATHER DATA SOURCES: AWOS–3 118.025 (432) 263–3842.
   COMMUNICATIONS: CTAF/UNICOM 122.8
      RCO 122.4 (SAN ANGELO RADIO)
      FORT WORTH CENTER APP/DEP CON 133.7
   RADIO AIDS TO NAVIGATION: NOTAM FILE BPG.
      (L) VORTACW 114.3   BGS   Chan 90   N32°23.14′
      W101°29.02′   180° 10.5 NM to fld. 2670/11E.

BIGGS AAF (FORT BLISS) (BIF)(KBIF) A   5 NE   UTC–7(–6DT)   N31°50.97′ W106°22.80′   EL PASO
   3948   B TPA—See Remarks NOTAM FILE ABQ   Not insp.   H–4L, L–6F
   RWY 03–21: H13554X150 (PEM)   PCN 120 R/C/W/T   HIRL   DIAP, AD
      RWY 03: PAPI(P4L)—GA 3.0° TCH 71′.
      RWY 21: ALSF1. PAPI(P4L)—GA 3.0° TCH 71′. Rgt tfc. 0.3% down.
   MILITARY SERVICE: LGT When unattended ACTIVATE 3–step HIRL Rwy 03–21, High Intensity ALS Category I configuration with
      sequenced Flashers (code) Rwy 21 and PAPI Rwy 21–127.9.   **JASU** 4(A/M32A–86) 2(A/M32–95)   **FUEL** A+ (Atlantic
      Avn, 1200–0400Z‡ Mon–Sun, C915–779–2831, 1 hr prior notice, after hr C915–861–2390, after hr call out fee $100.)
      FLUID SP   **TRAN ALERT** 1300–0500Z‡ Mon–Sun, exc holidays.
   MILITARY REMARKS: Attended Mon–Sun 1300–0500Z‡, except holidays. See FLIP AP/1 Supplementary Arpt Remark. **RSTD** PPR
      all acft. 24 hr prior notice, ctc Airfield Ops DSN 621–8811/8330, C915–744–8811/8330. Twr and svcs avbl for all acft
      with PPR. PPR time valid +/— 1 hr. All acft ctc Afld Ops via PTD 30 min prior to arr. Twr and svcs unavbl before 1 hr
      prior to PPR sked arr. **CAUTION** El Paso Intl Rwy 22 2 NM SE can be mistaken for Rwy 21. Coyote hazard. **TFC PAT** Fixed
      Wing 5002(1054), Fixed Wing Category BCDE turbo prop 5502(1554), Rotary Wing 4502(554), Jet 6002(2054).
      NS ABTMT VFR west arr/dep via mountain pass 15 NM NW of Biggs AAF. Avoid VFR over flight of city. Fly 1500′ AGL,
      1500′ horizontal distance from mountain dwellings. **MISC** Approval required for access to ramp. Temporary storage of
      classified material avbl at Afld Ops. Intl garbage cap ltd. Expect delays unless placed in garbage bags prior to arrival.
      Hangar space extremely limited for transient acft. KBIF manual obsn and wx forecaster avbl Mon–Fri 1300–0500Z‡, clsd
      holidays. DSN 621–1215/1214, C915–744–1215/1214, OT 25th OWS, Davis Monthan AFB, DSN 228–6598/6599.
   COMMUNICATIONS: ATIS 120.0 254.3 (C915–772–9412) **PTD** 122.7
   ®**EL PASO APP CON** 119.15 353.5 (South of V16) 124.25 298.85 (North of V16)
      TOWER 127.9 342.25 (Mon–Sun 1300–0500Z‡, except holidays). Advisory svc twr freq other times.
   ®**EL PASO DEP CON** 121.3 263.0
      EL PASO CLNC DEL 125.0 379.1
   AIRSPACE: CLASS D svc 1300–0500Z‡ Mon–Sat except holidays other times CLASS E.
   RADIO AIDS TO NAVIGATION: NOTAM FILE ABQ.
      NEWMAN (L) VORTACW 112.4   EWM   Chan 71   N31°57.10′ W106°16.34′   210° 8.2 NM to fld. 4040/12E.
      DME portion unusable:
         220°–255° byd 25 NM blo 12,000′
   COMM/NAV/WEATHER REMARKS: Radar—See Terminal FLIP for Radar Minima.

BIRD DOG AIRFIELD (See KRUM on page 297)

BISHOP (See DECATUR on page 245)

SC, 17 OCT 2013 to 12 DEC 2013

Figure 173

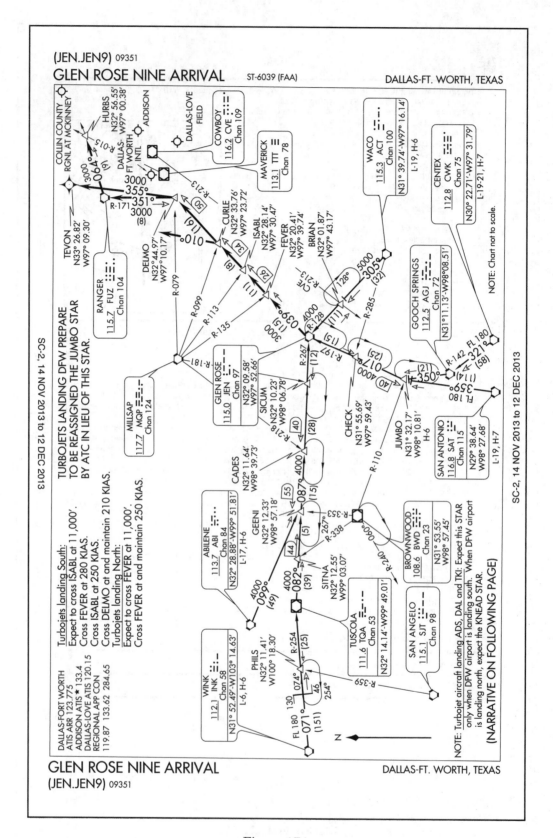

Figure 174

(JEN.JEN9) 09351

GLEN ROSE NINE ARRIVAL   ST-6039 (FAA)   DALLAS-FT. WORTH, TEXAS

ARRIVAL DESCRIPTION

SC-2, 14 NOV 2013 to 12 DEC 2013

SC-2, 14 NOV 2013 to 12 DEC 2013

ABILENE TRANSITION (ABI.JEN9): From over ABI VORTAC via R-099 to GEENI INT, then via JEN R-267 to JEN VORTAC. Thence. . . .
CENTEX TRANSITION (CWK.JEN9): From over CWK VORTAC via CWK R-321 and AGJ R-142 to AGJ VORTAC, then via AGJ R-350 to JUMBO INT, then via JEN R-197 to JEN VORTAC. Thence . . . .
JUMBO TRANSITION (JUMBO.JEN9): From over JUMBO INT via JEN R-197 to JEN VORTAC. Thence . . . .
SAN ANTONIO TRANSITION (SAT.JEN9): From over SAT VORTAC via SAT R-359 to JUMBO INT, then via JEN R-197 to JEN VORTAC. Thence . . . .
WACO TRANSITION (ACT.JEN9): From over ACT VORTAC via ACT R-305 and JEN R-128 to JEN VORTAC. Thence. . . .
WINK TRANSITION (INK.JEN9): From over INK VORTAC via INK R-071 and TQA R-254 to TQA VOR/DME, then via TQA R-082 to GEENI INT, then via JEN R-267 to JEN VORTAC. Thence. . . .

. . . . ALL AIRCRAFT: From over JEN VORTAC via JEN R-039, thence . . . .

ALL AIRCRAFT LANDING NORTH: To CURLE INT, expect vectors to final approach course.

JETS LANDING SOUTH: To DELMO, depart DELMO heading 355°.
For /E, /F, /G and /R (RNP 2.0) EQUIPMENT SUFFIXED AIRCRAFT: From over DELMO WP direct TEVON WP, expect vector to final approach course prior to TEVON WP. If not received by TEVON fly present heading.
NON TURBOJETS LANDING SOUTH: To CURLE INT, depart CURLE heading 010° for vectors to final approach course.

AIRCRAFT LANDING DAL, ADS, TKI: To DELMO INT, depart DELMO via FUZ R-171 to FUZ VORTAC then FUZ R-064 to HURBS INT, expect vectors to final approach course.

GLEN ROSE NINE ARRIVAL   DALLAS-FT. WORTH, TEXAS
(JEN.JEN9) 09351

Figure 175

TEXAS   **243**

DALLAS–FORT WORTH

DALLAS/FORT WORTH INTL (DFW)   12 NW   UTC–6(–5DT)   N32°53.81′ W97°02.28′   **DALLAS–FT WORTH**
607   B **FUEL** 100LL, JET A   OX 1, 3   AOE   Class I, ARFF Index E   NOTAM FILE DFW   **COPTER**
RWY 17C–35C: H13401X150 (CONC–GRVD) S–120, D–200, 2S–175, 2D–600, 2D/2D2–850   HIRL   H–6H, L–17C, A
CL   IAP, AD
  RWY 17C: ALSF2. TDZL. PAPI(P4L)—GA 3.0° TCH 74′.
  RWY 35C: ALSF2. TDZL. PAPI(P4L)—GA 3.0° TCH 76′.
RWY 17R–35L: H13401X200 (CONC–GRVD) S–120, D–200, 2S–175, 2D–600, 2D/2D2–850   HIRL CL
  RWY 17R: MALSR. TDZL. PAPI(P4L)—GA 3.0° TCH 68′.
  RWY 35L: MALSR. TDZL. PAPI(P4L)—GA 3.0° TCH 63′.
RWY 18L–36R: H13400X200 (CONC–GRVD) S–120, D–200, 2S–175, 2D–600, 2D/2D2–850   HIRL CL
  RWY 18L: MALSR. TDZL. PAPI(P4L)—GA 3.0° TCH 70′.
  RWY 36R: MALSR. TDZL. PAPI(P4L)—GA 3.0° TCH 66′.
RWY 18R–36L: H13400X150 (CONC–GRVD) S–120, D–200, 2S–175, 2D–600, 2D/2D2–850   HIRL CL
  RWY 18R: ALSF2. TDZL. PAPI(P4L)—GA 3.0° TCH 74′.
  RWY 36L: MALSR. TDZL. PAPI(P4L)—GA 3.0° TCH 72′.
RWY 13R–31L: H9301X150 (CONC–GRVD) S–120, D–200, 2S–175, 2D–600, 2D/2D2–850   HIRL   CL
  RWY 13R: MALSR. TDZL. PAPI(P4L)—GA 3.0° TCH 71′.
  RWY 31L: REIL. PAPI(P4L)—GA 3.13° TCH 72′.
RWY 13L–31R: H9000X200 (CONC–GRVD) S–120, D–200, 2S–175, 2D–600, 2D/2D2–850   HIRL   CL
  RWY 13L: REIL. PAPI(P4L)—GA 3.0° TCH 82′. Thld dsplcd 625′. 0.5% down.
  RWY 31R: MALSR. TDZL. PAPI(P4L)—GA 3.0° TCH 69′. 0.5% up.
RWY 17L–35R: H8500X150 (CONC–GRVD) S–120, D–200, 2S–175, 2D–600, 2D/2D2–850   HIRL   CL
  RWY 17L: ALSF2. TDZL. PAPI(P4L)—GA 3.0° TCH 77′. Antenna. 0.6% up.
  RWY 35R: ALSF2. TDZL. PAPI(P4R)—GA 3.0° TCH 73′. 0.6% down.
LAND AND HOLD–SHORT OPERATIONS

LDG RWY	HOLD–SHORT POINT	AVBL LDG DIST
RWY 17C	TWY B	10460
RWY 18R	TWY B	10100
RWY 35C	TWY EJ	9050
RWY 36L	TWY Z	10650

RUNWAY DECLARED DISTANCE INFORMATION
RWY 13L: TORA–9000 TODA–9000   ASDA–9000   LDA–8375
RWY 13R: TORA–9301 TODA–9301   ASDA–9301   LDA–9301
RWY 17C: TORA–13401 TODA–13401 ASDA–13401 LDA–13401
RWY 17L: TORA–8500 TODA–8500   ASDA–8500   LDA–8500
RWY 17R: TORA–13401 TODA–13401 ASDA–13401 LDA–13401
RWY 18L: TORA–13400 TODA–13400 ASDA–13400 LDA–13400
RWY 18R: TORA–13400 TODA–13400 ASDA–13400 LDA–13400
RWY 31L: TORA–9301 TODA–9301   ASDA–9301   LDA–9301
RWY 31R: TORA–8375 TODA–8375   ASDA–8375   LDA–8375
RWY 35C: TORA–13401 TODA–13401 ASDA–13401 LDA–13401
RWY 35L: TORA–13401 TODA–13401 ASDA–13401 LDA–13401
RWY 35R: TORA–8500 TODA–8500   ASDA–8500   LDA–8500
RWY 36L: TORA–13400 TODA–13400 ASDA–13400 LDA–13400
RWY 36R: TORA–13400 TODA–13400 ASDA–13400 LDA–13400

CONTINUED ON NEXT PAGE

SC, 17 OCT 2013 to 12 DEC 2013

Figure 176

244 **TEXAS**
CONTINUED FROM PRECEDING PAGE

AIRPORT REMARKS: Attended continuously. Rwy 17L–35R CLOSED 0400–1200Z‡ except PPR. Rwy 13R–31L CLOSED 0400–1200Z‡ except PPR. Rwy 13L–31R CLOSED 0400–1200Z‡ except PPR. Rwy 31R last 625´ CLOSED indef. Visual screen 20´ AGL 1180´ south AER 35C. Visual screen 22´ AGL 1179´ south AER 35L. ASDE–X SURVEILLANCE system in use: Pilots should opr transponders with mode C on all twys and rwys. PPR for acft with wingspan 215´ or greater (GROUP VI), call arpt ops 972–973–3112 for follow me services while taxiing to and from ramp and rwys. Rwy 13L, Rwy 17L, Rwy 31R, and Rwy 35R rwy visual range touchdown, midpoint and rollout avbl. Rwy 31L and Rwy 31R runway visual range touchdown and rollout avbl. Arpt under construction, PAEW in movement areas. Birds on and in vicinity of arpt. Tkf distance for Rwy 17L from Twy Q2 is 8196´. Tkf distance for Rwy 35R from Twy Q9 is 8196´. Tkf distance for Rwy 17R from Twy EG is 13082´ and from Twy EH is 12816´. Tkf distance for Rwy 35L from Twy EQ is 13084´ and from Twy EP is 12811´. Tkf distance for Rwy 36R from Twy WP is 12815´, from Twy WQ is 13082´. Tkf distance for Rwy 18L from Twy WG is 13082´, from Twy WH is 12815´. Tkf distance for Rwy 17C from Twy EG is 13,082´. Tkf distance for Rwy 18R from Twy WG is 13,082´. Land and hold–short signs on Rwy 17C at Twy B 10,460´ south of Rwy 17C thld, Rwy 18R at Twy B 10,100´ south of Rwy 18R thld, Rwy 35C at Twy EJ 9050´ north of Rwy 35C thld, Rwy 36L at Twy Z 10,650´ north of Rwy 36L thld, lgtd and marked with in–pavement pulsating white lgts. Twy G11 east of Twy G clsd to acft with wingspan 125´ and greater. Acft using gates D6–D17 must obtain approval from DFW ramp twr 129.95 prior to entering ramp and prior to pushback 1130–0430Z‡. Use extreme care at other times. Apron Terminal E ramp work in progress, ctc DFW ramp on 131.0 1530–1200Z‡ for Terminal E procedure change. Apron entrance/exit Points 32, 33, 34, 35, 36, 37, 38 and 39 clsd to acft with wingspan greater than 135´. Acft pushing back or powering back on Terminal B Apron have right of way. Frequent ground support equip under escort crossing Twys A and B at Twy HA. Apron entrance/exit points 5, 7, 42 and 44 clsd to acft with wingspan 118´ and greater. Apron entrance/exit points 42 and 44 clsd to acft with wingspan greater than 118´. Terminal B apron taxilane btn apron entrance/exit point taxilanes 110 and 115 clsd to acft with wingspan 118´ and greater. Apron entrance/exit points 22, 24, 105, 107 and 122 clsd to acft with wingspan 125´ and greater. Apron entrance/exit point 124 clsd to acft with wingspan 200´ and greater. Twy A5 clsd to acft with wingspan 171´ and greater. Twys may require judgemental oversteering for large acft. Apron entrance/exit points 52 and 53 clsd to acft with wingspan 171´ and greater. Acft exiting via apron entrance/exit points 42, 43 and 44 ctc Gnd Con prior to taxiing. PPR general aviation ops 0400–1200Z‡, call arpt ops 972–973–3112. PPR from arpt ops for general aviation acft to proceed to airline terminal gate except to general aviation facility. PPR from the primary tenant airlines to operate within the central terminal area. Proper minimum object free area distances may not be maintained for ramp/apron taxi lanes. Twy edge reflectors along all twys. Landing fee. Flight Notification Service (ADCUS) available. NOTE: See Land and Hold Short Operations, Intersection Departures During Periods of Darkness, Noise Abatement Procedures and Continuous Power Facilities.
WEATHER DATA SOURCES: ASOS (972) 453–0992 LLWAS.
COMMUNICATIONS: D–ATIS ARR 123.775 (972) 615–2701 **D–ATIS DEP** 135.925 (972) 615–2701 **UNICOM** 122.95
Ⓡ**RGNL APP CON** 125.025 133.525 (E) 119.875 133.625 (W)
DFW TOWER 126.55 127.5 (E) 124.15 134.9 (W) **GND CON** 121.65 121.8 (E) 121.85 (W)
CLNC DEL 128.25
Ⓡ**RGNL DEP CON** 118.55 (E) 126.475 (W) 124.825 (N) 125.125 (S)
AIRSPACE: CLASS B See VFR Terminal Area Chart
RADIO AIDS TO NAVIGATION: NOTAM FILE FTW.
MAVERICK (H) VORW/DME 113.1 TTT Chan 78 N32º52.15´ W97º02.43´ 358º 1.7 NM to fld. 540/6E.
ILS/DME 109.5 I–LWN Chan 32 Rwy 13R. Class IE.
ILS/DME 110.3 I–FLQ Chan 40 Rwy 17C. Class IIIE. DME also serves Rwy 35C.
ILS/DME 111.75 I–PPZ Chan 54(Y) Rwy 17L. Class IIIE. DME also serves Rwy 35R.
ILS/DME 111.35 I–JHZ Chan 50(Y) Rwy 17R. Class IE. DME also serves Rwy 35L.
ILS/DME 110.55 I–CIX Chan 42(Y) Rwy 18L. Class IE. DME also serves Rwy 36R.
ILS/DME 111.9 I–VYN Chan 56 Rwy 18R. Class IIIE. DME also serves Rwy 36L.
ILS/DME 110.9 I–RRA Chan 46 Rwy 31R. Class IE.
ILS/DME 110.3 I–PKQ Chan 40 Rwy 35C. Class IIIE. DME also serves Rwy 17C. OM/comlo also serves Rwy 35L.
ILS/DME 111.35 I–UWX Chan 50(Y) Rwy 35L. Class IE. OM/comlo also serves Rwy 35R. LOC unusable byd 14 NM blo 3,400´. DME also serves Rwy 17R.
ILS/DME 111.75 I–AJQ Chan 54(Y) Rwy 35R. Class IIIE. DME also serves Rwy 17L. LOC unusable byd 16 NM 5º right of course.
ILS/DME 111.9 I–BXN Chan 56 Rwy 36L. Class ID. DME also serves Rwy 18R. OM also serves Rwy 36R. LOC unusable byd 15 NM 5º right of course.
ILS/DME 110.55 I–FJN Chan 42(Y) Rwy 36R. Class IE. OM also serves Rwy 36L. DME also serves Rwy 18L.
COMM/NAV/WEATHER REMARKS: All acft arriving DFW are requested to turn DME off until dep due to tfc overload of Maverick DME.

DALLAS/FORT WORTH INTL (See DALLAS–FORT WORTH on page 243)

DAN E RICHARDS MUNI (See PADUCAH on page 325)

DAN JONES INTL (See HOUSTON on page 279)

SC, 17 OCT 2013 to 12 DEC 2013

Figure 176A

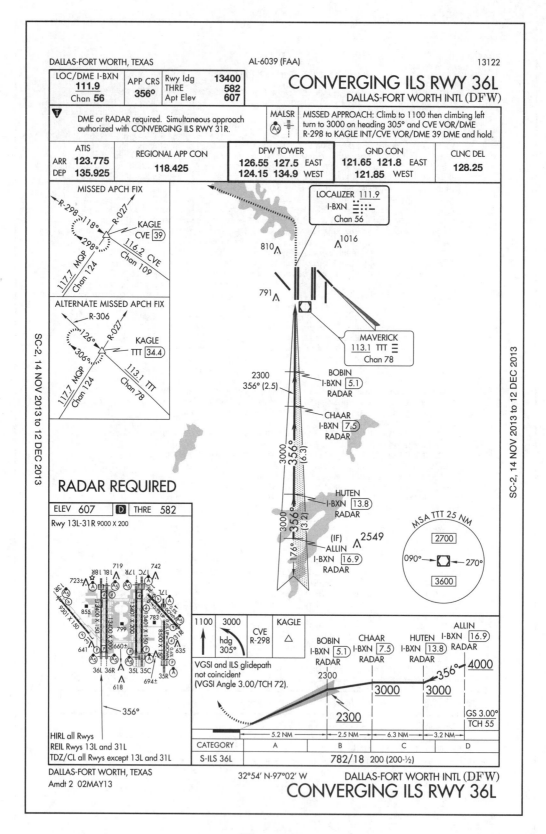

Figure 177

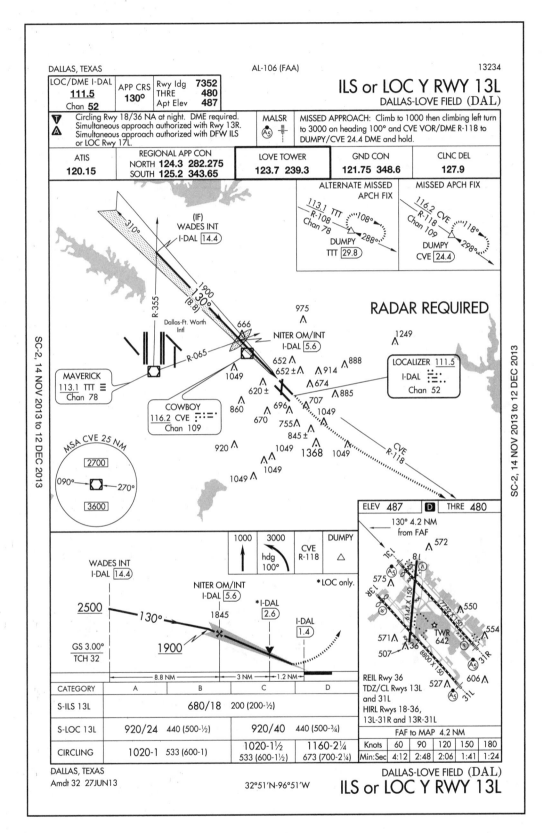

Figure 178

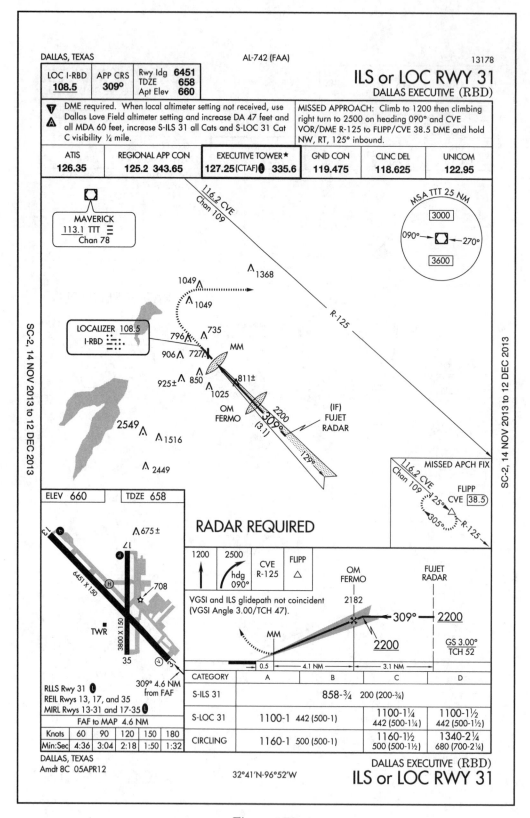

Figure 179

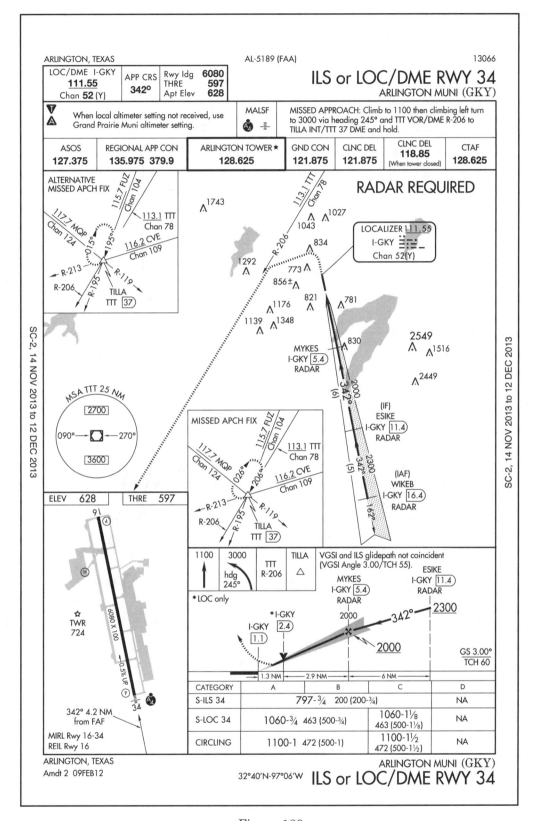

Figure 180

208   **TEXAS**

ARCHER CITY MUNI (T39)   1 SE   UTC–6(–5DT)   N33°34.94´ W98°37.12´   DALLAS–FT WORTH
  1065   S2   NOTAM FILE FTW   L–17B
  RWY 17–35: H3200X60 (ASPH)   S–12.5
    RWY 17: Road.
  AIRPORT REMARKS: Unattended. Wildlife on and invof arpt. 70´ AGL drilling
    rig 700´ northwest of Rwy 17–35. Rwy 17–35 loose grvl, tall grass and
    pot holes on rwy.
  COMMUNICATIONS: CTAF 122.9
  RADIO AIDS TO NAVIGATION: NOTAM FILE SPS.
    WICHITA FALLS (H) VORTACW 112.7   SPS   Chan 74   N33°59.24´
      W98°35.61´   173° 24.3 NM to fld. 1133/10E.

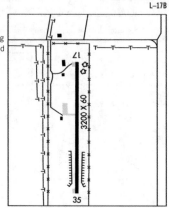

ARDYTH   N27°38.54´ W99°27.48´   NOTAM FILE SJT.   BROWNSVILLE
  NDB (MHW) 405   AGH   174° 5.9 NM to Laredo Intl.   L–20G

ARLEDGE FLD (See STAMFORD on page 351)

ARLINGTON MUNI (GKY)   4 S   UTC–6(–5DT)   N32°39.83´ W97°05.66´   DALLAS–FT WORTH
  628   B   S4   **FUEL** 100LL, JET A   OX 4   TPA—1628(1000)   NOTAM FILE GKY   COPTER
  RWY 16–34: H6080X100 (CONC)   S–60   MIRL   0.5% up NW   H–6H, L–17C, A
    RWY 16: REIL. PAPI(P4L)—GA 3.0° TCH 42´.   IAP, AD
    RWY 34: MALSF. PAPI(P4L)—GA 3.0° TCH 55´.
  AIRPORT REMARKS: Attended continuously. Self serve fuel with major credit
    card. Helicopter test facility at arpt mostly from private helipad
    adjoining ldg area. Extensive helicopter traffic west of rwy. Rwy 34
    PAPI unusable byd 8° right of centerline. MIRL Rwy 16–34 preset
    medium ints, higher ints by twr request. When twr clsd ACTIVATE
    MALSF Rwy 34—CTAF. PAPI Rwy 16 and Rwy 34 opr continuously.
  WEATHER DATA SOURCES: ASOS 127.375 (817) 557–0251.
  COMMUNICATIONS: CTAF 128.625
  Ⓡ **REGIONAL APP/DEP CON** 135.975
    TOWER 128.625 (1300–0300Z‡) **GND CON/CLNC DEL** 121.875
    CLNC DEL 118.85 (RGNL APP CON when twr clsd)
  AIRSPACE: CLASS D svc 1300–0300Z‡ other times **CLASS G.**
  RADIO AIDS TO NAVIGATION: NOTAM FILE FTW.
    MAVERICK (H) VORW/DME 113.1   TTT   Chan 78   N32°52.15´
      W97°02.43´   186° 12.6 NM to fld. 540/6E.
    All acft arriving DFW are requested to turn DME off until departure due
      to traffic overload of Maverick DME
    ILS/DME 111.55   I–GKY   Chan 52(Y)   Rwy 34.   Class IE.   LOC
      unusable byd 15° right of course. Unmonitored when ATCT clsd.

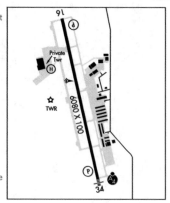

Figure 181

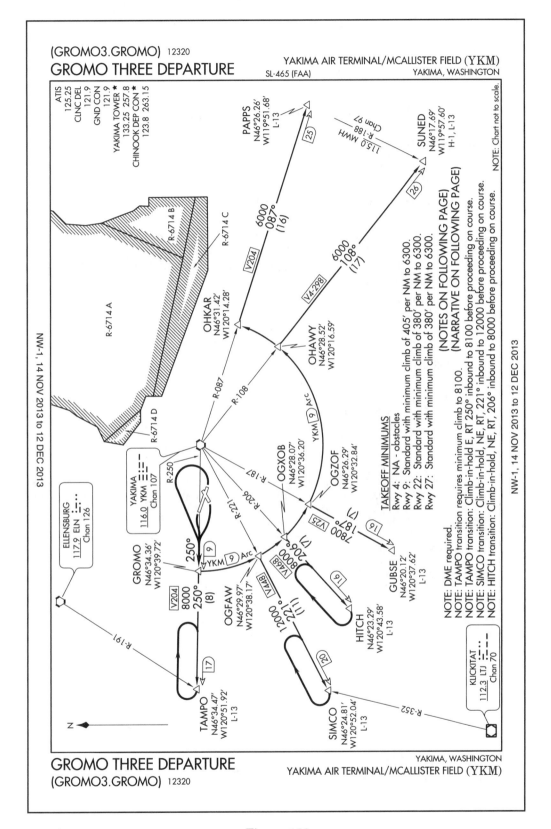

Figure 182

(GROMO3.GROMO) 12208
GROMO THREE DEPARTURE
SL-465 (FAA)

YAKIMA AIR TERMINAL/MCALLISTER FIELD (YKM)
YAKIMA, WASHINGTON

DEPARTURE ROUTE DESCRIPTION

<u>TAKEOFF RUNWAY 9,27</u>: Climbing left turn thence. . . .
<u>TAKEOFF RUNWAY 22</u>: Climbing right turn thence. . . .

. . . . intercept and proceed via YKM R-250 to GROMO/YKM 9 DME, then on assigned transition.

<u>GUBSE TRANSITION (GROMO3.GUBSE)</u>: From over GROMO DME Fix via YKM 9 DME Arc to OGZOF DME fix and YKM VORTAC R-187 to GUBSE DME fix.

<u>HITCH TRANSITION (GROMO3.HITCH)</u>: From over GROMO DME Fix via YKM 9 DME Arc to OGXOB DME fix and YKM VORTAC R-206 to HITCH DME fix.

<u>PAPPS TRANSITION (GROMO3.PAPPS)</u>: From over GROMO DME Fix via YKM 9 DME Arc to OKHAR DME fix and YKM VORTAC R-087 to PAPPS DME fix.

<u>SIMCO TRANSITION (GROMO3.SIMCO)</u>: From over GROMO DME Fix via YKM 9 DME Arc to OGFAW DME fix and YKM VORTAC R-221 to SIMCO INT.

<u>SUNED TRANSITION (GROMO3.SUNED)</u>: From over GROMO DME Fix via 9 DME Arc to OHAWY DME fix and KM R-108 to SUNED INT.

<u>TAMPO TRANSITION (GROMO3.TAMPO)</u>: From over GROMO DME Fix via YKM VORTAC R-250 to TAMPO INT.

<u>TAKEOFF OBSTACLE NOTES</u>
Rwy 9: OL on building 27' from DER, 507' right of centerline, 34' AGL/1074' MSL.
Pole 388' from DER, 561' right of centerline, 34' AGL/1073' MSL.
Trees beginning 586' from DER, 550' right of centerline, up to 100' AGL/1139' MSL.
Rwy 22: Fence beginning 27' from DER, 435' right of centerline, up to 10' AGL/1085' MSL.
Trees beginning 570' from DER, 228' left of centerline, up to 100' AGL/1199' MSL.
Trees beginning 3195' from DER, 202' right of centerline, up to 100' AGL/1199' MSL.
Trees beginning 1 NM from DER, 732' left of centerline, up to 100' AGL/1239' MSL.
Rwy 27: Ant on building 398' from DER, 282' left of centerline, 15' AGL/1117' MSL.
Trees beginning 3893' from DER, 1341' right of centerline, up to 100' AGL/1239' MSL.

GROMO THREE DEPARTURE
(GROMO3.GROMO) 12208

YAKIMA, WASHINGTON
YAKIMA AIR TERMINAL/MCALLISTER FIELD (YKM)

NW-1, 14 NOV 2013 to 12 DEC 2013

Figure 183

200   **WASHINGTON**

YAKIMA AIR TERMINAL/MCALLISTER FLD (YKM)   3 S   UTC–8(–7DT)   N46°34.09´ W120°32.64´   SEATTLE
1099   B   S4   **FUEL** 100LL, JET A   OX 1, 3   Class I, ARFF Index A   NOTAM FILE YKM   H–1C, L–13A
RWY 09–27: H7604X150 (ASPH–GRVD)   S–95, D–160, 2S–175, 2D–220, 2D/2D2–550 PCN 33 F/C/X/T   IAP, DIAP, AD
   HIRL   0.7% up W
   RWY 09: REIL. VASI(V4L)—GA 3.0° TCH 50´.
   RWY 27: MALSR. PAPI(P4L)—GA 3.0° TCH 57´.
RWY 04–22: H3835X150 (ASPH–PFC)   S–70, D–80, 2S–102, 2D–120 PCN 28 F/C/X/T   MIRL   0.5% up SW
   RWY 04: REIL. PAPI(P4L)—GA 3.0° TCH 57´.
   RWY 22: REIL. PAPI(P4L)—GA 3.0° TCH 45´.
   RUNWAY DECLARED DISTANCE INFORMATION
   RWY 04: TORA–3835   TODA–3835   ASDA–3835   LDA–3835
   RWY 09: TORA–7604   TODA–7604   ASDA–7604   LDA–7604
   RWY 22: TORA–3835   TODA–3835   ASDA–3535   LDA–3835
   RWY 27: TORA–7604   TODA–7604   ASDA–7604   LDA–7604
AIRPORT REMARKS: Attended 1400–0400Z‡. Sfc conditions unmonitored 0800–1330Z‡. Be alert, birds invof Yakima River 5
   NM east of apch to Rwy 27. Reflectors on Twy C only. Rwy 04–22 some spalling and raveling. PPR for unscheduled air
   carrier ops with more than 30 passenger seats, call arpt manger 509–575–6149/6150. Twy B from apch end of Rwy 22
   to Twy A rstd to acft with wingspans 79´ or less. MIRL Rwy 04–22, REIL Rwy 04 and Rwy 22, PAPI Rwy 04 and Rwy
   22 OTS when twr clsd. Twy B1 and Twy B2 twy lgts OTS when twr clsd. Twy B lgts south of Rwy 09–27 OTS when twr
   clsd. When twr clsd ACTIVATE HIRL Rwy 09–27 and MALSR Rwy 27—CTAF.
WEATHER DATA SOURCES: ASOS (509) 248–1502
COMMUNICATIONS: CTAF 133.25 **ATIS** 125.25 **UNICOM** 122.95
   RCO 122.5 (SEATTLE RADIO)
Ⓡ **CHINOOK APP/DEP CON** 123.8 (1400–0600Z‡)
Ⓡ **SEATTLE CENTER APP/DEP CON** 132.6 (0600–1400Z‡)
   TOWER 133.25 (1400–0600Z‡) **GND CON** 121.9 **CLNC DEL** 121.9
AIRSPACE: CLASS D svc 1400–0600Z‡ other times CLASS E.
RADIO AIDS TO NAVIGATION: NOTAM FILE YKM.
   (H) VORTACW 116.0   YKM   Chan 107   N46°34.21´ W120°26.68´   247° 4.1 NM to fld. 984/21E.
   DME unusable:
      095°–115° byd 26 NM blo 8,000´
      095°–115° byd 35 NM
      115°–207° byd 20 NM blo 8,500´
      115°–207° byd 36 NM blo 10,000´
      207°–230° byd 20 NM blo 10,000´
      290°–315° byd 20 NM blo 11,000´
      315°–080° byd 12 NM blo 15,000´
   VOR portion unusable:
      025°–035° byd 5 NM blo 6,000´
      080°–105° byd 35 NM blo 6,000´
      105°–107° byd 25 NM blo 6,000´
      109°–135° byd 25 NM blo 6,000´
      135°–180° byd 30 NM blo 7,500´
      195°–225° byd 30 NM blo 8,500´
      305°–335° byd 30 NM blo 9,000´
      350°–080° byd 25 NM blo 9,000´
   DONNY NDB (LOM) 371   YK   N46°31.54´ W120°22.33´ 274° 7.6 NM to fld. Unmonitored when ATCT closed.
   ILS 110.1   I–YKM   Rwy 27.   LOM DONNY NDB. Unmonitored when ATCT closed.
COMM/NAV/WEATHER REMARKS: During hrs twr is clsd all ops in vicinity of arpt rstd to acft with VHF radio capability, unless an
   emerg exist necessitating UHF equipped acft to land.

Figure 184

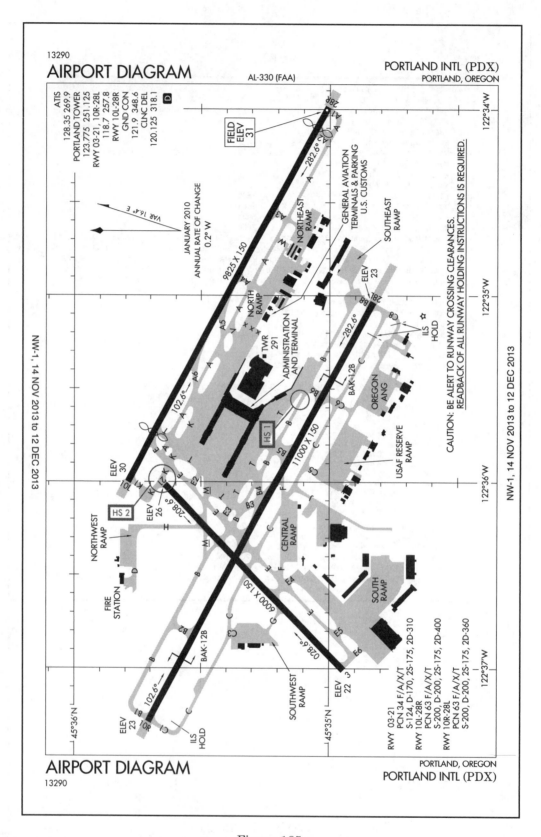

Figure 185

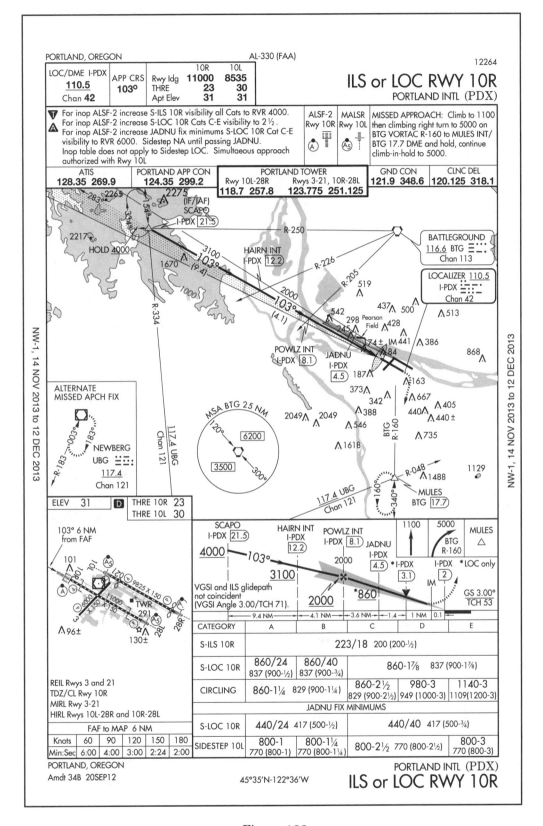

Figure 186

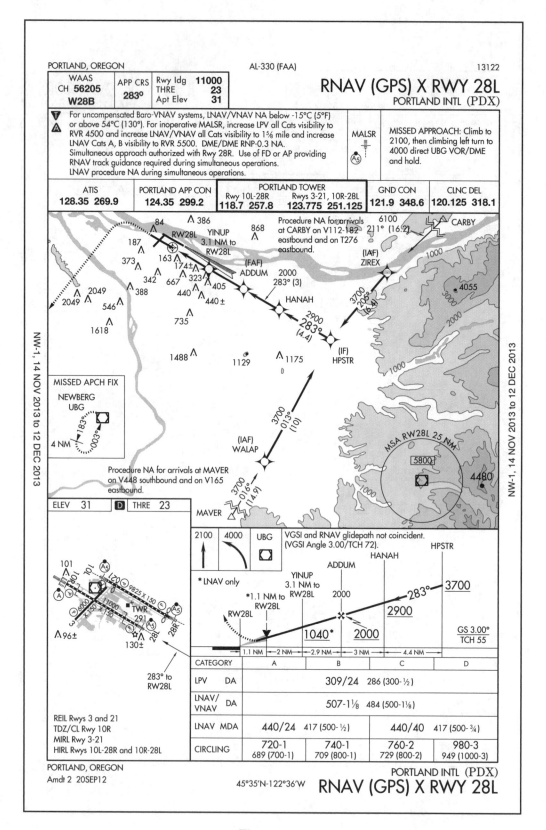

Figure 187

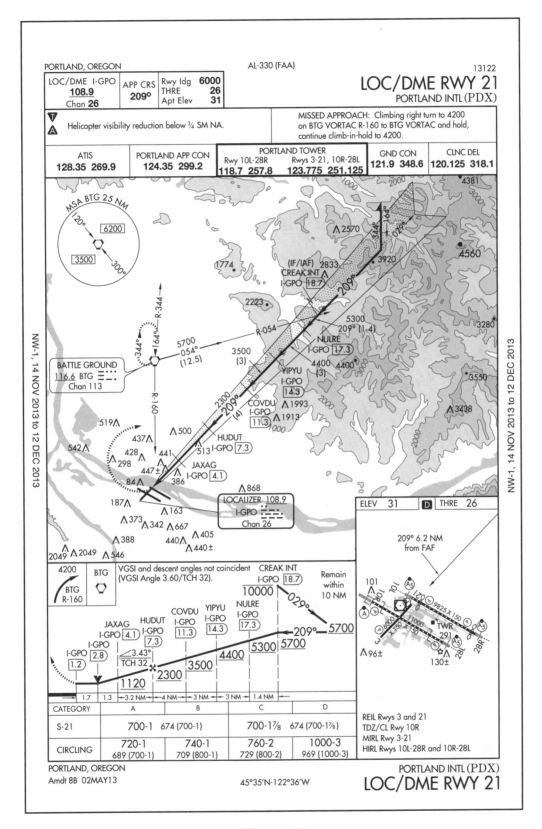

Figure 188

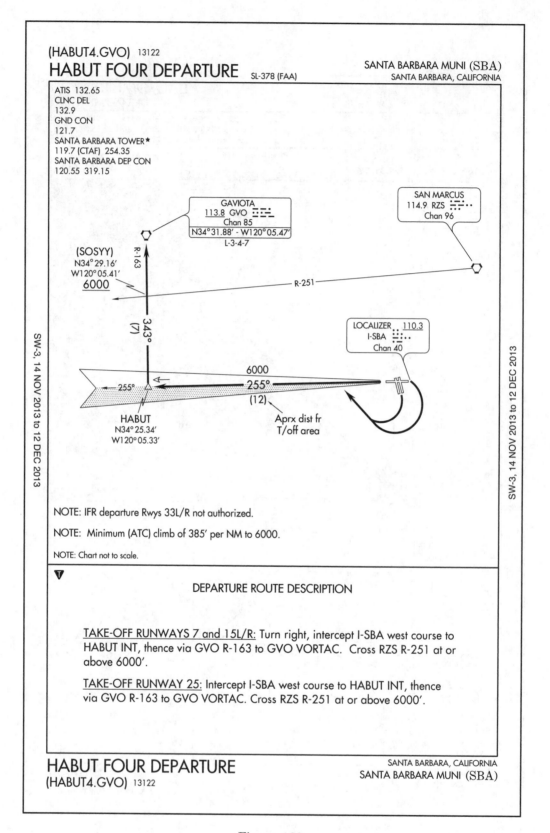

(HABUT4.GVO) 13122
HABUT FOUR DEPARTURE   SL-378 (FAA)

SANTA BARBARA MUNI (SBA)
SANTA BARBARA, CALIFORNIA

ATIS 132.65
CLNC DEL
132.9
GND CON
121.7
SANTA BARBARA TOWER★
119.7 (CTAF) 254.35
SANTA BARBARA DEP CON
120.55 319.15

GAVIOTA
113.8 GVO
Chan 85
N34°31.88' - W120°05.47'
L-3-4-7

SAN MARCUS
114.9 RZS
Chan 96

(SOSYY)
N34°29.16'
W120°05.41'
6000

R-163

R-251

343°
(7)

LOCALIZER   110.3
I-SBA
Chan 40

255°   6000
255°
(12)

HABUT
N34°25.34'
W120°05.33'

Aprx dist fr
T/off area

SW-3, 14 NOV 2013 to 12 DEC 2013

SW-3, 14 NOV 2013 to 12 DEC 2013

NOTE: IFR departure Rwys 33L/R not authorized.

NOTE: Minimum (ATC) climb of 385' per NM to 6000.

NOTE: Chart not to scale.

DEPARTURE ROUTE DESCRIPTION

TAKE-OFF RUNWAYS 7 and 15L/R: Turn right, intercept I-SBA west course to
HABUT INT, thence via GVO R-163 to GVO VORTAC. Cross RZS R-251 at or
above 6000'.

TAKE-OFF RUNWAY 25: Intercept I-SBA west course to HABUT INT, thence
via GVO R-163 to GVO VORTAC. Cross RZS R-251 at or above 6000'.

HABUT FOUR DEPARTURE
(HABUT4.GVO) 13122

SANTA BARBARA, CALIFORNIA
SANTA BARBARA MUNI (SBA)

Figure 189

186   **CALIFORNIA**

SANTA BARBARA MUNI (SBA)   7 W   UTC–8(–7DT)   N34°25.57´ W119°50.49´   LOS ANGELES
    13   B S4 **FUEL** 100LL, JET A   OX 1, 2, 3, 4   TPA—See Remarks   LRA   Class I, ARFF Index C   H–4H, L–3D, 4F, 7A
    NOTAM FILE SBA   IAP, AD
RWY 07–25: H6052X150 (ASPH–PFC)   S–110, D–160, 2S–175,
    2D–245   HIRL
    RWY 07: MALSR. Tree. Rgt tfc.
    RWY 25: REIL. PAPI(P4L)—GA 3.0° TCH 50´. Fence.
RWY 15R–33L: H4184X100 (ASPH)   S–48, D–63, 2S–80, 2D–100
    MIRL
    RWY 15R: REIL. Tree.
    RWY 33L: Tree. Rgt tfc.
RWY 15L–33R: H4178X75 (ASPH)   S–35, D–41, 2S–80, 2D–63
    RWY 15L: Thld dsplcd 217´. Bldg.
    RWY 33R: Rgt tfc.

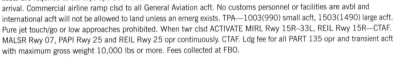

AIRPORT REMARKS: Attended 1330–0600Z‡. 100LL fuel 24 hr credit card
    svc avbl. Fee for Jet A fuel after hrs call 805–964–6733 or 967–5608.
    Numerous flocks of birds on and invof arpt. Deep creek located 300´
    from rwy end Rwy 07, Rwy 33L and Rwy 33R. Rwy 15L–33R dalgt
    hrs only. Arpt has noise abatement procedures ctc arpt ops
    805–692–6005. Due to ltd ramp space at the airline terminal
    non–scheduled transport category acft with more than 30 passenger
    seats are required to ctc arpt ops 805–692–6005 24 hour PPR to
    arrival. Commercial airline ramp clsd to all General Aviation acft. No customs personnel or facilities are avbl and
    international acft will not be allowed to land unless an emerg exists. TPA—1003(990) small acft, 1503(1490) large acft.
    Pure jet touch/go or low approaches prohibited. When twr clsd ACTIVATE MIRL Rwy 15R–33L, REIL Rwy 15R—CTAF.
    MALSR Rwy 07, PAPI Rwy 25 and REIL Rwy 25 opr continuously. CTAF. Ldg fee for all PART 135 opr and transient acft
    with maximum gross weight 10,000 lbs or more. Fees collected at FBO.
WEATHER DATA SOURCES: ASOS (805) 681–0583
COMMUNICATIONS: CTAF 119.7 **ATIS** 132.65 **UNICOM** 122.95
Ⓡ **APP/DEP CON** 120.55 (151°–329°) 125.4 (330°–150°) 124.15 127.725 (1400–0700Z‡)
Ⓡ **L.A. CENTER APP/DEP CON** 119.05 (0700–1400Z‡)
    TOWER 119.7 (1400–0700Z‡) **GND CON** 121.7 **CLNC DEL** 132.9
AIRSPACE: CLASS C svc ctc **APP CON** svc 1400–0700Z‡ other times CLASS E.
RADIO AIDS TO NAVIGATION: NOTAM FILE HHR.
    SAN MARCUS (H) VORTAC 114.9   RZS   Chan 96   N34°30.57´ W119°46.26´   201° 6.1 NM to fld. 3623/14E.
        HIWAS.
    VOR unusable:
        140°–178° byd 27 NM
    GAVIOTA (L) VORTACW 113.8   GVO   Chan 85   N34°31.88´ W120°05.47´   101° 13.9 NM to fld. 2616/16E.
    VORTAC unusable:
        117°–137° byd 35 NM
        310°–095° byd 10 NM blo 8,500´
        360°–095° byd 20 NM blo 12,500´
    ILS/DME 110.3 I–SBA   Chan 40   Rwy 07.   Class IA.   Unmonitored when ATCT clsd.

SANTA CATALINA   N33°22.50´ W118°25.19´   NOTAM FILE HHR.   LOS ANGELES
    (L) VORTACW 111.4   SXC   Chan 51   352° 1.8 NM to Catalina. 2090/15E.   H–4I, L–3E, 4G

Figure 190

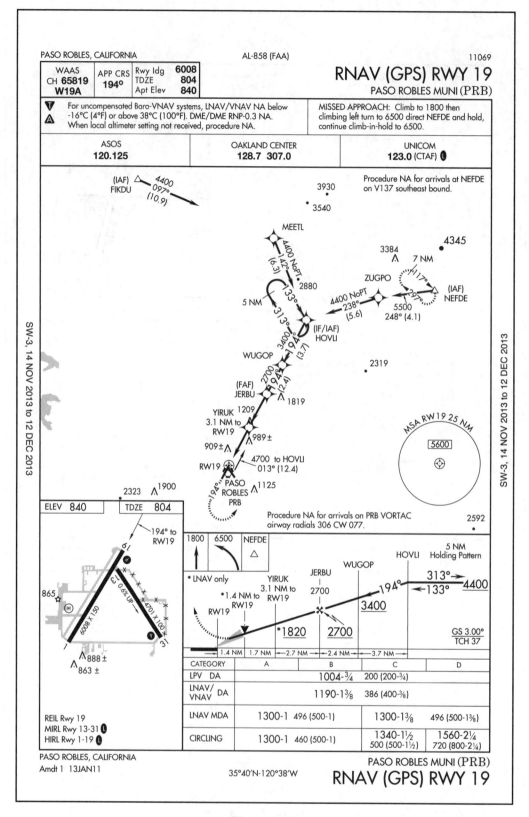

PASO ROBLES, CALIFORNIA   AL-858 (FAA)   11069

WAAS CH 65819 W19A	APP CRS 194°	Rwy Idg 6008 TDZE 804 Apt Elev 840

RNAV (GPS) RWY 19
PASO ROBLES MUNI (PRB)

For uncompensated Baro-VNAV systems, LNAV/VNAV NA below -16°C (4°F) or above 38°C (100°F). DME/DME RNP-0.3 NA. When local altimeter setting not received, procedure NA.

MISSED APPROACH: Climb to 1800 then climbing left turn to 6500 direct NEFDE and hold, continue climb-in-hold to 6500.

ASOS 120.125	OAKLAND CENTER 128.7 307.0	UNICOM 123.0 (CTAF) ⓛ

SW-3, 14 NOV 2013 to 12 DEC 2013

ELEV 840   TDZE 804

REIL Rwy 19
MIRL Rwy 13-31 ⓛ
HIRL Rwy 1-19 ⓛ

PASO ROBLES, CALIFORNIA
Amdt 1 13JAN11

35°40'N-120°38'W

* LNAV only

CATEGORY	A	B	C	D
LPV DA		1004-¾ 200 (200-¾)		
LNAV/ VNAV DA		1190-1⅜ 386 (400-⅜)		
LNAV MDA	1300-1 496 (500-1)		1300-1⅜ 496 (500-1⅜)	
CIRCLING	1300-1 460 (500-1)		1340-1½ 500 (500-1½)	1560-2¼ 720 (800-2¼)

PASO ROBLES MUNI (PRB)
RNAV (GPS) RWY 19

Figure 191

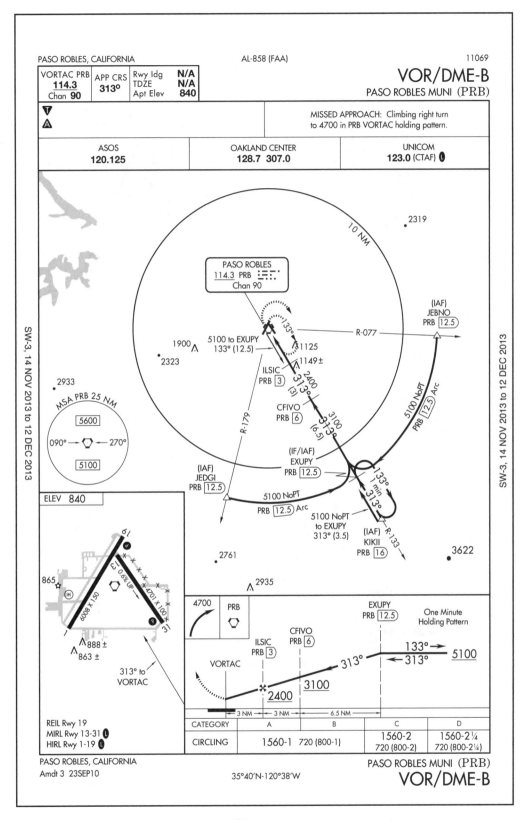

Figure 192

TEXAS   231

COLEMAN MUNI (COM)   2 NE   UTC–6(–5DT)   N31°50.47′ W99°24.22′   SAN ANTONIO
   1697   B S4 **FUEL** 100LL, JET A   NOTAM FILE FTW   L–19B
   RWY 15–33: H4506X75 (ASPH)   S–12.5   MIRL   0.4% up NW   IAP
      RWY 15: REIL. Road.
      RWY 33: REIL. Trees.
   AIRPORT REMARKS: Attended 1400–2300Z‡. Employee lives on premises.
      Multiple 65′ temporary cranes 1300′ NW AER 15. REIL Rwy 15 OTS
      indef. REIL Rwy 33 OTS indef.
   WEATHER DATA SOURCES: AWOS–3PT 119.1 (325) 625–3563.
   COMMUNICATIONS: CTAF/UNICOM 122.8
      FORT WORTH CENTER APP/DEP CON 127.45
   RADIO AIDS TO NAVIGATION: NOTAM FILE ABI.
      ABILENE (H) VORTACW 113.7   ABI   Chan 84   N32°28.88′
      W99°51.81′   138° 44.9 NM to fld. 1810/10E.
   COMM/NAV/WEATHER REMARKS: UNICOM unmonitored indef.

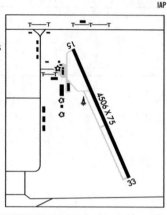

COLLEGE STATION
EASTERWOOD FLD (CLL)   3 SW   UTC–6(–5DT)   N30°35.32′ W96°21.83′   HOUSTON
   321   B S4 **FUEL** 100LL, JET A   Class I, ARFF Index A   NOTAM FILE CLL   H–7C, L–19D, 21A
   RWY 16–34: H7000X146 (ASPH–CONC–GRVD)   S–70, D–90, 2S–114,   IAP, AD
      2D–150   HIRL
      RWY 16: VASI(V4R)—GA 3.0° TCH 51′. Tree.
      RWY 34: MALSR.
   RWY 10–28: H5158X150 (ASPH–GRVD)   S–27, D–50, 2D–87   MIRL
      RWY 10: VASI(V4L)—GA 3.0° TCH 50′. Tree.
      RWY 28: REIL. VASI(V4L)—GA 3.0° TCH 54′. Tree.
   RWY 04–22: H5150X150 (CONC)   S–27, D–50, 2D–87
      RWY 04: Tree.
      RWY 22: Tree.
   RUNWAY DECLARED DISTANCE INFORMATION
      RWY 04: TORA–5149   TODA–5149   ASDA–5149   LDA–5149
      RWY 10: TORA–5159   TODA–5159   ASDA–5159   LDA–5159
      RWY 16: TORA–7000   TODA–7000   ASDA–7000   LDA–7000
      RWY 22: TORA–5149   TODA–5149   ASDA–5149   LDA–5149
      RWY 28: TORA–5159   TODA–5159   ASDA–5159   LDA–5159
      RWY 34: TORA–7000   TODA–7000   ASDA–7000   LDA–7000
   AIRPORT REMARKS: Attended 1200–0400Z‡. For fuel after hours PPR call
      979–845–4811 or ctc Texas A and M University police
      979–845–2345; late ngt fee. CLOSED to unscheduled air carrier ops
      with more than 30 passenger seats except 24 hours PPR call arpt manager 979–845–4811. Rwy 04–22 day VFR ops
      only. Rwy 10–28 mandatory hold short sign on Rwy 16–34 unlgtd. Itinerant acft park in front of twr, overnight parking
      fee. Ldg fee scheduled FAR 135 and all FAR 121 ops. Rwy 04–22 and Twy E S of Rwy 10–28 not avbl for air carrier acft
      with over 30 passenger seats. Rwy 16–34 first 1850′ Rwy 34 conc. PAEW adjacent all twys 1200–2200Z‡. When twr
      clsd ACTIVATE HIRL Rwy 16–34 and MALSR Rwy 34—CTAF. MIRL Rwy 10–28 and REIL Rwy 28 preset low ints only.
   WEATHER DATA SOURCES: ASOS (979) 846–1708 HIWAS 113.3 CLL.
   COMMUNICATIONS: CTAF 118.5 ATIS 126.85 UNICOM 122.95
      COLLEGE STATION RCO 122.65 122.2 (MONTGOMERY COUNTY RADIO).
   ®**HOUSTON APP/DEP CON** 134.3
      TOWER 118.5 (1400–0300Z‡) **GND CON/CLNC DEL** 128.7 **CLNC DEL** 120.4 (when twr clsd)
   AIRSPACE: CLASS D svc 1400–0300Z‡ other times CLASS E.

CONTINUED ON NEXT PAGE

SC, 17 OCT 2013 to 12 DEC 2013

Figure 193

232   **TEXAS**
                                    CONTINUED FROM PRECEDING PAGE

RADIO AIDS TO NAVIGATION: NOTAM FILE CLL.
    COLLEGE STATION (L) VORTACW 113.3   CLL   Chan 80   N30°36.30′ W96°25.24′   100° 3.1 NM to fld. 264/8E.
    HIWAS.
    DME unusable:
      101°–130° byd 25 NM blo 2,500′
      131°–148° byd 30 NM blo 2,500′
      149°–160° byd 30 NM blo 2,000′
      325°–349° byd 30 NM blo 2,500′
      350°–100° byd 25 NM blo 3,500′
    VOR portion unusable:
      131°–189° blo 7,000′
    ROWDY NDB (LOM) 260   CL   N30°29.62′ W96°20.26′ 341° 5.8 NM to fld. Unmonitored when ATCT clsd.
    ILS/DME 111.7   I–CLL   Chan 54   Rwy 34.   Class IB.   LOM ROWDY NDB. Unmonitored when ATCT clsd. DME
      unmonitored. Glideslope unusable for coupled apchs blo 1,050′ MSL.

COLLIN CO RGNL AT MC KINNEY (See DALLAS on page 241)

COLLINSVILLE
  SUDDEN STOP (T32)   1 NE   UTC–6(–5DT)   N33°34.29′ W96°54.43′   DALLAS–FT WORTH
    720   NOTAM FILE FTW
  RWY 17–35: 1550X60 (TURF)
    RWY 17: Trees.
    RWY 35: Road.
  AIRPORT REMARKS: Attended continuously. Student training prohibited.
  COMMUNICATIONS: CTAF 122.9

  COLORADO CITY (T88)   6 NW   UTC–6(–5DT)   N32°28.11′ W100°55.27′   DALLAS–FT WORTH
    2214   B   NOTAM FILE FTW   H–6G, L–17A
  RWY 17–35: H5479X60 (ASPH)   S–50   LIRL
    RWY 35: Tree.
  AIRPORT REMARKS: Attended irregularly. Rwy 17–35 pavement from Rwy 35
    thld lgts southward used as a twy and not maintained.
  COMMUNICATIONS: CTAF 122.9
  RADIO AIDS TO NAVIGATION: NOTAM FILE BPG.
    BIG SPRING (L) VORTACW 114.3   BGS   Chan 90   N32°23.14′
      W101°29.02′   069° 29.0 NM to fld. 2670/11E.

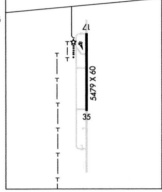

COLUMBUS
  ROBERT R WELLS JR (66R)   3 S   UTC–6(–5DT)   N29°38.49′ W96°30.96′   HOUSTON
    242   B   **FUEL** 100LL, JET A   NOTAM FILE CXO   L–19D, 21A
  RWY 15–33: H3800X60 (ASPH)   S–12.5   MIRL
    RWY 15: REIL. PAPI(P2L). Thld dsplcd 305′. Fence.
    RWY 33: REIL. PAPI(P2L). Thld dsplcd 177′. Brush.
  AIRPORT REMARKS: Unattended. Self svc fuel with major credit card. Ultra–light activity on and invof arpt. Rwy 33 REIL OTS
    indef. ACTIVATE MIRL Rwy 15–33—CTAF.
  COMMUNICATIONS: CTAF 122.9
  RADIO AIDS TO NAVIGATION: NOTAM FILE CXO.
    INDUSTRY (L) VORTACW 110.2   IDU   Chan 39   N29°57.36′ W96°33.73′   165° 19.0 NM to fld. 419/8E.

SC, 17 OCT 2013 to 12 DEC 2013

Figure 193A

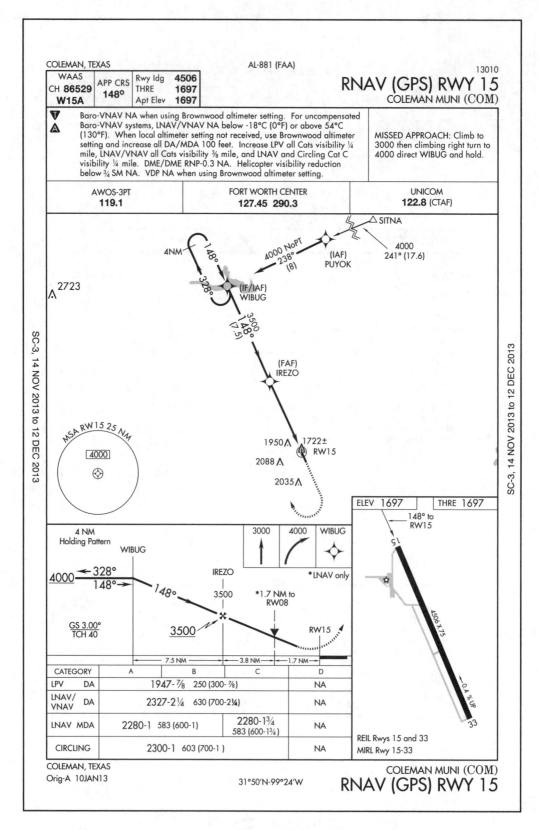

Figure 194

288   **TEXAS**

WESTHEIMER AIR PARK (O07)   20 W   UTC–6(–5DT)   N29°41.68´ W95°47.68´   HOUSTON
   117   B   S2   **FUEL** 100LL   NOTAM FILE CXO
   RWY 11–29: H2500X28 (CONC)   LIRL
     RWY 11: Trees.
     RWY 29: Tree.
     AIRPORT REMARKS: Attended 1400–0000Z‡. 90´ P–line 1500´ from Rwy 11 thld. Grass in cracks on rwy sfc. ACTIVATE
       rotating bcn—CTAF. ACTIVATE LIRL Rwy 11–29—CTAF.
     COMMUNICATIONS: CTAF/UNICOM 122.7

WILLIAM P HOBBY (HOU)   8 SE   UTC–6(–5DT)   N29°38.73´ W95°16.73´   HOUSTON
   46   B   S2   **FUEL** 100LL, JET A, A1   OX 1, 2, 3, 4   LRA   Class I, ARFF Index C   COPTER
   NOTAM FILE HOU   H–7C, L–19E, 21A, GOMW
                                                        IAP, AD
   RWY 04–22: H7602X150 (CONC–GRVD)   S–75, D–200, 2S–168,
     2T–461, 2D–400, 2D/D1–444, C5–717   HIRL   CL
     RWY 04: ALSF2. TDZL. PAPI(P4R)—GA 3.0° TCH 57´.
     RWY 22: MALS. VASI(V4L)—GA 3.0° TCH 52´. Pole.
   RWY 12R–30L: H7602X150 (ASPH–GRVD)   S–75, D–195, 2S–168,
     2T–461, 2D–220, 2D/D1–444, C5–717   HIRL   CL
     RWY 12R: MALSR. TDZL. PAPI(P4R)—GA 3.0° TCH 52´. Thld dsplcd
       1034´. Pole.
     RWY 30L: TDZL. REIL. PAPI(P4L)—GA 3.0° TCH 71´. Road.
   RWY 17–35: H6000X150 (ASPH–CONC–GRVD)   S–75, D–121, 2S–153,
     2D–195   MIRL
     RWY 17: VASI(V4L)—GA 3.0° TCH 38´. Antenna.
     RWY 35: REIL. VASI(V4R)—GA 3.0° TCH 41´. Bldg.
   RWY 12L–30R: H5148X100 (CONC–GRVD)   S–30, D–45, 2D–80   MIRL
     RWY 12L: PAPI(P4L)—GA 3.0° TCH 60´.
   RUNWAY DECLARED DISTANCE INFORMATION
     RWY 04: TORA–7602   TODA–7602   ASDA–7602   LDA–7602
     RWY 12L: TORA–5148   TODA–5148   ASDA–5148   LDA–5148
     RWY 12R: TORA–7602   TODA–7602   ASDA–7602   LDA–6568
     RWY 17: TORA–6000   TODA–6000   ASDA–6000   LDA–6000
     RWY 22: TORA–7602   TODA–7602   ASDA–7602   LDA–7602
     RWY 30L: TORA–7602   TODA–7602   ASDA–7602   LDA–7602
     RWY 30R: TORA–5148   TODA–5148   ASDA–5148   LDA–5148
     RWY 35: TORA–6000   TODA–6000   ASDA–6000   LDA–6000

Rwy 12L-30R: 5148 X 100

AIRPORT REMARKS: Attended continuously. Arpt CLOSED to acft with wingspan over 125´ except 24 hours PPR, call arpt
   manager 713–640–3000. Numerous birds on and invof arpt. ASDE–X Surveillance System in use: pilots should operate
   transponders with Mode C on all twys and rwys. Customs ramp has multiple obstructions, recommend large acft use
   customs overflow ramp. Acft in tkf position on Rwy 22 be alert for possible radio interference or null on frequency 118.7.
   Use upper antenna if so equipped. Rwy 04 runway visual range touchdown, midfield, rollout avbl. Rwy 22 runway visual
   range touchdown, midfield, rollout avbl. Rwy 12R runway visual range touchdown avbl. Rwy 30L runway visual range
   touchdown avbl. Twy G centerline to parked acft on W side only 68´. Twy G centerline to edge of adjacent svc vehicle
   road on W side only 48´. Due to complex rwy configuration, when taxiing to thlds 12L and 12R and 17 check compass
   heading before departing. Acft southbound on Twy C to Rwy 30L thld use extreme care, Twy C makes a 45° dogleg to the
   left crossing Twy K. PAPI Rwy 30L unusable byd 8° left and right of course. Flight Notification Service (ADCUS) available.
   NOTE: See Special Notices—U.S. Special Customs Requirement.
WEATHER DATA SOURCES: ASOS (713) 847–1462 TDWR.
COMMUNICATIONS: D–ATIS 124.6 (713) 847–1491 **UNICOM** 122.95
   HOBBY RCO 122.35 (MONTGOMERY COUNTY RADIO)
Ⓡ **HOUSTON APP CON** 134.45 (South) 124.35 (West) 120.05 (East)
   HOBBY TOWER 118.7
   HOUSTON GND CON 121.9 **CLNC DEL** 125.45 **PRE–TAXI CLNC** 125.45
Ⓡ **HOUSTON DEP CON** 134.45 (South) 123.8 (West) 119.7 (North)
   AIRSPACE: CLASS B See VFR Terminal Area Chart
VOR TEST FACILITY (VOT) 108.4
RADIO AIDS TO NAVIGATION: NOTAM FILE HOU.
   HOBBY (H) VORW/DME 117.1   HUB   Chan 118   N29°39.34´ W95°16.60´   at fld. 47/5E.
   ILS/DME 109.9   I–HUB   Chan 36   Rwy 04.   Class IIIE.   DME also serves Rwy 22.
   ILS/DME 111.3   I–PRQ   Chan 50   Rwy 12R.   Class IE.   DME also serves Rwy 30L.
   LOC/DME 109.9   I–OIB   Chan 36   Rwy 22.   DME also serves Rwy 04. DME unusable byd 17° right of course.
   ILS/DME 111.3   I–UPU   Chan 50   Rwy 30L.   Class IE.   DME also serves Rwy 12R.

HOUSTON   MCJ   N29°42.83´ W95°23.80´   HOUSTON
   AWOS–3 119.575   H–7C, L–19E, 21A, GOMW

SC, 17 OCT 2013 to 12 DEC 2013

Figure 195

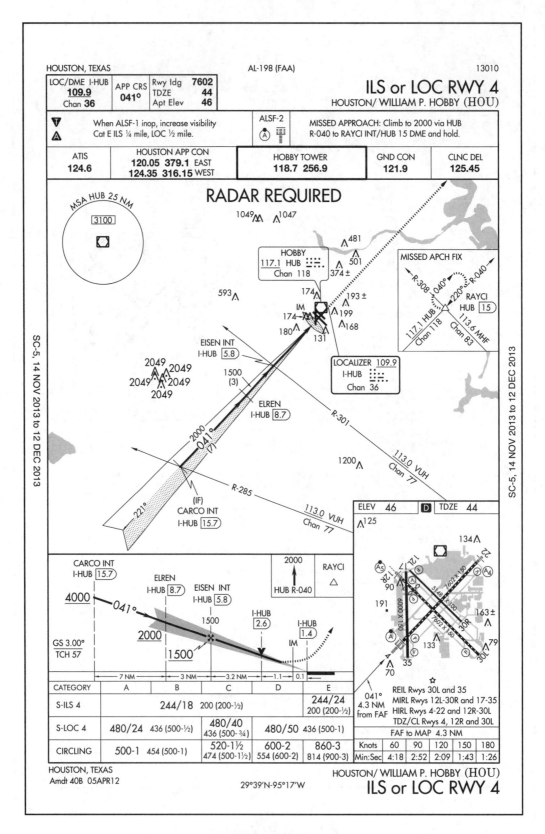

HOUSTON, TEXAS   AL-198 (FAA)   13010

| LOC/DME I-HUB **109.9** Chan **36** | APP CRS **041°** | Rwy Idg **7602** TDZE **44** Apt Elev **46** | | **ILS or LOC RWY 4** HOUSTON/ WILLIAM P. HOBBY (HOU) |

When ALSF-1 inop, increase visibility Cat E ILS ¼ mile, LOC ½ mile.

ALSF-2

MISSED APPROACH: Climb to 2000 via HUB R-040 to RAYCI INT/HUB 15 DME and hold.

| ATIS **124.6** | HOUSTON APP CON **120.05 379.1** EAST **124.35 316.15** WEST | HOBBY TOWER **118.7 256.9** | GND CON **121.9** | CLNC DEL **125.45** |

RADAR REQUIRED

MSA HUB 25 NM
3100

HOBBY 117.1 HUB Chan 118

LOCALIZER 109.9 I-HUB Chan 36

MISSED APCH FIX
R-308 040° R-040
220° RAYCI HUB 15
117.1 HUB Chan 118
113.6 MHF Chan 83

EISEN INT I-HUB 5.8
1500 (3)
ELREN I-HUB 8.7
R-301
113.0 VUH Chan 77
2000 041° (7)
221°
(IF) CARCO INT I-HUB 15.7
R-285
113.0 VUH Chan 77

1049 1047
481
501
374±
593
174
193±
174 199
180 168
131
2049 2049
2049 2049
2049
1200
125

SC-5, 14 NOV 2013 to 12 DEC 2013

		CARCO INT I-HUB 15.7	ELREN I-HUB 8.7	EISEN INT I-HUB 5.8				2000 RAYCI	

4000
041°
1500
I-HUB 2.6
I-HUB 1.4
2000
1500
IM
GS 3.00° TCH 57
HUB R-040

ELEV 46   D   TDZE 44
134
191
163±
79
133
35
70
041° 4.3 NM from FAF

REIL Rwys 30L and 35
MIRL Rwys 12L-30R and 17-35
HIRL Rwys 4-22 and 12R-30L
TDZ/CL Rwys 4, 12R and 30L
FAF to MAP 4.3 NM

	7 NM	3 NM	3.2 NM	1.1	0.1

CATEGORY	A	B	C	D	E
S-ILS 4		244/18 200 (200-½)			244/24 200 (200-½)
S-LOC 4	480/24 436 (500-½)		480/40 436 (500-¾)	480/50 436 (500-1)	
CIRCLING	500-1 454 (500-1)		520-1½ 474 (500-1½)	600-2 554 (600-2)	860-3 814 (900-3)

Knots	60	90	120	150	180
Min:Sec	4:18	2:52	2:09	1:43	1:26

HOUSTON, TEXAS
Amdt 40B 05APR12

29°39'N-95°17'W

HOUSTON/ WILLIAM P. HOBBY (HOU)
ILS or LOC RWY 4

SC-5, 14 NOV 2013 to 12 DEC 2013

Figure 196

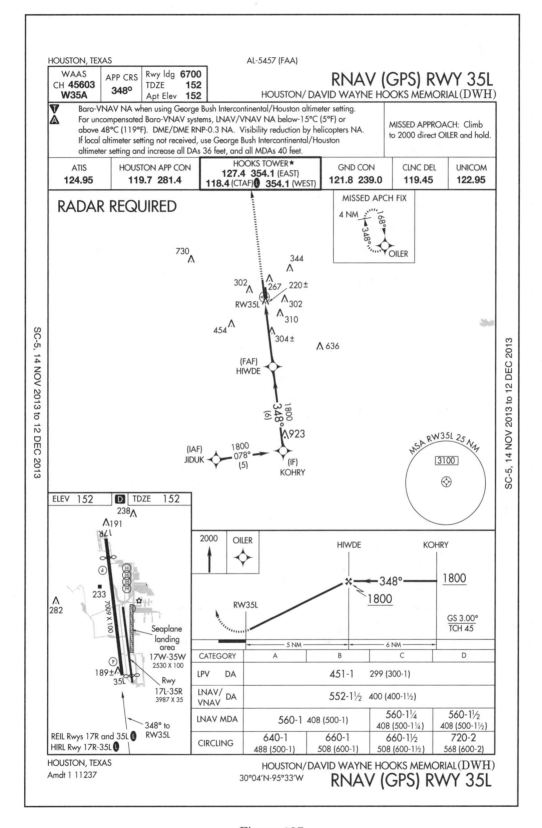

HOUSTON, TEXAS   AL-5457 (FAA)

| WAAS CH **45603** **W35A** | APP CRS **348°** | Rwy ldg **6700** TDZE **152** Apt Elev **152** | RNAV (GPS) RWY 35L HOUSTON/ DAVID WAYNE HOOKS MEMORIAL (DWH) |

Baro-VNAV NA when using George Bush Intercontinental/Houston altimeter setting. For uncompensated Baro-VNAV systems, LNAV/VNAV NA below-15°C (5°F) or above 48°C (119°F). DME/DME RNP-0.3 NA. Visibility reduction by helicopters NA. If local altimeter setting not received, use George Bush Intercontinental/Houston altimeter setting and increase all DAs 36 feet, and all MDAs 40 feet.

MISSED APPROACH: Climb to 2000 direct OILER and hold.

| ATIS **124.95** | HOUSTON APP CON **119.7 281.4** | HOOKS TOWER ★ **127.4 354.1** (EAST) **118.4** (CTAF) **354.1** (WEST) | GND CON **121.8 239.0** | CLNC DEL **119.45** | UNICOM **122.95** |

RADAR REQUIRED

MISSED APCH FIX
4 NM 168° 348° OILER

730 344
302 267 220±
RW35L 302
454 310
304± 636
(FAF) HIWDE
1800 348° (6)
923
(IAF) JIDUK 1800 078° (5) (IF) KOHRY

MSA RW35L 25 NM
3100

ELEV 152 D TDZE 152
238
191
17R
233
282
7009 X 100
Seaplane landing area
17W-35W
2530 X 100
189±
35L
Rwy 17L-35R
3987 X 35
348° to RW35L
REIL Rwys 17R and 35L
HIRL Rwy 17R-35L

	OILER		HIWDE		KOHRY
2000					1800
			←348°		
	RW35L		1800		
					GS 3.00° TCH 45
		5 NM		6 NM	

CATEGORY	A	B	C	D
LPV DA		451-1	299 (300-1)	
LNAV/ VNAV DA		552-1½	400 (400-1½)	
LNAV MDA	560-1 408 (500-1)		560-1¼ 408 (500-1¼)	560-1½ 408 (500-1½)
CIRCLING	640-1 488 (500-1)	660-1 508 (600-1)	660-1½ 508 (600-1½)	720-2 568 (600-2)

HOUSTON, TEXAS
Amdt 1 11237

HOUSTON/DAVID WAYNE HOOKS MEMORIAL (DWH)
30°04'N-95°33'W
RNAV (GPS) RWY 35L

SC-5, 14 NOV 2013 to 12 DEC 2013

Figure 197

84   **LOUISIANA**

LAFAYETTE RGNL (LFT)   2 SE   UTC–6(–5DT)   N30°12.30′ W91°59.27′   HOUSTON
   42   B S4 **FUEL** 100LL, JET A   OX 1, 4   Class I, ARFF Index B   NOTAM FILE LFT   **H–7D, L–21B, 22E, GOMC**
   RWY 04R–22L: H8001X150 (ASPH–GRVD)   S–140, D–170, 2S–175,   **IAP, AD**
      2D–290   HIRL
      RWY 04R: REIL. PAPI(P4L)—GA 3.0° TCH 53′. Pole. Rgt tfc.
      RWY 22L: MALSR. PAPI(P4L)—GA 3.0° TCH 52′. Thld dsplcd 342′.
      Trees.
   RWY 11–29: H5401X148 (ASPH–GRVD)   S–85, D–110, 2S–140,
      2D–175   MIRL
      RWY 11: REIL. PAPI(P4L)—GA 3.0° TCH 35′. Trees. Rgt tfc.
      RWY 29: REIL. PAPI(P4L)—GA 3.0° TCH 35′. Tree.
   RWY 04L–22R: H4099X75 (ASPH)   S–25, D–32   MIRL
      RWY 04L: REIL. PAPI(P2L)—GA 3.0° TCH 26′. Tree.
      RWY 22R: REIL. PAPI(P2L)—GA 3.0° TCH 27′. Tree. Rgt tfc.
   RUNWAY DECLARED DISTANCE INFORMATION
      RWY 04L: TORA–4099   TODA–4099   ASDA–4099   LDA–4099
      RWY 04R: TORA–8001   TODA–8001   ASDA–8001   LDA–8001
      RWY 11: TORA–5401   TODA–5401   ASDA–5401   LDA–5401
      RWY 22L: TORA–8001   TODA–8001   ASDA–8001   LDA–7659
      RWY 22R: TORA–4099   TODA–4099   ASDA–4099   LDA–4099
      RWY 29: TORA–5401   TODA–5401   ASDA–5401   LDA–5401
   ARRESTING GEAR/SYSTEM
      RWY 04R: EMAS
      RWY 22L: EMAS
   AIRPORT REMARKS: Attended continuously. Numerous birds on and invof arpt. PPR for unscheduled air carrier ops with more
      than 30 passenger seats call arpt manager 337–266–4400. Rwy 04L–22R not avbl for air carrier ops with more than 30
      passenger seats. Ctc ground control prior to push back from terminal. 155′ oil rig 1 NM southeast of arpt. Rwy 22L
      runway visual range touchdown avbl. Twy B between Twy C and Twy D clsd to acft with wingspan over 80′. Twy F south
      of Twy B clsd to single wheel acft over 25,000 lbs and dual wheel acft over 32,000 lbs. Twy F south of Twy B reduces
      to 40′ wide. When twr clsd ACTIVATE MALSR Rwy 22L—CTAF, MIRL Rwy 04L–22R not avbl.
   WEATHER DATA SOURCES: ASOS (337) 237–8153 **HIWAS** 109.8 LFT.
   COMMUNICATIONS: CTAF 118.5 ATIS 134.05 UNICOM 122.95
      RCO 122.35 (DE RIDDER RADIO)
   ®**APP/DEP CON** 121.1 (020°–210°) 128.7 (211°–019°) (1130–0430Z‡)
   ®**HOUSTON CENTER APP/DEP CON** 126.35 (0430–1130Z‡)
      TOWER 118.5 (1130–0430Z‡) **GND CON** 121.8 **CLNC DEL** 125.55
   AIRSPACE: CLASS C svc ctc **APP CON** svc 1130–0430Z‡ other times CLASS E.
   RADIO AIDS TO NAVIGATION: NOTAM FILE LFT.
      (L) VORTACW 109.8   LFT   Chan 35   N30°11.63′ W91°59.55′   at fld. 36/3E.   **HIWAS.**
      LAFFS NDB (LOM) 375   LF   N30°17.36′ W91°54.48′   216° 6.5 NM to fld. Unmonitored when ATCT clsd.
      ILS/DME 110.9   I–TYN   Chan 46   Rwy 04R.   Class IE.
      ILS/DME 109.5   I–LFT   Chan 32   Rwy 22L.   Class IE.   LOM LAFFS NDB. ILS and LOM unmonitored when ATCT clsd.
      ASR (1130–0430Z‡)

            •   •   •   •   •   •   •   •   •   •   •   •   •

   HELIPAD H1: H50X50 (ASPH)
      HELIPAD H1: RLLS.
   HELIPORT REMARKS: Rwy H1 circular pad. Helipad H1 perimeter lgts. Heliport ops to/from helipad between Twys B and F and
      the terminal ramp, avoid overflight of the terminal and other buildings in the 270°–020° quadrant from the helipad.
      Lead–in lgts two ingress paths. Helicopter parking pads avbl.

LAFFS   N30°17.36′ W91°54.48′   NOTAM FILE LFT.   HOUSTON
   NDB (LOM) 375   LF   216° 6.5 NM to Lafayette Rgnl. Unmonitored when ATCT clsd.   **L–21B, 22E**

SC, 17 OCT 2013 to 12 DEC 2013

Figure 198

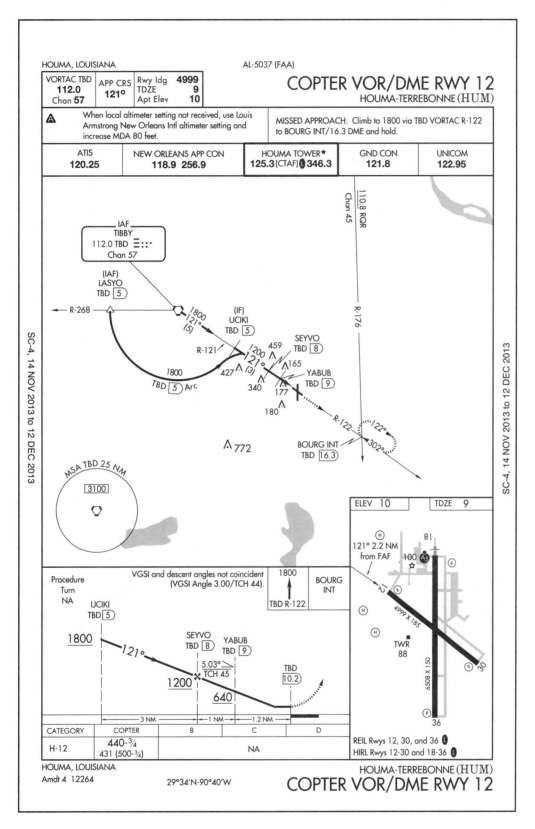

Figure 199

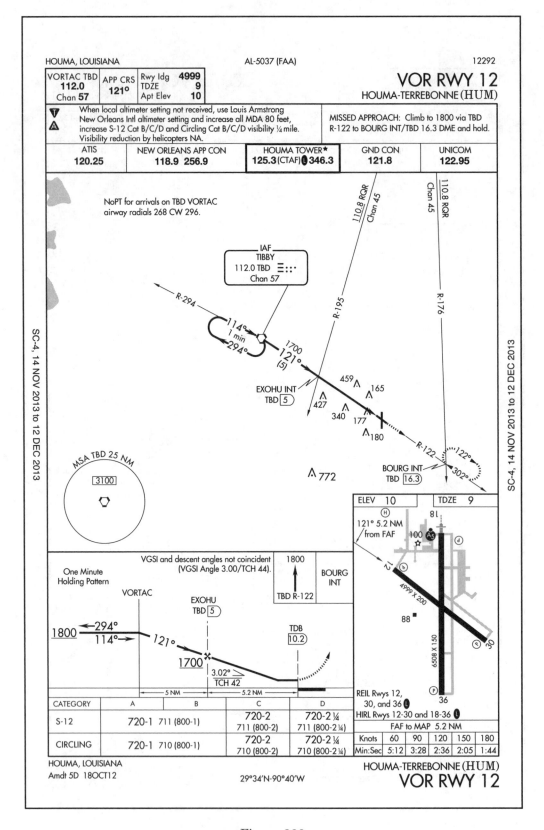

Figure 200

LOUISIANA 81

HOUMA–TERREBONNE (HUM) 3 SE UTC–6(–5DT) N29°33.99´ W90°39.63´ NEW ORLEANS
9 B S4 **FUEL** 100LL, JET A OX 1, 2, 3, 4 TPA—1009(1000) NOTAM FILE HUM H–7D, L–21B, 22F
RWY 18–36: H6508X150 (CONC–GRVD) S–50, D–70, 2S–89, 2D–137 IAP, AD
HIRL
  RWY 18: MALSR. PAPI(P2L)—GA 3.0° TCH 52´. Trees.
  RWY 36: REIL. PAPI(P2L)—GA 3.0° TCH 50´. Trees.
RWY 12–30: H4999X185 (CONC) S–50, D–70, 2S–89, 2D–137 HIRL
  RWY 12: REIL. PAPI(P2L)—GA 3.0° TCH 44´. Trees.
  RWY 30: REIL. PAPI(P2L)—GA 3.0° TCH 39´.
AIRPORT REMARKS: Attended 1200–0100Z‡. Fuel avbl 24 hrs with credit
card. Birds on and invof arpt. Numerous birds 500´AGL and blo 2.8 NM
south southwest AER 36, avoidance advised. Extensive helicopter ops
south thru west of arpt. Rwy 12–30 surface skid resistance fair when
wet. ACTIVATE HIRL Rwy 12–30 and Rwy 18–36 and MALSR Rwy 18
and REIL Rwy 12, Rwy 30 and Rwy 36—CTAF.
WEATHER DATA SOURCES: AWOS–3PT 120.25 (985) 876–4055. LAWRS.
COMMUNICATIONS: CTAF 125.3 **ATIS** 120.25 **UNICOM** 122.95
  RCO 122.45 (DE RIDDER RADIO)
Ⓡ**NEW ORLEANS APP/DEP CON** 118.9
  TOWER 125.3 (1200–0100Z‡) **GND CON** 121.8
AIRSPACE: CLASS D svc 1200–0100Z‡ other times CLASS G.
RADIO AIDS TO NAVIGATION: NOTAM FILE DRI.
  TIBBY (L) VORTAC 112.0 TBD Chan 57 N29°39.86´ W90°49.75´ 122° 10.6 NM to fld. 10/2E.
  VORTAC unusable:
    byd 30 NM blo 2,000´
  TACAN DME unusable:
    byd 30 NM blo 2,000´
  HOUMA NDB (LOM) 219 HU N29°39.80´ W90°39.58´ 179° 5.8 NM to fld. LOM unmonitored. Unmonitored when ATCT
  clsd.
  ILS 108.5 I–HUM Rwy 18. LOM HOUMA NDB. LOM unmonitored. Unmonitored when ATCT clsd.

IDA'S HELIPORT (L87) 0 N UTC–6(–5DT) N33°00.26´ W93°53.59´ MEMPHIS
286 NOTAM FILE DRI
HELIPAD H1: H40X40 (CONC)
HELIPORT REMARKS: Attended continuously. Helipad H1 perimeter lgts. Helipad H1 100´ water twr 300´ E and 149´ radio
twr 500´ S of pad. For perimeter lgts call 318–284–3231. Helipad H1 apch 180°–departure 000°.
COMMUNICATIONS: CTAF 122.9

INDEPENDENCE IPN N28°05.10´ W87°59.15´
AWOS–3 118.125 Winds unreliable.

JEANERETTE
LE MAIRE MEM (2R1) 1 S UTC–6(–5DT) N29°53.94´ W91°39.96´ HOUSTON
14 B **FUEL** 100LL NOTAM FILE DRI L–21B, 22F
RWY 04–22: H3000X75 (ASPH) S–6 MIRL
  RWY 04: REIL. PAPI(P2L)—GA 3.0° TCH 50´. Trees.
  RWY 22: REIL. PAPI(P2L)—GA 3.0° TCH 50´. Thld dsplcd 603´. Tree.
AIRPORT REMARKS: Unattended. For arpt attended call 337–365–7202. Fuel avbl 24 hrs self svc with credit card. MIRL Rwy
04–22 and REIL Rwys 04 and 22 preset low ints dusk to dawn, to incr ints ACTIVATE–CTAF.
COMMUNICATIONS: CTAF 122.9
RADIO AIDS TO NAVIGATION: NOTAM FILE LFT.
  LAFAYETTE (L) VORTACW 109.8 LFT Chan 35 N30°11.63´ W91°59.55´ 133° 24.5 NM to fld. 36/3E. HIWAS.

SC, 17 OCT 2013 to 12 DEC 2013

Figure 201

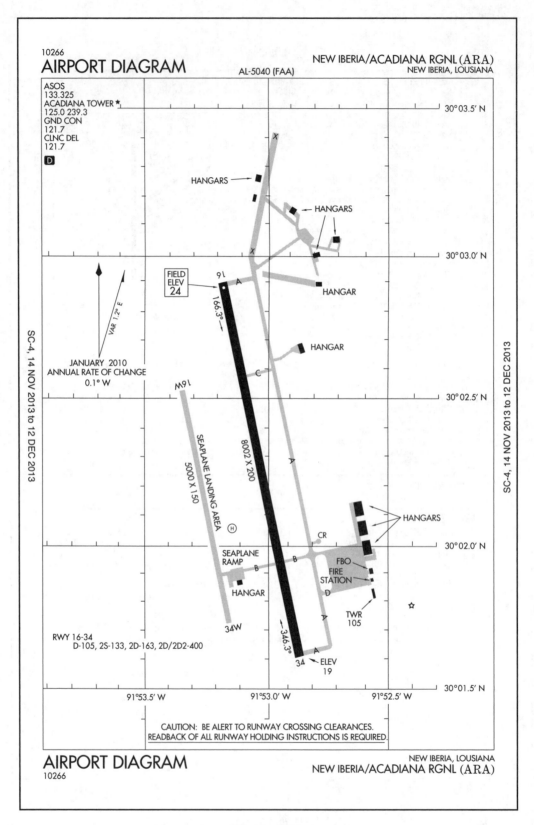

10266
AIRPORT DIAGRAM

AL-5040 (FAA)

NEW IBERIA/ACADIANA RGNL (ARA)
NEW IBERIA, LOUSIANA

ASOS
133.325
ACADIANA TOWER ★
125.0 239.3
GND CON
121.7
CLNC DEL
121.7

SC-4, 14 NOV 2013 to 12 DEC 2013

SC-4, 14 NOV 2013 to 12 DEC 2013

VAR 1.2° E

JANUARY 2010
ANNUAL RATE OF CHANGE
0.1° W

FIELD
ELEV
24

166.3°

8002 X 200

SEAPLANE LANDING AREA

5000 X 150

SEAPLANE
RAMP

HANGARS

HANGARS

HANGAR

HANGAR

HANGAR

HANGARS

FBO
FIRE
STATION

CR

TWR
105

346.3°

34W

HANGAR

RWY 16-34
D-105, 2S-133, 2D-163, 2D/2D2-400

34 ←ELEV
19

30°03.5' N

30°03.0' N

30°02.5' N

30°02.0' N

30°01.5' N

91°53.5' W   91°53.0' W   91°52.5' W

CAUTION: BE ALERT TO RUNWAY CROSSING CLEARANCES.
READBACK OF ALL RUNWAY HOLDING INSTRUCTIONS IS REQUIRED.

AIRPORT DIAGRAM
10266

NEW IBERIA, LOUSIANA
NEW IBERIA/ACADIANA RGNL (ARA)

Figure 202

90　　　　　　　　　　　　　　　**LOUISIANA**

NATCHITOCHES RGNL (IER)　2 S　UTC–6(–5DT)　N31°44.14′ W93°05.95′　　　HOUSTON
　121　B　S4　**FUEL** 100LL, JET A1+　NOTAM FILE IER　　　　　　　　　H–6I, L–22E
RWY 17–35: H5003X150 (ASPH)　S–30　MIRL　　　　　　　　　　　　　　IAP
　RWY 17: REIL. PAPI(P4L)—GA 3.0° TCH 45′. Tree.
　RWY 35: ODALS. PAPI(P4L)—GA 3.0° TCH 43′. Trees.
RWY 07–25: H4000X100 (ASPH)　S–21　MIRL
　RWY 07: Trees.
　RWY 25: P–line.
AIRPORT REMARKS: Attended dawn–dusk. For arpt attendant after hrs call
　318–471–2106. Fuel avbl 24 hr with credit card. MIRL Rwy 17–35
　and REIL Rwy 17 preset low ints dusk to dawn, to increase ints and
　ACTIVATE MIRL Rwy 07–25—CTAF. Rwy 35 ODALS operate low ints
　continuously, to increase ints ACTIVATE—CTAF.
WEATHER DATA SOURCES: AWOS–3 119.025 (318) 352–1575.
COMMUNICATIONS: CTAF/UNICOM 122.8
Ⓡ **POLK APP/DEP CON** 125.4
　GCO 135.075 (FORT POLK APCH AND DE RIDDER FSS)
RADIO AIDS TO NAVIGATION: NOTAM FILE AEX.
　ALEXANDRIA (H) VORTACW 116.1　AEX　Chan 108　N31°15.40′
　W92°30.06′　310° 42.0 NM to fld. 80/3E.　**HIWAS.**
　VOR unusable:
　035°–065° blo 2,000′
　066°–094° byd 35 NM blo 3,000′
　185°–200° byd 35 NM blo 3,000′
　201°–214° byd 35 NM blo 2,000′
　215°–260° blo 2,000′
　261°–285° byd 35 NM blo 2,000′
　357°–034° byd 35 NM blo 3,000′
　NDB (MHW) 407　OOC　N31°39.45′ W93°04.66′　343° 4.8 NM to fld.　NOTAM FILE IER.
　LOC 110.5　I–IER　Rwy 35.　LOC unmonitored 0000–1200Z‡.

NEW IBERIA
ACADIANA RGNL (ARA)　4 NW　UTC–6(–5DT)　N30°02.27′ W91°53.03′　　　HOUSTON
　24　B　S2　**FUEL** 100LL, JET A　OX 4　TPA—1024(1000)　Class IV, ARFF Index A　H–7D, L–21B, 22E, GOMC
　NOTAM FILE ARA　　　　　　　　　　　　　　　　　　　　　　　IAP, AD
RWY 16–34: H8002X200 (CONC)　D–105, 2S–133, 2D–163,
　2D/2D2–400　HIRL
　RWY 16: ODALS. PAPI(P4L)—GA 3.0° TCH 51′.
　RWY 34: MALSR. PAPI(P4L)—GA 3.0° TCH 52′. Rgt tfc.
RUNWAY DECLARED DISTANCE INFORMATION
　RWY 16: TORA–8002　TODA–8002　ASDA–8002　LDA–8002
　RWY 34: TORA–8002　TODA–8002　ASDA–8002　LDA–8002
AIRPORT REMARKS: Attended 1300–0300Z‡. For fuel after hrs call
　337–367–1401, FAX 337–367–1404. Seaplane landing area (water
　channel) West of and adjacent/parallel to runway. Rwy 16W–34W
　seaway edge lgts green; thld lgts amber. Bird activity on and invof arpt.
　ARFF PPR for more than 30 passenger seats call arpt manager
　337–365–7202. Rotor wing movement and landing area between the
　rwy and seaway. Intensive helicopter training. When twr closed HIRL
　Rwy 16–34 preset low ints, to increase ints and ACTIVATE MALSR Rwy
　34—CTAF.
WEATHER DATA SOURCES: ASOS 133.325 (337) 365–0128.
COMMUNICATIONS: CTAF 125.0　**UNICOM** 122.95
Ⓡ **LAFAYETTE APP/DEP CON** 121.1 (1130–0430Z‡)
　HOUSTON CENTER APP/DEP CON 126.35 (0430–1130Z‡)
　TOWER 125.0 (1200–0300Z‡) **GND CON** 121.7 **CLNC DEL** 121.7
　LAFAYETTE CLNC DEL 118.05
AIRSPACE: CLASS D svc 1200–0300Z‡ other times **CLASS G.**

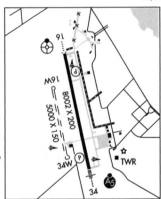

CONTINUED ON NEXT PAGE

SC, 17 OCT 2013 to 12 DEC 2013

Figure 203

LOUISIANA 91
CONTINUED FROM PRECEDING PAGE

RADIO AIDS TO NAVIGATION: NOTAM FILE LFT.
  LAFAYETTE (L) VORTACW 109.8 LFT Chan 35 N30°11.63′ W91°59.55′   146° 10.9 NM to fld. 36/3E.   **HIWAS.**
  ACADI NDB (MHW/LOM) 269 AR N29°57.38′ W91°51.80′   345° 5.0 NM to fld. NOTAM FILE ARA.
  ILS 108.9 I-ARA Rwy 34. Class IA. LOM ACADI NDB.

• • • • • • • • • • • • • • • • • • • •

WATERWAY 16W–34W: 5000X150 (WATER)   MIRL
  WATERWAY 16W: Rgt tfc.
RUNWAY DECLARED DISTANCE INFORMATION
  RWY 16W:TORA–5000 TODA–5000 ASDA–5000 LDA–5000
  RWY 34W:TORA–5000 TODA–5000 ASDA–5000 LDA–5000
SEAPLANE REMARKS: Waterway 16–34 seaway edge lgts green, thld lgts amber. ACTIVATE seaway edge lgts Waterway
  16–34—122.7. 3 clicks on 7 clicks off.

NEW ORLEANS
LAKEFRONT (NEW) 4 NE UTC-6(-5DT) N30°02.55′ W90°01.70′   **NEW ORLEANS**
  7 B S4 **FUEL** 100LL, JET A OX 1, 3 LRA NOTAM FILE NEW   H–7E, 8F, L–21B, 22F, GOMC
  RWY 18R–36L: H6879X150 (ASPH–GRVD) S–60, D–175, 2S–175,   IAP, AD
    2D–200, 2D/2D2–350 MIRL
    RWY 18R: MALSF. PAPI(P4L)—GA 3.0° TCH 51′. Thld dsplcd 239′.

Rwy 9-27: 3114 X 75
    Pier. Rgt tfc.
    RWY 36L: REIL. PAPI(P4L)—GA 3.0° TCH 50′. Thld dsplcd 820′. Wall.
  RWY 18L–36R: H3697X75 (ASPH) S–35, D–55, 2D–80 MIRL
    RWY 18L: REIL.
    RWY 36R: REIL. PAPI(P4L)—GA 3.0° TCH 45′. Bldg. Rgt tfc.
  RWY 09–27: H3114X75 (ASPH) S–50, D–80, 2S–102, 2D–100 MIRL
    RWY 09: REIL. PAPI(P4L)—GA 3.0° TCH 40′. Berm.
    RWY 27: PAPI(P4R)—GA 3.0° TCH 40′. Road. Rgt tfc.
RUNWAY DECLARED DISTANCE INFORMATION
  RWY 09: TORA–3113 TODA–3113 ASDA–3113 LDA–3113
  RWY 18L:TORA–3697 TODA–3697 ASDA–3697 LDA–3697
  RWY 18R:TORA–6880 TODA–6880 ASDA–6035 LDA–5510
  RWY 27: TORA–3113 TODA–3113 ASDA–3113 LDA–3113
  RWY 36L:TORA–6880 TODA–6880 ASDA–5955 LDA–5135
  RWY 36R:TORA–3697 TODA–3697 ASDA–3697 LDA–3697
AIRPORT REMARKS: Attended continuously. For field conditions after 2200Z‡
  ctc arpt manager on 504–914–5721. Birds on and invof arpt. Boats as
  high as 80′ pass within 400′ of Rwy 09 thld. Rwy 18R–36L few low spots near intersection of Rwy 09–27 holding water.
  When twr clsd MIRL Rwy 18R–36L preset med ints and twy lgts for Twys A, B, D, E, F and H preset on medium. ARFF
  capability equivalent to Index B. Acft transporting any items listed in Part 175 title 49 PPR to land. Landing fee. Landing
  fee waived with minimum fuel purchase. Flight Notification Service (ADCUS) temporarily not available. NOTE: See Special
  Notices—U.S. Special Customs Requirement.
WEATHER DATA SOURCES: ASOS (504) 245–4366 LAWRS.
COMMUNICATIONS: CTAF 119.9 ATIS 124.9
  NEW ORLEANS RCO 122.6 (DE RIDDER RADIO)
Ⓡ NEW ORLEANS APP/DEP CON 133.15 (North) 123.85 (South)
  TOWER 119.9 (1400–0000Z‡) GND CON 121.7 CLNC DEL 127.4 (NEW ORLEANS APP/DEP CON when twr clsd)
AIRSPACE: CLASS D svc 1400–0000Z‡ other times CLASS E.
RADIO AIDS TO NAVIGATION: NOTAM FILE NEW.
  HARVEY (H) VORTACW 114.1 HRV Chan 88 N29°51.01′ W90°00.18′   351° 11.6 NM to fld. 2/2E.
  VORTAC unusable:
    004°–125° byd 30 NM blo 2,000′
    126°–136° byd 25 NM blo 3,000′
    137°–174° byd 30 NM blo 2,000′
    175°–190° byd 30 NM blo 3,000′
    191°–239° byd 30 NM blo 2,000′
    240°–255° byd 25 NM blo 6,000′
    256°–279° byd 30 NM blo 2,000′
    280°–290° byd 30 NM
    291°–352° byd 30 NM blo 2,000′
    353°–003° byd 30 NM blo 3,000′
  ILS/DME 111.3 I-NEW Chan 50 Rwy 18R.

Figure 203A

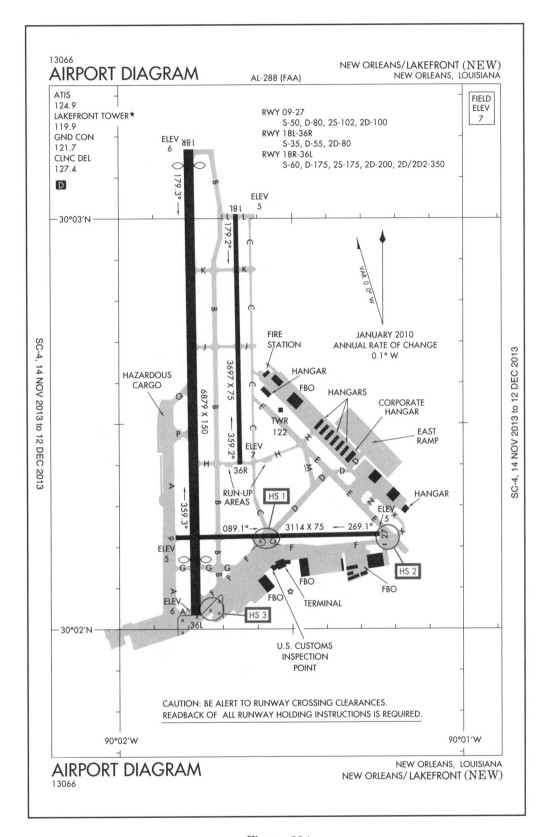

Figure 204

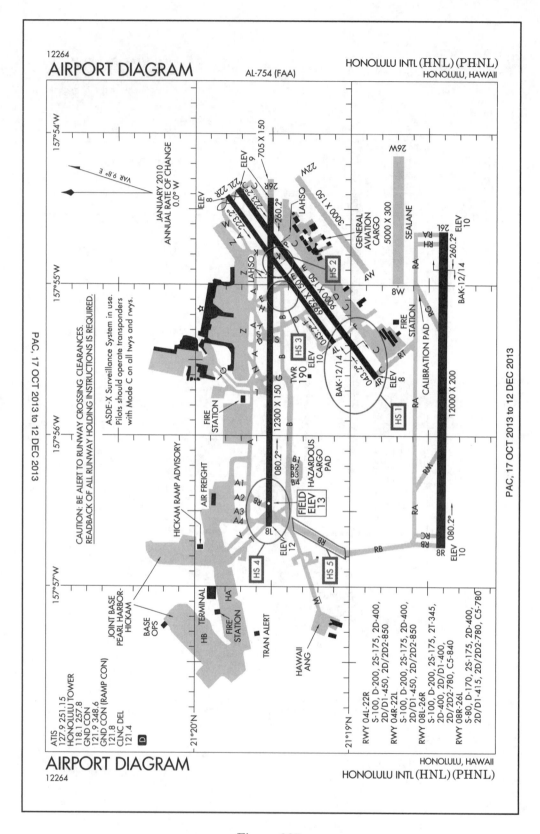

Figure 205

AIRPORT/FACILITY DIRECTORY

29

- -

HONOLULU INTL (JOINT BASE PEARL HARBOR–HICKAM) (HNL)(PHNL)   3 NW   UTC−10   **HAWAIIAN–MARIANA**

   N21°19.12′ W157°55.35′   P–1C, 2G

   13   B   S4   **FUEL** 80, 100, JET A, A1+, B   OX 1, 2, 3, 4   TPA—See Remarks   IAP

   LRA   Class I, ARFF Index E   NOTAM FILE HNL

RWY 08L–26R: H12300X150 (ASPH–GRVD)   S–100, D–200, 2S–175, 2T–345, 2D–400, 2D/D1–400,

   D2D/2D2–780   HIRL

   RWY 08L: MALSR. PAPI(P4L)—GA 3.0° TCH 80′.

   RWY 26R: REIL. PAPI(P4L)—GA 3.0 TCH 71′.

RWY 08R–26L: H12000X200 (ASPH–GRVD)   S–80, D–170, 2S–175, 2D–400, D/2D2–780   HIRL

   RWY 08R: REIL. PAPI(P4L)—GA 3.25° TCH 99′.

   RWY 26L: MALSF. PAPI(P4L)—GA 3.0° TCH 75′. 3 cranes.

RWY 04R–22L: H9000X150 (ASPH–GRVD)   S–100, D–200, 2S–175, 2D–400, D/2D2–850   HIRL

   RWY 04R: MALSR. PAPI(P4L)—GA 3.0° TCH 71′. Tree.

   RWY 22L: REIL. PAPI(P4L)—GA 3.44° TCH 80′. Stack.

RWY 04L–22R: H6952X150 (ASPH)   S–100, D–200, 2S–175, 2D–400, D/2D2–850   MIRL

   RWY 04L: REIL. PAPI(P4L)—GA 3.0° TCH 50′.   **RWY 22R:** REIL. Antenna. Thld dsplcd 150′.

LAND AND HOLD-SHORT OPERATIONS

LDG RWY	HOLD-SHORT POINT	AVBL LDG DIST
RWY 04L	08L–26R	3700
RWY 04R	08L–26R	6250
RWY 08L	04L–22R	9300

RUNWAY DECLARED DISTANCE INFORMATION

RWY 04R:	TORA–9000	TODA–9000	ASDA–8950	LDA–8950
RWY 22L:	TORA–9000	TODA–9000	ASDA–8937	LDA–8937

ARRESTING GEAR/SYSTEMS

   RWY 04R BAK–14 BAK–12B (1500′)

   HOOK MB 60 (200′) → **RWY 26R**

   BAK–14 BAK 12B(B) (1500) **RWY 26L**

AIRPORT REMARKS: Attended continuously. 80 and 100 octane fuel avbl thru FBO. Bird strike hazard all runways. Mil acft opr during Bird Watch Condition MODERATE (initial tkof or full stop ldg only, no multiple IFR/VFR approaches) and SEVERE (tkof and ldg prohibited w/o 15 OG/CC approval or 154 OG/CC approval for HIANG acft) ctc HIK ramp, PTD, 15 WG command post, 735 AMC command post, 154 WG command post for current conditions. See FLIP AP/3 Supplementary arpt information, route and area rstd, and Oakland FIR flt haz. Use caution for obstruction 76′ from Twy M centerline on Oceanside, approximately 200′ from parking apron. Crane 290′ AGL approximately 2,600′ north of Rwy 08L, 2500′ west of Inter Island Terminal 1630–0330Z daily. PAEW 600′–1300′E Rwy 22L and Rwy 22R thld, 1700–0130Z Mon–Fri. Rwys CLOSED 1730–0630 every month as follows: Rwy 04R–22L first Tue; Rwy 08R–26R second Tue; and Rwy 08L–26R third Tue. Rwy 08R–26L 200′ pavement width with lgts outside, pavement striped 150′ wide. Thld of Rwy 08L difficult to determine due to Twy T. All jet acft ctc ramp control prior to engine start at gate or hard stand. Foreign object debris hazard exits on all movement areas east of Twy S. Fighter acft exercise extreme caution when taxiing. To minimize foreign object damage potential, all acft should use minimum thrust, especially outboard engines, when taxiing past the F–22 alert facility on Twy T. Twys G and L between Twy A and Inter–Island ramp clsd to wide–bodied and 4–engine turbo–jet acft under power without PPR from arpt ops manager 808–836–6428 Mon–Fri 1745–0230Z. Twy K not a high speed exit twy. Wide body and 4 engine turbojets ldg on Rwy 04R roll to end of rwy, no left turn at Twy K without approval. Tfc pattern overhead altitude 2000(1987), restricted to HIANG acft. Rwy 04R–22L and Rwy 08R–26L sfc grvd within 10′ of A–G system. Potential for fighter acft tail hook skip exists. Due to sensitivities of citizens, fighter acft and water–augmented acft dep only authorized from Mon–Sat 1700–0700Z, and Sun and holidays 1800–0700Z. All request for waivers will be sent to the 15/OG/CC at least 5 working days in advance. Waivers will be granted on extreme necessary. If short notice mission essential waivers are necessary, ctc 150G/CC by phone thru 15 WG Comd Post (15 WG/CP). 15 WG Comd Post will pass approval to Hickam flight svc and Hickam ramp advisory. Tfc pattern altitude for small acft entering from NW 800(787). Tfc pattern altitude for small acft entering from S 1000(987). Tfc pattern altitude for large acft entering from S 1500(1487). No F–16 transient support avbl in accordance with Area Control Center LSET flash safety 06–02. Transient F–16 units should provide their own maintenance support. PPR all acft units planning to stage ops from Hickam AFB must ctc 15 OSS/OSX DSN 315–449–1596/1597 at least 60 days prior to arrival. All military acft rqr Customs/Agriculture/Immigration inspection must ctc 15 WG command post or if Air Mobility Command ctc Hickam AMCC, no later than 3 hrs prior to arrival with departure location estimated block time, number of aircrew, Civilian/Military Passengers/Foreign Nationals/and Distinguished Visitor codes. JBPH–H is PPR to all non–AMC acft and AMC trng msn (QEN, KEN, PEN, AEN, and ANC C130's). All tran acft not on an AMC/TWCF msn and home stn acft terminating at JBPH–H, will provide a 3 hr out call (COMM 808–448–6900) as well as a 20–30 min out call on 292.5 to the 15 WG/CP (KOA CONTROL). All transient acft, not on an Air Mobility Command mission, will provide a 2–3 hr out call, as well as 20–30 minute out call on 292.5 to the 15 WG/CP (KOA Control). 15 WG can provide eqpt but crews must provide own pers when needed. Upon arrival, crews will proceed directly to Command Post (Bldg 2050) and complete an outbound setup sheet to facilitate departure requirements. No COMSEC material avbl thru Hickam Airfield Ops. Transient aircrews should plan to arrive with appropriate amount of COSMEC to complete entire mission. Arfld

CONTINUED ON NEXT PAGE

Figure 206

30   **AIRPORT/FACILITY DIRECTORY**

CONTINUED FROM PRECEDING PAGE

Management Ops has no COMSEC storage avbl for tran aircrew. COMSEC storage avbl at Command Post.
Bedtime All Coronet W tankers use 311.0 for tanker-fighter inter-plane on launch day. After duty hr DSN
448–8888 613AOC/AMD, Flt Management. Twy M unlgted between M combat acft parking apron (CAPA) and
F22 apron. Due to non–visibility twr unable to determine if the following areas are clear of obstructions and/or
tfc: portions of Twy RB between Twy B and Rwy 08R, portions of inter–island acft parking ramp. Due to location
of twr, controllers unable to determine whether acft are on correct final apch to Rwy 04L, Rwy 04R, Rwy 22L and
Rwy 22R. Remain at least 1 mile offshore of Waikiki Diamond Head Koko Head and EWA Beach. Arrival Rwy 08L,
fly ILS apch procedure or a close–in base leg remaining over center of Pearl Harbor Channel. Arrival Rwy 26L and
Rwy 26R, remain at tfc pattern altitudes as long as possible before beginning descent for ldg. All military acft
with VIP code 7 or abv ctc 15WG command post or relay thru HF/SSB airway 1 hour out to confirm blocktime. All
acft inbd to JBPH–H should address flt plan to PHIK. All inbound helicopters ctc HIK ramp at fld boundary prior to
ldg. JBPH–H Base Wx station open Mon–Fri 1400Z–0800Z, clsd weekends/holidays except during local flying, as
manning permits.Limited wx brief support. Remote flt wx briefings ctc 17th Wx Sq H24, DSN
315–449–7950/8333, FAX DSN 315–449–8336; 2 hr prior notice rqr for timely brief. Official obsn taken by
FAA. Cooperative wx watch procedures do not exist between Wx and ATC. Recreational boating activities on and
invof waterways. During periods of repeated precipitation anticipate wet rwy conditions, if current conditions rqr
confirmation ctc Honolulu twr on initial ctc. Rwy 04L REIL operates continuously. Rwy 26L PAPI aligned 05° left
of rwy centerline. Rwy 26L PAPI unusable byd 05° right of rwy centerline. Rwy 26R PAPI unusable byd 3.6 NM
from thld/obstruction. Rwy 04R–22L DC–10 450,000 L–1011 450,000+ Rwy 04L–22R DC–10 450,000+
L–1011 450,000+ Rwy 08L–26R DC–10 400,000 L–1011 410,000 Rwy 08R–26L DC–10 415,000 L–1011
400,000. ASDE–X surveillance system in use: pilots should opr transponders with Mode C on all twys and rwys.
Flight Notification Service (ADCUS) avbl, 2 hrs advance notice rqr outside regular business hrs. Ldg fee and
storage charges collectable on arrival. PPR from arpt manager for transportation of Class A and B explosives in
and out of HNL. SPECIAL VFR OPERATIONS PROHIBITED to fixed wing acft.

    NOTE—See Area Notices. NOTE—See General Notices—GENERAL INFORMATION ON FLYING TO HAWAII.
    NOTE—See Special Notices—Tower Data Link System, Continuous Power Facilities.
WEATHER DATA SOURCES: ASOS (808) 836–0449. WSP.
COMMUNICATIONS: D–ATIS 127.9
    HONOLULU RCO 122.1R 114.8T (HONOLULU FSS)
®️ **HONOLULU CONTROL FACILITY APP CON** 118.3
    TOWER 118.1 123.9   **GND CON** 121.9   **ADVISORY RAMP** 121.8 (HNL INTL) 133.6 234.8 (HICKAM)
    CLNC DEL 121.4
®️ **HONOLULU CONTROL FACILITY DEP CON** 118.3 (West) 124.8 (East)
AIRSPACE: CLASS B: See VFR Terminal Area Chart.
    VOLMET 13282 8828 6679 2863 Broadcast H+ 00 and 30.
VOR TEST FACILITY (VOT) 111.0
RADIO AIDS TO NAVIGATION: NOTAM FILE HNL.
    (H) VORTAC 114.8   HNL   Chan 95   N21°18.50′ W157°55.83′   at fld. 10/11E.
    VOR Unusable:
        100°–115° byd 30 NM blo 4000′
        120°–140° byd 35 NM blo 5000′
        170°–210° byd 20 NM blo 3000′
        240°–250° byd 30 NM blo 3000′
        241°–250° byd 35 NM blo 4000′
        351°–359° byd 25 NM blo 7500′
    DME unusable
        055°–085° byd 15 NM blo 7000′
        251°–260° byd 20 NM blo 2200′
        261°–280° byd 20 NM blo 3000′
        281°–305° byd 20 NM blo 7500′
        306°–330° byd 30 NM blo 7500′
        331°–340° byd 32 NM blo 5500′
        360°–085° byd 30 NM blo 12000′
    EWABE NDB (MHW/LOM) 242   HN   N21°19.49′ W158°02.93′   082° 7.1 NM to fld.
    ILS 111.7   I–HNL   Rwy 08L.   LOM EWABE NDB. LOC unusable byd 26° left and right of course.
    ILS/DME 110.5   I–IUM   Chan 42   Rwy 04R.   Class IE.
    LDA/DME 109.1   I–EPC   Chan 28   Rwy 26L.   Class I. Unusable byd 25° N of centerline due to terrain.
COMM/NAV/WEATHER REMARKS: Aeronautical Radio, Inc. (ARINC) see Associated Data. Excessive needle oscillation can
be expected over mountainous terrain NE of NDB—CAUTION advised. Hickam ramp twr (Non–ATC facility) All acft
on HIK flightline including haz cargo pad will ctc HIK Ramp prior to eng start/taxi. HIK Ramp will provide advisory
directions and will relay to AFLD Ops via VHF capable acft. All acft departing to CONUS must complete USDA
inspection prior to eng start/taxi.

• •
WATERWAY 08–26: 5000X300 (WATER)
WATERWAY 04–22: 3000X150 (WATER)
SEAPLANE REMARKS: Rwy 04W–22W and Rwy 08W–26W recreational boating activities on and invof waterways.

- -

PAC, 17 OCT 2013 to 12 DEC 2013

Figure 206A

32 **CONNECTICUT**

WINDSOR LOCKS
BRADLEY INTL (BDL) 3 W UTC–5(–4DT) N41°56.35′ W72°41.00′ **NEW YORK**

173 B S4 **FUEL** 100LL, JET A H–10I, 11D, 12K, L–33C, 34I

OX 1, 2, 3, 4 TPA—See Remarks LRA Class I, ARFF Index D NOTAM FILE BDL **IAP, AD**

RWY 06–24: H9510X200 (ASPH–GRVD) S–200, D–200, 2S–175,
2D–350, 2D/2D2–710 HIRL CL

RWY 06: ALSF2. TDZL. PAPI(P4L)—GA 3.0° TCH 71′. Trees.

RWY 24: MALSR. TDZL. PAPI(P4L)—GA 3.0° TCH 71′. Trees.

RWY 15–33: H6847X150 (ASPH–GRVD) S–200, D–200, 2S–175,
2D–350 HIRL

RWY 15: REIL. PAPI(P4L)—GA 3.5° TCH 61′. Trees.

RWY 33: MALSF. PAPI(P4R)—GA 3.0° TCH 72′. Trees.

RWY 01–19: H4268X100 (ASPH) S–60, D–190, 2S–175, 2D–328
MIRL

RWY 01: Thld dsplcd 475′. Acft.

RWY 19: Trees.

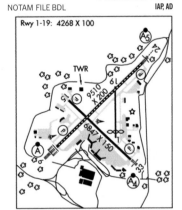

Rwy 1-19: 4268 X 100

LAND AND HOLD–SHORT OPERATIONS

LDG RWY	HOLD–SHORT POINT	AVBL LDG DIST
RWY 06	01–19	6000
RWY 24	15–33	5850
RWY 33	06–24	4550

RUNWAY DECLARED DISTANCE INFORMATION

RWY 01: TORA–4268	TODA–4268	ASDA–4268	
RWY 06: TORA–9509	TODA–9509	ASDA–9509	LDA–9509
RWY 15: TORA–6847	TODA–6847	ASDA–6847	LDA–6847
RWY 19:			LDA–4268
RWY 24: TORA–9509	TODA–9509	ASDA–9509	LDA–9509
RWY 33: TORA–6847	TODA–6847	ASDA–6847	LDA–6847

AIRPORT REMARKS: Attended continuously. Numerous birds frequently on or invof arpt. No training flts, no practice apchs, no touch and go ldgs between Mon–Sat 0400–1200Z‡ and Sun 0400–1700Z‡. Exc for taxiing, Rwy 01–19 open for acft with wingspan less than 79′. Rwy 01 clsd for arrivals to all fixed wing acft. Rwy 19 clsd for departures to all fixed wing acft. Twy J clsd between Twy S and Twy R to acft with wingspans in excess of 171′. ANG ramp PAEW barricaded adjacent northeast side. Bird acft strike haz Phase I Apr to Sep and Oct to Mar, bird acft strike haz Phase II wildlife activity Sep and Oct and Mar and Apr. ANG ramp markings may not be appropriate for large acft, follow marshallers instructions. KC35 acft use caution, fire hydrants are 33″ and are less than 84′ from taxilane centerline. Parallel twy ops on Twy C and Twy B rstd to acft with wingspan of 171′ or less. ASDE X Surveilance System in use. Pilots should opr transponders with Mode C on all twys and rwys. Rwy 33 touchdown rwy visual range avbl. TPA—1873(1700) heavy acft. Rwy 06 VGSI and glidepath not coincident. Rwy 24 VGSI and glidepath not coincident. Rwy 33 VGSI and glidepath not coincident. Afld manager does not issue or store COMSEC for tran crews. Ldg fee for business, corporate and revenue producing acft. Flight Notification Service (ADCUS) avbl. Acft req U.S. customs svc must park on the customs spot with the nose of the acft facing SW. Ctc customs at 860 292 1314 when parked. NOTE: See Special Notices–Land and Hold Short Lights.

WEATHER DATA SOURCES: ASOS (860) 627–9732 WSP.

COMMUNICATIONS: D–ATIS 118.15 (860–386–3570) **UNICOM** 122.95

WINDSORLOCKS RCO 122.3 (BRIDGEPORT RADIO)

Ⓡ **BRADLEY APP/DEP CON** 123.95 (061°–240°) 125.35 (241°–060°) 127.225

TOWER 120.3 **GND CON** 121.9 **CLNC DEL** 121.75

AIRSPACE: CLASS C svc ctc **APP CON**

VOR TEST FACILITY (VOT) 111.4

RADIO AIDS TO NAVIGATION: NOTAM FILE HFD.

HARTFORD (L) VORW/DME 114.9 HFD Chan 96 N41°38.47′ W72°32.85′ 354° 18.9 NM to fld. 849/13W.
HIWAS.

ILS/DME 111.1 I–BDL Chan 48 Rwy 06. Class IIIE.

ILS/DME 111.1 I–MYQ Chan 48 Rwy 24. Class IT. DME unusable from 4 NM inbound to Rwy 24.

ILS/DME 108.55 I–IKX Chan 22(Y) Rwy 33. Class IE.

YALESVILLE HELIPORT (4C3) 2 N UTC–5(–4DT) N41°29.51′ W72°48.67′

65 B **FUEL** 100LL, JET A NOTAM FILE BDR

HELIPAD H1: H65X65 (CONC)

HELIPORT REMARKS: Attended 1400–2300Z‡. Pilots unfamiliar with heliport ctc 203–294–8800 prior to arrival for a briefing on current procedures. ACTIVATE rotating bcn—123.5

COMMUNICATIONS: CTAF/UNICOM 123.05

Figure 207

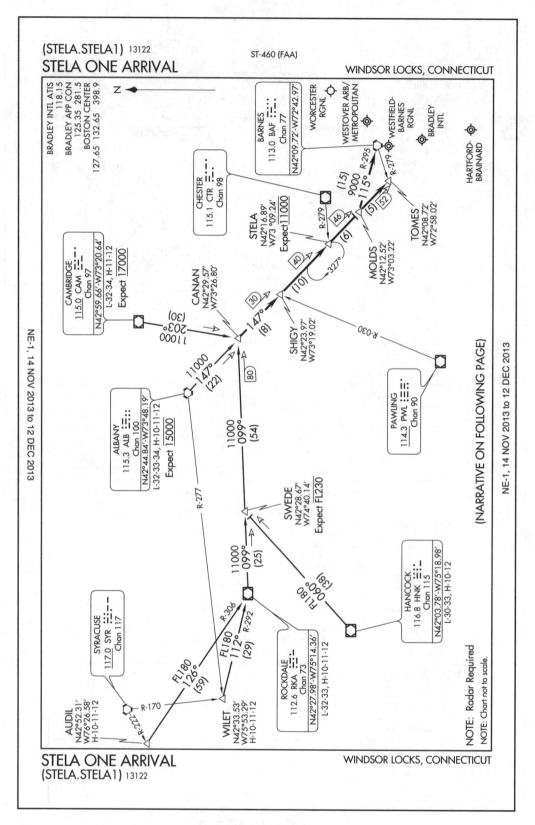

Figure 208

(STELA.STELA1) 12152   ST-460 (FAA)
STELA ONE ARRIVAL   WINDSOR LOCKS, CONNECTICUT

ARRIVAL ROUTE DESCRIPTION

ALBANY TRANSITION (ALB.STELA1): From over ALB VORTAC via ALB R-147 to
CANAN INT. Thence. . . .
AUDIL TRANSITION (AUDIL.STELA1): From over AUDIL INT via RKA R-306 to
RKA VOR/DME, then via RKA R-099 to CANAN INT. Thence. . . .
CAMBRIDGE TRANSITION (CAM.STELA1): From over CAM VOR/DME via
CAM R-203 to CANAN INT. Thence. . . .
HANCOCK TRANSITION (HNK.STELA1): From over HNK VOR/DME via HNK
R-060 to SWEDE INT, then via RKA R-099 to CANAN INT. Thence. . . .
WILET TRANSITION (WILET.STELA1): From over WILET INT via RKA R-292 to
RKA VOR/DME, then via RKA R-099 TO CANAN INT. Thence. . . .

KBDL and KHFD ARRIVALS: From over CANAN INT via ALB R-147 to TOMES INT.
Expect radar vectors to final approach course prior to TOMES INT.

KBAF, KCEF and KORH ARRIVALS: From over CANAN INT via ALB R-147 to MOLDS
INT. Then via BAF R-295 to BAF VORTAC. Expect radar vectors to final approach
course prior to BAF VORTAC.

NE-1, 14 NOV 2013 to 12 DEC 2013

NE-1, 14 NOV 2013 to 12 DEC 2013

STELA ONE ARRIVAL   WINDSOR LOCKS, CONNECTICUT
(STELA.STELA1) 12152

Figure 209

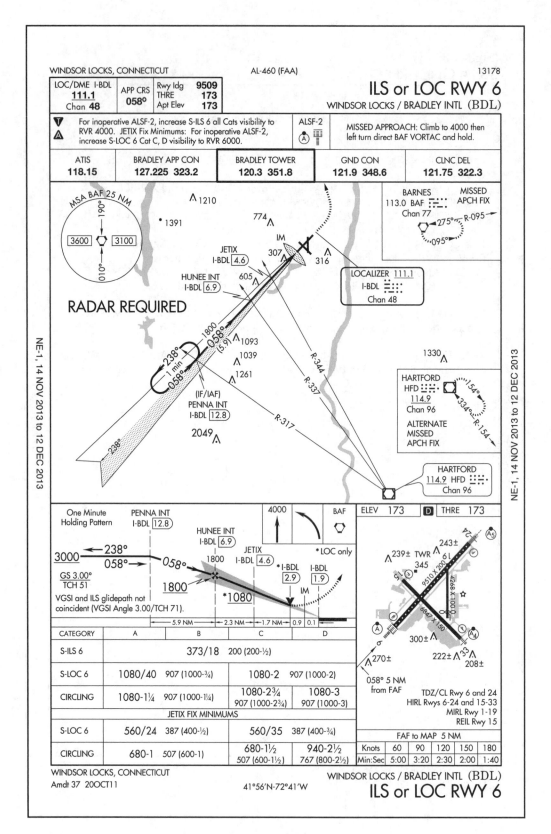

ILS or LOC RWY 6
WINDSOR LOCKS / BRADLEY INTL (BDL)

Figure 210

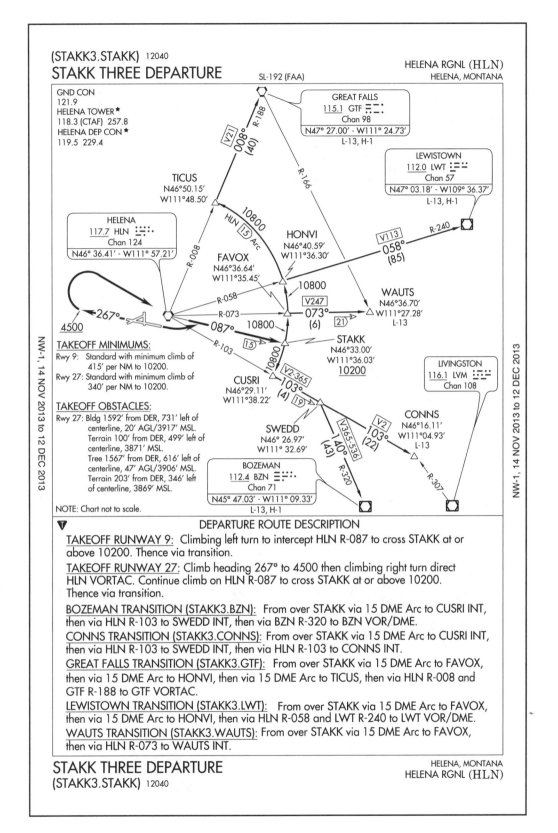

(STAKK3.STAKK) 12040
STAKK THREE DEPARTURE
SL-192 (FAA)

HELENA RGNL (HLN)
HELENA, MONTANA

GND CON
121.9
HELENA TOWER ★
118.3 (CTAF) 257.8
HELENA DEP CON ★
119.5 229.4

NW-1, 14 NOV 2013 to 12 DEC 2013

NW-1, 14 NOV 2013 to 12 DEC 2013

TAKEOFF MINIMUMS:
Rwy 9: Standard with minimum climb of
415' per NM to 10200.
Rwy 27: Standard with minimum climb of
340' per NM to 10200.

TAKEOFF OBSTACLES:
Rwy 27: Bldg 1592' from DER, 731' left of
centerline, 20' AGL/3917' MSL.
Terrain 100' from DER, 499' left of
centerline, 3871' MSL.
Tree 1567' from DER, 616' left of
centerline, 47' AGL/3906' MSL.
Terrain 203' from DER, 346' left
of centerline, 3869' MSL.

NOTE: Chart not to scale.

▼ DEPARTURE ROUTE DESCRIPTION

TAKEOFF RUNWAY 9: Climbing left turn to intercept HLN R-087 to cross STAKK at or
above 10200. Thence via transition.

TAKEOFF RUNWAY 27: Climb heading 267° to 4500 then climbing right turn direct
HLN VORTAC. Continue climb on HLN R-087 to cross STAKK at or above 10200.
Thence via transition.

BOZEMAN TRANSITION (STAKK3.BZN): From over STAKK via 15 DME Arc to CUSRI INT,
then via HLN R-103 to SWEDD INT, then via BZN R-320 to BZN VOR/DME.

CONNS TRANSITION (STAKK3.CONNS): From over STAKK via 15 DME Arc to CUSRI INT,
then via HLN R-103 to SWEDD INT, then via HLN R-103 to CONNS INT.

GREAT FALLS TRANSITION (STAKK3.GTF): From over STAKK via 15 DME Arc to FAVOX,
then via 15 DME Arc to HONVI, then via 15 DME Arc to TICUS, then via HLN R-008 and
GTF R-188 to GTF VORTAC.

LEWISTOWN TRANSITION (STAKK3.LWT): From over STAKK via 15 DME Arc to FAVOX,
then via 15 DME Arc to HONVI, then via HLN R-058 and LWT R-240 to LWT VOR/DME.

WAUTS TRANSITION (STAKK3.WAUTS): From over STAKK via 15 DME Arc to FAVOX,
then via HLN R-073 to WAUTS INT.

STAKK THREE DEPARTURE
(STAKK3.STAKK) 12040

HELENA, MONTANA
HELENA RGNL (HLN)

Figure 211

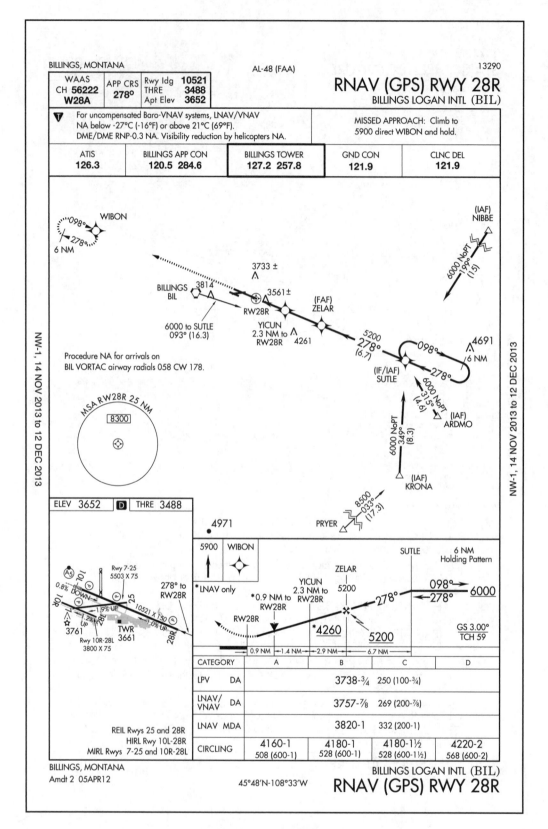

Figure 212

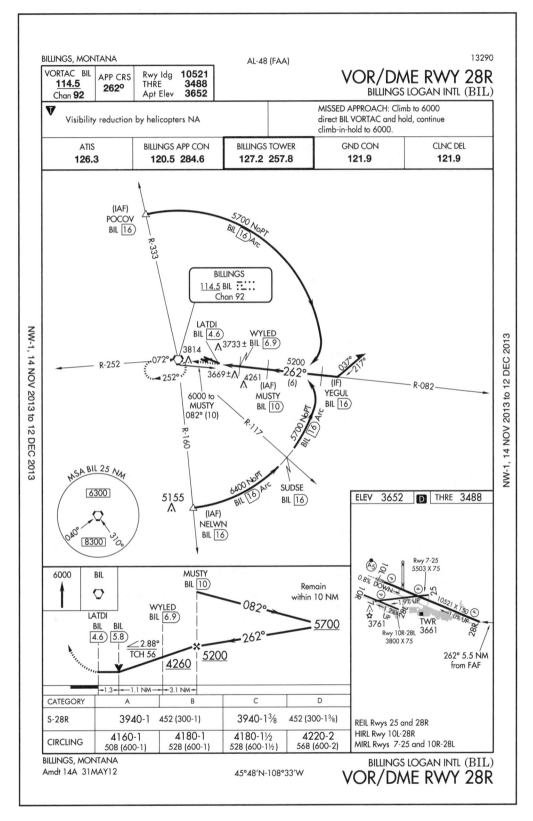

Figure 213

MONTANA

BILLINGS LOGAN INTL (BIL)   2 NW   UTC–7(–6DT)   N45°48.46′ W108°32.57′   **BILLINGS**
    3652   B S4 **FUEL** 100LL, JET A   OX 1, 2, 3, 4   ARFF Index—See Remarks   NOTAM FILE BIL   **H–1E, L–13D**
    RWY 10L–28R: H10521X150 (ASPH–GRVD) S–130, D–170, 2S–175,   **IAP, AD**
      2D–285 HIRL.

Rwy 10R-28L: 3800 X 75
Rwy 7-25: 5503 X 75

    RWY 10L: MALSR. PAPI(P4L)—GA 3.0° TCH 51′. 0.8% down.
    RWY 28R: REIL. PAPI(P4R)—GA 3.0° TCH 56′. Ground. 1.0% up.
    RWY 07–25: H5503X75 (ASPH–GRVD) S–12.5 MIRL 1.9% up SW
    RWY 07: PAPI(P4L)—GA 3.0° TCH 31′. Ground.
    RWY 25: REIL. PAPI(P4R)—GA 3.0° TCH 36′.
    RWY 10R–28L: H3800X75 (ASPH) S–12.5 MIRL 1.2% up NW
    RWY 10R: Ground.
    RUNWAY DECLARED DISTANCE INFORMATION
    RWY 07: TORA–5503   TODA–5503   ASDA–5503   LDA–5503
    RWY 10L: TORA–10521 TODA–10521 ASDA–10521 LDA–10521
    RWY 10R: TORA–3800   TODA–3800   ASDA–3800   LDA–3800
    RWY 25: TORA–5503   TODA–5503   ASDA–5503   LDA–5503
    RWY 28L: TORA–3800   TODA–3800   ASDA–3800   LDA–3800
    RWY 28R: TORA–10521 TODA–10521 ASDA–10521 LDA–10521
    AIRPORT REMARKS: Attended continuously. Rwy 07–25 and Rwy 10R–28L
      CLOSED to acft over 12,500 lbs. No customs, remote acft parking, ltd
      ground handling svc. Migratory waterfowl invof arpt. Twy D 35′ wide
      clsd to acft over 12,500 lbs. Class I, ARFF Index C. PPR unscheduled
    air carrier ops with more than 30 passenger seats ctc arpt ops 406–657–8496. ARFF Index B from 0900–1300Z‡. 180°
    turns Rwy 10L–28R by acft over 25,000 lbs prohibited. For MIRL Rwy 10R–28L and Rwy 07–25, HIRL Rwy 10L–28R,
    MALSR Rwy 10L and REIL Rwy 25 and Rwy 28R ctc twr.
    WEATHER DATA SOURCES: ASOS (406) 248–2773 LLWAS.
    COMMUNICATIONS: ATIS 126.3   **UNICOM** 122.95
      RCO 122.55 (GREAT FALLS RADIO)
    Ⓡ **APP/DEP CON** 119.2 (EAST) 120.5 (WEST)
      TOWER 127.2   **GND CON** 121.9   **CLNC DEL** 121.9
      PRE TAXI CLNC 121.9
    AIRSPACE: CLASS C svc ctc **APP CON**
    RADIO AIDS TO NAVIGATION: NOTAM FILE BIL.
      (H) VORTACW 114.5   BIL   Chan 92   N45°48.51′ W108°37.48′   077° 3.4 NM to fld. 3811/14E.
      SAIGE NDB (LOM) 251   BI   N45°51.13′ W108°41.67′ 099° 6.9 NM to fld.
      ILS 110.3   I–BIL   Rwy 10L. Class IB. LOM SAIGE NDB.
      ILS/DME 111.5   I–BMO   Chan 52   Rwy 28R. Class IA. Localizer unusable beyond 20° left and right of course.

BLACK BUTTE NORTH (See WINIFRED on page 106)

BOULDER (3U9)   2 S   UTC–7(–6DT)   N46°12.70′ W112°06.46′   **GREAT FALLS**
    4968   NOTAM FILE GTF
    RWY 11–29: 3675X72 (TURF)   1.6% up W
    RWY 11: Hill.
    RWY 29: Road.
    AIRPORT REMARKS: Unattended. No snow removal. Rwy 11–29 thlds marked with faded red cones, edges marked with white
      cones. –2′ drainage ditch +1′ berm W side of rwy full length, 43′ from Rwy 11–29 centerline.
    COMMUNICATIONS: CTAF 122.9

BOWMAN FLD (See ANACONDA on page 62)

Figure 214

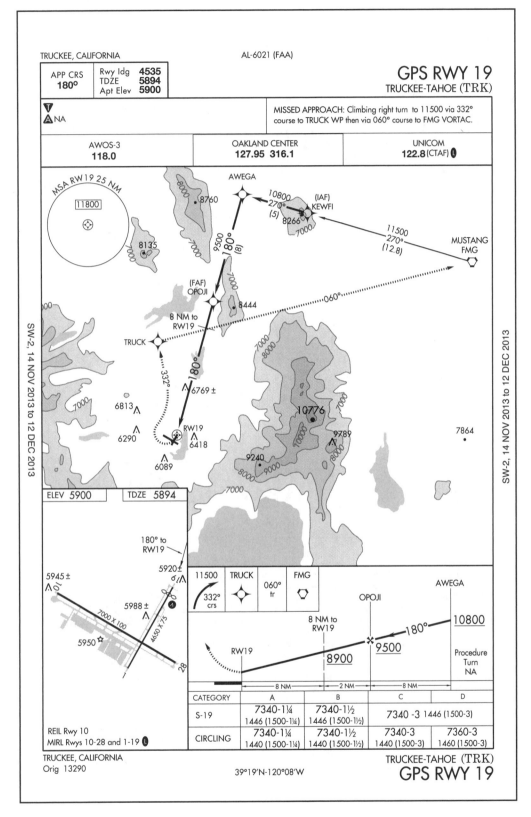

TRUCKEE, CALIFORNIA

AL-6021 (FAA)

GPS RWY 19
TRUCKEE-TAHOE (TRK)

APP CRS 180°	Rwy Idg	4535
	TDZE	5894
	Apt Elev	5900

MISSED APPROACH: Climbing right turn to 11500 via 332° course to TRUCK WP then via 060° course to FMG VORTAC.

AWOS-3 118.0	OAKLAND CENTER 127.95 316.1	UNICOM 122.8 (CTAF)

TRUCKEE, CALIFORNIA
Orig 13290

39°19'N-120°08'W

TRUCKEE-TAHOE (TRK)
GPS RWY 19

CATEGORY	A	B	C	D
S-19	7340-1¼ 1446 (1500-1¼)	7340-1½ 1446 (1500-1½)	7340 -3 1446 (1500-3)	
CIRCLING	7340-1¼ 1440 (1500-1¼)	7340-1½ 1440 (1500-1½)	7340-3 1440 (1500-3)	7360-3 1460 (1500-3)

REIL Rwy 10
MIRL Rwys 10-28 and 1-19

Figure 215

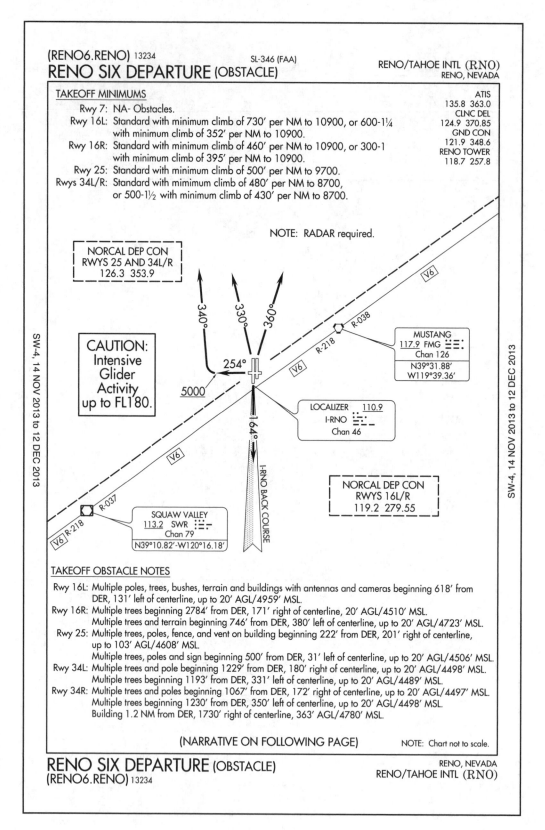

(RENO6.RENO) 13234   SL-346 (FAA)   RENO/TAHOE INTL (RNO)
RENO SIX DEPARTURE (OBSTACLE)   RENO, NEVADA

TAKEOFF MINIMUMS   ATIS
                                                                                135.8 363.0
   Rwy 7: NA- Obstacles.   CLNC DEL
   Rwy 16L: Standard with minimum climb of 730' per NM to 10900, or 600-1¼   124.9 370.85
            with minimum climb of 352' per NM to 10900.   GND CON
   Rwy 16R: Standard with minimum climb of 460' per NM to 10900, or 300-1   121.9 348.6
            with minimum climb of 395' per NM to 10900.   RENO TOWER
   Rwy 25: Standard with minimum climb of 500' per NM to 9700.   118.7 257.8
   Rwys 34L/R: Standard with mimimum climb of 480' per NM to 8700,
               or 500-1½ with minimum climb of 430' per NM to 8700.

                                          NOTE: RADAR required.

   NORCAL DEP CON
   RWYS 25 AND 34L/R
      126.3 353.9

   CAUTION: MUSTANG
   Intensive   117.9 FMG
   Glider   254°   Chan 126
   Activity   N39°31.88'
   up to FL180.   5000   W119°39.36'

                                                         LOCALIZER   110.9
                                                          I-RNO
                                                           Chan 46

                                                         NORCAL DEP CON
                                                         RWYS 16L/R
                                                          119.2 279.55

         SQUAW VALLEY
         113.2 SWR
            Chan 79
         N39°10.82'-W120°16.18'

TAKEOFF OBSTACLE NOTES

   Rwy 16L: Multiple poles, trees, bushes, terrain and buildings with antennas and cameras beginning 618' from
            DER, 131' left of centerline, up to 20' AGL/4959' MSL.
   Rwy 16R: Multiple trees beginning 2784' from DER, 171' right of centerline, 20' AGL/4510' MSL.
            Multiple trees and terrain beginning 746' from DER, 380' left of centerline, up to 20' AGL/4723' MSL.
   Rwy 25: Multiple trees, poles, fence, and vent on building beginning 222' from DER, 201' right of centerline,
            up to 103' AGL/4608' MSL.
            Multiple trees, poles and sign beginning 500' from DER, 31' left of centerline, up to 20' AGL/4506' MSL.
   Rwy 34L: Multiple trees and pole beginning 1229' from DER, 180' right of centerline, up to 20' AGL/4498' MSL.
            Multiple trees beginning 1193' from DER, 331' left of centerline, up to 20' AGL/4489' MSL.
   Rwy 34R: Multiple trees and poles beginning 1067' from DER, 172' right of centerline, up to 20' AGL/4497' MSL.
            Multiple trees beginning 1230' from DER, 350' left of centerline, up to 20' AGL/4498' MSL.
            Building 1.2 NM from DER, 1730' right of centerline, 363' AGL/4780' MSL.

                        (NARRATIVE ON FOLLOWING PAGE)   NOTE: Chart not to scale.

RENO SIX DEPARTURE (OBSTACLE)   RENO, NEVADA
(RENO6.RENO) 13234   RENO/TAHOE INTL (RNO)

SW-4, 14 NOV 2013 to 12 DEC 2013

Figure 216

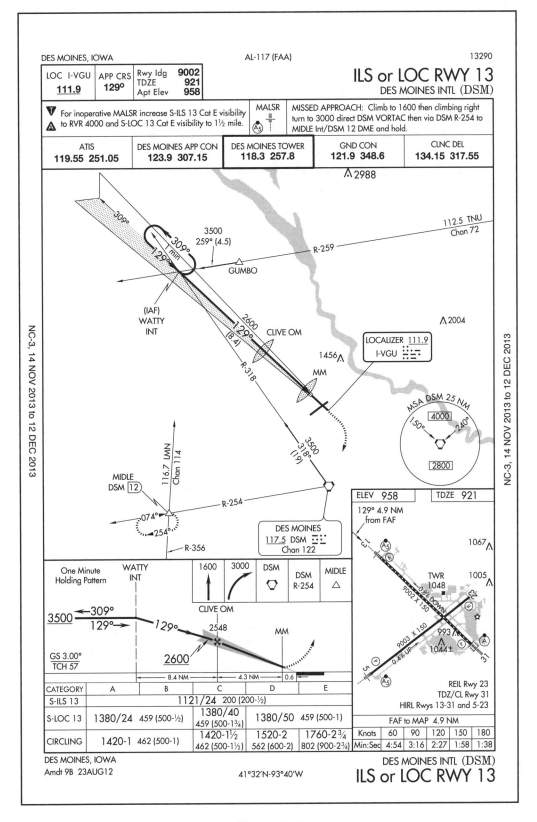

Figure 217

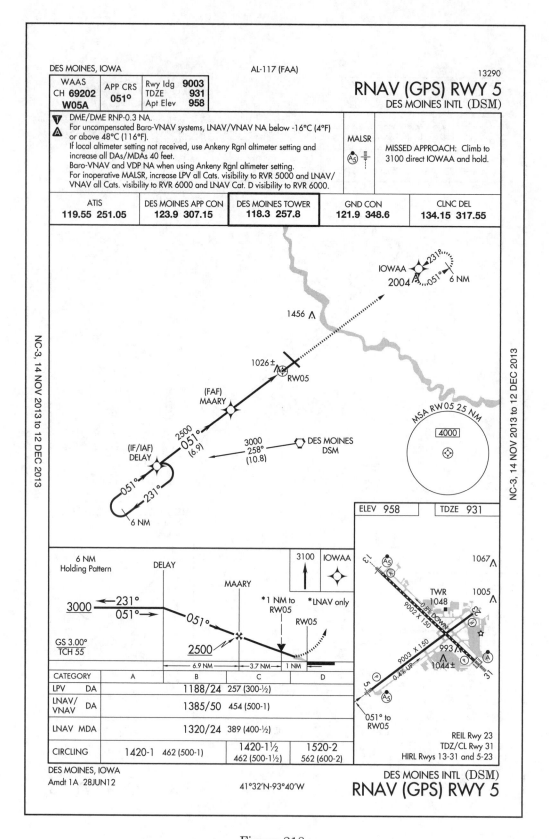

Figure 218

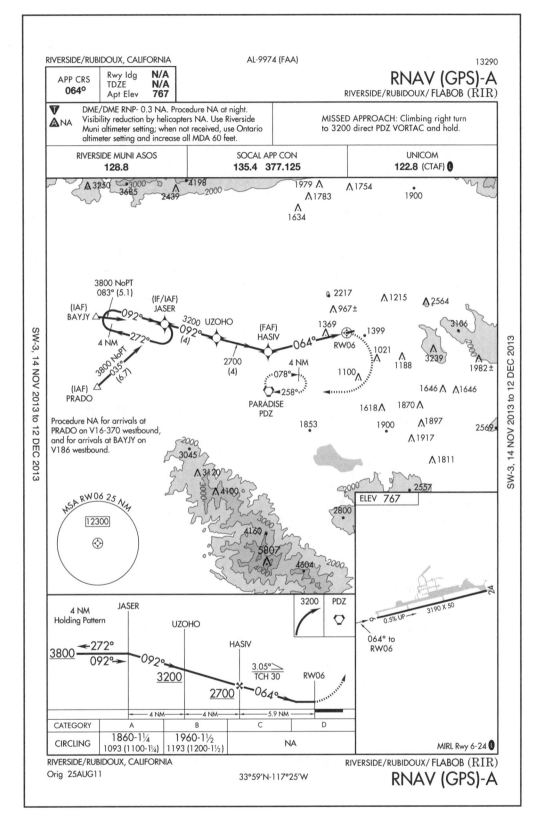

Figure 219

L11

TAKEOFF MINIMUMS AND (OBSTACLE) DEPARTURE PROCEDURES

13234

RIVERSIDE/RUBIDOUX, CA
FLABOB (RIR)
ORIG 11181 (FAA)
> TAKEOFF MINIMUMS: **Rwy 6,** std. w/min. climb of 670' per NM to 4000 or 400-2 w/min. climb of 480' per NM to 4000 or 2100-3 for climb in visual conditions. **Rwy 24,** std. w/min. climb of 630' per NM to 3000 or 800-2¾ w/min. climb of 305' per NM to 4600 or 2100-3 for climb in visual conditions.
> DEPARTURE PROCEDURE: **Rwy 6,** climb via heading 064° to 4000 then right turn direct PDZ VORTAC, or for climb in visual conditions cross Flabob Airport Southwest bound at or above 2700 then via PDZ R-039 to PDZ VORTAC. **Rwy 24,** climb via heading 244° and PDZ R-031 to PDZ VORTAC, or for climb in visual conditions cross Flabob airport Southwest bound at or above 2700 then via PDZ R-039 to PDZ VORTAC.
> All aircraft climb in PDZ VORTAC holding pattern (hold East, right turns, 258° inbound) to cross PDZ VORTAC at or above MEA for direction of flight before proceeding on course.
> NOTE: **Rwy 6,** trees beginning 3763' from DER, 1152' right of centerline, up to 40' AGL/1119' MSL. **Rwy 24,** antenna on tank 6193' from DER, 2057' right of centerline, 38' AGL/1237' MSL. Trees beginning 2494' from DER, 434' right of centerline, up to 40' AGL/1519' MSL. Pole 6261' from DER, 1950' right of centerline, 30' AGL/1230' MSL. Building 1.52 NM from DER, 1154' right of centerline, up to 29' AGL/1369' MSL. Antenna on tank 1.26 NM from DER, 2047' right of centerline, 54' AGL/1254' MSL. Tank 4043' from DER, 794' right of centerline, 66' AGL/961' MSL. Tree 1.79 NM from DER, 434' right of centerline, 58' AGL/1138' MSL.

SAN BERNARDINO, CA
SAN BERNARDINO INTL (SBD)
ORIG 93343 (FAA)
> TAKEOFF MINIMUMS: **Rwy 6,** CAT A,B 2100-2 or std. with a min. climb of 340' per NM to 3700. CAT C,D 3100-2 or std. with a min. climb of 480' per NM to 4600.
> DEPARTURE PROCEDURE: **Rwy 6,** climbing right turn. **Rwy 24,** climbing left turn. **All aircraft** climb direct PDZ VORTAC. Aircraft departing PDZ R-091 CW R-140 and R-231 CW R-280 climb on course. All others continue climb in PDZ holding pattern (Hold NE, right turns, 210° inbound) to cross PDZ VORTAC at or above: R-281 CW R-090, 7700; R-141 CW R-230, 4900.

SAN CLEMENTE ISLAND NALF
(FREDERICK SHERMAN FLD)(KNUC)
SAN CLEMENTE ISLAND, CA 12208
> **Rwy 5:** Diverse departures authorized 090° to 233° CCW.
> **Rwy 23:** Diverse departures authorized 160° to 053° CW.
> TAKE-OFF OBSTACLES: **Rwy 5,** Pylon 198' MSL, 44' from DER, 274' left of centerline. Terrain 192' MSL, 50' from DER, 500' right of centerline. Terrain 194' MSL, 264' from DER, 509' right of centerline. Terrain 209' MSL, 824' from DER, 721' right of centerline. Terrain 199' MSL, 957' from DER, 612' right of centerline.

SAN DIEGO, CA
BROWN FIELD MUNI (SDM)
AMDT 4 10154(FAA)
> TAKEOFF MINIMUMS: **Rwy 8L,** std. w/ min. climb of 570' per NM to 3100. **Rwys 8R,26L,** NA - ATC.
> DEPARTURE PROCEDURE: **Rwy 8L,** climbing left turn, thence...**Rwy 26R,** climbing right turn, thence...
> ...via heading 280° to intercept MZB R-160 to MZB VORTAC.
> NOTE: **Rwy 26R,** tree 1284' from DER, 778' left of centerline, 52' AGL/561' MSL.

MONTGOMERY FIELD (MYF)
AMDT 3A 10210 (FAA)
> TAKEOFF MINIMUMS: **Rwy 5,** 1500-2 or std. with a min. climb of 290' per NM to 1700.
> DEPARTURE PROCEDURE: **Rwys 5, 10L/R,** climbing right turn. **Rwys 28L/R,** climbing left turn. **All aircraft** climb direct to MZB VORTAC. Aircraft departing MZB R-090 CW R-360 climb on course. All others climb in MZB holding pattern (W, right turns, 075° inbound) to cross MZB VORTAC at or above 1800.
> NOTE: **Rwy 5,** trees and bushes beginning 244' from DER, 161' left of centerline, up to 99' AGL/524' MSL. Tree 1287' from DER, 103' right of centerline, up to 49' AGL/474' MSL. **Rwy 23,** tree, flag pole, and transmission towers beginning 1594' from DER, 82' right of centerline, up to 125' AGL/545' MSL. Transmission towers beginning 2627' from DER, 414' left of centerline up to 125' AGL/524' MSL. **Rwy 10L,** trees beginning 230' from DER, 494' left of centerline, up to 57' AGL/486' MSL. Trees beginning 1172' from DER, 591' right of centerline, up to 69' AGL/488' MSL. **Rwy 10R,** rod on electrical equipment 40' from DER, 66' left of centerline, 7' AGL/426' MSL. Trees beginning 2107' from DER, 199' right of centerline, up to 69' AGL/488' MSL. **Rwy 28L,** bushes and poles beginning 35' from DER, 160' right of centerline, up to 37' AGL/451' MSL. Trees beginning 1008' from DER, 7' left of centerline, up to 37' AGL/451' MSL.**Rwy 28R,** bushes, trees, and poles beginning 34' from DER, 162' left of centerline, up to 38' AGL/451' MSL. Trees, signs, and poles beginning 768' from DER, 98' right of centerline, up to 67' AGL/488' MSL.

14 NOV 2013 to 12 DEC 2013

14 NOV 2013 to 12 DEC 2013

13234

TAKEOFF MINIMUMS AND (OBSTACLE) DEPARTURE PROCEDURES

L11   SW-3

Figure 220

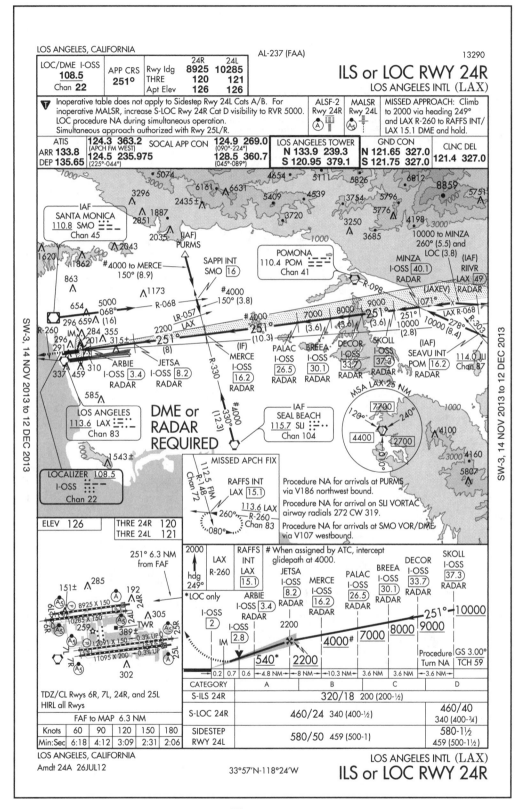

Figure 221

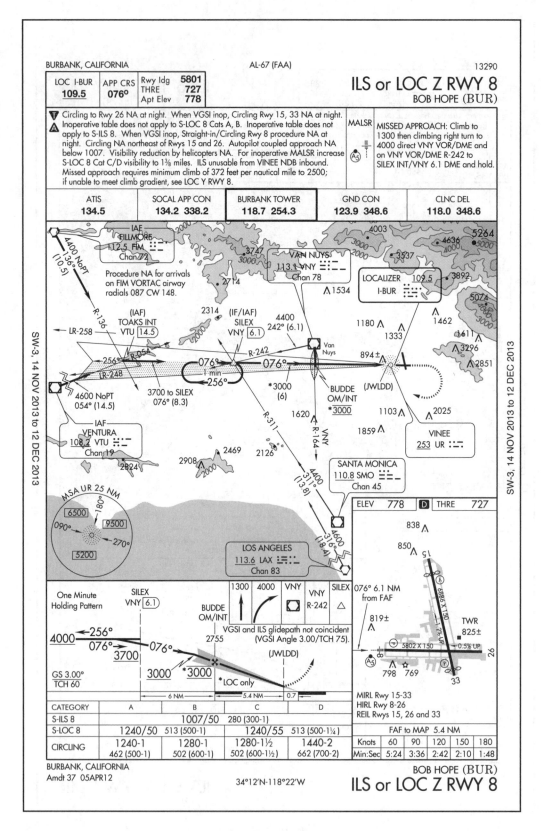

Figure 222

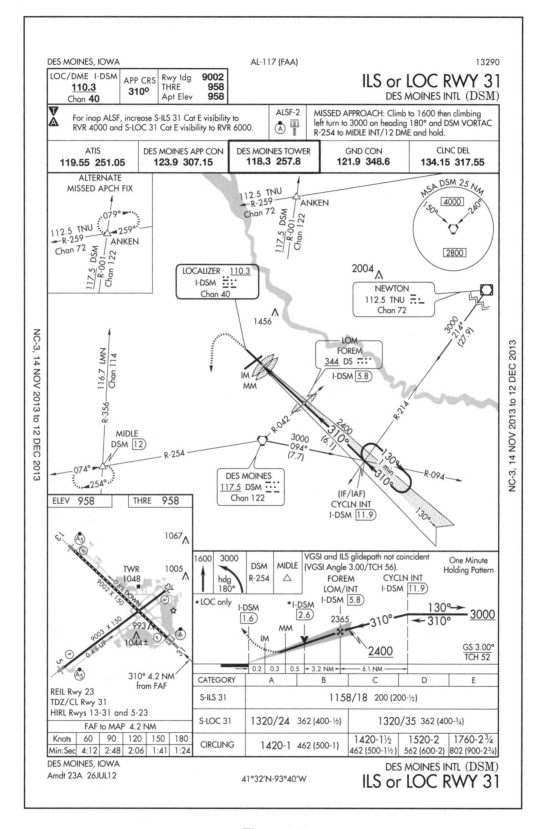

Figure 223

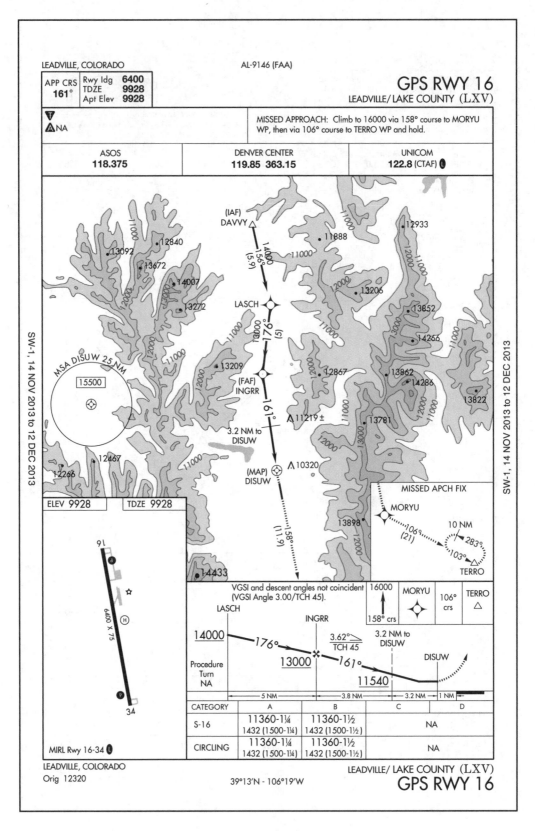

LEADVILLE, COLORADO   AL-9146 (FAA)

APP CRS	Rwy Idg	6400
161°	TDZE	9928
	Apt Elev	9928

GPS RWY 16
LEADVILLE/ LAKE COUNTY (LXV)

MISSED APPROACH: Climb to 16000 via 158° course to MORYU WP, then via 106° course to TERRO WP and hold.

ASOS	DENVER CENTER	UNICOM
118.375	**119.85 363.15**	**122.8** (CTAF)

ELEV 9928   TDZE 9928

MIRL Rwy 16-34

LEADVILLE, COLORADO
Orig 12320   39°13'N - 106°19'W

VGSI and descent angles not coincident (VGSI Angle 3.00/TCH 45).

CATEGORY	A	B	C	D
S-16	11360-1¼ 1432 (1500-1¼)	11360-1½ 1432 (1500-1½)	NA	
CIRCLING	11360-1¼ 1432 (1500-1¼)	11360-1½ 1432 (1500-1½)	NA	

LEADVILLE/ LAKE COUNTY (LXV)

GPS RWY 16

Figure 224

L8

 TAKEOFF MINIMUMS AND (OBSTACLE) DEPARTURE PROCEDURES

13262

KREMMLING, CO
MC ELROY AIRFIELD (20V)
TAKEOFF MINIMUMS: **Rwy 9,** 2600-2 or std. with a
min. climb of 370' per NM to 12700. **Rwy 27,** 3200-2
or std. with a min. climb of 500' per NM to 12700.
DEPARTURE PROCEDURE: **Rwy 9,** climb runway
heading to 10000, then climbing right turn. **Rwy 27,**
climb runway heading to 10900, then climbing left
turn. **All aircraft** proceed direct RLG VOR/DME.
Continue climb to 13,000 in RLG holding pattern
(hold SW, left turns, 051° inbound).

LA JUNTA, CO
LA JUNTA MUNI (LHX)
AMDT 3 03191 (FAA)
DEPARTURE PROCEDURE: **Rwy 8,** climb via
heading 080°. **Rwy 12,** climb via heading 120°.
Rwy 26, turn left heading 160°. **Rwy 30,** turn left
heading 140°.   **All aircraft,** intercept LAA R-
238 (V210) to LAA VOR/DME. When at or above
8000 proceed on course.

LAMAR, CO
LAMAR MUNI (LAA)
DEPARTURE PROCEDURE: **Rwys 8,36,** turn left.
Rwy 18, turn left/right. **Rwy 26,** turn right. Direct LAA
VOR/DME. Aircraft departing LAA R-048 CW R-118
climb on course. All others continue climbing in LAA
holding pattern (N, right turns, 169° inbound) to 6000
before proceeding on course.

LAS CRUCES, NM
LAS CRUCES INTL (LRU)
AMDT 1 96340 (FAA)
DEPARTURE PROCEDURE: **Rwys 4, 8,** climbing
right turn. **Rwy 12,** CAT A,B, climb runway heading
CAT C,D, NA. **Rwys 22, 26,** climbing left turn. **Rwy
30,** climbing runway heading to 5100 then climbing
left turn.
All aircraft climb direct HAWKE LOM. Continue
climb in HAWKE holding pattern (SE, left turns, 304°
inbound) to cross HAWKE LOM at or above 10000
before proceeding on course.

LAS VEGAS, NM
LAS VEGAS MUNI (LVS)
AMDT 1 06103 (FAA)
DEPARTURE PROCEDURE: **Rwys 2, 14** turn left/
right. **Rwy 20,** turn left (except via FTI R-215).   **Rwy
32,** turn right.
Departures via FTI VORTAC R-001 CW R-215 climb
on course. Departures via FTI VORTAC R-216 CW
R-360 proceed direct FTI VORTAC. Climb in FTI
VORTAC holding pattern (hold north, left turn, 192°
inbound) to cross FTI at airway MEA/MCA. (NOTE:
climb in hold not authorized for turbojet aircraft).

LEADVILLE, CO
LAKE COUNTY (LXV)
AMDT 2 08101 (FAA)
DEPARTURE PROCEDURE: **Rwy 16,** use LOZUL
(RNAV) DEPARTURE. **Rwy 34,** use DAVVY
(RNAV) DEPARTURE.

LONGMONT, CO
VANCE BRAND (LMO)
AMDT 1 12040 (FAA)
DEPARTURE PROCEDURE: **Rwy 11,** climbing left turn to
intercept GLL VOR/DME R-221 to 7000 ... **Rwy 29,**
climbing right turn to intercept GLL VOR/DME R-221 to
7000 ...
... All aircraft proceed on GLL R-221 to GLL VOR/DME.
Cross GLL VOR/DME at or above MEA/MCA for route of
flight.
NOTE: **Rwy 11,** trees beginning 130' from DER, 191' right
of centerline, up to 80' AGL/5119' MSL. Vehicles on
roadway, 449' from DER, 395' left and right of centerline,
17' AGL/5046' MSL. Trees beginning 1383' from DER,
434' left of centerline, up to 80' AGL/5109' MSL. **Rwy
29,** trees beginning 4105' from DER, 220' left of
centerline, up to 80' AGL/5189' MSL.

LOS ALAMOS, NM
LOS ALAMOS (LAM)
AMDT 1 12152 (FAA)
TAKEOFF MINIMUMS: **Rwy 27,** NA-obstacles and airport
restriction.
DEPARTURE PROCEDURE: **Rwy 9,** climb heading 092°
to intercept SAF R-354. Northbound climbing to 11000
on V83. Southbound climbing to 9000 on V83.
NOTE: **Rwy 9,** terrain and trees beginning 101' from
DER, 178' left and right of centerline, up to 60' AGL/7139'
MSL.

LOVINGTON, NM
LEA COUNTY-ZIP FRANKLIN MEMORIAL (E06)
AMDT 1 99364 (FAA)
DEPARTURE PROCEDURE: **Rwy 3,** climb runway
heading to 4700 before turning on course.
NOTE: **Rwy 12,** 35' AGL power line 1250' from DER 150'
right of centerline. **Rwy 21,** 40' AGL tower 936' from DER
273' right of centerline. **Rwy 30,** 50' AGL windmill 1800'
from DER 50' right of centerline.

MEEKER, CO
MEEKER (EEO)
AMDT 1 08157 (FAA)
TAKEOFF MINIMUMS: **Rwys 3, 21,** 4100-3 for climb in
visual conditions.
DEPARTURE PROCEDURE: **Rwys 3, 21,** for climb in
visual conditions: cross Meeker Airport at or above
10500 before proceeding on course.
NOTE: **Rwy 21,** multiple trees beginning 843' from DER,
20' left of centerline, up to 100' AGL/7190' MSL. Multiple
trees beginning 227' from DER, 187' right of centerline,
up to 100' AGL/6862' MSL.

MONTE VISTA, CO
MONTE VISTA MUNI (MVI)
AMDT 3 01025 (FAA)
DEPARTURE PROCEDURE: **Rwy 2,** climbing right turn.
Rwy 20, climbing left turn. **All aircraft,** climb direct ALS
VORTAC, continue climb in ALS holding pattern (SE,
right turns, 301° inbound) to cross ALS VORTAC at or
above 11000, except V210 westbound 11200 and J102
northeast bound 13700, before proceeding enroute.

14 NOV 2013 to 12 DEC 2013

14 NOV 2013 to 12 DEC 2013

13262

 TAKEOFF MINIMUMS AND (OBSTACLE) DEPARTURE PROCEDURES

Figure 225

242   **COLORADO**

LAMAR MUNI (LAA)   3 SW   UTC–7(–6DT)   N38°04.18´ W102°41.31´   WICHITA
  3706   B   S4   **FUEL** 100LL, JET A   OX 1, 3   NOTAM FILE LAA   H–5A, L–10G
  RWY 18–36: H6304X100 (CONC–GRVD)   S–45, D–55, 2D–100   MIRL   IAP
    0.4% up S
    RWY 18: REIL. VASI(V4L)—GA 3.0° TCH 45´. Road.
    RWY 36: REIL. PAPI(P4L)—GA 3.0° TCH 45´. Hill.
  RWY 08–26: H5001X60 (ASPH–PFC)   S–35, D–50, 2D–95   MIRL
    RWY 08: PAPI(P2L)—GA 3.0° TCH 30´. Road.
    RWY 26: REIL. PAPI(P2L)—GA 3.0° TCH 31´. Fence.
  AIRPORT REMARKS: Attended 1500–0100Z‡. For svc after hrs phone
    719–336–7701. Be alert, intensive USAF student training invof
    Colorado Springs and Pueblo Colorado. Rwy 18–36 now has distance
    remaining signs. Twr 500´ AGL 4.5 mile SE unlighted. ACTIVATE MIRL
    Rwy 08–26 and Rwy 18–36—CTAF. NOTE: See Special
    Notices—Aerobatic Operations in Colorado. USAF 306 FTG Flight
    Training Areas, Vicinity of Colorado Springs and Pueblo Colorado.
  WEATHER DATA SOURCES: ASOS 135.625 (719) 336–3854.
  COMMUNICATIONS: CTAF/UNICOM 122.8
    DENVER CENTER APP/DEP CON 133.4
  RADIO AIDS TO NAVIGATION: NOTAM FILE LAA.
    (H) VORW/DME 116.9   LAA   Chan 116   N38°11.83´
      W102°41.25´   168° 7.6 NM to fld. 3944/12E.

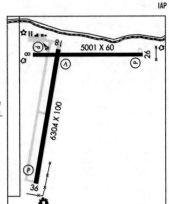

LAS ANIMAS

CITY OF LAS ANIMAS – BENT CO (7V9)   1 S   UTC–7(–6DT)   N38°03.24´ W103°14.31´   WICHITA
  3915   S4   NOTAM FILE DEN   L–10F
  RWY 08–26: H3870X40 (ASPH)   S–5   HIRL   0.4% up W
    RWY 08: REIL. Fence.
    RWY 26: REIL. Road.
  AIRPORT REMARKS: Attended Mon–Sat 1500–0000Z‡. Be alert, intensive USAF student training invof Colorado Springs and
    Pueblo Colorado. Rwy 26 has +30´ poles 105´ from thld 210´ left of extd rwy centerline, +15´ tank 321´ from rwy
    end 270´ right of centerline. Thld lgts NSTD; three lgts each end. Thld lgts OTS indef. Rwy 08 thld lgts 23´ from thld.
    Rwy 26 thld lgts 12´ from thld. Rwy 08 numbers located 216´ from pavement end, Rwy 08–26 numbers smaller than
    standard, no centerline markings. ACTIVATE HIRL Rwy 08–26—CTAF. Med ints 5 clicks, high ints 7 clicks. See Special
    Notices—USAF 306 FTG Flight Training Areas, Vicinity of Colorado Springs and Pueblo Colorado.
  COMMUNICATIONS: CTAF 122.9
  RADIO AIDS TO NAVIGATION: NOTAM FILE LAA.
    LAMAR (H) VORW/DME 116.9   LAA   Chan 116   N38°11.83´ W102°41.25´   240° 27.5 NM to fld. 3944/12E.

LEACH (See CENTER on page 220)

LEADVILLE

LAKE CO (LXV)   2 SW   UTC–7(–6DT)   N39°13.17´ W106°18.99´   DENVER
  9934   B   **FUEL** 100LL, JET A   NOTAM FILE LXV   H–3F, 5A, L–9E
  RWY 16–34: H6400X75 (ASPH)   S–20, D–20   MIRL   IAP
    RWY 16: PAPI(P2L)—GA 3.0° TCH 45´. Rgt tfc.
    RWY 34: PAPI(P2L)—GA 3.0° TCH 45´.
  AIRPORT REMARKS: Attended May–Oct 1430–2330Z‡, Nov–Apr
    1500–2330Z‡. For svc after hrs call sheriff dispatch 719–486–1249.
    PPR for svc after hrs call 719–293–5110. Rwy 34 has +50´ power
    lines 750´ from right of thld. Twy C and old ramp have potholes and
    loose aggregate. All twys and new ramp area marked with blue and
    white reflectors. ACTIVATE MIRL Rwy 16–34 and PAPI Rwy 16 and
    Rwy 34—CTAF.
  WEATHER DATA SOURCES: ASOS 118.375 (719) 486–2735.
  COMMUNICATIONS: CTAF/UNICOM 122.8
    DENVER CENTER APP/DEP CON 119.85
  RADIO AIDS TO NAVIGATION: NOTAM FILE DEN.
    RED TABLE (H) VORW/DME 113.0   DBL   Chan 77   N39°26.36´
      W106°53.68´   104° 30.0 NM to fld. 11800/12E.
  • • • • • • • • • • • • • • • •
  HELIPAD H1: H150X100 (ASPH–CONC)
  HELIPORT REMARKS: Rwy H1 has 6–8 inch lip all around edges, concrete has
    longitudinal and corner cracking. Rwy H1 has 20´ to 30´ trees 130´ east of pad.

SW, 17 OCT 2013 to 12 DEC 2013

Figure 226

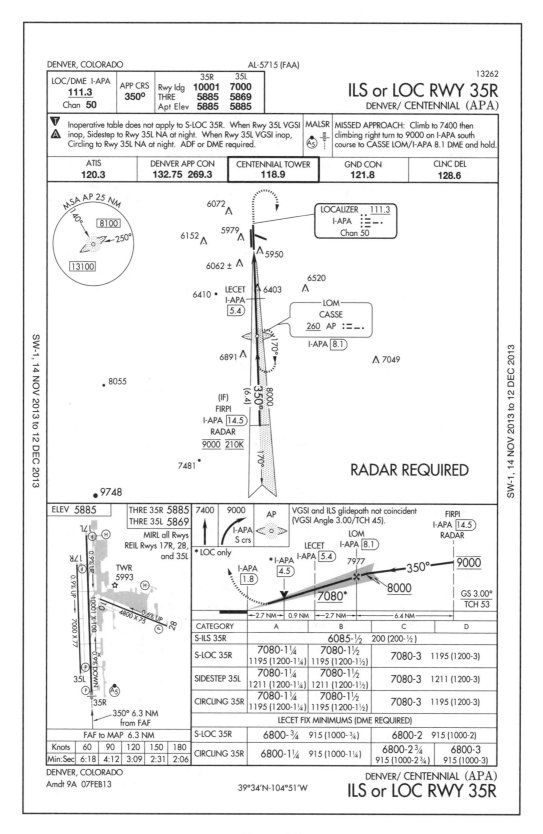

Figure 227

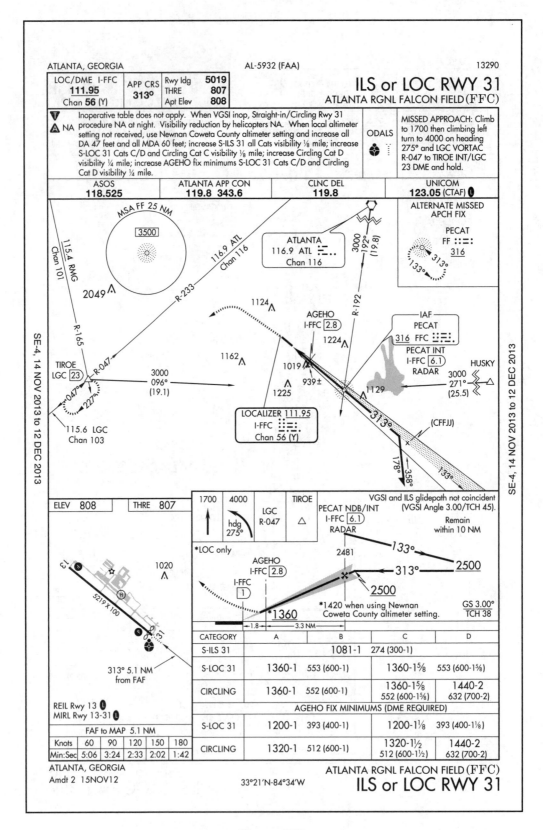

Figure 228

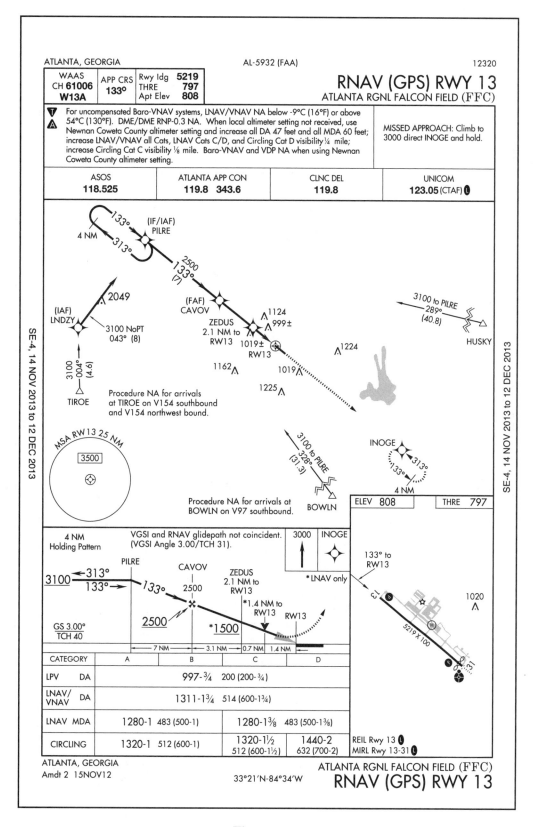

Figure 229

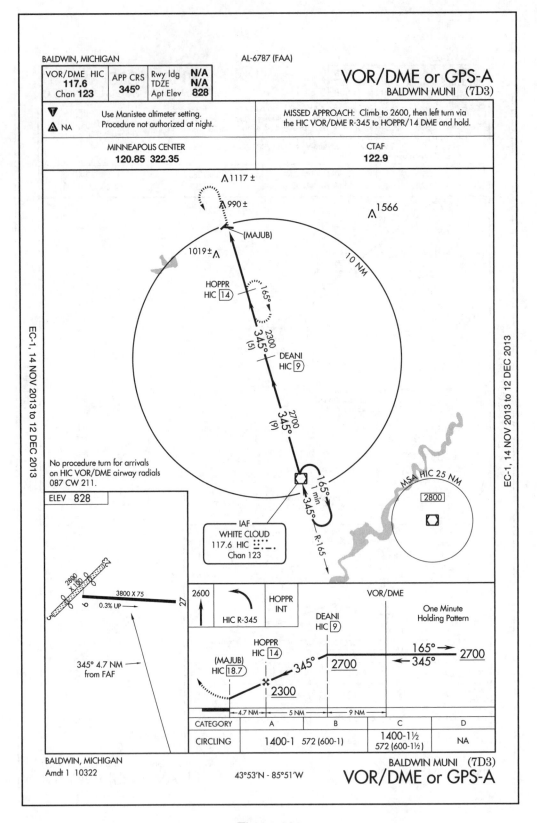

BALDWIN, MICHIGAN   AL-6787 (FAA)

VOR/DME HIC **117.6** Chan **123**	APP CRS **345°**	Rwy ldg **N/A** TDZE **N/A** Apt Elev **828**	VOR/DME or GPS-A

BALDWIN MUNI   (7D3)

▽ Use Manistee altimeter setting. Procedure not authorized at night.
⚠ NA

MISSED APPROACH: Climb to 2600, then left turn via the HIC VOR/DME R-345 to HOPPR/14 DME and hold.

MINNEAPOLIS CENTER **120.85 322.35**	CTAF **122.9**

EC-1, 14 NOV 2013 to 12 DEC 2013

No procedure turn for arrivals on HIC VOR/DME airway radials 087 CW 211.

ELEV 828

IAF
WHITE CLOUD
117.6 HIC
Chan 123

MSA HIC 25 NM
2800

2800 X 100

3800 X 75
0.3% UP →

345° 4.7 NM
from FAF

2600	↶ HIC R-345	HOPPR INT

VOR/DME

DEANI HIC [9]

One Minute Holding Pattern

165° → 2700
← 345°

HOPPR HIC [14]

(MAJUB) HIC [18.7]

345° → 2700

2300

2700

	←4.7 NM→	←5 NM→	←9 NM→	
CATEGORY	A	B	C	D
CIRCLING	1400-1 572 (600-1)		1400-1½ 572 (600-1½)	NA

BALDWIN, MICHIGAN
Amdt 1 10322

43°53'N - 85°51'W

BALDWIN MUNI   (7D3)
VOR/DME or GPS-A

EC-1, 14 NOV 2013 to 12 DEC 2013

Figure 230

130   **MICHIGAN**

BALDWIN MUNI (7D3)   2 S   UTC–5(–4DT)   N43°52.53´ W85°50.53´   CHICAGO
  828 TPA—1828(1000) NOTAM FILE LAN   L–281
  RWY 09–27: H3800X75 (ASPH) S–10 0.3% up E   IAP
    RWY 09: Trees.
    RWY 27: Trees.
  RWY 05–23: 2800X100 (TURF)
    RWY 05: Thld dsplcd 800´. Trees.
    RWY 23: Thld dsplcd 800´. Trees.
  AIRPORT REMARKS: Unattended. Deer on and invof arpt. Arpt CLOSED Nov
    thru Apr; no snow removal. Arpt manager cell 231–250–2551. Rwy
    09–27 sfc considerable pavement cracking with vegetation growing
    through cracks. Rwy 05–23 and dsplcd thlds marked with 3´ yellow
    cones.
  COMMUNICATIONS: CTAF 122.9
  Ⓡ **MINNEAPOLIS CENTER APP/DEP CON** 120.85
  RADIO AIDS TO NAVIGATION: NOTAM FILE LAN.
    WHITE CLOUD (L) VOR/DME 117.6 HIC Chan 123 N43°34.49´
    W85°42.97´ 344° 18.9 NM to fld. 920/1W.
    VOR/DME unusable:
      020°–090° byd 30 NM blo 3,000´
    DME portion unusable:
      270°–290° byd 35 NM blo 3,000´

BANGU N45°00.88´ W84°48.49´ NOTAM FILE GLR.   LAKE HURON
  NDB (LOM) 375 GL 097° 4.5 NM to Gaylord Rgnl. Unmonitored.

BANNISTER

SHADY LAWN FLD (4M4)   2 E   UTC–5(–4DT)   N43°07.72´ W84°22.88´   CHICAGO
  680 TPA—1680(1000) NOTAM FILE LAN
  RWY 09–27: 1850X50 (TURF)   LIRL
    RWY 09: Bldg.
    RWY 27: Trees.
  AIRPORT REMARKS: Attended irregularly. Ultralight and AG activity on and invof arpt. Deer and birds on and invof arpt. Crops
    adjacent to rwy during summer months. NSTD LIRL color and configuration, by prior arrangement. Rwy 09 and Rwy 27
    marked by 3´ yellow cones.
  COMMUNICATIONS: CTAF 122.9

BARAGA (2P4)   4 W   UTC–5(–4DT)   N46°47.10´ W88°34.67´   GREEN BAY
  845 TPA—1845(1000) NOTAM FILE GRB
  RWY 09–27: 2200X100 (TURF)
    RWY 09: Trees.
    RWY 27: Trees.
  AIRPORT REMARKS: Unattended. Arpt CLOSED Nov–Apr except to ski equipped acft. 25´ p–line 850´ from thld Rwy 27. Deer
    and birds on and invof arpt.
  COMMUNICATIONS: CTAF 122.9

BATH

UNIVERSITY AIRPARK (41G)   2 NW   UTC–5(–4DT)   N42°50.42´ W84°28.75´   DETROIT
  856 B S2 NOTAM FILE LAN
  RWY 08–26: 1988X100 (TURF)   LIRL
    RWY 08: Trees.
    RWY 26: Tree.
  AIRPORT REMARKS: Attended irregularly. Rwy 08–26 occasionally soft/wet areas E end during spring thaw and after heavy rain.
    ACTIVATE LIRL Rwy 08–26 and NSTD rotating bcn—122.85. NSTD flashing strobe and alternating white/red bcn. Rwy
    08–26 marked with 3´ yellow cones.
  COMMUNICATIONS: CTAF 122.9

BATOL N42°21.72´ W85°11.07´ NOTAM FILE BTL.   CHICAGO
  NDB (MHW/LOM) 272 BT 225° 4.4 NM to W K Kellogg.   L–281

EC, 17 OCT 2013 to 12 DEC 2013

Figure 231

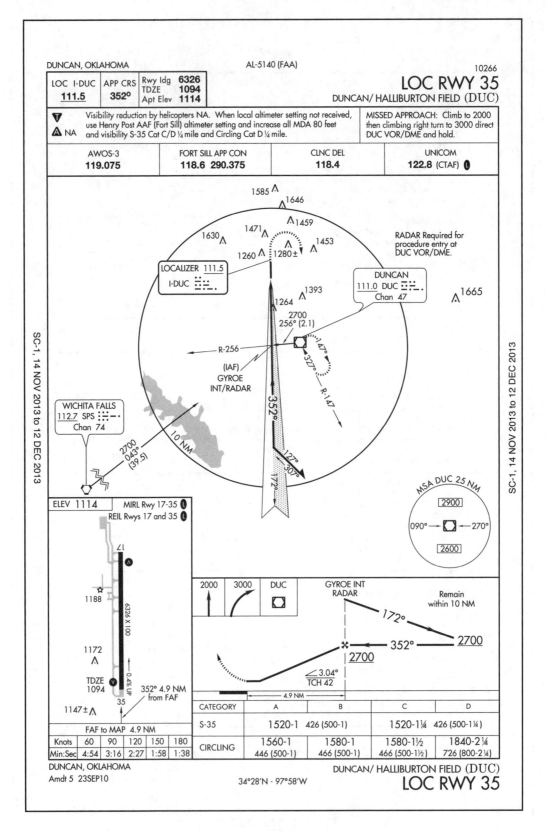

DUNCAN, OKLAHOMA   AL-5140 (FAA)   10266

LOC I-DUC	APP CRS	Rwy Idg	6326
111.5	**352°**	TDZE	**1094**
		Apt Elev	**1114**

LOC RWY 35
DUNCAN/ HALLIBURTON FIELD (DUC)

Visibility reduction by helicopters NA. When local altimeter setting not received, use Henry Post AAF (Fort Sill) altimeter setting and increase all MDA 80 feet and visibility S-35 Cat C/D ¼ mile and Circling Cat D ¼ mile.

NA

MISSED APPROACH: Climb to 2000 then climbing right turn to 3000 direct DUC VOR/DME and hold.

AWOS-3	FORT SILL APP CON	CLNC DEL	UNICOM
119.075	**118.6 290.375**	**118.4**	**122.8 (CTAF)**

RADAR Required for procedure entry at DUC VOR/DME.

LOCALIZER 111.5
I-DUC

DUNCAN
111.0 DUC
Chan 47

R-256

(IAF)
GYROE
INT/RADAR

WICHITA FALLS
112.7 SPS
Chan 74

MSA DUC 25 NM
2900
090° — 270°
2600

ELEV 1114	MIRL Rwy 17-35
	REIL Rwys 17 and 35

1188

1172

TDZE
1094

1147±

6326 X 100

0.4% UP

352° 4.9 NM
from FAF

35

2000	3000	DUC

GYROE INT
RADAR

Remain within 10 NM

172°

2700

352°

2700

3.04°
TCH 42

4.9 NM

FAF to MAP 4.9 NM

Knots	60	90	120	150	180
Min:Sec	4:54	3:16	2:27	1:58	1:38

CATEGORY	A	B	C	D
S-35	1520-1	426 (500-1)	1520-1¼	426 (500-1¼)
CIRCLING	1560-1	1580-1	1580-1½	1840-2¼
	446 (500-1)	466 (500-1)	466 (500-1½)	726 (800-2¼)

DUNCAN, OKLAHOMA
Amdt 5 23SEP10

DUNCAN/ HALLIBURTON FIELD (DUC)
LOC RWY 35

34°28'N - 97°58'W

Figure 232

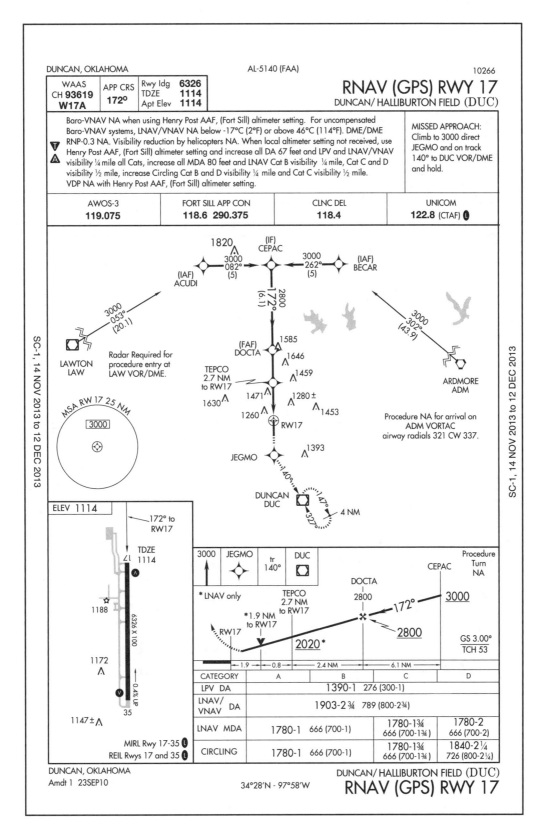

Figure 233

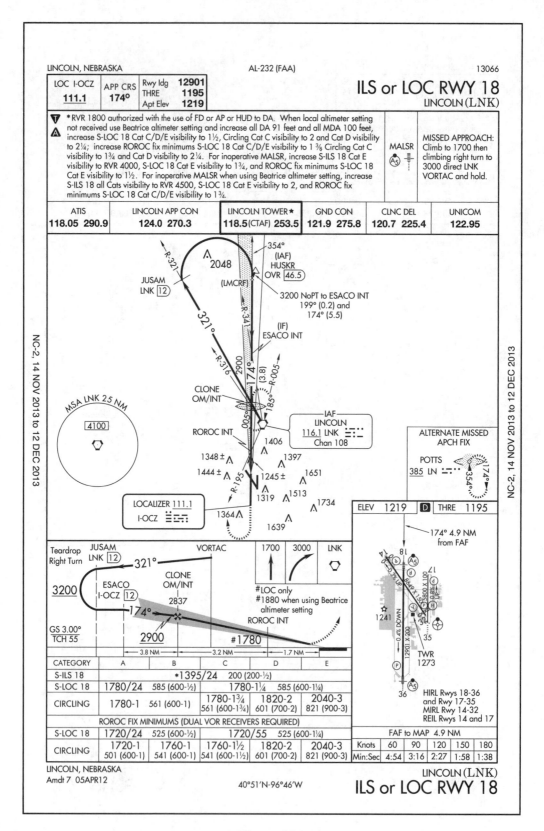

Figure 234

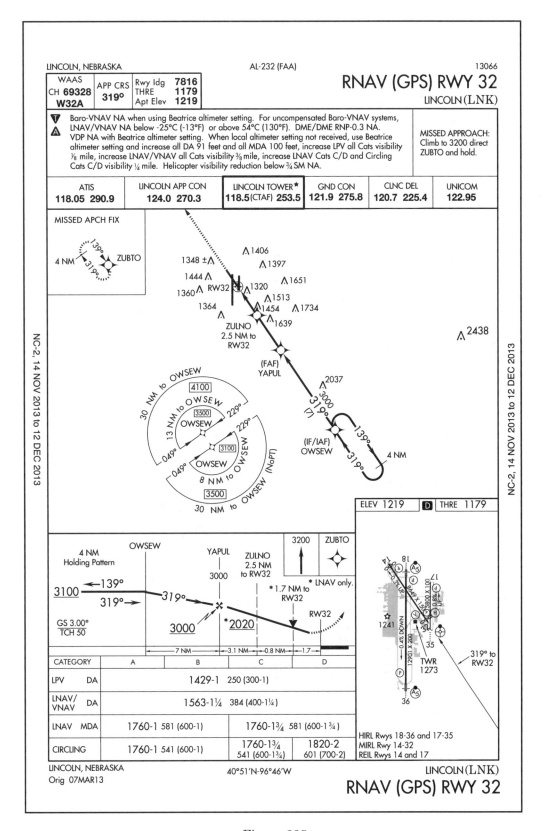

Figure 235

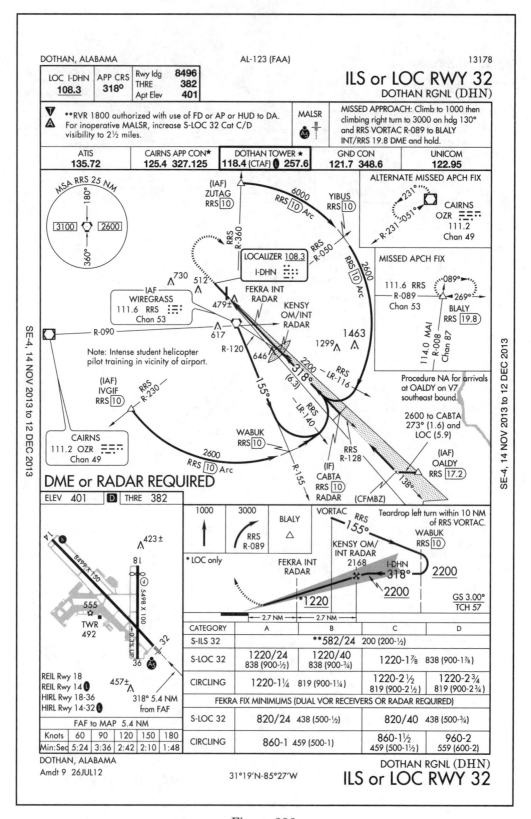

Figure 236

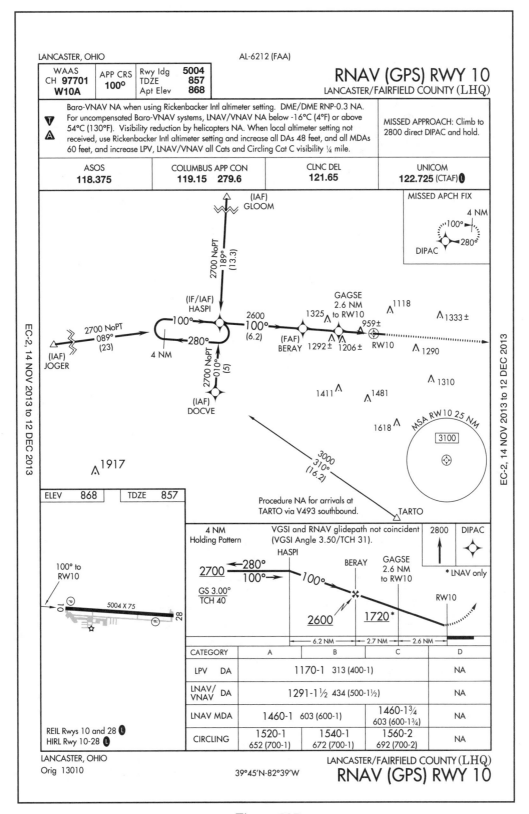

Figure 237

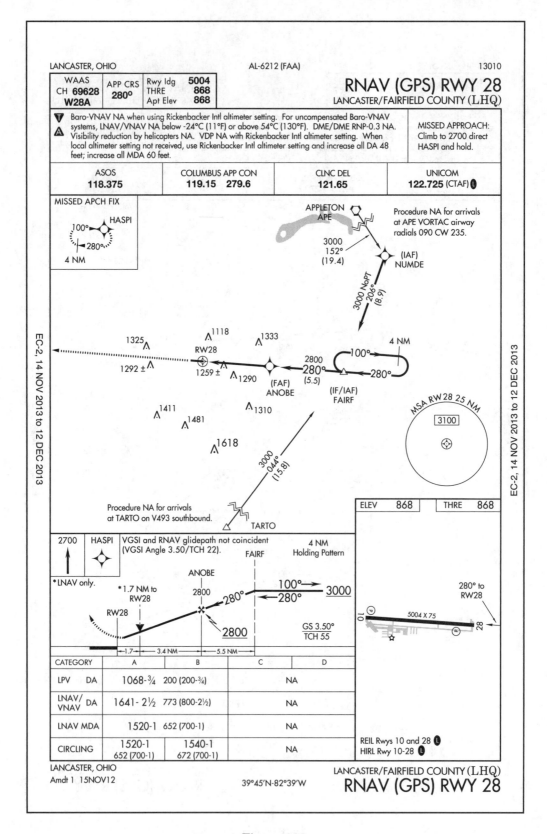

Figure 238

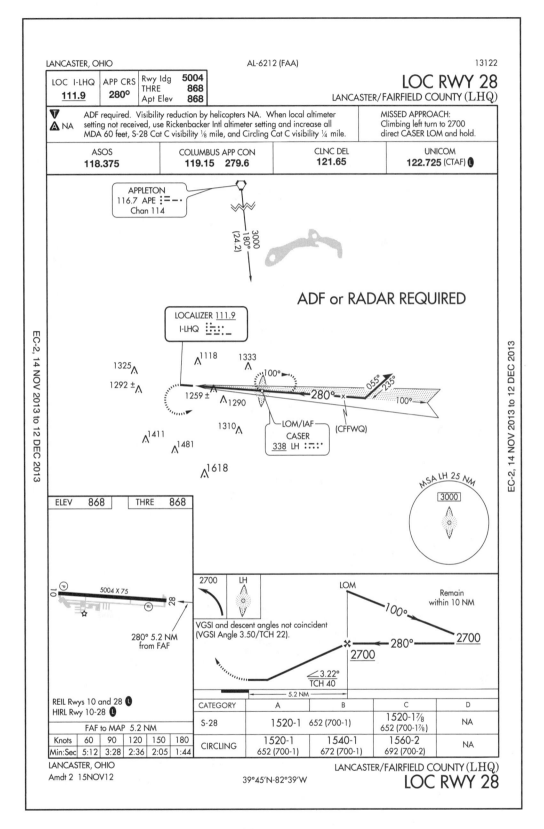

Figure 239

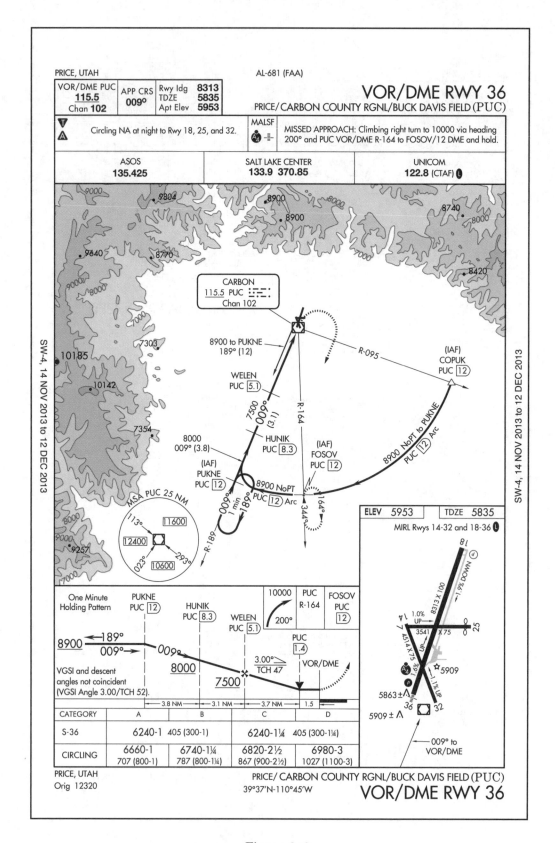

PRICE, UTAH

VOR/DME PUC	APP CRS	Rwy Idg	8313
115.5	**009°**	TDZE	**5835**
Chan **102**		Apt Elev	**5953**

AL-681 (FAA)

VOR/DME RWY 36
PRICE/CARBON COUNTY RGNL/BUCK DAVIS FIELD (PUC)

Circling NA at night to Rwy 18, 25, and 32.

MALSF

MISSED APPROACH: Climbing right turn to 10000 via heading 200° and PUC VOR/DME R-164 to FOSOV/12 DME and hold.

ASOS	SALT LAKE CENTER	UNICOM
135.425	**133.9 370.85**	**122.8 (CTAF)**

CARBON
115.5 PUC
Chan 102

8900 to PUKNE
189° (12)

R-095

(IAF)
COPUK
PUC 12

WELEN
PUC 5.1

7500
009°
(3.1)

R-164

8000
009° (3.8)

HUNIK
PUC 8.3

8900 NoPT to PUKNE
PUC 12 Arc

(IAF)
FOSOV
PUC 12

(IAF)
PUKNE
PUC 12

8900 NoPT
PUC 12 Arc

009°
1 min

189°

344°

164°

9804
8900
8900
8740
8000

9640
8770
8420

7303
10185
10142
7354
9257

R-189

MSA PUC 25 NM

113°   11600
12400
023°   293°
10600

ELEV 5953 | TDZE 5835
MIRL Rwys 14-32 and 18-36

18
8313 X 100
1.9% DOWN
25
3541 X 75
4514 X 75
5909
5863±
36   32
5909 ±

009° to
VOR/DME

One Minute Holding Pattern	PUKNE PUC 12	HUNIK PUC 8.3	WELEN PUC 5.1	10000 PUC R-164 FOSOV PUC 12		
				200°		
8900 ←189°				PUC 1.4		
009° →	009°			VOR/DME		
		8000				
VGSI and descent angles not coincident (VGSI Angle 3.00/TCH 52).		7500	3.00° / TCH 47			
		3.8 NM	3.1 NM	3.7 NM	1.5	

CATEGORY	A	B	C	D
S-36	6240-1 405 (300-1)		6240-1¼ 405 (300-1¼)	
CIRCLING	6660-1 707 (800-1)	6740-1¼ 787 (800-1¼)	6820-2½ 867 (900-2½)	6980-3 1027 (1100-3)

PRICE, UTAH
Orig 12320

PRICE/ CARBON COUNTY RGNL/BUCK DAVIS FIELD (PUC)
39°37'N-110°45'W

VOR/DME RWY 36

Figure 240

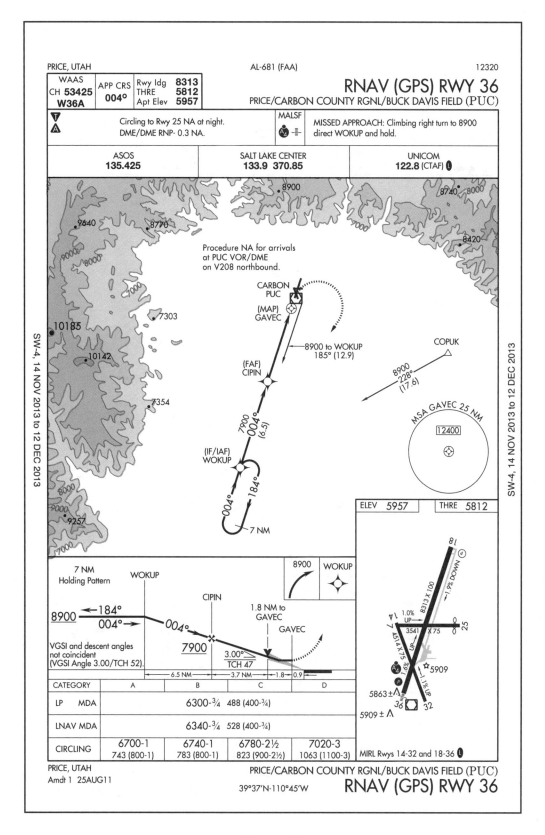

PRICE, UTAH

AL-681 (FAA)

12320

WAAS
CH 53425
W36A

APP CRS
004°

Rwy Idg 8313
THRE 5812
Apt Elev 5957

RNAV (GPS) RWY 36
PRICE/CARBON COUNTY RGNL/BUCK DAVIS FIELD (PUC)

Circling to Rwy 25 NA at night.
DME/DME RNP- 0.3 NA.

MALSF

MISSED APPROACH: Climbing right turn to 8900
direct WOKUP and hold.

ASOS
135.425

SALT LAKE CENTER
133.9 370.85

UNICOM
122.8 (CTAF)

Procedure NA for arrivals
at PUC VOR/DME
on V208 northbound.

MSA GAVEC 25 NM

12400

ELEV 5957

THRE 5812

7 NM
Holding Pattern

8900 ← 184°
004° →

WOKUP

CIPIN

004°

7900

1.8 NM to
GAVEC

GAVEC

VGSI and descent angles
not coincident
(VGSI Angle 3.00/TCH 52).

3.00°
TCH 47

6.5 NM   3.7 NM   1.8   0.9

8900

WOKUP

CATEGORY	A	B	C	D
LP MDA	6300-¾ 488 (400-¾)			
LNAV MDA	6340-¾ 528 (400-¾)			
CIRCLING	6700-1 743 (800-1)	6740-1 783 (800-1)	6780-2½ 823 (900-2½)	7020-3 1063 (1100-3)

MIRL Rwys 14-32 and 18-36

PRICE, UTAH
Amdt 1 25AUG11

39°37'N-110°45'W

PRICE/CARBON COUNTY RGNL/BUCK DAVIS FIELD (PUC)
RNAV (GPS) RWY 36

Figure 241

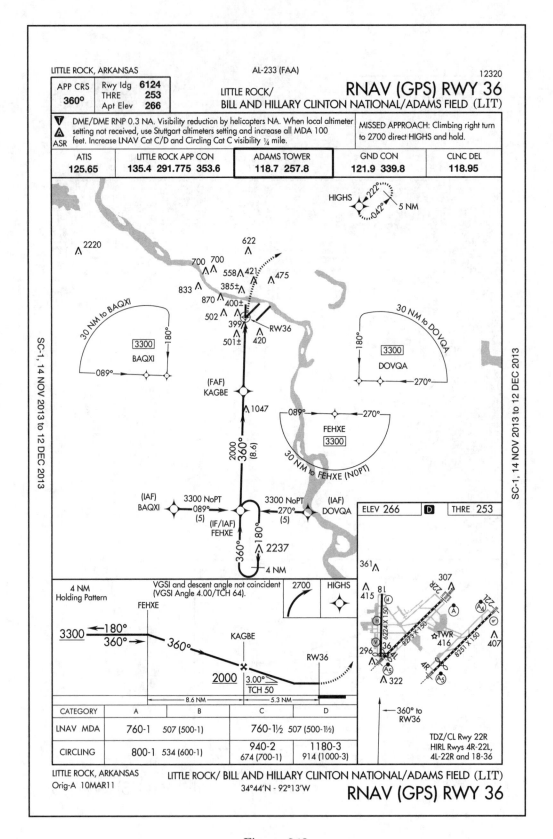

Figure 242

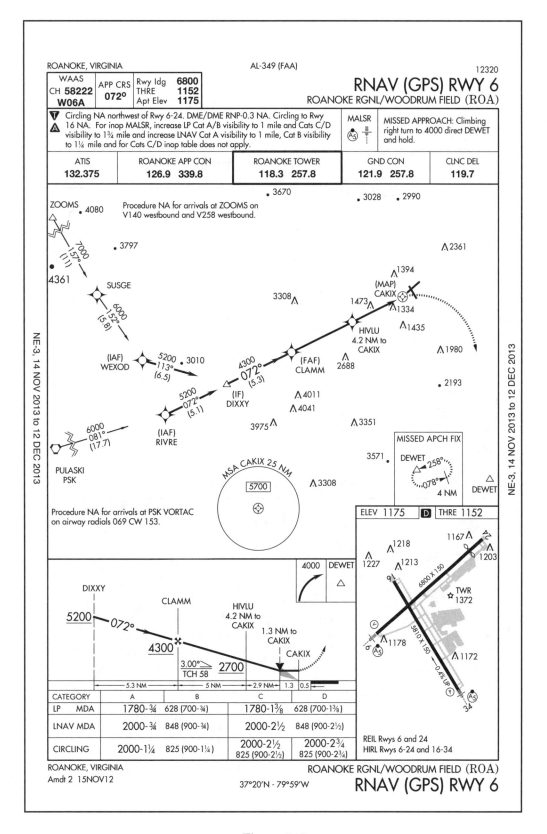

Figure 243

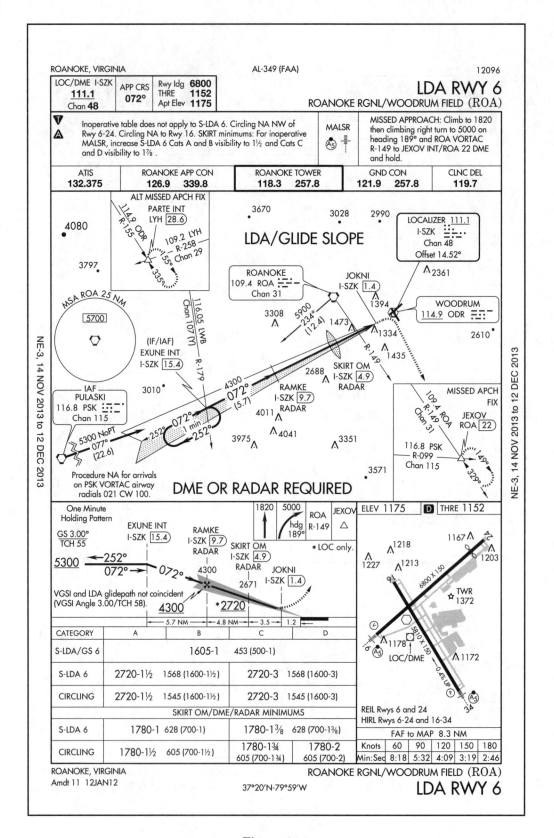

Figure 244

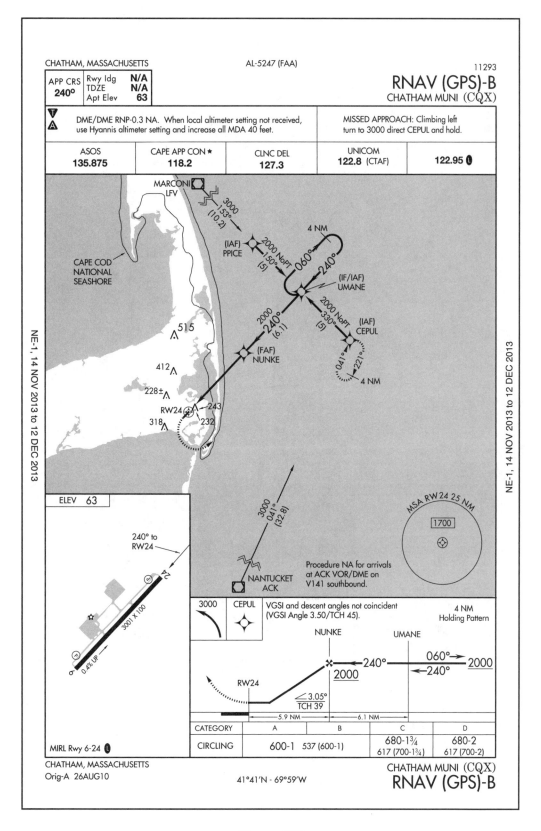

Figure 245

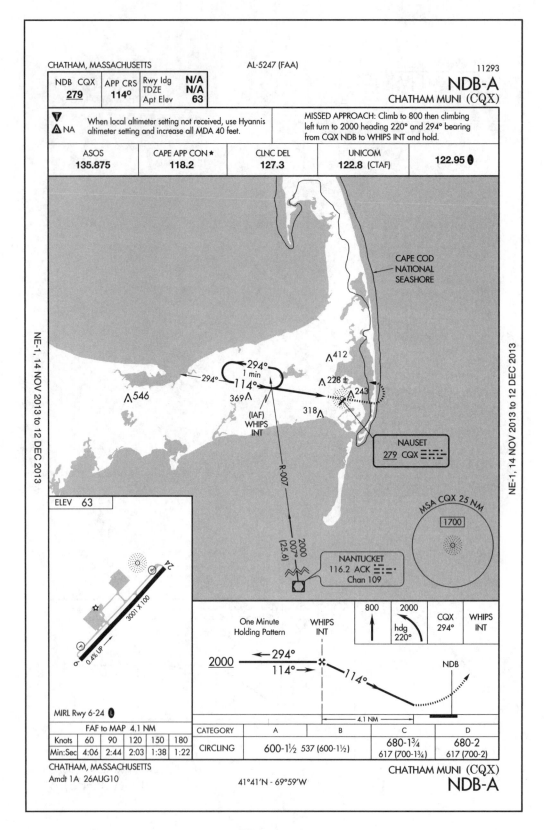

Figure 246

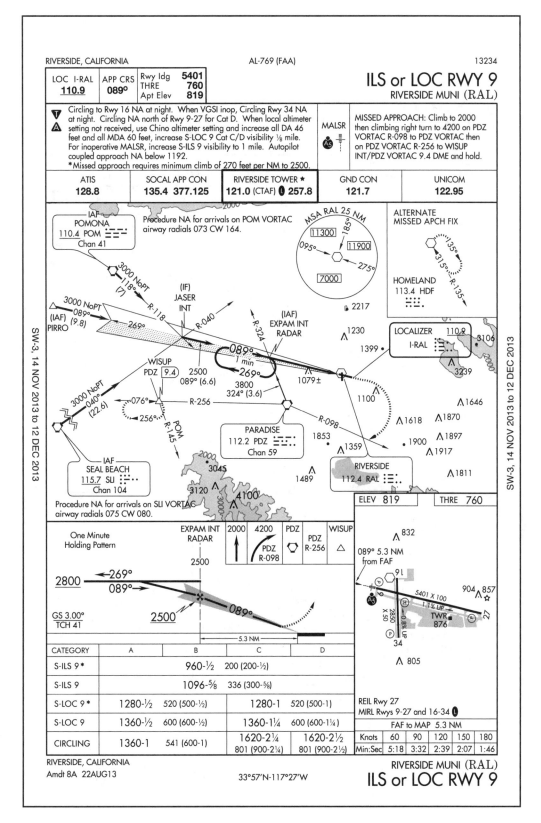

Figure 247

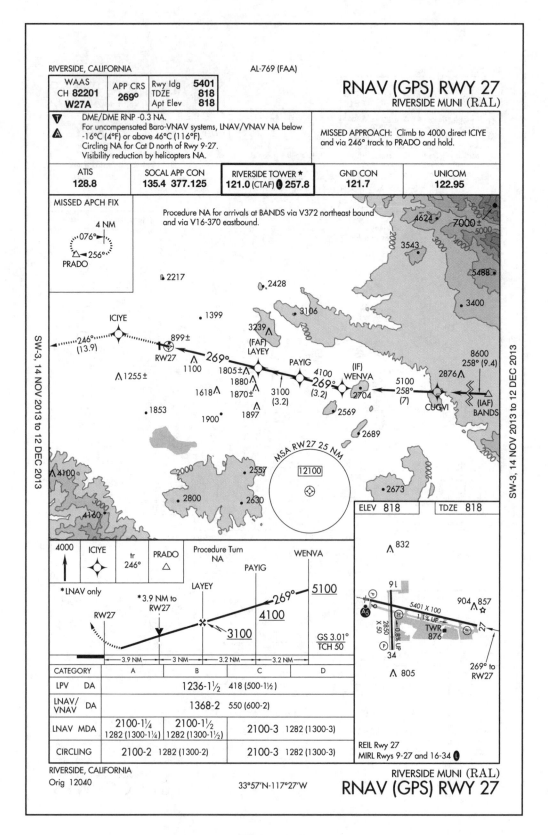

RIVERSIDE, CALIFORNIA   AL-769 (FAA)

| WAAS CH 82201 W27A | APP CRS 269° | Rwy Idg 5401 TDZE 818 Apt Elev 818 | **RNAV (GPS) RWY 27** RIVERSIDE MUNI (RAL) |

DME/DME RNP -0.3 NA.
For uncompensated Baro-VNAV systems, LNAV/VNAV NA below -16°C (4°F) or above 46°C (116°F).
Circling NA for Cat D north of Rwy 9-27.
Visibility reduction by helicopters NA.

MISSED APPROACH: Climb to 4000 direct ICIYE and via 246° track to PRADO and hold.

| ATIS 128.8 | SOCAL APP CON 135.4 377.125 | RIVERSIDE TOWER ★ 121.0 (CTAF) ❶ 257.8 | GND CON 121.7 | UNICOM 122.95 |

MISSED APCH FIX

4 NM
076°
256°
PRADO

Procedure NA for arrivals at BANDS via V372 northeast bound and via V16-370 eastbound.

ELEV 818   TDZE 818

REIL Rwy 27
MIRL Rwys 9-27 and 16-34 ❶

CATEGORY	A	B	C	D
LPV DA	1236-1½ 418 (500-1½)			
LNAV/VNAV DA	1368-2 550 (600-2)			
LNAV MDA	2100-1¼ 1282 (1300-1¼)	2100-1½ 1282 (1300-1½)	2100-3 1282 (1300-3)	
CIRCLING	2100-2 1282 (1300-2)		2100-3 1282 (1300-3)	

RIVERSIDE, CALIFORNIA
Orig 12040

33°57'N-117°27'W

RIVERSIDE MUNI (RAL)
RNAV (GPS) RWY 27

Figure 248

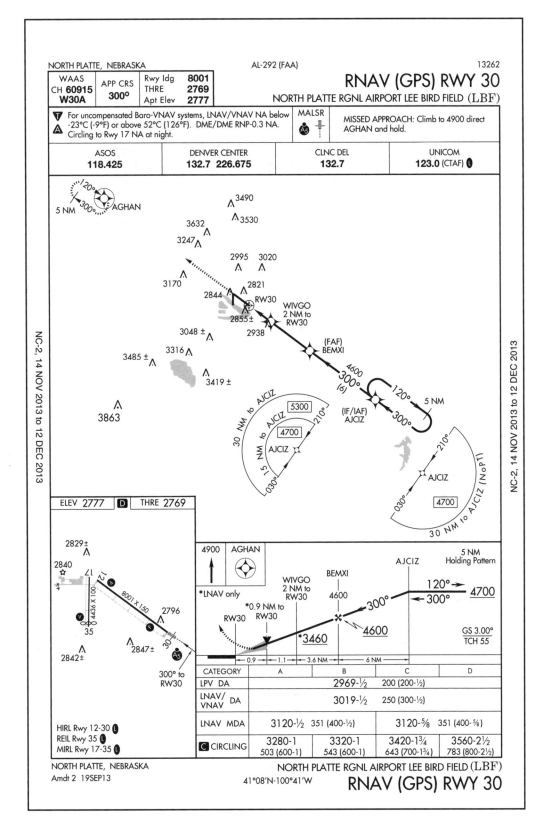

Figure 249

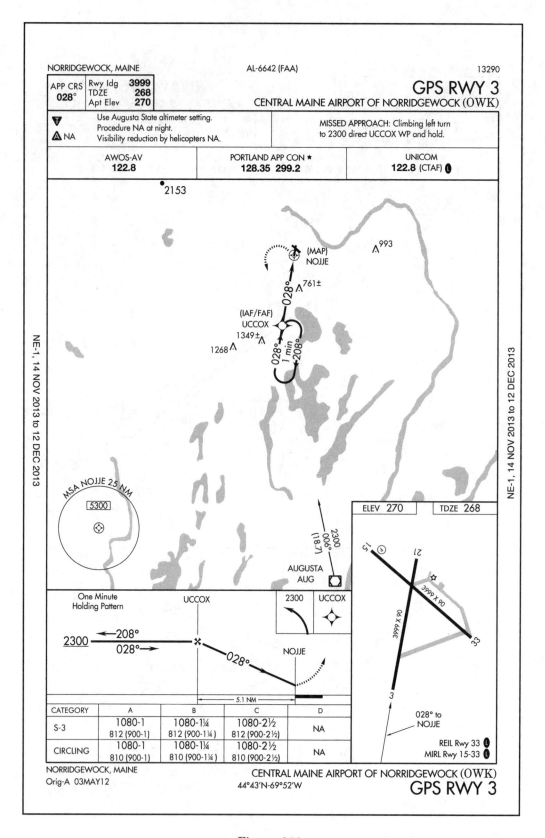

Figure 250

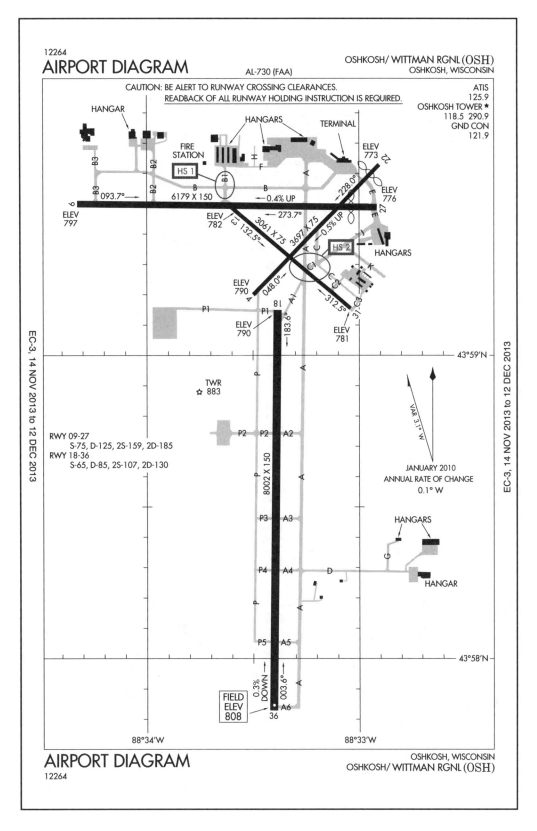

Figure 251

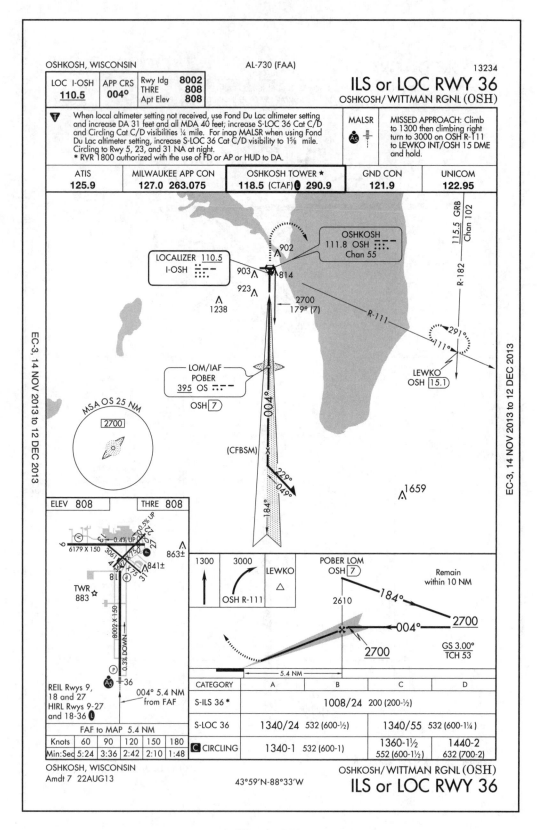

Figure 252

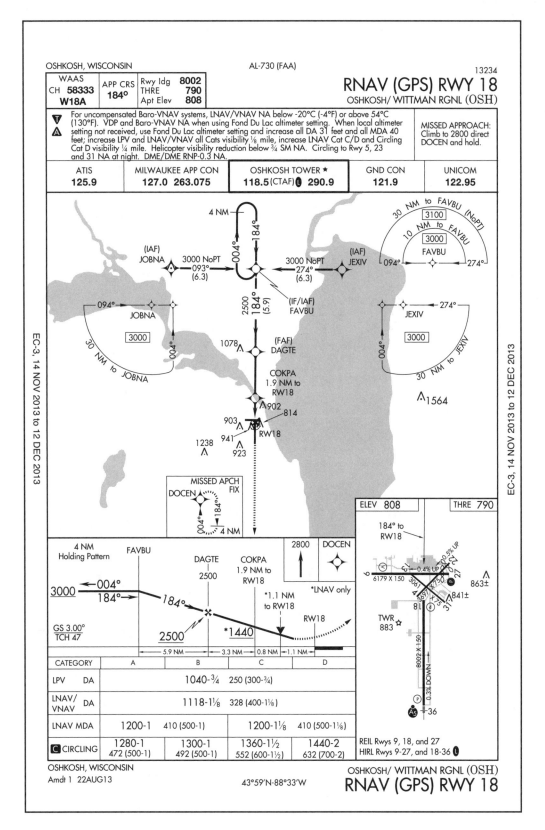

Figure 253

LEARNING STATEMENT CODES AND LEARNING STATEMENTS

To determine the knowledge area in which a particular question was incorrectly answered, compare the learning statement code(s) on the Federal Aviation Administration Airmen Computer Test Report to the following learning statement outline. The total number of test items missed may differ from the number of learning statement codes shown on the test report, since you may have missed more than one question in a specific learning statement code.

Learning Statement Codes and Learning Statements for Pilots, Instructors, Flight Engineers, Dispatchers, Navigators, and Pilot Examiners Exams

Code	Learning Statement
PLT001	Calculate a course intercept
PLT002	Calculate aircraft performance—airspeed
PLT003	Calculate aircraft performance—center of gravity
PLT004	Calculate aircraft performance—climb / descent / maneuvering
PLT005	Calculate aircraft performance—density altitude
PLT006	Calculate aircraft performance—glide
PLT007	Calculate aircraft performance—IAS / EPR
PLT008	Calculate aircraft performance—landing
PLT009	Calculate aircraft performance—turbine temperatures (MGT, EGT, ITT, T4, etc) / torque / horsepower
PLT010	Calculate aircraft performance—STAB TRIM
PLT011	Calculate aircraft performance—takeoff
PLT012	Calculate aircraft performance—time/speed/distance/course/fuel/wind
PLT013	Calculate crosswind / headwind components
PLT014	Calculate distance / bearing from/to a station
PLT015	Calculate flight performance / planning—range
PLT016	Calculate fuel—dump time / weight / volume / quantity / consumption
PLT017	Calculate L/D ratio
PLT018	Calculate load factor / stall speed / velocity / angle of attack
PLT019	Calculate pressure altitude
PLT020	Calculate turbulent air penetration
PLT021	Calculate weight and balance
PLT022	Define Aeronautical Decision Making (ADM)
PLT023	Define altitude—absolute / true / indicated / density / pressure
PLT024	Define atmospheric adiabatic process
PLT025	Define Bernoulli`s principle
PLT026	Define ceiling
PLT027	Define coning

Code	Learning Statement
PLT028	Define crewmember
PLT029	Define critical phase of flight
PLT030	Define false lift
PLT031	Define isobars / associated winds
PLT032	Define MACH speed regimes
PLT033	Define MEA / MOCA / MRA
PLT034	Define stopway / clearway
PLT035	Define Vne / Vno
PLT036	Interpret a MACH meter reading
PLT037	Interpret a radar weather report
PLT038	Interpret aircraft Power Schedule Chart
PLT039	Interpret airport landing indicator
PLT040	Interpret airspace classes—charts / diagrams
PLT041	Interpret altimeter—readings / settings
PLT042	Interpret Constant Pressure charts / Isotachs Chart
PLT043	Interpret Analysis Heights / Temperature Chart
PLT044	Interpret ATC communications / instructions / terminology
PLT045	Interpret Descent Performance Chart
PLT046	Interpret drag ratio from charts
PLT047	Interpret/Program Flight Director/FMS/Automation—modes / operation / indications / errors
PLT048	Interpret Hovering Ceiling Chart
PLT049	Interpret ILS—charts / RMI / CDI / indications
PLT050	Interpret information on a Brake Energy Limit Chart
PLT051	Interpret information on a Convective Outlook
PLT052	Interpret information on a Departure Procedure Chart
PLT053	Interpret information on a Flight Plan
PLT054	Interpret information on a Glider Performance Graph
PLT055	Interpret information on a High Altitude Chart
PLT056	Interpret information on a Horizontal Situation Indicator (HSI)
PLT057	Interpret information on a Hot Air Balloon Performance Graph
PLT058	Interpret information on a Low Altitude Chart
PLT059	Interpret information on a METAR / SPECI report
PLT060	Interpret information on a Performance Curve Chart
PLT061	Interpret information on a PIREP
PLT062	Interpret information on a Pseudo-Adiabatic Chart
PLT063	Interpret information on a Radar Summary Chart
PLT064	Interpret information on a Sectional Chart
PLT065	Interpret information on a Service Ceiling Engine Inoperative Chart
PLT066	Interpret information on a Convective Outlook Chart
PLT067	Interpret information on a SIGMET
PLT068	Interpret information on a Significant Weather Prognostic Chart
PLT069	Interpret information on a Slush/Standing Water Takeoff Chart
PLT070	Interpret information on a Stability Chart
PLT071	Interpret information on a Surface Analysis Chart
PLT072	Interpret information on a Terminal Aerodrome Forecast (TAF)

Code	Learning Statement
PLT073	Interpret information on a Tower Enroute Control (TEC)
PLT074	Interpret information on a Velocity/Load Factor Chart
PLT075	Interpret information on a Weather Depiction Chart
PLT076	Interpret information on a Winds and Temperatures Aloft Forecast (FB)
PLT077	Interpret information on an Airport Diagram
PLT078	Interpret information in an Airport Facility Directory (AFD)
PLT079	Interpret information on an Airways Chart
PLT080	Interpret information on an Arrival Chart
PLT081	Interpret information on an Aviation Area Forecast (FA)
PLT082	Interpret information on an IFR Alternate Airport Minimums Chart
PLT083	Interpret information on an Instrument Approach Procedures (IAP)
PLT084	Interpret information on an Observed Winds Aloft Chart
PLT085	Interpret information on Takeoff Obstacle / Field / Climb Limit Charts
PLT086	Interpret readings on a Turn and Slip Indicator
PLT087	Interpret readings on an Aircraft Course and DME Indicator
PLT088	Interpret speed indicator readings
PLT089	Interpret Takeoff Speeds Chart
PLT090	Interpret VOR—charts / indications / CDI / ADF / NAV
PLT091	Interpret VOR / ADF / NDB / CDI / RMI—illustrations / indications / procedures
PLT092	Interpret weight and balance—diagram
PLT093	Recall administration of medical oxygen
PLT094	Recall aerodynamics—airfoil design / pressure distribution / effects of altitude
PLT095	Recall aerodynamics—longitudinal axis / lateral axis
PLT096	Recall aeromedical factors—effects of altitude
PLT097	Recall aeromedical factors—effects of carbon monoxide poisoning
PLT098	Recall aeromedical factors—fitness for flight
PLT099	Recall aeromedical factors—scanning procedures
PLT100	Recall aeronautical charts—IFR En Route Low Altitude
PLT101	Recall aeronautical charts—pilotage
PLT102	Recall aeronautical charts—terminal procedures
PLT103	Recall Aeronautical Decision Making (ADM)—hazardous attitudes
PLT104	Recall Aeronautical Decision Making (ADM)—human factors / CRM
PLT105	Recall airborne radar / thunderstorm detection equipment—use / limitations
PLT106	Recall aircraft air-cycle machine
PLT107	Recall aircraft alternator / generator system
PLT108	Recall aircraft anti-icing / deicing—methods / fluids
PLT109	Recall aircraft batteries—capacity / charging / types / storage / rating / precautions
PLT110	Recall aircraft brake system
PLT111	Recall aircraft circuitry—series / parallel
PLT112	Recall aircraft controls—proper use / techniques
PLT113	Recall aircraft design—categories / limitation factors
PLT114	Recall aircraft design—construction / function
PLT115	Recall aircraft engine—detonation/backfiring/after firing, cause/characteristics
PLT116	Recall aircraft general knowledge / publications / AIM / navigational aids
PLT117	Recall aircraft heated windshields

Code	Learning Statement
PLT118	Recall aircraft instruments—gyroscopic
PLT119	Recall aircraft lighting—anti-collision / landing / navigation
PLT120	Recall aircraft limitations—turbulent air penetration
PLT121	Recall aircraft loading—computations
PLT122	Recall aircraft operations—checklist usage
PLT123	Recall aircraft performance—airspeed
PLT124	Recall aircraft performance—atmospheric effects
PLT125	Recall aircraft performance—climb / descent
PLT126	Recall aircraft performance—cold weather operations
PLT127	Recall aircraft performance—density altitude
PLT128	Recall aircraft performance—effects of icing
PLT129	Recall aircraft performance—effects of runway slope / slope landing
PLT130	Recall aircraft performance—fuel
PLT131	Recall aircraft performance—ground effect
PLT132	Recall aircraft performance—instrument markings / airspeed / definitions / indications
PLT133	Recall aircraft performance—normal climb / descent rates
PLT134	Recall aircraft performance—takeoff
PLT135	Recall aircraft pressurization—system / operation
PLT136	Recall aircraft systems—anti-icing / deicing
PLT137	Recall aircraft systems—environmental control
PLT138	Recall aircraft landing gear/tires—types / characteristics
PLT139	Recall aircraft warning systems—stall / fire / retractable gear / terrain awareness
PLT140	Recall airport operations—LAHSO
PLT141	Recall airport operations—markings / signs / lighting
PLT142	Recall airport operations—noise avoidance routes
PLT143	Recall airport operations—rescue / fire fighting vehicles and types of agents
PLT144	Recall airport operations—runway conditions
PLT145	Recall airport operations—runway lighting
PLT146	Recall airport operations—traffic pattern procedures / communication procedures
PLT147	Recall airport operations—visual glideslope indicators
PLT148	Recall airport operations lighting—MALS / ALSF / RCLS / TDZL
PLT149	Recall airport preflight / taxi operations—procedures
PLT150	Recall airport traffic patterns—entry procedures
PLT151	Recall airship—buoyancy
PLT152	Recall airship—flight characteristics / controllability
PLT153	Recall airship—flight operations
PLT154	Recall airship—ground weigh-off / static / trim condition
PLT155	Recall airship—maintaining pressure
PLT156	Recall airship—maximum headway / flight at equilibrium
PLT157	Recall airship—pressure height / dampers / position
PLT158	Recall airship—pressure height / manometers
PLT159	Recall airship—pressure height / super heat / valving gas
PLT160	Recall airship—stability / control / positive superheat
PLT161	Recall airspace classes—limits / requirements / restrictions / airspeeds / equipment

Code	Learning Statement
PLT162	Recall airspace requirements—operations
PLT163	Recall airspace requirements—visibility / cloud clearance
PLT164	Recall airspeed—effects during a turn
PLT165	Recall altimeter—effect of temperature changes
PLT166	Recall altimeter—settings / setting procedures
PLT167	Recall altimeters—characteristics / accuracy
PLT168	Recall angle of attack—characteristics / forces / principles
PLT169	Recall antitorque system—components / functions
PLT170	Recall approach / landing / taxiing techniques
PLT171	Recall ATC—reporting
PLT172	Recall ATC—system / services
PLT173	Recall atmospheric conditions—measurements / pressure / stability
PLT174	Recall autopilot / yaw damper—components / operating principles / characteristics / failure modes
PLT175	Recall autorotation
PLT176	Recall balance tab—purpose / operation
PLT177	Recall balloon—flight operations
PLT178	Recall balloon—flight operations / gas
PLT179	Recall balloon—ground weigh-off / static equilibrium / load
PLT180	Recall balloon gas/hot air—lift / false lift / characteristics
PLT181	Recall balloon—hot air / physics
PLT182	Recall balloon—inspecting the fabric
PLT183	Recall balloon flight operations—ascent / descent
PLT184	Recall balloon flight operations—launch / landing
PLT185	Recall basic instrument flying—fundamental skills
PLT186	Recall basic instrument flying—pitch instruments
PLT187	Recall basic instrument flying—turn coordinator / turn and slip indicator
PLT188	Recall cabin atmosphere control
PLT189	Recall carburetor—effects of carburetor heat / heat control
PLT190	Recall carburetor ice—factors affecting / causing
PLT191	Recall carburetors—types / components / operating principles / characteristics
PLT192	Recall clouds—types / formation / resulting weather
PLT193	Recall cockpit voice recorder (CVR)—operating principles / characteristics / testing
PLT194	Recall collision avoidance—scanning techniques
PLT195	Recall collision avoidance—TCAS
PLT196	Recall communications—ATIS broadcasts
PLT197	Recall Coriolis effect
PLT198	Recall course / heading—effects of wind
PLT199	Recall cyclic control pressure—characteristics
PLT200	Recall dead reckoning—calculations / charts
PLT201	Recall departure procedures—ODP / SID
PLT202	Recall DME—characteristics / accuracy / indications / Arc
PLT203	Recall earth's atmosphere—layers / characteristics / solar energy
PLT204	Recall effective communication—basic elements

Code	Learning Statement
PLT205	Recall effects of alcohol on the body
PLT206	Recall effects of temperature—density altitude / icing
PLT207	Recall electrical system—components / operating principles / characteristics / static bonding and shielding
PLT208	Recall emergency conditions / procedures
PLT209	Recall engine pressure ratio—EPR
PLT210	Recall engine shutdown—normal / abnormal / emergency / precautions
PLT211	Recall evaluation testing characteristics
PLT212	Recall fire extinguishing systems—components / operating principles / characteristics
PLT213	Recall flight characteristics—longitudinal stability / instability
PLT214	Recall flight characteristics—structural / wing design
PLT215	Recall flight instruments—magnetic compass
PLT216	Recall flight instruments—total energy compensators
PLT217	Recall flight maneuvers—quick stop
PLT218	Recall flight operations—common student errors
PLT219	Recall flight operations—maneuvers
PLT220	Recall flight operations—night and high altitude operations
PLT221	Recall flight operations—takeoff / landing maneuvers
PLT222	Recall flight operations—takeoff procedures
PLT223	Recall flight operations multiengine—engine inoperative procedures
PLT224	Recall flight plan—IFR
PLT225	Recall flight plan—requirements
PLT226	Recall fog—types / formation / resulting weather
PLT227	Recall FOI techniques—integrated flight instruction
PLT228	Recall FOI techniques—lesson plans
PLT229	Recall FOI techniques—professionalism
PLT230	Recall FOI techniques—responsibilities
PLT231	Recall FOI techniques / human behavior—anxiety / fear / stress
PLT232	Recall FOI techniques / human behavior—dangerous tendencies
PLT233	Recall FOI techniques / human behavior—defense mechanisms
PLT234	Recall forces acting on aircraft—3 axis intersect
PLT235	Recall forces acting on aircraft—aerodynamics
PLT236	Recall forces acting on aircraft—airfoil / center of pressure / mean camber line
PLT237	Recall forces acting on aircraft—airspeed / air density / lift / drag
PLT238	Recall forces acting on aircraft—aspect ratio
PLT239	Recall forces acting on aircraft—buoyancy / drag / gravity / thrust
PLT240	Recall forces acting on aircraft—CG / flight characteristics
PLT241	Recall forces acting on aircraft—drag / gravity / thrust / lift
PLT242	Recall forces acting on aircraft—lift / drag / thrust / weight / stall / limitations
PLT243	Recall forces acting on aircraft—propeller / torque
PLT244	Recall forces acting on aircraft—stability / controllability
PLT245	Recall forces acting on aircraft—stalls / spins
PLT246	Recall forces acting on aircraft—steady state climb / flight
PLT247	Recall forces acting on aircraft—thrust / drag / weight / lift

Code	Learning Statement
PLT248	Recall forces acting on aircraft—turns
PLT249	Recall fuel—air mixture
PLT250	Recall fuel—types / characteristics / contamination / fueling / defueling / precautions
PLT251	Recall fuel characteristics / contaminants / additives
PLT252	Recall fuel dump system—components / methods
PLT253	Recall fuel system—components / operating principles / characteristics / leaks
PLT254	Recall fuel tank—components / operating principles / characteristics
PLT255	Recall fueling procedures—safety / grounding / calculating volume
PLT256	Recall glider performance—effect of loading
PLT257	Recall glider performance—speed / distance / ballast / lift / drag
PLT258	Recall ground reference maneuvers—ground track diagram
PLT259	Recall ground resonance—conditions to occur
PLT260	Recall gyroplane—aerodynamics / rotor systems
PLT261	Recall hail—characteristics / hazards
PLT262	Recall helicopter hazards—dynamic rollover / Low G / LTE
PLT263	Recall hazardous weather—fog / icing / turbulence / visibility restriction
PLT264	Recall helicopter approach—settling with power
PLT265	Recall helicopter takeoff / landing—ground resonance action required
PLT266	Recall high lift devices—characteristics / functions
PLT267	Recall hot air balloon—weigh-off procedure
PLT268	Recall hovering—aircraft performance / tendencies
PLT269	Recall human behavior—defense mechanism
PLT270	Recall human behavior—social / self fulfillment / physical
PLT271	Recall human factors (ADM)—judgment
PLT272	Recall human factors—stress management
PLT273	Recall hydraulic systems—components / operating principles / characteristics
PLT274	Recall icing—formation / characteristics
PLT275	Recall ILS—indications / HSI
PLT276	Recall ILS—indications / OBS / CDI
PLT277	Recall ILS—marker beacon / indicator lights / codes
PLT278	Recall indicating systems—airspeed / angle of attack / attitude / heading / manifold pressure / synchro / EGT
PLT279	Recall Inertial/Doppler Navigation System principles / regulations / requirements / limitations
PLT280	Recall inflight illusions—causes / sources
PLT281	Recall information in an Airport Facility Directory
PLT282	Recall information in the certificate holder's manual
PLT283	Recall information on a Constant Pressure Analysis Chart
PLT284	Recall information on a Forecast Winds and Temperatures Aloft (FB)
PLT285	Recall information on a Height Velocity Diagram
PLT286	Recall information on a Significant Weather Prognostic Chart
PLT287	Recall information on a Surface Analysis Chart
PLT288	Recall information on a Terminal Aerodrome Forecast (TAF)
PLT289	Recall information on a Weather Depiction Chart
PLT290	Recall information on AIRMETS / SIGMETS

Code	Learning Statement
PLT291	Recall information on an Aviation Area Forecast (FA)
PLT292	Recall information on an Instrument Approach Procedures (IAP)
PLT293	Recall information on an Instrument Departure Procedure Chart
PLT294	Recall information on Inflight Aviation Weather Advisories
PLT295	Recall instructor techniques—obstacles / planning / activities / outcome
PLT296	Recall instrument procedures—holding / circling
PLT297	Recall instrument procedures—unusual attitude / unusual attitude recovery
PLT298	Recall instrument procedures—VFR on top
PLT300	Recall instrument/navigation system checks/inspections—limits / tuning / identifying / logging
PLT301	Recall inversion layer—characteristics
PLT302	Recall jet stream—types / characteristics
PLT303	Recall L/D ratio
PLT304	Recall launch procedures
PLT305	Recall leading edge devices—types / effect / purpose / operation
PLT306	Recall learning process—levels of learning / transfer of learning / incidental learning
PLT307	Recall learning process—memory / fact / recall
PLT308	Recall learning process—laws of learning elements
PLT309	Recall load factor—angle of bank
PLT310	Recall load factor—characteristics
PLT311	Recall load factor—effect of airspeed
PLT312	Recall load factor—maneuvering / stall speed
PLT313	Recall loading – limitations / terminology
PLT314	Recall longitudinal axis—aerodynamics / center of gravity / direction of motion
PLT315	Recall Machmeter—principles / functions
PLT316	Recall meteorology—severe weather watch (WW)
PLT317	Recall microburst—characteristics / hazards
PLT318	Recall minimum fuel advisory
PLT319	Recall navigation – celestial / navigation chart / characteristics
PLT320	Recall navigation—true north / magnetic north
PLT321	Recall navigation—types of landing systems
PLT322	Recall navigation—VOR / NAV system
PLT323	Recall NOTAMS—classes / information / distribution
PLT324	Recall oil system—types / components / functions / oil specifications
PLT325	Recall operations manual—transportation of prisoner
PLT326	Recall oxygen system—components / operating principles / characteristics
PLT327	Recall oxygen system—install / inspect / repair / service / precautions / leaks
PLT328	Recall performance planning—aircraft loading
PLT329	Recall physiological factors—cabin pressure
PLT330	Recall physiological factors—cause / effects of hypoxia
PLT331	Recall physiological factors—effects of scuba diving / smoking
PLT332	Recall physiological factors—hyperventilation
PLT333	Recall physiological factors—night vision
PLT334	Recall physiological factors—spatial disorientation

Code	Learning Statement
PLT335	Recall pilotage—calculations
PLT336	Recall pitch control—collective / cyclic
PLT337	Recall pitot-static system—components / operating principles / characteristics
PLT338	Recall pneumatic system—operation
PLT340	Recall positive exchange of flight controls
PLT341	Recall power settling—characteristics
PLT342	Recall powerplant—controlling engine temperature
PLT343	Recall powerplant—operating principles / operational characteristics / inspecting
PLT344	Recall precipitation—types / characteristics
PLT345	Recall pressure altitude
PLT346	Recall primary / secondary flight controls—types / purpose / functionality / operation
PLT347	Recall principles of flight—critical engine
PLT348	Recall principles of flight—turns
PLT349	Recall procedures for confined areas
PLT350	Recall propeller operations—constant / variable speed
PLT351	Recall propeller system—types / components / operating principles / characteristics
PLT352	Recall purpose / operation of a stabilizer
PLT353	Recall Radar Summary Chart
PLT354	Recall radio—GPS / RNAV / RAIM
PLT355	Recall radio—HSI
PLT356	Recall radio—ILS / compass locator
PLT357	Recall radio—ILS / LDA
PLT358	Recall radio—LOC / ILS
PLT359	Deleted
PLT360	Recall radio—Microwave Landing System
PLT361	Recall radio—SDF / ILS
PLT362	Recall radio – VHF / Direction Finding
PLT363	Recall radio—VOR / VOT
PLT364	Recall radio system—licence requirements / frequencies
PLT365	Recall reciprocating engine—components / operating principles / characteristics
PLT366	Recall regulations—accident / incident reporting and preserving wreckage
PLT367	Recall regulations—additional equipment/operating requirements large transport aircraft
PLT368	Recall regulations—admission to flight deck
PLT369	Recall regulations—aerobatic flight requirements
PLT370	Recall regulations—Air Traffic Control authorization / clearances
PLT371	Recall regulations—Aircraft Category / Class
PLT372	Recall regulations—aircraft inspection / records / expiration
PLT373	Recall regulations—aircraft operating limitations
PLT374	Recall regulations—aircraft owner / operator responsibilities
PLT375	Recall regulations—aircraft return to service
PLT376	Recall regulations—airspace special use / TFRS
PLT377	Recall regulations—airworthiness certificates / requirements / responsibilities
PLT378	Recall regulations—Airworthiness Directives
PLT379	Recall regulations—alternate airport requirements

Code	Learning Statement
PLT380	Recall regulations—alternate airport weather minima
PLT381	Recall regulations—altimeter settings
PLT382	Recall regulations—approach minima
PLT383	Recall regulations—basic flight rules
PLT384	Recall regulations—briefing of passengers
PLT385	Recall regulations—cargo in passenger compartment
PLT386	Recall regulations—certificate issuance / renewal
PLT387	Recall regulations—change of address
PLT388	Recall regulations—cockpit voice / flight data recorder(s)
PLT389	Recall regulations—commercial operation requirements / conditions / OpSpecs
PLT390	Recall regulations—communications enroute
PLT391	Recall regulations—communications failure
PLT392	Recall regulations—compliance with local regulations
PLT393	Recall regulations—controlled / restricted airspace—requirements
PLT394	Recall regulations—declaration of an emergency
PLT395	Recall regulations—definitions
PLT396	Recall regulations—departure alternate airport
PLT397	Recall regulations—destination airport visibility
PLT398	Recall regulations—dispatch
PLT399	Recall regulations—display / inspection of licences and certificates
PLT400	Recall regulations—documents to be carried on aircraft during flight
PLT401	Recall regulations—dropping / aerial application / towing restrictions
PLT402	Recall regulations—ELT requirements
PLT403	Recall regulations—emergency deviation from regulations
PLT404	Recall regulations—emergency equipment
PLT405	Recall regulations—equipment / instrument / certificate requirements
PLT406	Recall regulations—equipment failure
PLT407	Recall regulations—experience / training requirements
PLT408	Recall regulations—fire extinguisher requirements
PLT409	Recall regulations—flight / duty time
PLT410	Recall regulations—flight engineer qualifications / privileges / responsibilities
PLT411	Recall regulations—flight instructor limitations / qualifications
PLT412	Recall regulations—flight release
PLT413	Recall regulations—fuel requirements
PLT414	Recall regulations—general right-of-way rules
PLT415	Recall regulations—IFR flying
PLT416	Recall regulations—immediate notification
PLT417	Recall regulations—individual flotation devices
PLT418	Recall regulations—instructor demonstrations / authorizations
PLT419	Recall regulations—instructor requirements / responsibilities
PLT420	Recall regulations—instrument approach procedures
PLT421	Recall regulations—instrument flight rules
PLT422	Recall regulations—intermediate airport authorizations
PLT423	Recall regulations—knowledge and skill test checks

Code	Learning Statement
PLT424	Recall regulations—limits on autopilot usage
PLT425	Recall regulations—maintenance reports / records / entries
PLT426	Recall regulations—maintenance requirements
PLT427	Recall regulations—medical certificate requirements / validity
PLT428	Recall regulations—minimum equipment list
PLT429	Recall regulations—minimum flight / navigation instruments
PLT430	Recall regulations—minimum safe / flight altitude
PLT431	Recall regulations—operating near other aircraft
PLT432	Recall regulations—operational control functions
PLT433	Recall regulations—operational flight plan requirements
PLT434	Recall regulations—operational procedures for a controlled airport
PLT435	Recall regulations—operational procedures for an uncontrolled airport
PLT436	Recall regulations—operations manual
PLT437	Recall regulations—overwater operations
PLT438	Recall regulations—oxygen requirements
PLT439	Recall regulations—persons authorized to perform maintenance
PLT440	Recall regulations—Pilot / Crew duties and responsibilities
PLT441	Recall regulations—pilot briefing
PLT442	Recall regulations—pilot currency requirements
PLT443	Recall regulations—pilot qualifications / privileges / responsibilities / crew complement
PLT444	Recall regulations—pilot-in-command authority / responsibility
PLT445	Recall regulations—preflight requirements
PLT446	Recall regulations—preventative maintenance
PLT447	Recall regulations—privileges / limitations of medical certificates
PLT448	Recall regulations—privileges / limitations of pilot certificates
PLT449	Recall regulations—proficiency check requirements
PLT450	Recall regulations—qualifications / duty time
PLT451	Recall regulations—ratings issued / experience requirements / limitations
PLT452	Recall regulations—re-dispatch
PLT453	Recall regulations—records retention for domestic / flag air carriers
PLT454	Recall regulations—required aircraft / equipment inspections
PLT455	Recall regulations—requirements of a flight plan release
PLT456	Recall regulations—runway requirements
PLT457	Recall regulations—student pilot endorsements / other endorsements
PLT458	Recall regulations—submission / revision of Policy and Procedure Manuals
PLT459	Recall regulations—takeoff procedures / minimums
PLT460	Recall regulations—training programs
PLT461	Recall regulations—use of aircraft lights
PLT462	Recall regulations—use of microphone / megaphone / interphone / public address system
PLT463	Recall regulations alcohol or drugs
PLT464	Recall regulations—use of safety belts / harnesses (crew member)
PLT465	Recall regulations—use of seats / safety belts / harnesses (passenger)
PLT466	Recall regulations—V speeds
PLT467	Recall regulations—visual flight rules and limitations

Code	Learning Statement
PLT468	Recall regulations—Visual Meteorological Conditions (VMC)
PLT469	Recall regulations—weather radar
PLT470	Recall rotor system—types / components / operating principles / characteristics
PLT471	Recall rotorcraft transmission—components / operating principles / characteristics
PLT472	Recall rotorcraft vibration—characteristics / sources
PLT473	Recall secondary flight controls—types / purpose / functionality
PLT474	Recall soaring—normal procedures
PLT475	Recall squall lines—formation / characteristics / resulting weather
PLT476	Recall stabilizer—purpose / operation
PLT477	Recall stalls—characteristics / factors / recovery / precautions
PLT478	Recall starter / ignition system—types / components / operating principles / characteristics
PLT479	Recall starter system—starting procedures
PLT480	Recall static/dynamic stability/instability—characteristics
PLT481	Recall student evaluation—learning process
PLT482	Recall student evaluation—written tests / oral quiz / critiques
PLT483	Recall supercharger—characteristics / operation
PLT484	Recall symbols—chart / navigation
PLT485	Recall taxiing / crosswind / techniques
PLT486	Recall taxiing / takeoff—techniques / procedures
PLT487	Recall teaching methods—demonstration / performance
PLT488	Recall teaching methods—group / guided discussion / lecture
PLT489	Recall teaching methods—known to unknown
PLT490	Recall teaching methods—motivation / student feelings of insecurity
PLT491	Recall teaching methods—organizing material / course of training
PLT492	Recall temperature—effects on weather formations
PLT493	Recall the dynamics of frost / ice / snow formation on an aircraft
PLT494	Recall thermals—types / characteristics / formation / locating / maneuvering / corrective actions
PLT495	Recall thunderstorms—types / characteristics / formation / hazards / precipitation static
PLT496	Recall towrope—strength / safety links / positioning
PLT497	Recall transponder—codes / operations / usage
PLT498	Recall Transportation Security Regulations
PLT499	Recall turbine engines—components / operational characteristics / associated instruments
PLT500	Recall turboprop engines—components / operational characteristics
PLT501	Recall turbulence—types / characteristics / reporting / corrective actions
PLT502	Recall universal signals—hand / light / visual
PLT503	Recall use of narcotics / drugs / intoxicating liquor
PLT504	Recall use of training aids—types / function / purpose
PLT505	Recall use of training aids—usefulness / simplicity / compatibility
PLT506	Recall V speeds—maneuvering / flap extended / gear extended / V1, V2, r, ne, mo, mc, mg, etc.
PLT507	Recall VOR—indications / VOR / VOT / CDI
PLT508	Recall VOR/altimeter/transponder checks—identification / tuning / identifying / logging
PLT509	Recall wake turbulence—characteristics / avoidance techniques
PLT510	Recall weather—causes / formation

Code	Learning Statement
PLT511	Recall weather associated with frontal activity / air masses
PLT512	Recall weather conditions—temperature / moisture / dewpoint
PLT513	Recall weather information—TWEB broadcasts / FAA Avcams
PLT514	Recall weather reporting systems—briefings / forecasts / reports / AWOS / ASOS
PLT515	Recall weather services—EFAS / TIBS / TPC / WFO / AFSS / HIWAS
PLT516	Recall winds—types / characteristics
PLT517	Recall winds associated with high / low-pressure systems
PLT518	Recall windshear—characteristics / hazards / power management
PLT519	Recall wing spoilers—purpose / operation
PLT520	Calculate density altitude
PLT521	Recall helicopter takeoff / landing – slope operations
PLT522	Recall helicopter – Pinnacle / Ridgeline operations
PLT523	Recall vortex generators – purpose / effects / aerodynamics
PLT524	Interpret / Program information on an avionics display
PLT525	Interpret table – oxygen / fuel / oil / accumulator / fire extinguisher
PLT526	Recall near midair collision report
PLT527	Recall BASIC VFR weather minimums